K¹² Math⁺

Lesson Guide

About K12 Inc.

K12 Inc., a technology-based education company, is the nation's leading provider of
proprietary curriculum and online education programs to students in grades K–12. K^{12}
provides its curriculum and academic services to online schools, traditional classroom
blended school programs, and directly to families. K12 Inc. also operates the K^{12} Internal
Academy, an accredited, diploma-granting online private school serving students worle.
K^{12}'s mission is to provide any child the curriculum and tools to maximize success in life
regardless of geographic, financial, or demographic circumstances. K12 Inc. is accredite
CITA. More information can be found at www.K12.com.

ISBN: 978-1-60153-082-0
Printed by RR Donnelley & Sons, Roanoke, VA, USA, April 2013, Lot 040513

Contents

Add, Subtract, Number Composition

Inverse Operations: Add and Subtract

Measurement

Add or Subtract: Problem Solving

Problem Solving: Reason and Connect

Semester Review and Checkpoint

Numbers Through 1,000

Plane and Solid Figures

Add or Subtract Numbers Through 1,000

Multiplication and Number Patterns

Multiplication and Addition Properties

Introduction to Division

Data Representations and Analysis

Introduction to Fractions

Semester Review and Checkpoint

Program Overview

Lesson Overview

The table at the beginning of each lesson tells you what activities are in the lesson and whether students are on the computer (**ONLINE**) or at a table or desk (**OFFLINE**). The expected time for each activity is given.

Objectives and Prerequisite Skills

Each lesson teaches the Lesson Objectives. The lesson assumes that students know the Prerequisite Skills from their previous math experience. The Get Ready activity is designed to remind students of the prerequisite skills, and to prepare them for the lesson.

Common Errors and Misconceptions

Research shows that students might misunderstand certain concepts, which then leads to misunderstanding of more advanced concepts. When certain research applies to a lesson, the lesson has a Common Errors and Misconceptions section.

Content Background

The Content Background tells you what the students will learn in the lesson, and it explains any complex math concepts, putting the lesson into perspective with wider math knowledge.

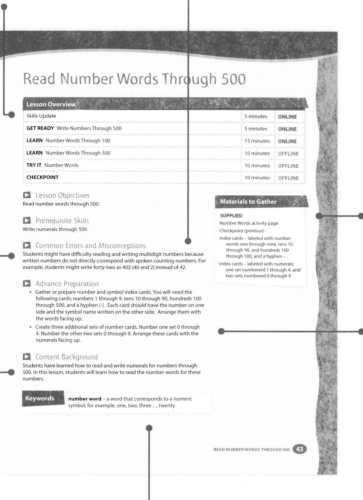

Read Number Words Through 500

Lesson Overview		
Skills Update	5 minutes	ONLINE
GET READY Write Numbers Through 500	5 minutes	ONLINE
LEARN Number Words Through 100	15 minutes	ONLINE
LEARN Number Words Through 500	10 minutes	OFFLINE
TRY IT Number Words	10 minutes	OFFLINE
CHECKPOINT	10 minutes	OFFLINE

▶ Lesson Objectives
Read number words through 500.

▶ Prerequisite Skills
Write numerals through 500.

▶ Common Errors and Misconceptions
Students might have difficulty reading and writing multidigit numbers because written numbers do not directly correspond with spoken counting numbers. For example, students might write forty-two as 402 (40 and 2) instead of 42.

▶ Advance Preparation
- Gather or prepare number and symbol index cards. You will need the following cards: numbers 1 through 9, tens 10 through 90, hundreds 100 through 500, and a hyphen (-). Each card should have the number on one side and the symbol name written on the other side. Arrange them with the words facing up.
- Create three additional sets of number cards. Number one set 0 through 4. Number the other two sets 0 through 9. Arrange these cards with the numerals facing up.

▶ Content Background
Students have learned how to read and write numerals for numbers through 500. In this lesson, students will learn how to read the number words for these numbers.

Keywords   **number word** – a word that corresponds to a numeric symbol; for example, one, two, three…, twenty

Materials to Gather

SUPPLIED
Number Words activity page
Checkpoint (printout)
index cards – labeled with number words one through nine, tens 10 through 90, and hundreds 100 through 500, and a hyphen – .
index cards – labeled with numerals; one set numbered 1 through 4, and two sets numbered 0 through 9

READ NUMBER WORDS THROUGH 500 **43**

Materials

This box tells you what materials students will need in this lesson. More information about the materials is included on page x.

Advance Preparation

Some lessons require preparation that extends beyond gathering materials. In these cases, the lesson includes an Advance Preparation section.

Keywords

Definitions of keywords are included in the lesson in which the math term is introduced. The Unit Review includes of a list of all keywords for the unit.

Materials

K[12] supplies math materials, including this Lesson Guide and the Activity Book, the student practice book.

The **block set** includes various counters as well as 2-D and 3-D shapes. Note that the blocks are labeled with letters. The materials lists in each lesson refer to these blocks by their letter (for instance, B blocks or BB blocks or C blocks). The O blocks refer to the cubes. These blocks aren't labeled with the letter O, but the hole in each block resembles this letter. Within the lesson, you might see a more descriptive term, such as "circles" for the B blocks. A set of base-10 blocks contains blocks representing ones, tens, and hundreds.

Printouts, Plastic Sheet Cover, and Dry-Erase Markers

A lesson may ask you to print a document showing a number line, place-value chart, or other math tool. These documents will be reused throughout the course. We recommend that you obtain a plastic sheet cover and dry-erase markers so students can place the sheet over the printout and write answers on the sheet. They can then erase the answers and reuse the printout multiple times.

Number and Symbol Cards

Index cards labeled with numbers or symbols are frequently called for in the lessons. We recommend that you create a set of index cards numbered 0–100, and use them throughout the course. You can also create the symbols that will be used most frequently: $-$ (minus), $+$ (plus), $=$ (equals), $>$ (greater than), $<$ (less than).

Paper and Pencil

Students should always have notebook paper and a pencil handy. These materials are not listed in each lesson.

Also Needed

Other common items are called for in lessons, designated in the materials list as "Also Needed." Common materials include, but are not limited to, the following: calendar, containers, crayons, glue, glue stick, index cards, markers (permanent and coloring), paper (construction, drawing, and wide-line handwriting), pipe cleaners, play money, scissors (adult and round-end safety), sticky notes, tape (clear, double-stick, and masking), and yarn.

Working Through a Lesson

When you go online with students to do a math lesson, you will see a list of the activities that are included in the lesson. Students will warm up for their math lesson by answering questions in the Skills Update. Answers will be shown as students work through each question.

The Lesson Guide will give you an overview of the entire lesson.

Instructions for online activities are online, so you should expect to work at the computer with students, reading instructions and activities to them as necessary. The Lesson Guide may, however, include a teaching tip or other information. In some cases, such as when an open-ended Learning Tool is used, there will be instructions to follow in the Lesson Guide. The online screen will guide you to follow the instructions in the Lesson Guide.

Instructions for offline activities are in the Lesson Guide. These activities may use supplied or common materials, and some include pages from the Activity Book.

Types of Activities

Skills Update Short online problem set for warm-up. These problems should take about 5 minutes to complete.

Get Ready Review of previous math knowledge that will be needed for this lesson. The Get Ready can be online or offline.

Learn Presentation of math concepts, or guided practice. The Learn activities can be online or offline.

Try It Students practice what they have just learned, without guidance. The Try It activities are usually found in the Activity Book.

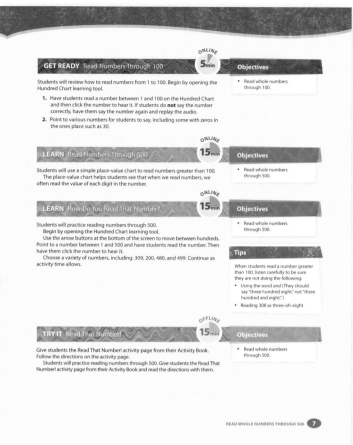

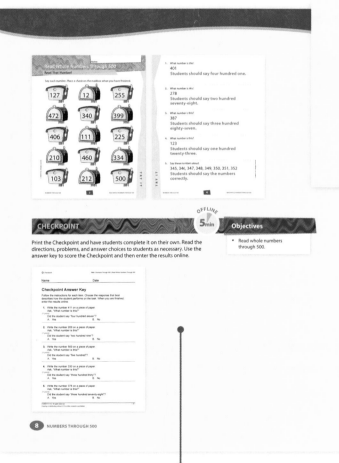

The Lesson Guide includes the answers, shown in magenta, to the Activity Book pages and offline Checkpoints.

Checkpoint Assessments of whether students have learned the objectives taught in the lesson or lessons. Not every lesson has a Checkpoint. In some Checkpoints, students show or explain their answers, and you record their performance.

In addition to the regular Checkpoints, **Unit Reviews** and **Unit Checkpoints** are lessons at the end of each unit. Each semester ends with a **Semester Review** and **Semester Checkpoint**.

Online Activities

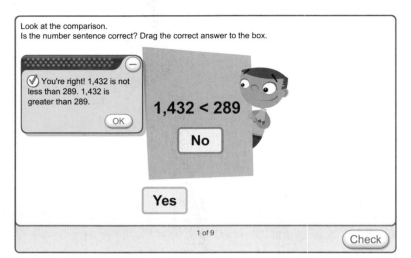

Online activities will show whether students answer correctly.

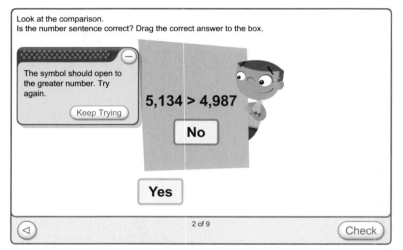

If students answer incorrectly, they will see feedback. They should click Keep Trying to try again. If they answer incorrectly a second time, they can click Show Me to see the correct answer.

Learning Tools are online activities that you set up to give students math exercises that will apply to what they are learning in a specific lesson.

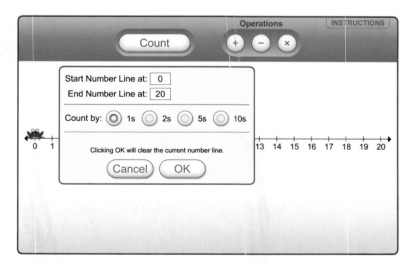

Numbers Through 500

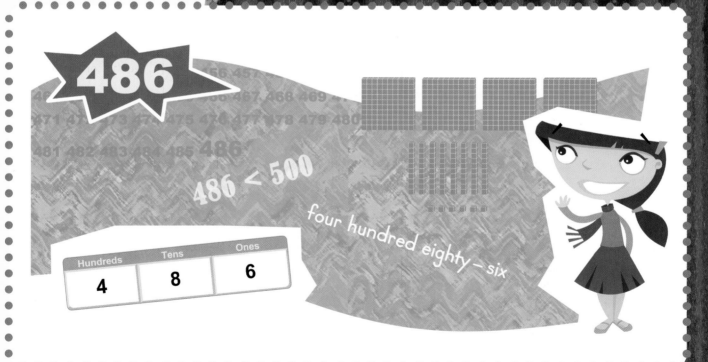

486

465 466 467 468 469 470
471 472 473 474 475 476 477 478 479 480
481 482 483 484 485 **486**

486 < 500

four hundred eighty-six

Hundreds	Tens	Ones
4	8	6

▶ Unit Objectives

- Count aloud whole numbers through 500.
- Read whole numbers through 500.
- Write number words through 500.
- Identify the place value for each digit in whole numbers through 500.
- Use models to represent regrouping in addition or subtraction problems.

- Use expanded forms to represent numbers through 500, such as 345 = 3 hundreds + 4 tens + 5 ones = 300 + 40 + 5.
- Compare whole numbers through 500 by using the symbols <, =, >. Order three or more whole numbers through 500 by using the symbols <, =, >.
- Write numerals through 500.

▶ Big Ideas

- Numbers tell us the results of counting.
- Place-value notation makes it easier to write and operate on large numbers.

▶ Unit Introduction

In this unit, students will investigate three different ways to represent numbers: concrete models, numerals, and number words.

Students will use models to build numbers through 500 while focusing on counting, reading, and writing numbers. For example, they will use ones cubes, tens rods, and hundreds flats to model numbers and demonstrate their understanding of place value. From this concrete foundation, students will be able to move more easily into the abstract representations of numerals and number words.

Count Aloud Through 500

Lesson Overview

GET READY Penny Collection	5 minutes	ONLINE
LEARN Count to 500	20 minutes	ONLINE
LEARN Let's Keep Counting	20 minutes	ONLINE
TRY IT Let's Count!	10 minutes	OFFLINE
CHECKPOINT	5 minutes	OFFLINE

▶ Lesson Objectives

Count aloud whole numbers through 500.

▶ Prerequisite Skills

Count aloud whole numbers through 100.

▶ Common Errors and Misconceptions

Students might skip a number as they count.

▶ Advance Preparation

In the Get Ready activity, students will count from 1 to 100. You may want to gather 100 countable objects and a jar or bowl to help students keep track as they count. For counting objects, use small, durable household items (for example, dry macaroni, shells, or twists).

▶ Content Background

Students will learn to count whole numbers through 500. They will learn to recognize the patterns repeated in each hundred.

Materials to Gather

SUPPLIED
Let's Count! activity page
Checkpoint (printout)

ALSO NEEDED
jar or bowl (optional)
counting objects–100 (optional)

GET READY Penny Collection

ONLINE
5min

Students will listen as Rosa counts her pennies from 93 to 100. They will then count aloud from 1 to 100.

Objectives

- Count aloud whole numbers through 100.

Tips

To provide extra practice, give students other objects to count, such as paper clips, pieces of pasta, or toothpicks.

LEARN Count To 500

Students will practice counting to 500. They will also begin to connect the spoken name of a number to its numeric form.

Objectives

Objectives

- Count aloud whole numbers through 500.

Tips

Remind students that they should not insert an unnecessary "and" when saying numbers in the hundreds. For example, they should read 101 as one hundred one, **not** one hundred and one or one-oh-one.

LEARN Let's Keep Counting

Students will practice counting across hundreds.

Objectives

- Count aloud whole numbers through 500.

TRY IT Let's Count!

Students will practice counting aloud through 500. Give students the Let's Count! activity page from their Activity Book and read the directions with them.

Objectives

- Count aloud whole numbers through 500.

Count Aloud Through 500
Let's Count!

Name: _____

Count aloud.

1. Count aloud from 126 to 146. **Students should count aloud from 126 to 146.**

2. Count aloud from 294 to 302. **Students should count aloud from 294 to 302.**

3. Count aloud from 387 to 405. **Students should count aloud from 387 to 405.**

4. Count aloud from 100 to 200. **Students should count aloud from 100 to 200.**

5. Pretend you are going to count from 300 to 400. Count for a few seconds. How does counting from 300 to 400 sound the same as counting from 100 to 200? How does it sound different? **You say the same numbers except you say three hundred in front.**

6. Say the numbers in order from 185 to 205. **Students should count aloud from 185 to 205.**

7. Say the numbers in order from 250 to 275. **Students should count aloud from 250 to 275.**

8. Say the numbers in order from 480 to 490. **Students should count aloud from 480 to 490.**

9. Say the numbers in order from 310 to 325. **Students should count aloud from 310 to 325.**

10. Say the numbers in order from 290 to 305. **Students should count aloud from 290 to 305.**

TRY IT

NUMBERS THROUGH 500   1   COUNT ALOUD THROUGH 500

NUMBERS THROUGH 500   2   COUNT ALOUD THROUGH 500

CHECKPOINT

Objectives

- Count aloud whole numbers through 500.

Print the Checkpoint and have students complete it on their own. Read the directions, problems, and answer choices to students as necessary. Use the answer key to score the Checkpoint and then enter the results online.

⚙ Checkpoint   Math | Numbers Through 500 | Count Aloud Through 500

Name _____   Date _____

Checkpoint Answer Key

Follow the instructions for each item. Choose the response that best describes how the student performs on the task. When you are finished, enter the results online.

1. Say, "Say the numbers in order from 340 to 350."
(1 point)
Did the student correctly count in order from 340 to 350?
  A. Yes   B. No

2. Say, "Say the numbers in order from 175 to 200."
(1 point)
Did the student correctly count in order from 175 to 200?
  A. Yes   B. No

3. Say, "Say the numbers in order from 475 to 485."
(1 point)
Did the student correctly count in order from 475 to 485?
  A. Yes   B. No

4. Say, "Say the numbers in order from 296 to 300."
(1 point)
Did the student correctly count in order from 296 to 300?
  A. Yes   B. No

5. Say, "Say the numbers in order from 210 to 220."
(1 point)
Did the student correctly count in order from 210 to 220?
  A. Yes   B. No

Read Whole Numbers Through 500

Lesson Overview

Skills Update	5 minutes	ONLINE
GET READY Read Numbers Through 100	5 minutes	ONLINE
LEARN Read Numbers Through 500	15 minutes	ONLINE
LEARN How Do You Read That Number?	15 minutes	ONLINE
TRY IT Read That Number!	15 minutes	OFFLINE
CHECKPOINT	5 minutes	OFFLINE

▶ Lesson Objectives

Read whole numbers through 500.

▶ Prerequisite Skills

Read whole numbers through 100.

▶ Common Errors and Misconceptions

Students might have difficulty writing multidigit numbers because numerals do not correspond exactly to English number words. For example, students might write twenty-five as 205 (20 and 5) instead of 25.

▶ Content Background

Students will learn to read whole numbers through 500.

Materials to Gather

SUPPLIED
Read That Number! activity page
Checkpoint (printout)

Keywords

counting numbers – the numbers 1, 2, 3, 4, 5, 6, …
digit – any one of the numerals 0, 1, 2, 3, 4, 5, 6, 7, 8, 9
hundred chart – a 10-by-10 grid displaying the numbers from 1 to 100 in order from left to right
multidigit number – a number with more than one digit, such as 26 or 547
place-value chart – a chart or arrangement that shows the value of each digit in a number
whole numbers – zero and the counting numbers (0, 1, 2, 3, 4, 5, 6, …)

GET READY Read Numbers Through 100

Objectives

- Read whole numbers through 100.

Students will review how to read numbers from 1 to 100. Begin by opening the Hundred Chart Learning Tool.

DIRECTIONS FOR USING THE HUNDRED CHART LEARNING TOOL

1. Have students read a number between 1 and 100 on the hundred chart and then click the number to hear it. If students do **not** say the number correctly, have them say the number again and replay the audio.

2. Point to various numbers for students to say, including some with zeros in the ones place, such as 30.

LEARN Read Numbers Through 500

Objectives

- Read whole numbers through 500.

Students will use a simple place-value chart to read numbers greater than 100.

The place-value chart helps students see that when we read numbers, we often read the value of each digit in the number.

LEARN How Do You Read That Number?

Objectives

- Read whole numbers through 500.

Students will practice reading numbers through 500.

Begin by opening the Hundred Chart Learning Tool.

Use the arrow buttons at the bottom of the screen to move between hundreds. Point to a number between 1 and 500 and have students read the number. Then have them click the number to hear it.

Choose a variety of numbers, including: 309, 200, 480, and 499. Continue as activity time allows.

Tips

When students read a number greater than 100, listen carefully to be sure they are not doing the following:

- Using the word *and* (They should say "three hundred eight," not "three hundred and eight.")
- Reading 308 as three-oh-eight

TRY IT Read That Number!

Objectives

- Read whole numbers through 500.

Give students the Read That Number! activity page from their Activity Book. Follow the directions on the activity page.

Students will practice reading numbers through 500. Give students the Read That Number! activity page from their Activity Book and read the directions with them.

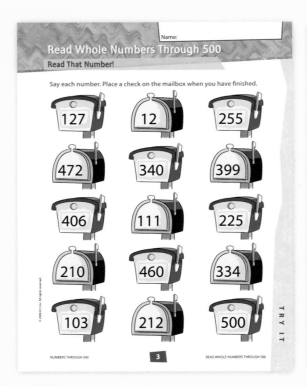

Read Whole Numbers Through 500

Read That Number!

Say each number. Place a check on the mailbox when you have finished.

127 12 255
472 340 399
406 111 225
210 460 334
103 212 500

NUMBERS THROUGH 500   **3**   READ WHOLE NUMBERS THROUGH 500

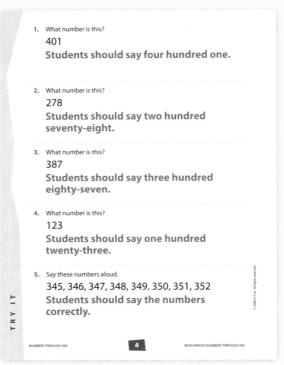

1. What number is this?

   401

   Students should say four hundred one.

2. What number is this?

   278

   Students should say two hundred seventy-eight.

3. What number is this?

   387

   Students should say three hundred eighty-seven.

4. What number is this?

   123

   Students should say one hundred twenty-three.

5. Say these numbers aloud.

   345, 346, 347, 348, 349, 350, 351, 352

   Students should say the numbers correctly.

NUMBERS THROUGH 500   **4**   READ WHOLE NUMBERS THROUGH 500

CHECKPOINT

OFFLINE

5 min

Objectives

Print the Checkpoint and have students complete it on their own. Read the directions, problems, and answer choices to students as necessary. Use the answer key to score the Checkpoint and then enter the results online.

- Read whole numbers through 500.

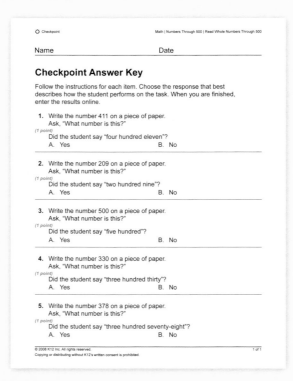

⚙ Checkpoint   Math | Numbers Through 500 | Read Whole Numbers Through 500

Name _____   Date _____

Checkpoint Answer Key

Follow the instructions for each item. Choose the response that best describes how the student performs on the task. When you are finished, enter the results online.

1. Write the number 411 on a piece of paper.
   Ask, "What number is this?"
   (1 point)
   Did the student say "four hundred eleven"?
   A. Yes   B. No

2. Write the number 209 on a piece of paper.
   Ask, "What number is this?"
   (1 point)
   Did the student say "two hundred nine"?
   A. Yes   B. No

3. Write the number 500 on a piece of paper.
   Ask, "What number is this?"
   (1 point)
   Did the student say "five hundred"?
   A. Yes   B. No

4. Write the number 330 on a piece of paper.
   Ask, "What number is this?"
   (1 point)
   Did the student say "three hundred thirty"?
   A. Yes   B. No

5. Write the number 378 on a piece of paper.
   Ask, "What number is this?"
   (1 point)
   Did the student say "three hundred seventy-eight"?
   A. Yes   B. No

1 of 1

Write Numerals Through 500

Lesson Overview

Skills Update	5 minutes	**ONLINE**
GET READY Write Numerals Through 100	10 minutes	**OFFLINE**
LEARN Writing Numerals on Hundred Charts	30 minutes	**OFFLINE**
TRY IT Writing Numerals Through 500	10 minutes	**OFFLINE**
CHECKPOINT	5 minutes	**OFFLINE**

▶ Lesson Objectives

Write numerals through 500.

▶ Prerequisite Skills

Write numerals through 100.

▶ Common Errors and Misconceptions

Students might have difficulty writing multidigit numbers because numerals do not correspond exactly to English number words. For example, students might write twenty-five as 205 (20 and 5) instead of 25.

▶ Advance Preparation

Print the Hundred Grid and fill in all of the numbers except the following: 4, 15, 22, 37, 41, 55, 61, 73, 80, 82, and 90.

▶ Content Background

Students will learn to write numerals through 500 by filling in numbers on Hundred Charts from 101 to 500. As they write the numerals on each chart, they will identify patterns of what changes and what stays the same.

   Mathematically, the distinction between the terms numeral and number is that a numeral is a symbol and number represents a quantity. So, a numeral, such as 1, 2, 3, and so on, symbolically represents the number, or quantity. In everyday language, we say number most often to refer to both the symbol and the quantity. As you speak with your students, the use of number is appropriate. This lesson is titled "Write Numerals Through 500" to convey correct mathematical terminology.

Materials to Gather

SUPPLIED

Writing Numerals on Hundred Charts activity page

Writing Numerals Through 500 activity page

Hundred Grid (printout)

Checkpoint (printout)

place-value mat

ALSO NEEDED

dry-erase marker

dry-erase eraser

Keywords

numeral – a symbol that stands for a number

GET READY Write Numerals Through 100

OFFLINE 10 min

Students will write the numbers that are missing from the Hundred Grid as you say them. They should write the following numbers: 4, 15, 22, 37, 41, 55, 61, 73, 80, 82, and 90.

Objectives

- Write numerals through 100.

LEARN Writing Numerals on Hundred Charts

OFFLINE 30 min

Objectives

- Write numerals through 500.

Students will practice writing numerals through 500.

Gather the place-value mat, marker, tissue or eraser, and the Writing Numerals on Hundred Charts activity pages from the Activity Book.

1. **Say:** Write the number 182. How many hundreds are there in one hundred eighty-two?
   ANSWER: 1

   Say: Write a 1 in the hundreds place.

2. **Ask:** How many tens are there in one hundred eighty-two?
   ANSWER: 8 (If students do not know, ask them how many tens there are in 80, and have them count by tens to check.)

   Say: Write an 8 in the tens place.

3. **Ask:** How many ones are there in one hundred eighty-two?
   ANSWER: 2

   Say: Write a 2 in the ones place.

4. **Say:** Read the number you wrote.
   ANSWER: 182

5. Repeat Steps 1–4 with the following numbers: 205, 311, 470, 300, 99.

6. Give students a blank sheet of paper, and have them write the following numbers by writing the hundreds, the tens, and then the ones: 119, 304, 475, 500.

7. Give students the Writing Numerals on Hundred Charts activity pages, and read the directions with them. As students work, have them point out the patterns that repeat on each Hundred Chart.

Tips

Be sure students understand that they must write a 0 when there are zero tens or ones in a number.

Write Numerals Through 500
Writing Numerals on Hundred Charts

Hundred Chart 1

101	102	103	104	105	106	107	108	109	110
111	112	113	114	115	116	117	118	119	120
121	122	123	124	125	126	127	128	129	130
131	132	133	134	135	136	137	138	139	140
141	142	143	144	145	146	147	148	149	150
151	152	153	154	155	156	157	158	159	160
161	162	163	164	165	166	167	168	169	170
171	172	173	174	175	176	177	178	179	180
181	182	183	184	185	186	187	188	189	190
191	192	193	194	195	196	197	198	199	200

LEARN

Hundred Chart 2

201	202	203	204	205	206	207	208	209	210
211	212	213	214	215	216	217	218	219	220
221	222	223	224	225	226	227	228	229	230
231	232	233	234	235	236	237	238	239	240
241	242	243	244	245	246	247	248	249	250
251	252	253	254	255	256	257	258	259	260
261	262	263	264	265	266	267	268	269	270
271	272	273	274	275	276	277	278	279	280
281	282	283	284	285	286	287	288	289	290
291	292	293	294	295	296	297	298	299	300

LEARN

Hundred Chart 3

301	302	303	304	305	306	307	308	309	310
311	312	313	314	315	316	317	318	319	320
321	322	323	324	325	326	327	328	329	330
331	332	333	334	335	336	337	338	339	340
341	342	343	344	345	346	347	348	349	350
351	352	353	354	355	356	357	358	359	360
361	362	363	364	365	366	367	368	369	370
371	372	373	374	375	376	377	378	379	380
381	382	383	384	385	386	387	388	389	390
391	392	393	394	395	396	397	398	399	400

LEARN

Hundred Chart 4

401	402	403	404	405	406	407	408	409	410
411	412	413	414	415	416	417	418	419	420
421	422	423	424	425	426	427	428	429	430
431	432	433	434	435	436	437	438	439	440
441	442	443	444	445	446	447	448	449	450
451	452	453	454	455	456	457	458	459	460
461	462	463	464	465	466	467	468	469	470
471	472	473	474	475	476	477	478	479	480
481	482	483	484	485	486	487	488	489	490
491	492	493	494	495	496	497	498	499	500

LEARN

OFFLINE
10 min

- Write numerals through 500.

Students will practice writing numerals from 1 through 500. Give students the Writing Numerals Through 500 activity page from their Activity Book and read the directions with them.

For Problems 1–5, use the following numbers:

1. three hundred forty-seven
2. one hundred six
3. one hundred twelve
4. four hundred fifty-nine
5. two hundred seventy-two

Name: _____

Write Numerals Through 500
Writing Numerals Through 500

Write the numbers as you hear them.

1. __347__
2. __106__
3. __112__
4. __459__
5. __272__

6. Fill in the missing numbers in the partial hundred charts.

431	432	**433**	434	435	436	437	**438**	439	440
201	202	203	**204**	**205**	206	207	208	209	**210**
391	392	393	394	395	396	**397**	398	**399**	**400**
271	**272**	273	274	275	276	277	278	279	**280**

TRY IT

Complete Problems 7–12.

7. Write the number for two hundred sixty-two. __262__

8. Write the numbers for one hundred twenty-nine through one hundred thirty-nine.

   __129__, __130__, __131__, __132__, __133__, __134__,
   __135__, __136__, __137__, __138__, __139__

9. Write the number for three hundred sixty-six. __366__

10. Write the number for four hundred. __400__

11. Write the number for three hundred three. __303__

12. Write the numbers for four hundred fifty-five through four hundred sixty-five.

    __455__, __456__, __457__, __458__, __459__, __460__,
    __461__, __462__, __463__, __464__, __465__

TRY IT

CHECKPOINT

OFFLINE 5 min

Print the Checkpoint and have students complete it on their own. Read the directions, problems, and answer choices to students as necessary. Use the answer key to score the Checkpoint and then enter the results online.

Objectives

- Write numerals through 500.

☼ Checkpoint   Math | Numbers Through 500 | Write Numerals Through 500

Name _____ Date _____

Checkpoint Answer Key

Follow the instructions for each item. Choose the response that best describes how the student performs on the task. When you are finished, enter the results online.

1. Say, "Write the number one hundred one."
(1 point)
Did the student write the number 101?

  A. Yes   B. No

---

2. Say, "Write the number two hundred twenty-two."
(1 point)
Did the student write the number 222?

  A. Yes   B. No

---

3. Say, "Write the number three hundred three."
(1 point)
Did the student write the number 303?

  A. Yes   B. No

---

4. Say, "Write the number four hundred eighteen."
(1 point)
Did the student write the number 418?

  A. Yes   B. No

---

5. Say, "Write the number three hundred eighty."
(1 point)
Did the student write the number 380?

  A. Yes   B. No

Identify Place Value

Lesson Overview

Skills Update	5 minutes	ONLINE
GET READY Tens and Ones	5 minutes	ONLINE
LEARN What's the Value?	15 minutes	ONLINE
LEARN Represent Numbers Through 500	15 minutes	OFFLINE
TRY IT Place Value	20 minutes	OFFLINE

▶ Lesson Objectives

Identify the place value for each digit in whole numbers through 500.

▶ Prerequisite Skills

- Count and group objects in ones and tens, such as 4 groups of 10 objects with 2 more objects = 40 + 2 = 42.
- Demonstrate understanding of place value by grouping given numbers into sets of tens and ones, such as 64 = 6 tens and 4 ones.

▶ Common Errors and Misconceptions

- Students might not realize that a digit's place-value position determines its value. For example, students might think the digits in 14 have values of 1 and 4, not 10 and 4.
- Students might have difficulty modeling multidigit numbers with counting objects. For example, when asked to model 23, students might use two objects to represent the 2 rather than using twenty objects.

▶ Content Background

In this lesson, students will learn about place value and the value of each digit in a number. They will use base-10 blocks to model numbers and identify the value of each digit in a 3-digit number.

The numbers 0 through 9 are called *digits*. The digits 0 through 9 can be used to write any number in the base-10 system that we use. Each digit's value in a number is called its *place value*.

Materials to Gather

SUPPLIED

base-10 blocks

place-value mat

Place Value activity page

ALSO NEEDED

dry-erase marker

dry-erase eraser

GET READY Tens and Ones

ONLINE 5 min

Students will show understanding of place value by arranging beads into groups of tens and ones and then answering questions about the groups.

Objectives

- Count and group objects in ones and tens, such as 4 groups of 10 objects with 2 more objects = 40 + 2 = 42.

- Demonstrate understanding of place value by grouping given numbers into sets of tens and ones, such as 64 = 6 tens and 4 ones.

Tips

If students have difficulty seeing that combining the tens and ones makes a whole number, have students count each bead to see that the result is the same. For example, 2 tens and 6 ones is the same as 26 ones.

LEARN What's the Value?

ONLINE 15 min

Students will see how groups of 1, 10, and 100 items can be used to represent numbers and that each digit in a number represents a value.

Objectives

- Identify the place value for each digit in whole numbers through 500.

LEARN Represent Numbers Through 500

Objectives

- Identify the place value for each digit in whole numbers through 500.

Students will be introduced to base-10 blocks, and use the blocks to model numbers. They will use the written number and the blocks to find the value of each digit in the number.

Gather the base-10 blocks, the place-value mat, and a dry-erase marker and eraser.

1. Have students write the number 462 on the place-value mat, putting one digit in each place. The 4 should be in the hundreds place, the 6 should be in the tens place, and the 2 should be in the ones place.

2. Show students the ones cubes and explain that each cube stands for 1. Tell them they are called ones cubes.

   Ask: How many ones cubes do you need to show the ones in 462?
   ANSWER: 2

   Have students place 2 ones cubes below the 2 on the place-value mat.

3. Show students the tens rods and ask them what each tens rod stands for. If they are unsure, have them line up ones cubes next to a tens rod to find out how many it represents. Tell them they are called tens rods.

   Ask: How many tens rods do you need to show the tens in 462?
   ANSWER: 6

   Have students place 6 tens rods below the 6 on the place-value mat.

   Ask: What does the 6 stand for in 462?
   ANSWER: 6 tens or 60

4. Show students the hundreds flats and ask them what each flat stands for. If they are unsure, have them line up tens rods on the hundreds flat and count by 10s to find out how many it represents. Tell them they are called hundreds flats.

   Ask: How many hundreds flats do you need to show the hundreds in 462?
   ANSWER: 4

   Have students place 4 hundreds flats on the place-value mat below the 4.

   Ask: What does the 4 stand for in 462?
   ANSWER: 4 hundreds or 400.

5. Place 2 hundreds flats, 3 tens rods, and 5 ones cubes on the place-value mat.

   Ask: How many hundreds are there in this number?
   ANSWER: 2
   Say: Write the 2 in the hundreds place.

   Repeat for tens and ones.

6. Have students read the number aloud and then tell you the value of each digit. (The value of the 2 is 200. The value of the 3 is 30. The value of the 5 is 5.)

7. Repeat Steps 5–6 with the numbers:
   - 403 (The value of the 4 is 400. The value of the 0 is 0. The value of the 3 is 3.)
   - 340 (The value of the 3 is 300. The value of the 4 is 40. The value of the 0 is 0.)
   - 116 (The value of the first 1 is 100. The value of the second 1 is 10. The value of the 6 is 6.)

8. Write the number 279 on the place-value mat. Ask students to read the number aloud and then tell you the value of each digit. Repeat with the numbers 401 and 199.

Ones Cube

Tens Rod

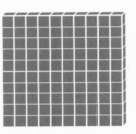

Hundreds Flat

Tips

If students have difficulty finding the number represented by the base-10 blocks, have them physically count each block. For example, if students count 3 hundreds flats, they should record a 3 in the hundreds column of the place-value mat.

TRY IT Place Value

Students will practice writing numbers in a place-value chart and identifying the value of a digit in a number. Give students the Place Value activity page from their Activity Book and read the directions with them. Use the answer key to check students' answers, and then enter the results online.

Objectives

- Identify the place value for each digit in whole numbers through 500.

Tips

If students confuse the face value of the digit (e.g., 2 in 245) with its actual value (200), have them say each digit with its place value. For example, for the number 245, students would say, "2 hundreds, 4 tens, 5 ones." Students can then find the value of each digit.

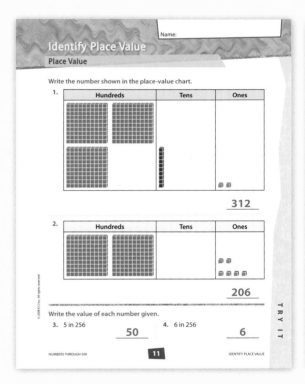

Name:

Identify Place Value
Place Value

Write the number shown in the place-value chart.

1.

Hundreds	Tens	Ones

312

2.

Hundreds	Tens	Ones

206

Write the value of each number given.

3. 5 in 256   **50**   4. 6 in 256   **6**

T R Y   I T

Write the value of each number given.

5. 4 in 437   **400**   6. 3 in 437   **30**

Circle the value for the underlined number.

7. 329
   A. 2
   B. 20
   C. 200

8. 475
   A. 5
   B. 50
   C. 500

9. 198
   A. 8 ones
   B. 8 tens
   C. 8 hundreds

10. 241
   A. 2 ones
   B. 2 tens
   C. 2 hundreds

11. 461
   A. 4
   B. 40
   C. 400

12. 367
   A. 6 ones
   B. 6 tens
   C. 6 hundreds

Complete the place value for each problem.

13. 409
   4 hundreds   **0** tens   **9** ones

14. 330
   3 hundreds   **3** tens   **0** ones

15. 160
   1 hundreds   **6** tens   **0** ones

16. 202
   2 hundreds   **0** tens   **2** ones

Use Expanded Form: Numbers Through 500

Skills Update	5 minutes	ONLINE
GET READY Grouping Tens and Ones	5 minutes	ONLINE
LEARN Expanded Form Through 500	20 minutes	ONLINE
LEARN Writing Numbers in Expanded Form	20 minutes	OFFLINE
TRY IT Expand a Number	10 minutes	OFFLINE

▶ Lesson Objectives

Use expanded forms to represent numbers through 500, such as
345 = 3 hundreds + 4 tens + 5 ones = 300 + 40 + 5.

▶ Prerequisite Skills

Demonstrate understanding of place value by grouping given numbers into sets of tens and ones, such as 64 = 6 tens and 4 ones.

▶ Advance Preparation

Number index cards 1, 3, 5, 20, 90, 100, 300, and 500. Label two other index cards as follows: **0 tens** and **0 ones**. Label two other index cards with the plus symbol (+).

▶ Content Background

When numbers are written in the conventional way, such as 365, they are said to be written in *standard form*. In this lesson, students will learn to write numbers through 500 in *expanded form*. For example, the number 365 can be written in expanded form as: 300 + 60 + 5 or 3 hundreds + 6 tens + 5 ones.

Materials to Gather

SUPPLIED

Expand a Number activity page

base-10 blocks (optional)

place-value mat

ALSO NEEDED

index cards – numbered 1, 3, 5, 20, 90, 100, 300, and 500

index cards – labeled **0 tens**, **0 ones**, and + (two cards)

dry-erase marker

dry-erase eraser

Keywords

expanded form – a way to write a number that shows the place value of each of its digits; for example, 428 = 400 + 20 + 8 or 4 hundreds + 2 tens + 8 ones
hundreds place – the third digit to the left of the decimal point in a number; the digit represents zero hundreds through 9 hundreds
ones place – the first digit to the left of the decimal point in a number; the digit represents zero ones through 9 ones
standard form – the conventional way of writing numbers; 348 is standard form whereas 300 + 40 + 8 is expanded form
tens place – the second digit to the left of the decimal point in a number; the digit represents zero tens through 9 tens

GET READY Grouping Tens and Ones

Objectives

Students will review place value by grouping a number into sets of tens and ones. Be sure to emphasize that a digit in the tens place represents how many tens are in the number.

- Demonstrate understanding of place value by grouping given numbers into sets of tens and ones, such as 64 = 6 tens and 4 ones.

LEARN Expanded Form Through 500

Objectives

Students will learn to connect place value to writing a number in expanded form by modeling numbers in groups of hundreds, tens, and ones.

- Use expanded forms to represent numbers through 500, such as 345 = 3 hundreds + 4 tens + 5 ones = 300 + 40 + 5.

DIRECTIONS FOR USING THE PLACE VALUE LEARNING TOOL

1. Click Begin Setup and choose the following:
   - Work with NUMBERS up to: 500
   - Use regrouping: NO
   - Teacher or parent makes question
2. Enter the number 365, and then have students build the number.
3. Point out the expanded form shown at the bottom of the place-value chart.

   Say: When you write a number in expanded form, you show the value of each digit as an addition expression. Three hundreds equals 300. Six tens equals 60. Five ones equals 5. So 300 + 60 + 5 = 365.
4. Repeat the process for the following numbers. Before students click Check, have them tell you what the expanded form will be.
   - 274
   - 402
5. Explain that a zero in a place value means that there are no groups in that place. In 402, there are no groups of 10, so there is a 0 in the tens place.

Tips

If students seem to be missing the connection between place value and expanded form, consider using base-10 blocks. Point out that the rods and flats are made up of ones cubes.

LEARN Writing Numbers in Expanded Form

- Use expanded forms to represent numbers through 500, such as 345 = 3 hundreds + 4 tens + 5 ones = 300 + 40 + 5.

Students will use number cards and a place-value chart to write numbers in expanded form and in standard form.

Gather the number and symbol cards, place-value mat, marker, and eraser.

1. Slide the 100 card, the 20 card, and the 5 card together to show 125.

   Say: This number is in standard form. That means this is the way we usually write the number. To write the same number in expanded form, we will start by finding the value of each digit. Then we will write the digits as an addition expression. What is the value of the 1?

   ANSWER: 100, or 1 hundred. If students are unsure, prompt them by asking if the 1 stands for 1, 1 ten, or 1 hundred.

   Say: Write 100 in the hundreds place on the place-value mat, and then write a plus symbol next to it.

2. **Ask:** What is the value of the 2?
   ANSWER: 20, or 2 tens.

   Say: Write 20 in the tens place on the place-value mat, and then write a plus symbol next to it.

3. **Ask:** What is the value of the 5?
   ANSWER: 5, or 5 ones. If students are unsure, prompt them by asking if the 5 stands for 5, 5 tens, or 5 hundreds.

   Say: Write 5 in the ones place on the place-value mat. Now read the expanded form aloud.

4. Slide the cards apart, and place a plus symbol card between the 100 and 20 and between the 20 and 5. Have students check their written expanded form by comparing it to the cards.

5. Repeat these steps for the numbers 409 (400 card, 0 tens card, and 9 card), and 290 (200 card, 90 card and 0 ones card). Have students separate the number cards to check their written work.

6. **Say:** Now we will go the opposite way! We will see a number in expanded form first, and try to write it in standard form.

7. Follow the steps below for the numbers 193, 301, and 500.

   - Arrange the three place-value cards with plus symbols in between to show the expanded form.

   - Have students write the digit for each place on the place-value mat. Then have them read the number aloud.

   - Have students slide the cards together to show the standard form of the number and compare it to their written work.

When students see a number in expanded form such as 125 = 100 + 20 + 5 and are asked how many hundreds are in the number, they might say 100 at first rather than 1. Help them to recognize 100 as 1 hundred, and, similarly, help them to see 20 as 2 tens.

TRY IT Expand a Number

Objectives

Students will practice putting numbers in expanded form and in standard form. Give students the Expand a Number activity page from their Activity Book and read the directions with them. Use the answer key to check students' answers, and then enter the results online.

- Use expanded forms to represent numbers through 500, such as 345 = 3 hundreds + 4 tens + 5 ones = 300 + 40 + 5.

Name: _____

Use Expanded Form: Numbers Through 500

Expand a Number

Write each number in expanded form.

1. 345 = __3__ hundreds + __4__ tens + __5__ ones

2. 204 = __2__ hundreds + __0__ tens + __4__ ones

3. 460 = __4__ hundreds + __6__ tens + __0__ ones

4. 369 = __300__ + __60__ + __9__

5. 273 = __200__ + __70__ + __3__

Write each number in standard form.

6. 2 hundreds + 8 tens + 7 ones = __287__

7. 3 hundreds + 3 tens + 0 ones = __330__

8. 200 + 60 + 6 = __266__   9. 300 + 20 + 4 = __324__

TRY IT

Choose the expanded form of each number.

10. 485
  - A. 4 hundreds + 80 tens + 5 ones
  - B. 40 hundreds + 8 tens + 5 ones
  - C. 4 hundreds + 8 tens + 5 ones *(circled)*
  - D. 48 hundreds + 5 ones

11. 77
  - A. 7 + 7
  - B. 7 + 0 + 7
  - C. 70 + 70
  - D. 70 + 7 *(circled)*

Write the answer.

12. What is 299 written in expanded form?

  __2__ hundreds + __9__ tens + __9__ ones

Circle the answer.

13. Which of the following shows 453 in expanded form?
  - A. 4 + 5 + 3
  - B. 45 + 3
  - C. 400 + 50 + 3 *(circled)*
  - D. 450 + 50 + 30

14. Which of the following shows 340 in expanded form?
  - A. 34 + 0
  - B. 3 + 4 + 0
  - C. 3 + 40 + 0
  - D. 300 + 40 + 0 *(circled)*

TRY IT

Model Addition Problems

Skills Update	5 minutes	**ONLINE**
GET READY What's the Number?	5 minutes	OFFLINE
LEARN Model to Add 3-Digit Numbers	15 minutes	OFFLINE
TRY IT Use Counting Blocks	5 minutes	OFFLINE
LEARN Model Addition with Regrouping	20 minutes	**ONLINE**
TRY IT Model and Solve	15 minutes	OFFLINE

▶ Lesson Objectives

Use models to represent regrouping in addition problems or subtraction problems.

▶ Prerequisite Skills

- Count and group objects in ones and tens, such as 4 groups of 10 objects with 2 more objects = 40 + 2 = 42.
- Demonstrate understanding of place value by grouping given numbers into sets of tens and ones, such as 64 = 6 tens and 4 ones.

▶ Common Errors and Misconceptions

- Students might not think of numbers as groups of tens, hundreds, and so forth. For example, students might think of 24 only as 24 single units, not 2 tens and 4 ones.
- Students might not realize that a digit's place-value position determines its value. For example, students might think the digits in 14 have values of 1 and 4, not 10 and 4.
- Students might have difficulty modeling multidigit numbers with counting objects. For example, when asked to model 23, students might use two objects to represent the 2 rather than using twenty objects.

▶ Content Background

Students will use base-10 blocks to model and solve 3-digit addition problems. In this lesson, students will do problems that do not require regrouping, and then they will do problems with regrouping.

Base-10 models make it is easy for students to see that when they have 10 blocks in one place-value column they can exchange them for a larger block. For example, if the ones column has 13 ones cubes, they can regroup 10 of them into 1 tens rod and place it in the tens column.

The term *carrying* used to be used to describe regrouping in addition, and *borrowing* was used for regrouping in subtraction. Since these terms simply refer to a regrouping of a number in a different way, *regrouping* has replaced both terms.

Materials to Gather

SUPPLIED

base-10 blocks

place-value mat

Model and Solve activity page

addend – one of the two or more numbers that are added to determine a sum

addition – the process of combining, or putting together, groups of objects or numbers; a mathematical operation

regroup; regrouping – to use place-value concepts to rename numbers, such as 1 ten and 3 ones = 13 ones; often used in addition and subtraction

sum – the solution to an addition problem

GET READY What's the Number?

OFFLINE
5min

Objectives

Students will identify the number modeled by base-10 blocks, regrouping when necessary. Gather the base-10 blocks and the place-value mat.

- Count and group objects in ones and tens, such as 4 groups of 10 objects with 2 more objects = 40 + 2 = 42.

- Demonstrate understanding of place value by grouping given numbers into sets of tens and ones, such as 64 = 6 tens and 4 ones.

1. Set out 5 tens rods and 8 ones cubes on the place-value mat. Write a 5 below the tens rods and an 8 below the ones cubes.

   Say: What number is this?
   ANSWER: 58

2. **Say:** I am going to model another number. See if you can figure out what number it is.

   Set out 6 tens rods and 12 ones cubes on the place-value mat. Write a 6 under the tens rods and a 12 under the ones cubes. Students may count by 10s and then add on ones to find the correct number.
   ANSWER: 72

3. **Say:** Look at the numbers I wrote. There are 6 tens and 12 ones. There are enough ones cubes that we can make another ten. Take out 10 of the ones cubes, and exchange them for 1 tens rod.

4. Cross off the written numbers and change the 6 to a 7 and the 12 to a 2.

   Say: This is called regrouping. We had too many ones, so we regrouped 10 of them into 1 tens rod. What number is this?
   ANSWER: 72

5. Set out 3 tens rods and 15 ones cubes. Write a 3 under the tens rods and a 15 under the ones cubes. Have students regroup before counting. Students should then cross off the 3 and the 15 and write the correct numbers.
   ANSWER: 45

6. Set out 1 hundreds flat and 18 tens rods. Write a 1 in the hundreds column and an 18 in the tens column. Point out that you can regroup 10 tens into 1 hundred, and exchange the tens rods for a hundreds flat. Have students cross off the numbers on the mat and write the correct numbers.
   ANSWER: 280

LEARN Model to Add 3-Digit Numbers

Objectives

- Use models to represent regrouping in addition or subtraction problems.

Students will use base-10 blocks to solve addition problems with 3-digit numbers. Gather the base-10 blocks and place-value mat.

1. Have students model the numbers 132 and 145 on the place-value mat. They should leave enough space between the two numbers so that they can clearly see both.

2. **Say:** Now let's add 132 plus 145. Combine your two groups of blocks.

3. **Ask:** How many ones are there
   ANSWER: 7

   Ask: How many tens do you have?
   ANSWER: 7

   Ask: How many hundreds?
   ANSWER: 2

4. **Ask:** What is the sum?
   ANSWER: 277

   Ask: Did you have to regroup any blocks to find the sum?
   ANSWER: No

5. Write the following problem on a sheet of paper: 315 + 124

   Say: Let's try another one. Show the numbers with your blocks on the place-value mat. Then solve the addition problem.

6. Check that students correctly show each addend and combine the blocks to find the answer.

   Ask: What is the sum of 315 plus 124?
   ANSWER: 439

7. **Say:** Sometimes you may have 10 or more ones cubes, and you will need to regroup them into 1 tens rod before you can find your sum.

   Use your blocks to show 146 on the place-value mat. Then use your blocks to show 128.

8. **Say:** Combine your two groups to show 146 plus 128. Begin with the ones.

   Ask: How many ones are there?
   ANSWER: 14

   Say: There are more than 10 ones cubes, so you need to regroup. Trade 10 ones for 1 ten. Now add the tens.

   Ask: How many tens are there?
   ANSWER: 7

   Say: Add the hundreds.

   Ask: How many hundreds do you have?
   ANSWER: 2

   Ask: What is the sum of 146 and 128?
   ANSWER: 274

9. Give students additional 3-digit problems with regrouping to model with blocks and solve as time permits.

   a. 257 + 318 (575)
   b. 411 + 279 (690)
   c. 135 + 216 (351)

TRY IT Use Counting Blocks

OFFLINE 5 min

Objectives

- Use models to represent regrouping in addition or subtraction problems.

Have students use base-10 blocks to find the following sums. Note how students perform, and then enter the results online.

1. Use the base-10 blocks to add 46 and 21.
   ANSWER: 67

2. Use the base-10 blocks to add 32 and 24.
   ANSWER: 56

LEARN Model Addition with Regrouping

ONLINE 20 min

Objectives

- Use models to represent regrouping in addition or subtraction problems.

Students will use base-10 blocks to show 3-digit numbers and combine the blocks to show addition of the numbers. They will regroup as needed to find the sum.

DIRECTIONS FOR USING THE PLACE VALUE ADDITION LEARNING TOOL

1. Click Begin Setup and choose the following:
   - Present addition problems with SUMS up to: 500
   - Allow REGROUPING in problems: YES
   - Computer Makes Questions
2. Show students the addition problem in the upper left corner. Point out the first addend model on the place-value chart and the second addend model below it. Click Begin.
3. As students follow the directions, make sure they see the problem being completed in the upper left corner.

Tips

If necessary, students may use their own base-10 blocks to copy the blocks on the screen. Students can physically manipulate the blocks when they combine the addends to reinforce the regrouping concept.

TRY IT Model and Solve

OFFLINE 15 min

Objectives

- Use models to represent regrouping in addition or subtraction problems.

Students will practice modeling and solving addition problems. Give students the base-10 blocks and Model and Solve activity page from their Activity Book. Read the directions with them. Use the answer key to check students' answers, and then enter the results online.

Tips

Remind students to regroup 10 ones as 1 ten when necessary.

Model Addition Problems

Model and Solve

Use base-10 blocks to show the numbers and find the sum for each problem.

1. 37
   + 12
   49

2. 45
   + 34
   79

3. 68
   + 19
   87

4. 54
   + 27
   81

5. 211
   + 157
   368

6. 340
   + 236
   576

7. 246
   + 125
   371

8. 414
   + 349
   763

T R Y   I T

Use base-10 blocks to show the numbers and find the sum for each problem.

9. 29
   + 12
   41

10. 19
    + 29
    48

11. 79
    + 36
    115

12. 207
    + 39
    246

13. 127
    + 127
    254

14. 346
    + 134
    480

15. 119
    + 222
    341

16. 255
    + 176
    431

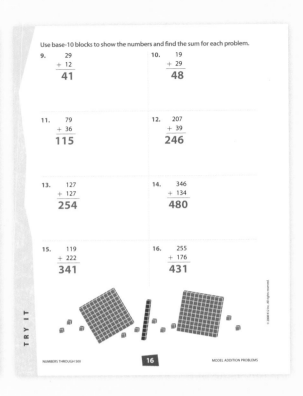

T R Y   I T

Place Value and Regrouping

Skills Update	5 minutes	**ONLINE**
GET READY Grouping and Place Value	5 minutes	**ONLINE**
LEARN Model Numbers in Expanded Form	15 minutes	**ONLINE**
LEARN Add Numbers with Regrouping	15 minutes	**OFFLINE**
TRY IT Regrouping and Expanded Form	10 minutes	**OFFLINE**
CHECKPOINT	10 minutes	**OFFLINE**

▶ Lesson Objectives

- Identify the place value for each digit in whole numbers through 500.
- Use models to represent regrouping in addition or subtraction problems.
- Use expanded forms to represent numbers through 500, such as $345 = 3$ hundreds $+ 4$ tens $+ 5$ ones $= 300 + 40 + 5$.

▶ Prerequisite Skills

- Count and group objects in ones and tens, such as 4 groups of 10 objects with 2 more objects $= 40 + 2 = 42$.
- Demonstrate understanding of place value by grouping given numbers into sets of tens and ones, such as $64 = 6$ tens and 4 ones.

▶ Content Background

In this lesson, students will practice modeling numbers in expanded form, identify the value of each digit in a number, and add 3-digit numbers with regrouping.

Materials to Gather

SUPPLIED

base-10 blocks

place-value mat

Regrouping and Expanded Form activity page

Checkpoint (printout)

ALSO NEEDED

dry-erase marker

dry-erase eraser

GET READY Grouping and Place Value

Students will count and group objects in groups of tens and ones.

- Count and group objects in ones and tens, such as 4 groups of 10 objects with 2 more objects = 40 + 2 = 42.
- Demonstrate understanding of place value by grouping given numbers into sets of tens and ones, such as 64 = 6 tens and 4 ones.

Tips

Have students skip count by 10s to 100. Make sure they say each 10 in sequential order.

LEARN Model Numbers in Expanded Form

Students will model numbers using base-10 blocks and then write the numbers in expanded form.

DIRECTIONS FOR USING THE PLACE VALUE LEARNING TOOL

1. Click Begin Setup and choose the following:
   - Work with NUMBERS up to: 500
   - Use regrouping: NO
   - Teacher or parent makes question
2. Enter the number 341 and then have students build the number. Ask students to explain how they showed the number. For example, I used 3 hundreds flats, 4 tens rods, and 1 ones cube.
3. Point out the expanded form shown at the bottom of the place-value chart. Explain that when a number is written in expanded form, the values for each digit are written as a sum. For example, 341 = 300 + 40 + 1.
4. Repeat the process for the following numbers. Before students click Check, have them write the expanded form on paper.
   - 162
   - 226
   - 403
5. Remind students that a zero in a place value means that there are no groups to represent that place. For example, 403 has no groups of 10. In math, the way to say "no tens" is to say and write that there are zero tens.

Objectives

- Identify the place value for each digit in whole numbers through 500.
- Use expanded forms to represent numbers through 500, such as 345 = 3 hundreds + 4 tens + 5 ones = 300 + 40 + 5.

Tips

If students have difficulty writing the numbers in expanded form, allow them to use base-10 blocks until they are comfortable reading the value of each digit.

LEARN Add Numbers with Regrouping

- Use models to represent regrouping in addition or subtraction problems.

Students will use base-10 blocks to model, regroup, and add 3-digit numbers. Gather the base-10 blocks, the place-value mat, and a dry-erase marker and eraser.

1. Have students model the number 328 using base-10 blocks. Below 328, have them model the number 157.

   Say: We are going to add these two numbers.

2. Put all of the ones cubes together to add the ones.

   Ask: How many ones cubes do you have altogether?
   ANSWER: 15

3. **Say:** When you have 10 or more blocks in a group, it's time to regroup. For example, you can regroup this group of 15 ones into 10 ones cubes and 5 ones cubes. Now take the group of 10 ones cubes and exchange them for 1 tens rod. Put this tens rod with the other tens rods. You will use this idea of regrouping a lot in addition and subtraction.

4. **Ask:** How many ones cubes do you have left?
   ANSWER: 5

   Ask: Do you need to regroup again?
   ANSWER: No

5. **Say:** Now combine the tens rods and count them. Do you need to regroup?
   ANSWER: No

6. **Say:** Now add the hundreds flats together. Do you need to regroup?
   ANSWER: No

   Ask: What is the sum?
   ANSWER: 485

7. Repeat Steps 3–5 using the following numbers:

   - 147 + 283 (430)
   - 263 + 149 (412)

Tips

Point out to students that sometimes they might need to regroup in one place, and at other times they might need to regroup in two places. Ask questions such as "Which places did you need to regroup?" or give instructions such as "Describe how you regrouped."

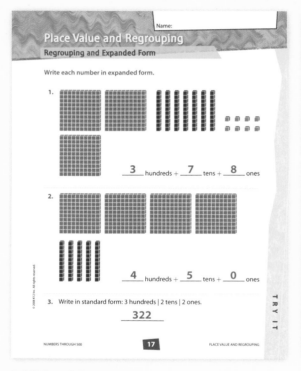

TRY IT Regrouping and Expanded Form

OFFLINE 10 min

Students will practice writing numbers in expanded form and standard form and identify the value of each digit. They will use regrouping to add 3-digit numbers. Give students the base-10 blocks and Regrouping and Expanded Form activity page from their Activity Book. Read the directions with them.

Objectives

- Identify the place value for each digit in whole numbers through 500.
- Use models to represent regrouping in addition or subtraction problems.
- Use expanded forms to represent numbers through 500, such as 345 = 3 hundreds + 4 tens + 5 ones = 300 + 40 + 5.

Name: _____

Place Value and Regrouping
Regrouping and Expanded Form

Write each number in expanded form.

1.

____3____ hundreds + ____7____ tens + ____8____ ones

2.

____4____ hundreds + ____5____ tens + ____0____ ones

3. Write in standard form: 3 hundreds | 2 tens | 2 ones.

____322____

NUMBERS THROUGH 500   **17**   PLACE VALUE AND REGROUPING

TRY IT

TRY IT

4. Explain the value of the digits in the tens and ones places in Problem 3.

See below. _____

_____

Model the numbers with base-10 blocks.
Then regroup and add. Write the sum on the line.

5. The sum of 236 and 147 is ____383____

Circle the answer.

6. What is the value of the 9 in 389?
   - A. 90
   - (B.) 9
   - C. 19
   - D. 900

7. What is the value of the 4 in 243?
   - A. 4 ones
   - (B.) 4 tens
   - C. 4 hundreds
   - D. 40 tens

8. Draw base-10 blocks to model and solve this problem.

   The sum of 255 and 177 is ____432____

   See below.

9. Choose the expanded form of the following number: 485.
   - A. 4 hundreds + 80 tens + 5 ones
   - B. 40 hundreds + 8 tens + 5 ones
   - (C.) 4 hundreds + 8 tens + 5 ones
   - D. 48 hundreds + 5 ones

NUMBERS THROUGH 500   **18**   PLACE VALUE AND REGROUPING

Additional Answers

4. The 2 in the tens place has a value of 20 and the 2 in the ones place has a value of 2.

8. Model should include 2 hundreds, 5 tens, 5 ones for 255 and 1 hundred, 7 tens, 7 ones for 177.

CHECKPOINT

Objectives

- Identify the place value for each digit in whole numbers through 500.
- Use models to represent regrouping in addition or subtraction problems.
- Use expanded forms to represent numbers through 500, such as $345 = 3$ hundreds $+ 4$ tens $+ 5$ ones $= 300 + 40 + 5$.

Print the Checkpoint and have students complete it on their own. Read the directions, problems, and answers to students as necessary. Use the answer key to score the Checkpoint, and then enter the results online.

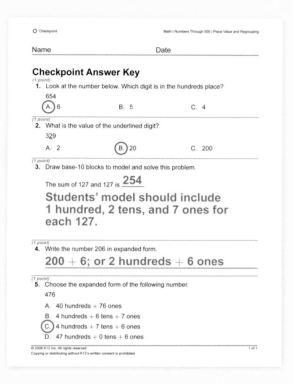

○ Checkpoint   Math | Numbers Through 500 | Place Value and Regrouping

Name _____ Date _____

Checkpoint Answer Key

(1 point)
1. Look at the number below. Which digit is in the hundreds place?

654

(A.) 6   B. 5   C. 4

(1 point)
2. What is the value of the underlined digit?

329

A. 2   (B.) 20   C. 200

(1 point)
3. Draw base-10 blocks to model and solve this problem.

The sum of 127 and 127 is 254.

Students' model should include 1 hundred, 2 tens, and 7 ones for each 127.

(1 point)
4. Write the number 206 in expanded form.

200 + 6; or 2 hundreds + 6 ones

(1 point)
5. Choose the expanded form of the following number.

476

A. 40 hundreds + 76 ones
B. 4 hundreds + 6 tens + 7 ones
(C.) 4 hundreds + 7 tens + 6 ones
D. 47 hundreds + 0 tens + 6 ones

Compare Numbers Through 500

Lesson Overview

Skills Update	5 minutes	ONLINE
GET READY Compare Numbers Through 20	5 minutes	ONLINE
LEARN Compare Numbers Through 500	20 minutes	OFFLINE
LEARN Which Number Is Greater?	10 minutes	ONLINE
TRY IT Compare Numbers	20 minutes	OFFLINE

▶ Lesson Objectives

Compare whole numbers through 500 by using the symbols $<$, $=$, $>$.

▶ Prerequisite Skills

Use the symbols for less than, equal to, or greater than ($<$, $=$, $>$) to compare and order whole numbers through 100.

▶ Common Errors and Misconceptions

- Students might not think of numbers as groups of tens, hundreds, and so forth. For example, students might think of 24 only as 24 single units, not 2 tens and 4 ones.

- Students might not realize that a digit's place-value position determines its value. For example, students might think the digits in 14 have values of 1 and 4, not 10 and 4.

- Students might compare numbers based on the ones digits as opposed to the digits in the greatest place-value position. For example, students might think 69 is greater than 71 because 9 is greater than 1.

▶ Advance Preparation

Label index cards with the following symbols: ?, $<$, $>$, and $=$. Write **less than**, **greater than**, and **equals** on the reverse side of the corresponding card.

▶ Content Background

In this lesson, students will use the greater-than ($>$), less-than ($<$), and equals ($=$) symbols to compare numbers. The greater-than symbol points to the right, and the less-than symbol points to the left. However, for ease in use, students can know that these comparison symbols point to the lesser number and open to the greater number.

Although the word *sign* is used often in everyday language, the word *symbol* is more accurate as a mathematical term. In math, *sign* specifically refers to the positive sign and negative sign that are used with numbers.

Materials to Gather

SUPPLIED

base-10 blocks

Compare Numbers activity page

ALSO NEEDED

index cards – labeled with symbols: ?, $>$, $<$, and $=$

compare – to find the similarities or differences among sizes, values, or amounts

equals symbol (=) – a symbol that shows the relationship between two equal values

greater-than symbol (>) – a symbol indicating that an amount or number is greater than another amount or number

less-than symbol (<) – a symbol indicating that an amount or number is less than another amount or number

GET READY Compare Numbers Through 20

ONLINE 5 min

Objectives

Students will compare numbers through 20 using online flash cards.

- Use the symbols for less than, equal to, or greater than (<, =, >) to compare and order whole numbers through 100.

LEARN Compare Numbers Through 500

OFFLINE 20 min

Objectives

Students will compare numbers through 500. They will learn to compare the value of each digit—hundreds, tens, and ones—to see if a number is greater than, less than, or equal to another number.

Gather the base-10 blocks and the labeled index cards.

- Compare whole numbers through 500 by using the symbols <, =, >.

1. Have students model the number 483 using the base-10 blocks. Then have them model 239 to the right of 483. Place the "?" card between the two models.

2. **Say:** Let's compare the numbers. When you compare numbers, you "read" the numbers from left to right. Both numbers have hundreds, so start by comparing the hundreds.

   Ask: How many hundreds are in 483?
   ANSWER: 4

   Ask: How many hundreds are in 239?
   ANSWER: 2

3. **Say:** 4 hundreds is greater than 2 hundreds, so you say "483 is greater than 239."

4. Give students the cards with the greater-than (>), less-than (<), and equals (=) symbols. Have them read the symbols on the cards. Then have them turn the cards over to see if they are correct.

5. Have students choose the correct card to use to compare 483 and 239. (They should choose the greater-than symbol.)

   Say: Place the greater-than symbol on top of the "?" card, and say "483 is greater than 239." Point to each number as you say it.

6. Have students move the models so that 239 is to the left of 483. Ask them to place the correct symbol between the numbers. Then have students say "239 is less than 483."

7. Have students model 394 and 311 placing the "?" card between the two numbers. Explain that both numbers have 3 hundreds, so students will need to compare the tens to decide which number is bigger. Repeat Steps 5–6.

8. Repeat the same steps for 287 and 280. This time students will have to compare the ones place, because both numbers have 2 hundreds and 8 tens.

9. Have students model 123 and 123.

   Ask: How many hundreds, tens, and ones does each number have?
   ANSWER: 1 hundred, 2 tens, and 3 ones

10. **Say:** When two numbers have the same number of hundreds, tens, and ones, the numbers are equal.

11. Place the equals symbol between the numbers. Point to each number and symbol.

    Say: 147 is equal to 147.

12. Have students compare more pairs of numbers. For example, compare 203 and 98, 291 and 291, 457 and 500, and 138 and 140.

ONLINE **10**min

LEARN Which Number Is Greater?

Students will compare numbers without using a model by looking at the numbers in the hundreds place, the tens place, and the ones place.

Objectives

- Compare whole numbers through 500 by using the symbols $<, =, >$.

OFFLINE **20**min

TRY IT Compare Numbers

Students will practice comparing numbers by looking at the numbers in the hundreds place, the tens place, and the ones place. Give students the Compare Numbers activity page from their Activity Book and read the directions with them. Use the answer key to check students' answers, and then enter the results online.

Objectives

- Compare whole numbers through 500 by using the symbols $<, =, >$.

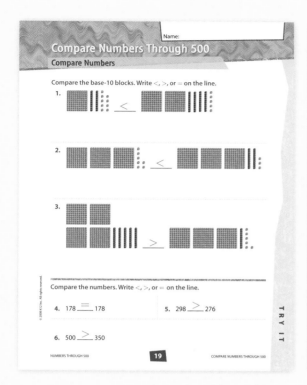

Compare Numbers Through 500

Compare Numbers

Compare the base-10 blocks. Write <, >, or = on the line.

1. ___<___

2. ___<___

3. ___>___

Compare the numbers. Write <, >, or = on the line.

4. 178 ___=___ 178   **5.** 298 ___>___ 276

6. 500 ___>___ 350

TRY IT

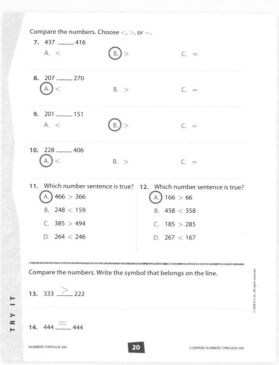

Compare the numbers. Choose <, >, or =.

7. 437 _____ 416
   A. <   B. >   C. =

8. 207 _____ 270
   A. <   B. >   C. =

9. 201 _____ 151
   A. <   B. >   C. =

10. 228 _____ 406
   A. <   B. >   C. =

11. Which number sentence is true?
   A. 466 > 366
   B. 248 < 159
   C. 385 > 494
   D. 264 < 246

12. Which number sentence is true?
   A. 166 > 66
   B. 458 < 358
   C. 185 > 285
   D. 267 < 167

Compare the numbers. Write the symbol that belongs on the line.

13. 333 ___>___ 222

14. 444 ___=___ 444

TRY IT

Comparing and Ordering

Lesson Overview

Skills Update	5 minutes	**ONLINE**
GET READY Compare and Order Numbers	10 minutes	**ONLINE**
LEARN Jump to Compare Numbers	15 minutes	**ONLINE**
LEARN Kick to Order Numbers	15 minutes	**ONLINE**
TRY IT Put the Numbers in Order	15 minutes	OFFLINE

▶ ## Lesson Objectives

- Compare whole numbers through 500 by using the symbols $<$, $=$, $>$.
- Order three or more whole numbers through 500 by using the symbols $<$, $=$, $>$.

▶ ## Prerequisite Skills

Use the symbols for less than, equal to, or greater than ($<$, $=$, $>$) to compare and order whole numbers through 100.

▶ ## Common Errors and Misconceptions

- Students might not think of numbers as groups of tens, hundreds, and so forth. For example, students might think of 24 only as 24 single units, not 2 tens and 4 ones.
- Students might not realize that a digit's place-value position determines its value. For example, students might think the digits in 14 have values of 1 and 4, not 10 and 4.
- Students might compare numbers based on the ones digits as opposed to the digits in the greatest place-value position. For example, students might think 69 is greater than 71 because 9 is greater than 1.

▶ ## Content Background

In this lesson, students will use the greater-than ($>$), less-than ($<$), and equals ($=$) symbols to compare numbers with and without a place-value chart. Students will also use symbols to order numbers through 500 from least to greatest value and from greatest to least value.

The greater-than symbol points to the right, and the less-than symbol points to the left. However, for ease in use, students can know that these comparison symbols *point* to the lesser number and *open* to the greater number.

Although the word *sign* is used often in everyday language, the word *symbol* is more accurate as a mathematical term. In math, *sign* specifically refers to the positive sign and negative sign that are used with numbers.

Materials to Gather

SUPPLIED

Put the Numbers in Order activity page

place-value mat (optional)

ALSO NEEDED

dry-erase marker (optional)

dry-erase eraser (optional)

ONLINE **10** min

GET READY Compare and Order Numbers

Students will use base-10 blocks and the place-value chart to compare and order numbers through 100.

Objectives

- Use the symbols for less than, equal to, or greater than ($<$, $=$, $>$) to compare and order whole numbers through 100.

ONLINE **15** min

LEARN Jump to Compare Numbers

Students will practice identifying and ordering numbers using a place-value chart.

Objectives

- Compare whole numbers through 500 by using the symbols $<$, $=$, $>$.

ONLINE **15** min

LEARN Kick to Order Numbers

Students will order a set of numbers from least to greatest and from greatest to least using the greater-than, less-than and equals symbols.

If students are having trouble ordering numbers, they can use their place-value mat to compare place values.

Objectives

- Order three or more whole numbers through 500 by using the symbols $<$, $=$, $>$.

OFFLINE **15** min

TRY IT Put the Numbers in Order

Students will practice comparing and ordering numbers. Give students the Put the Numbers in Order activity page from their Activity Book and read the directions with them. Use the answer key to check students' answers, and then enter the results online.

Objectives

- Compare whole numbers through 500 by using the symbols $<$, $=$, $>$.
- Order three or more whole numbers through 500 by using the symbols $<$, $=$, $>$.

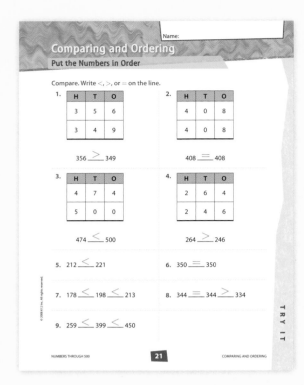

Comparing and Ordering

Put the Numbers in Order

Name:

Compare. Write <, >, or = on the line.

1.

H	T	O
3	5	6
3	4	9

356 > 349

2.

H	T	O
4	0	8
4	0	8

408 = 408

3.

H	T	O
4	7	4
5	0	0

474 < 500

4.

H	T	O
2	6	4
2	4	6

264 > 246

5. 212 < 221

6. 350 = 350

7. 178 < 198 < 213

8. 344 = 344 > 334

9. 259 < 399 < 450

T R Y   I T

NUMBERS THROUGH 500   **21**   COMPARING AND ORDERING

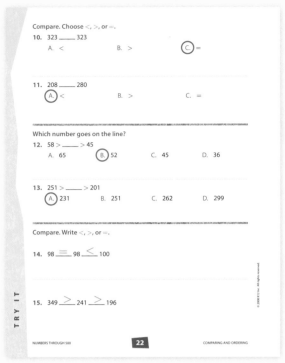

Compare. Choose <, >, or =.

10. 323 _____ 323

   A. <   B. >   (C.) =

11. 208 _____ 280

   (A.) <   B. >   C. =

Which number goes on the line?

12. 58 > _____ > 45

   A. 65   (B.) 52   C. 45   D. 36

13. 251 > _____ > 201

   (A.) 231   B. 251   C. 262   D. 299

Compare. Write <, >, or =.

14. 98 = 98 < 100

15. 349 > 241 > 196

T R Y   I T

NUMBERS THROUGH 500   **22**   COMPARING AND ORDERING

Order Whole Numbers Through 500

Lesson Overview

Skills Update	5 minutes	**ONLINE**
GET READY Comparing Numbers Through 100	5 minutes	**ONLINE**
LEARN Compare Whole Numbers Through 500	15 minutes	**OFFLINE**
LEARN Order Three Whole Numbers Through 500	15 minutes	**OFFLINE**
TRY IT Order These Numbers	10 minutes	**OFFLINE**
CHECKPOINT	10 minutes	**OFFLINE**

▶ Lesson Objectives

- Compare whole numbers through 500 by using the symbols $<, =, >$.
- Order three or more whole numbers through 500 by using the symbols $<, =, >$.

▶ Prerequisite Skills

Use the symbols for less than, equal to, or greater than ($<, =, >$) to compare and order whole numbers through 100.

▶ Common Errors and Misconceptions

- Students might not think of numbers as groups of tens, hundreds, and so forth. For example, students might think of 24 only as 24 single units, not 2 tens and 4 ones.
- Students might not realize that a digit's place-value position determines its value. For example, students might think the digits in 14 have values of 1 and 4, not 10 and 4.
- Students might compare numbers based on the ones digits as opposed to the digits in the greatest place-value position. For example, students might think 69 is greater than 71 because 9 is greater than 1.

▶ Content Background

In this lesson, students will use the greater-than ($>$), less-than ($<$), and equals ($=$) symbols to compare and order numbers and to make a true number sentence. The greater-than symbol points to the right, and the less-than symbol points to the left. However, for ease in use, students can know that these comparison symbols point to the lesser number and open to the greater number.

Although the word *sign* is used often in everyday language, the word *symbol* is more accurate as a mathematical term. In math, *sign* specifically refers to the positive sign and negative sign that are used with numbers.

Materials to Gather

SUPPLIED

Order These Numbers activity page
Checkpoint (printout)

GET READY Comparing Numbers Through 100

Students will compare numbers through 100 using online flash cards.

Objectives

- Use the symbols for less than, equal to, or greater than ($<$, $=$, $>$) to compare and order whole numbers through 100.

LEARN Compare Whole Numbers Through 500

Students will write a number that is less than ($<$), greater than ($>$), or equal to ($=$) a given number.
  There are no materials to gather for this activity.

1. Write $126 < \underline{\quad}$. Have students read the number aloud and tell you the value of each digit. Then have them read the symbol.

2. Ask students to write a number on the blank line that makes the statement true. (Possible answer: 199)

3. Have students explain why the number they have written is correct. For example, students might say that 129 has fewer tens than 199, so 129 is less than 199.

4. Repeat with the following numbers and symbols:

    $307 > \underline{\quad}$

    $420 = \underline{\quad}$

    $\underline{\quad} < 168$

    $235 < \underline{\quad}$

    $368 = \underline{\quad}$

    $\underline{\quad} > 307$

    $\underline{\quad} = 402$

    $470 > \underline{\quad}$

    $\underline{\quad} < 136$

Objectives

- Compare whole numbers through 500 by using the symbols $<$, $=$, $>$.

Tips

Remind students that the less-than and greater-than symbols point to the lesser number and open to the greater number.
  If necessary, fill in the number and review why it is less or greater than the other number. For example, $126 < 135$ because 126 has the same number of hundreds, but fewer tens.

LEARN Order Three Whole Numbers Through 500

Students will write a number that is between two given numbers. Then they will write the correct comparison symbols between the three numbers.
  There are no materials to gather for this activity.

1. Write $364 \underline{\quad} 375$. Leave enough space between the two numbers to write another number and two comparison symbols.

2. Ask students to pick a number that is between the two numbers. This number will be greater than 364 and less than 375. (Possible answer: $364 < 370 < 375$)

3. Write the number on the blank line. Have students explain why their number is greater than the first number and less than the second number. For example, 370 has more tens than the 364, but fewer ones than 375.

Objectives

- Order three or more whole numbers through 500 by using the symbols $<$, $=$, $>$.

4. Explain that the first number is less than the second number as you write a less-than symbol (<) between them. Explain that the second number is less than the third number as you write a less-than symbol (<) between them.

5. Repeat with the following numbers and symbols:

299 ___ 257 (>)

127 ___ 151 (<)

242 ___ 201 (>)

319 ___ 364 (<)

456 ___ 471 (<)

500 ___ 399 (>)

OFFLINE
10 min

TRY IT Order These Numbers

Students will compare and order numbers using symbols. They will also find the number that makes a number sentence true. Give students the Order These Numbers activity page from their Activity Book and read the directions with them. Use the answer key to check students' answers, and then enter the results online.

Objectives

- Compare whole numbers through 500 by using the symbols <, =, >.
- Order three or more whole numbers through 500 by using the symbols <, =, >.

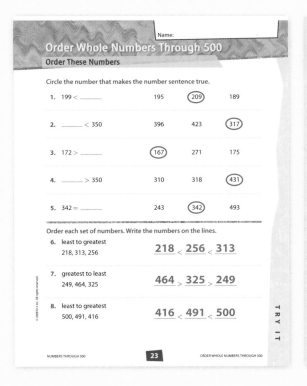

Name: _____

Order Whole Numbers Through 500

Order These Numbers

Circle the number that makes the number sentence true.

1. 199 < _____   195   (209)   189

2. _____ < 350   396   423   (317)

3. 172 > _____   (167)   271   175

4. _____ > 350   310   318   (431)

5. 342 = _____   243   (342)   493

Order each set of numbers. Write the numbers on the lines.

6. least to greatest
218, 313, 256   **218** < **256** < **313**

7. greatest to least
249, 464, 325   **464** > **325** > **249**

8. least to greatest
500, 491, 416   **416** < **491** < **500**

TRY IT

NUMBERS THROUGH 500   **23**   ORDER WHOLE NUMBERS THROUGH 500

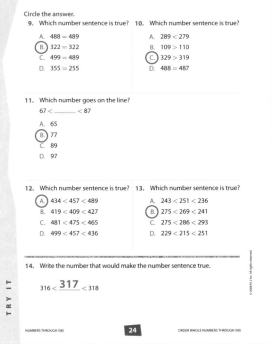

Circle the answer.

9. Which number sentence is true?
A. 488 = 489
B. 322 = 322
C. 499 = 489
D. 355 = 255

10. Which number sentence is true?
A. 289 < 279
B. 109 > 110
C. 329 > 319
D. 488 = 487

11. Which number goes on the line?
67 < _____ < 87
A. 65
B. 77
C. 89
D. 97

12. Which number sentence is true?
A. 434 < 457 < 489
B. 419 < 409 < 427
C. 481 < 475 < 465
D. 499 < 457 < 436

13. Which number sentence is true?
A. 243 < 251 < 236
B. 275 < 269 < 241
C. 275 < 286 < 293
D. 229 < 215 < 251

14. Write the number that would make the number sentence true.

316 < **317** < 318

TRY IT

NUMBERS THROUGH 500   **24**   ORDER WHOLE NUMBERS THROUGH 500

CHECKPOINT

Objectives

- Compare whole numbers through 500 by using the symbols $<, =, >$.
- Order three or more whole numbers through 500 by using the symbols $<, =, >$.

Print the Checkpoint and have students complete it on their own. Read the directions to students if necessary. Use the answer key to score the Checkpoint, and then enter the results online.

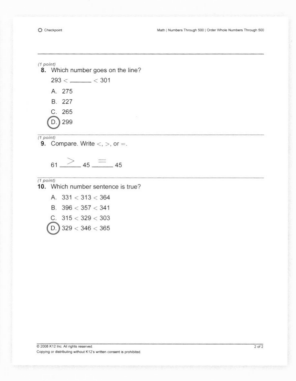

⚙ Checkpoint   Math | Numbers Through 500 | Order Whole Numbers Through 500

Name _____   Date _____

Checkpoint Answer Key
(1 point)
1. What symbol belongs on the line?

    353 _____ 343

    A. $<$ B. $=$ Ⓒ $>$

Write the symbol that belongs on the line.

(1 point)	*(1 point)*	*(1 point)*
2. 171 $\underline{>}$ 160	3. 218 $\underline{=}$ 218	4. 401 $\underline{<}$ 410

(1 point)
5. Compare. Write $<$, $>$, or $=$.

    393 $\underline{>}$ 339

(1 point)
6. Which number sentence is true?

    A. $185 < 164 < 159$
    B. $135 > 196 > 171$
    Ⓒ $123 < 134 < 155$
    D. $162 > 177 > 148$

(1 point)
7. Which number goes on the line?

    $255 >$ _____ > 231

    A. 275
    B. 227
    C. 265
    Ⓓ 241

⚙ Checkpoint   Math | Numbers Through 500 | Order Whole Numbers Through 500

_____

(1 point)
8. Which number goes on the line?

    $293 <$ _____ < 301

    A. 275
    B. 227
    C. 265
    Ⓓ 299

(1 point)
9. Compare. Write $<$, $>$, or $=$.

    61 $\underline{>}$ 45 $\underline{=}$ 45

(1 point)
10. Which number sentence is true?

    A. $331 < 313 < 364$
    B. $396 < 357 < 341$
    C. $315 < 329 < 303$
    Ⓓ $329 < 346 < 365$

Read Number Words Through 500

Skills Update	5 minutes	ONLINE
GET READY Write Numbers Through 500	5 minutes	ONLINE
LEARN Number Words Through 100	15 minutes	ONLINE
LEARN Number Words Through 500	10 minutes	OFFLINE
TRY IT Number Words	10 minutes	OFFLINE
CHECKPOINT	10 minutes	OFFLINE

▶ Lesson Objectives

Read number words through 500.

▶ Prerequisite Skills

Write numerals through 500.

▶ Common Errors and Misconceptions

Students might have difficulty writing multidigit numbers because numerals do not correspond exactly to English number words. For example, students might write twenty-five as 205 (20 and 5) instead of 25.

▶ Advance Preparation

- Gather or prepare number and symbol index cards. You will need the following cards: numbers 0 through 19, tens 20 through 90, hundreds 100 through 500, and a hyphen (-). Each card should have the number on one side and the number word or symbol name written on the other side. Arrange them with the words facing up.
- Create three additional sets of number cards. Number one set 0 through 4. Number the other two sets 0 through 9. Arrange these cards with the numerals facing up.
- Print the Number Words Chart.

▶ Content Background

Students have learned how to read and write numerals for numbers through 500. In this lesson, students will learn how to read the number words for these numbers.

Keywords

number word – a word that corresponds to a numeric symbol; for example, one, two, three..., twenty

Materials to Gather

SUPPLIED

Number Words activity page

Checkpoint (printout)

Number Words Chart (printout)

ALSO NEEDED

index cards – labeled with numerals and number words 0 through 19, tens 20 through 90, and hundreds 100 through 500, and a hyphen -

index cards – labeled with numerals; one set numbererd 1 through 4, and two sets numbered 0 through 9

GET READY Write Numbers Through 500

5 min

Objectives

Students will use the keyboard to write numbers to 500 when they hear the number said aloud.

- Write numerals through 500.

LEARN Number Words Through 100

15 min

Objectives

Students will learn how to read the word form for numbers from 1 through 100. They will also learn how to place a hyphen correctly between the tens and ones in 2-digit numbers greater than 20.

- Read number words through 500.

LEARN Number Words Through 500

10 min

Objectives

Students will learn how to read the word form for numbers from 100 through 500. Gather the index cards and the Number Words Chart.

- Read number words through 500.

Part 1

1. Place the three groups of numeral index cards (0–4, 1–9, and 1–9) in a row in front of students. (Make sure the stack with the numbers 0–4 is on the left side and that the numerals are facing up.) Explain that the stack on the right is the ones place, the middle stack is the tens place, and the stack on the left is the hundreds place.

2. Have students form a number in the hundreds by choosing one card from each stack. Have students read the number aloud.

3. Give students the three groups of number-word cards (0 through 19, tens, and hundreds) and the card with the hyphen. Have them choose the correct cards to create the number that they formed. Then have them read the number word aloud to check that it matches the number they created.

4. Repeat the activity four times.

Part 2

5. Now reverse the process. Have students choose the word cards (and the hyphen, if needed) to form a number. Have them read the number aloud. Then have them create the same number with the numeral cards.

6. Repeat the activity four times.

Tips

Allow students to look at the Number Words Chart before they go through the activity.

Remind students that they need to use a hyphen to separate the tens and the ones in number words.

TRY IT Number Words

Students will read and write number words. Give students the Number Words activity page from their Activity Book and read the directions with them.

- Read number words through 500.

Name: _____

Read Number Words Through 500
Number Words

Write a number for each number word.

1. eighty

   80

2. one hundred eleven

   111

3. nineteen

   19

4. four hundred fifty-one

   451

5. two hundred seventeen

   217

6. ninety-nine

   99

7. three hundred seventy-six

   376

8. two hundred eight

   208

9. forty-three

   43

10. four hundred eighty

    480

11. sixteen

    16

12. fifty-two

    52

TRY IT

TRY IT

13. Write the number 200 in word form.

    two hundred

14. Write the number 400 in word form.

    four hundred

15. Write the number 233 in word form.

    two hundred thirty-three

16. Write the number 155 in word form.

    one hundred fifty-five

17. Write the number 309 in word form.

    three hundred nine

18. Write the number 104 in word form.

    one hundred four

19. Write the number 168 in word form.

    one hundred sixty-eight

20. Write the number 446 in word form.

    four hundred forty-six

CHECKPOINT

- Read number words through 500.

Print the Checkpoint. Read Problems 1 and 2 in Part 1 aloud to students. Then have students complete Part 2 on their own. Use the answer key to score the Checkpoint, and then enter the results online.

Name _____ Date _____

Checkpoint Answer Key

Part 1

Follow the instructions for each item. Choose the response that best describes how the student performed on the task. When you have finished, enter the results online.

1. Say, "Write the number 322 in word form."
   (1 point)
   Did students write three hundred twenty-two?
   A. Yes   B. No

2. Say, "Write the number 497 in word form."
   (1 point)
   Did students write four hundred ninety-seven?
   A. Yes   B. No

Give students Part 2 of the assessment.

Name _____ Date _____

Part 2

Choose the correct answer.
(1 point)

3. Which of the following shows the number 36 in word form?
   A. $3 + 6$
   B. three six
   C. thirty-six ✓
   D. three hundred six

(1 point)
4. Which of the following shows the number 216 in word form?
   A. $2 + 1 + 6$
   B. two hundred sixteen ✓
   C. two six
   D. twenty-one six

(1 point)
5. Which of the following shows the number 475 in word form?
   A. $4 + 7 + 5$
   B. forty-seven hundred five
   C. four hundred seventy-five ✓
   D. four hundred seven five

Unit Review

Lesson Overview

UNIT REVIEW Look Back	20 minutes	**ONLINE**
UNIT REVIEW Checkpoint Practice	20 minutes	**OFFLINE**
⏩ **UNIT REVIEW** Prepare for the Checkpoint		

▶ Unit Objectives

This lesson reviews the following objectives:

- Count aloud whole numbers through 500.
- Read whole numbers through 500.
- Write numerals through 500.
- Identify the place value for each digit in whole numbers through 500.
- Use models to represent regrouping in addition or subtraction problems.
- Use expanded forms to represent numbers through 500, such as 345 = 3 hundreds + 4 tens + 5 ones = 300 + 40 + 5.
- Compare whole numbers through 500 by using the symbols $<, =, >$.
- Order three or more whole numbers through 500 by using the symbols $<, =, >$.
- Read number words through 500.

Materials to Gather

SUPPLIED
Checkpoint Practice activity page

▶ Advance Preparation

In this lesson, students will have an opportunity to review previous activities in the Numbers Through 500 unit. Look at the suggested activities in Unit Review: Prepare for the Checkpoint online and gather any needed materials.

Keywords

addend	number word
addition	numeral
base-10 blocks	ones place
compare	order numbers
counting numbers	place value
digit	place-value chart
equals symbol (=)	place-value mat
expanded form	place-value notation
greater-than symbol (>)	regroup; regrouping
hundred chart	standard form
hundreds place	sum
less-than symbol (<)	tens place
model (verb)	whole numbers
multidigit number	

UNIT REVIEW Look Back

ONLINE 20min

Objectives

- Review unit objectives.

In this unit, students have learned to count, read, write, compare, and order numbers through 500. They have learned to read number words through 500. They have also developed a greater understanding of place value as a foundation for understanding number operations, such as addition or subtraction. Students will review these concepts to prepare for the Unit Checkpoint.

UNIT REVIEW Checkpoint Practice

OFFLINE 20min

Objectives

- Review unit objectives.

Students will complete a Checkpoint Practice activity page to prepare for the Unit Checkpoint. If necessary, read the directions, questions, and answer choices to students. Have students answer the problems on their own. Carefully review the answers with students.

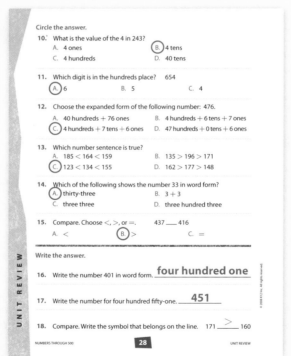

Unit Review
Checkpoint Practice

Name: _____

Fill in the missing numbers.

1. 361, 362, **363**, 364, 365, **366**, 367, 368, 369, **370**

2. **191**, 192, 193, **194**, 195, 196, **197**, 198, 199, 200

3. Circle the greatest number.   24 (214) 145

4. Circle the least number.   376 (318) 352

5. Write the numbers in order from least to greatest.
    217 189 108 213   **108 189 213 217**

Write the number in expanded form.

6. 419 **400 + 10 + 9**
    or 4 hundreds + 1 ten + 9 ones

7. 186 **100 + 80 + 6**
    or 1 hundreds + 8 tens + 6 ones

Write the number for each number word.

8. twenty-seven **27**

9. two hundred ninety-four **294**

NUMBERS THROUGH 500   **27**   UNIT REVIEW

Circle the answer.

10. What is the value of the 4 in 243?
     A. 4 ones   (B.) 4 tens
     C. 4 hundreds   D. 40 tens

11. Which digit is in the hundreds place?   654
     (A.) 6   B. 5   C. 4

12. Choose the expanded form of the following number: 476.
     A. 40 hundreds + 76 ones   B. 4 hundreds + 6 tens + 7 ones
     (C.) 4 hundreds + 7 tens + 6 ones   D. 47 hundreds + 0 tens + 6 ones

13. Which number sentence is true?
     A. 185 < 164 < 159   B. 135 > 196 > 171
     (C.) 123 < 134 < 155   D. 162 > 177 > 148

14. Which of the following shows the number 33 in word form?
     (A.) thirty-three   B. 3 + 3
     C. three three   D. three hundred three

15. Compare. Choose <, >, or =.   437 ___ 416
     A. <   (B.) >   C. =

Write the answer.

16. Write the number 401 in word form. **four hundred one**

17. Write the number for four hundred fifty-one. **451**

18. Compare. Write the symbol that belongs on the line.   171 __**>**__ 160

NUMBERS THROUGH 500   **28**   UNIT REVIEW

➔ UNIT REVIEW Prepare for the Checkpoint

What you do next depends on how students performed in the previous activity, Unit Review: Checkpoint Practice. If students had difficulty with any of the problems, complete the appropriate review activity listed in the table online.

Unit Checkpoint

Lesson Overview		
UNIT CHECKPOINT Online	30 minutes	**ONLINE**
UNIT CHECKPOINT Offline	30 minutes	**OFFLINE**

▶ Unit Objectives

This lesson assesses the following objectives:

- Count aloud whole numbers through 500.
- Read whole numbers through 500.
- Write numerals through 500.
- Identify the place value for each digit in whole numbers through 500.
- Use models to represent regrouping in addition or subtraction problems.
- Use expanded forms to represent numbers through 500, such as $345 = 3$ hundreds $+ 4$ tens $+ 5$ ones $= 300 + 40 + 5$.
- Compare whole numbers through 500 by using the symbols $<, =, >$.
- Order three or more whole numbers through 500 by using the symbols $<, =, >$.
- Write number words through 500.

Materials to Gather

SUPPLIED
Unit Checkpoint (printout)
base-10 blocks

ONLINE **30**min

UNIT CHECKPOINT Online

Students will complete this part of the Unit Checkpoint online. Read the directions, problems, and answer choices to students. If necessary, help students with keyboard or mouse operations.

Objectives

- Review unit objectives.

OFFLINE **30**min

UNIT CHECKPOINT Offline

Students will complete this part of the Unit Checkpoint offline. In Part 1, students will take a performance-based assessment. In Part 2, students will complete the problems on their own. Print the Unit Checkpoint. Read the directions, problems, and answer choices to students if necessary. Use the answer key to score the Unit Checkpoint, and then enter the results online.

For Problem 2, give students the base-10 blocks.

Objectives

- Review unit objectives.

Name   Date

Unit Checkpoint Answer Key

Part 1

Follow the instructions for each item. Choose the response that best describes how the student performs on the task. When you have finished, enter the results online.

1. Say "Count aloud from 340 to 350."
(5 points)
Did the student correctly count aloud from 340 to 350?

  A. Yes   B. No

2. Say, "Use the blocks to model the number 208."

Possible model: 2 hundreds flats, 8 ones cubes.
(5 points)
Did the student correctly model the number 208?

  A. Yes   B. No

3. Write the number 123 on a piece of paper.
Ask, "What number is this?"
(5 points)
Did the student say "one hundred twenty-three"?

  A. Yes   B. No

Give students Part 2 of the assessment.

Name   Date

Part 2

For Problems 4–7, circle the answer.

(5 points)
4. Look at the number below. In which place is the 6?

    615

  A. ones

  B. tens

  (C.) hundreds

(5 points)
5. Which number sentence is true?

  A. $366 > 367$

  B. $258 < 149$

  (C.) $485 > 484$

  D. $364 < 346$

(5 points)
6. Which of the following shows the number 131 in word form?

  A. $100 + 31$

  (B.) one hundred thirty-one

  C. $1 + 3 + 1$

  D. one hundred thirteen

(5 points)
7. Which of these numbers is the number one hundred seventy-one?

  (A.) 171

  B. 711

  C. 10,071

  D. 17

For Problems 8–13, write the answer in the space.

(5 points)
8. Write the number three hundred three.

    303

(5 points)
9. Write the number 206 in expanded form.

  2 hundreds + 0 tens + 6 ones
  or 200 + 6

Name   Date

(5 points)
10. Compare the numbers below. Write $<$, $>$, or $=$ on the line.

  221 $=$ 221

(5 points)
11. Order the numbers 355, 127, 234 from least to greatest, using the symbols $<$ or $>$.

  $127 < 234 < 355$

(5 points)
12. Order the numbers 88, 92, 63, and 93 from greatest to least, using the symbols $<$ or $>$.

  $93 > 92 > 88 > 63$

(5 points)
13. Write the number 210 in word form.

  two hundred ten

Time and Money

▶ Unit Objectives

- Tell time to the nearest quarter hour.
- Identify relationships between units of time, such as minutes in an hour, days in a month, weeks in a year.
- Determine elapsed time in hours, such as 11:00 a.m. to 4:00 p.m.
- Identify the value of a combination of coins and bills.
- Use dollar and cent symbols for money.
- Use decimal notation for money.
- Find the fewest number of bills and coins to represent an amount of money.
- Solve problems by using combinations of coins and bills.

▶ Unit Introduction

In this unit, students will learn about time and money. Students will begin by learning how to tell when the time is exactly or about a quarter past, half past, or a quarter 'til the hour. They will learn about relationships between units of time. (For example, they will learn that 60 seconds = 1 minute and 60 minutes = 1 hour.) Then students will learn about a.m. and p.m. and how to find elapsed time in hours.

In the lessons about money, students will find the value of groups of coins by counting on from the coin with the greatest value to the coin with the least value. They will use the same technique for counting bills, up to and including the $20 bill.

Students will write money amounts using the cent sign, the dollar sign, and the decimal point. They will practice counting groups of coins and bills and writing the amount using the correct notation. Students will trade coins or bills of lesser value for coins or bills of greater value to end up with the fewest coins or bills.

Time to the Nearest Quarter Hour

Lesson Overview

Skills Update	5 minutes	ONLINE
GET READY Time to the Nearest Half Hour	10 minutes	ONLINE
LEARN A Quarter After the Hour	15 minutes	OFFLINE
LEARN A Quarter 'til the Hour	15 minutes	OFFLINE
TRY IT Time Will Tell	10 minutes	OFFLINE
CHECKPOINT	5 minutes	OFFLINE

▶ Lesson Objectives

Tell time to the nearest quarter hour.

▶ Prerequisite Skills

Tell time to the nearest half hour.

▶ Common Errors and Misconceptions

- Students might have difficulty using digital clocks to tell approximate times. For example, to understand that 7:58 is almost 8:00 on a digital clock, students must know that there are 60 minutes in an hour, that 58 is near 60, and that 2 minutes is a short amount of time. On an analog clock, students can more easily see that 7:58 is almost 8:00.
- Students might confuse the hour hand and minute hand.

▶ Advance Preparation

Print and assemble the paper clock model by cutting out the two hands and attaching them to the center dot using a brad.

▶ Content Background

Digital clocks do not provide a clear relationship between minutes and hours. This means that many students read time from a digital clock without really understanding what it means. In this lesson, students will learn how to tell time to the nearest quarter hour using analog clocks to help them make the connection between minutes and hours.

Materials to Gather

SUPPLIED
Paper Clock Model (printout)
A Quarter After the Hour activity page
A Quarter 'til the Hour activity page
Time Will Tell activity page
Checkpoint (printout)

ALSO NEEDED
crayons
metal brad

Keywords

analog clock – a clock that displays the time with the continual movement of an hour and a minute hand

GET READY Time to the Nearest Half Hour

Objectives

- Tell time to the nearest half hour.

Students will review the parts of a clock and telling time to the nearest half hour using an analog clock. If students need more practice, have them model times on their paper clock model.

LEARN A Quarter After the Hour

Objectives

- Tell time to the nearest quarter hour.

Students will learn to tell time to the nearest quarter hour when the time is around a quarter past the hour. They should not be concerned with telling time to the minute, but should stay focused on telling time to the nearest quarter hour.

Gather the paper clock model, the A Quarter After the Hour activity page, and crayons.

Part 1

1. Show students the paper clock model with both the hour and minute hands in the one o'clock position. Have students tell you what time the clock shows. Then have students count the minutes by five with you as you point to the numbers 1, 2, and 3.

   Say: We can count by fives to find the number of minutes after one o'clock. Count with me: 5, 10, 15.

2. Move the minute hand so that the clock reads 3:15.

   Say: We counted to 15, so when the minute hand points to the 3, it is 15 minutes after one o'clock. You can say this time as fifteen minutes past one, one fifteen, or a quarter past one. You can also say a quarter after one.

3. Point to the numbers on the clock as you continue.

   Say: There are four quarter hours in 1 hour.

   Notice that one quarter goes from 12 to 3, another quarter goes from 3 to 6, another quarter goes from 6 to 9, and another quarter goes from 9 to 12. The numbers 3, 6, 9, and 12 mark the quarter hours. When you tell time to the nearest quarter hour, you look to see which one of these numbers the minute hand is closest to.

4. Position the hands on the clock so that they show 6:15.

   Ask: What is the time shown on the clock?
   ANSWER: 6:15

   Ask: What is another way to say this time?
   ANSWER: a quarter past six or fifteen minutes past six

5. Move the minute hand so that it points to the 2.

   Say: The minute hand is between two quarter hour marks: the 12 and the 3. It is closer to the 3, so the time is about 6:15. The time to the nearest quarter hour is 6:15, a quarter past six, or fifteen minutes past six.

6. Move the minute hand so that the time shown is 6:21.

Ask: Between which two quarter hour marks is the minute hand?
ANSWER: between 3 and 6

Ask: Is the minute hand closer to 3 or 6?
ANSWER: 3

Say: The minute hand is closer to the 3. The time to the nearest quarter hour is still 6:15.

7. Show students the following times on the clock: 3:13, 12:19, and 9:15. Ask them to say the time shown to the nearest quarter hour in three ways. Then ask them to explain how they found their answers.

Part 2

8. Give students the A Quarter After the Hour activity page.

Say: Now you are going to draw hands on the clocks to show different times. Which hand is shorter?
ANSWER: the hour hand

9. Position the hands on the paper clock model to show 1:15.

Ask: What time does the clock show?
ANSWER: 1:15

10. Say: Draw the hands on the first clock on your activity page to show one fifteen. Then write the time on the line below the clock.

11. Position the hands on the clock so that the clock shows 7:15.

Ask: What time does the clock show?
ANSWER: 7:15

Ask: What is another way to say this time?
ANSWER: a quarter past seven or fifteen minutes past seven

12. Say: Draw the hands on the second clock on your activity page to show 7:15. Then write the time on the line below the clock.

13. Repeat the activity with the following times: 12:15, 3:15, 10:15, and 6:15.

LEARN A Quarter 'til the Hour

Objectives

- Tell time to the nearest quarter hour.

Students will learn to tell time to the nearest quarter hour when the time is around a quarter 'til the hour.

Gather the paper clock model, the A Quarter 'til the Hour activity page, and crayons.

1. Give students the paper clock model. Make sure that both hands point toward 12.

    Say: Show me a time that, to the nearest quarter hour, is 3:15. (Encourage students to show a time near 3:15 but not exactly 3:15.) Now show me a time that, to the nearest quarter hour, is 3:30. A time can also be a quarter 'til the hour.

2. Return the hour hand to the 12 o'clock position and move the minute hand so that it points to the 9.

    Say: Count aloud by 5s until you reach the 9.

    Ask: How many minutes after the hour is it when the minute hand points to the 9?
    ANSWER: 45 minutes

3. Position the hands on the clock so that they show 3:45.

    Ask: What time is shown on the clock?
    ANSWER: 3:45

    Say: At 3:45 there is only one quarter of an hour left until 4 o'clock, so you can also say that it is a quarter 'til 4 o'clock. You can say this time as three forty-five, forty-five minutes after three, fifteen minutes to four, or a quarter 'til four.

4. Move the minute hand so that it points to the 10.

    Ask: What time is shown to the nearest quarter hour?
    ANSWER: 3:45

    Ask: How did you find your answer?
    ANSWER: The minute hand is between 9 and 12. It's closer to the 9.

5. Move the minute hand so that the time shown is 3:39.

    Ask: Now what time is shown to the nearest quarter hour?
    ANSWER: 3:45

    Ask: How did you find your answer?
    ANSWER: The minute hand is between 9 and 6. It's closer to the 9.

    Ask: What is another way to give the time to the nearest quarter hour?
    ANSWER: a quarter 'til four, or fifteen minutes to four

6. Show students the following times on the clock: 2:45, 9:48, and 10:41. Ask them to say the time shown to the nearest quarter hour in three ways. Then ask them to explain how they found their answers.

7. Give students the A Quarter 'til the Hour activity page. Have students draw hands to show 9:45, 2:45, 7:45, 11:45, 6:45, and 1:45. For each time, have students say the time four different ways, for example, as forty-five minutes after nine, nine forty-five, fifteen minutes to ten, and a quarter 'til ten.

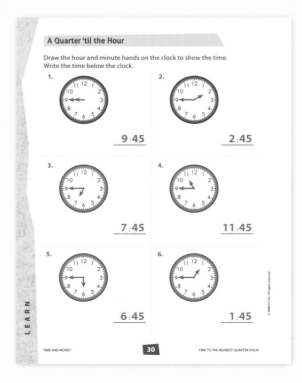

A Quarter 'til the Hour

Draw the hour and minute hands on the clock to show the time. Write the time below the clock.

1. 9:45   2. 2:45

3. 7:45   4. 11:45

5. 6:45   6. 1:45

LEARN

TIME AND MONEY   30   TIME TO THE NEAREST QUARTER HOUR

TRY IT Time Will Tell

Students will practice telling time to the nearest quarter hour. Give students the Time Will Tell activity page from their Activity Book and read the directions with them. Students may use their paper clock model as they work through the problems.

- Tell time to the nearest quarter hour.

Name: _____

Time to the Nearest Quarter Hour
Time Will Tell

Write the time shown on the clock to the nearest quarter hour.

1. **3 : 00**

2. **10 : 15**

3. **12 : 30**

4. **11 : 45**

Draw hands on the clock to show the time.

5. 4 : 45

6. 12 : 45

7. 6 : 15

8. 2 : 30

TIME AND MONEY **31** TIME TO THE NEAREST QUARTER HOUR

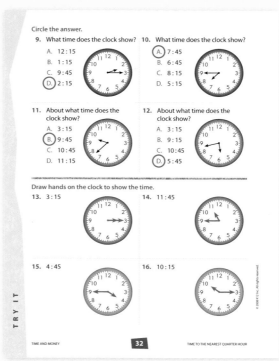

Circle the answer.

9. What time does the clock show?
   A. 12 : 15
   B. 1 : 15
   C. 9 : 45
   D. 2 : 15

10. What time does the clock show?
   A. 7 : 45
   B. 6 : 45
   C. 8 : 15
   D. 5 : 15

11. About what time does the clock show?
   A. 3 : 15
   B. 9 : 45
   C. 10 : 45
   D. 11 : 15

12. About what time does the clock show?
   A. 3 : 15
   B. 9 : 15
   C. 10 : 45
   D. 5 : 45

Draw hands on the clock to show the time.

13. 3 : 15

14. 11 : 45

15. 4 : 45

16. 10 : 15

TIME AND MONEY **32** TIME TO THE NEAREST QUARTER HOUR

Print the Checkpoint and have students complete it on their own. Read the directions, problems, and answer choices to students if necessary. Use the answer key to score the assessment, and then enter the results online.

OFFLINE
5min

- Tell time to the nearest quarter hour.

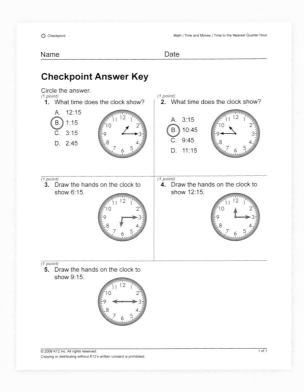

Time Relationships

▶ Lesson Objectives

Identify relationships between units of time, such as minutes in an hour, days in a month, weeks in a year.

▶ Prerequisite Skills

- Tell time to the nearest half hour.
- Tell time to the nearest quarter hour.

▶ Common Errors and Misconceptions

- Students might have difficulty using digital clocks to tell approximate times. For example, to understand that 7:58 is almost 8:00 on a digital clock, students must know that there are 60 minutes in an hour, that 58 is near 60, and that 2 minutes is a short amount of time. On an analog clock, students can more easily see that 7:58 is almost 8:00.
- Students might confuse the hour hand and minute hand.

▶ Advance Preparation

- Assemble the paper clock model by cutting out the two hands and attaching them to the center dot using a brad.
- Prepare index cards with the numbers 7, 12, 24, 52, and 60.

▶ Content Background

Students will learn about relationships between units of time, such as minutes in an hour, days in a week, and months in a year.

Materials to Gather

SUPPLIED

Paper Clock Model (printout)

Equivalent Times activity page

Checkpoint (printout)

ALSO NEEDED

index cards – labeled with numbers 7, 12, 24, 52, and 60

12-month calendar

metal brad

GET READY Time to the Nearest Quarter Hour

Students will practice telling time to the nearest hour, half hour, and quarter hour by looking at an analog clock.

- Tell time to the nearest quarter hour.
- Tell time to the nearest half hour.

LEARN Serena's Time Tale

Students will learn about the following relationships between units of time:

- 60 seconds = 1 minute
- 60 minutes = 1 hour
- 24 hours = 1 day
- 7 days = 1 week
- 52 weeks = 1 year
- 12 months = 1 year

- Identify relationships between units of time, such as minutes in an hour, days in a week, months in a year.

LEARN Time Relationships

Students will answer questions about time relationships using the index cards. Then they will make up their own "time statements."

Gather the numbered index cards, the paper clock model, and the 12-month calendar.

- Identify relationships between units of time, such as minutes in an hour, days in a week, months in a year.

1. Give students the index cards, the paper clock model, and a 12-month calendar.

   Say: I am going to ask you a question. Then you are going to choose the card that correctly answers the question. You can use the clock and the calendar to help you.

2. Ask students the following questions. Correct them if necessary.
   - How many minutes are there in 1 hour? (60)
   - How many hours are there in 1 day? (24)
   - How many days are there in 1 week? (7)
   - How many weeks are there in 1 year? (52)
   - How many seconds are there in 1 minute? (60)
   - How many months are there in 1 year? (12)

3. Shuffle the index cards and place them face down in a stack.

   Say: Pick a card and then tell me a time fact about that number. For example, if you choose the 24 card, you should say "There are 24 hours in 1 day."

4. Continue until students have chosen every card.

TRY IT   Equivalent Times

Students will practice matching equivalent times. Give students the paper clock model, the 12-month calendar, and the Equivalent Times activity page. Read the directions with them.

- Identify relationships between units of time, such as minutes in an hour, days in a month, weeks in a year.

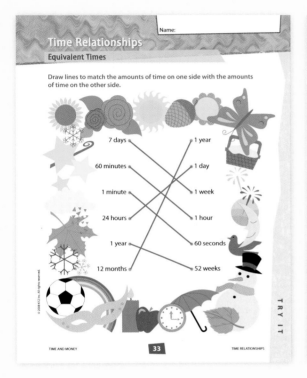

Name: _____

Time Relationships
Equivalent Times

Draw lines to match the amounts of time on one side with the amounts of time on the other side.

7 days

60 minutes

1 minute

24 hours

1 year

12 months

1 year

1 day

1 week

1 hour

60 seconds

52 weeks

TIME AND MONEY   **33**   TIME RELATIONSHIPS

T R Y   I T

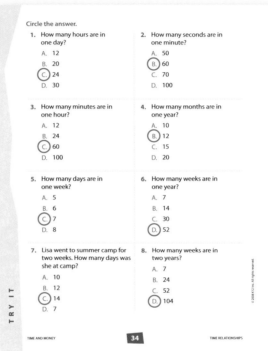

T R Y   I T

Circle the answer.

1. How many hours are in one day?
   A. 12
   B. 20
   C. 24
   D. 30

2. How many seconds are in one minute?
   A. 50
   B. 60
   C. 70
   D. 100

3. How many minutes are in one hour?
   A. 12
   B. 24
   C. 60
   D. 100

4. How many months are in one year?
   A. 10
   B. 12
   C. 15
   D. 20

5. How many days are in one week?
   A. 5
   B. 6
   C. 7
   D. 8

6. How many weeks are in one year?
   A. 7
   B. 14
   C. 30
   D. 52

7. Lisa went to summer camp for two weeks. How many days was she at camp?
   A. 10
   B. 12
   C. 14
   D. 7

8. How many weeks are in two years?
   A. 7
   B. 24
   C. 52
   D. 104

TIME AND MONEY   **34**   TIME RELATIONSHIPS

Objectives

- Identify relationships between units of time, such as minutes in an hour, days in a month, weeks in a year.

Print the assessment and have students complete it on their own. Read the directions, problems, and answer choices to students if necessary. Use the answer key to score the assessment, and then enter the results online.

○ Checkpoint   Math | Time and Money | Time Relationships

Name _____   Date _____

Checkpoint Answer Key

Circle the answer.

(1 point)
1. How many hours are in one day?
   - A. 12
   - B. 20
   - C. 24
   - D. 30

(1 point)
2. How many minutes are in one hour?
   - A. 12
   - B. 24
   - C. 60
   - D. 100

(1 point)
3. How many weeks are in one year?
   - A. 7
   - B. 14
   - C. 30
   - D. 52

(1 point)
4. How many months are in one year?
   - A. 10
   - B. 12
   - C. 15
   - D. 20

(1 point)
5. How many seconds are in one minute?
   - A. 50
   - B. 60
   - C. 70
   - D. 100

1 of 1

Elapsed Time

▶ Lesson Objectives

Determine elapsed time in hours, such as 11:00 a.m. to 4:00 p.m.

▶ Prerequisite Skills

Tell time to the nearest quarter hour.

▶ Common Errors and Misconceptions

- Students might have difficulty using digital clocks to tell approximate times. For example, to understand that 7:58 is almost 8:00 on a digital clock, students must know that there are 60 minutes in an hour, that 58 is near 60, and that 2 minutes is a short amount of time. On an analog clock, students can more easily see that 7:58 is almost 8:00.
- Students might confuse the hour hand and minute hand.

▶ Advance Preparation

Assemble the paper clock model by cutting out the two hands and attaching them to the center dot using a brad.

▶ Content Background

The concept of amount of time passed is commonly called *elapsed time*. In this lesson, students will learn to determine how much time has passed from one on-the-hour time to another. For example, the elapsed time from 2:00 p.m. to 6:00 p.m. would be 4 hours. Students will also learn about a.m. and p.m., and they will find elapsed times that cross over from a.m. to p.m. or from p.m. to a.m.

Keywords	**elapsed time** – the amount of time that passes between a starting time and an ending time

Materials to Gather

SUPPLIED

Paper Clock Model (printout)
blocks – B (10 of any color)
Show Elapsed Time activity page

ALSO NEEDED

metal brad

GET READY What Time Is It?

ONLINE
5min

Students will practice telling time to the nearest quarter hour using an analog clock.

Objectives

- Tell time to the nearest quarter hour.

Tips

Help students remember the names of the hands on a clock by writing and comparing the words. *Hour* is a short word, so it goes with the short hand. *Minute* is a long word, so it goes with the long hand.

LEARN A.M. and P.M.

ONLINE
15min

Students will learn that a.m. and p.m. are used to indicate whether the time is morning, afternoon, evening, or night.

Objectives

- Determine elapsed time in hours, such as 11:00 a.m. to 4:00 p.m.

LEARN Passing Time

ONLINE
10min

Students will practice finding elapsed time using online clocks and their paper clock model.

Gather the paper clock model and circle blocks to help students count the hours between two times.

Objectives

- Determine elapsed time in hours, such as 11:00 a.m. to 4:00 p.m.

LEARN How Much Time Has Passed?

Objectives

- Determine elapsed time in hours, such as 11:00 a.m. to 4:00 p.m.

Students will learn how to find elapsed time from an a.m. hour to a p.m. hour and from a p.m. hour to an a.m. hour.

1. **Say:** The first 12 hours in a day are from 12 midnight to 12 noon. These are the a.m. hours. The second 12 hours in a day are from 12 noon to 12 midnight. These are the p.m. hours.

   Let's say you begin your schoolwork at 9:00 a.m. and finish at 2:00 p.m. Let's find the number of hours between 9:00 a.m. and 2:00 p.m.

2. Have students set the time on the Clock learning tool to 9:00 a.m. Then have them move the minute hand around the clock until the time is 2:00 p.m. Count aloud each time the clock shows a new hour. Point out that the hour hand is moving 1 hour each time around.

   Say: The elapsed time between 9:00 a.m. and 2:00 p.m. is 5 hours.

3. **Ask:** Why do you think we start with 1 again after the hour hand reaches the 12?

   ANSWER: The clock only goes to 12.

4. **Say:** Notice that the time changed from a.m. to p.m. This is because p.m. is used to show times after 12 noon and before 12 midnight.

5. Have students find the elapsed time between 11:00 a.m. and 5:00 p.m. and between 10:00 a.m. and 1:00 p.m.

6. **Say:** Say you go to bed at 9:00 p.m. and wake up at 7:00 a.m. Let's find the number of hours between 9:00 p.m. and 7:00 a.m.

   Have students set the time on the Clock learning tool to 9:00 p.m. Then have them move the minute hand around the clock until the time is 7:00 a.m. Count aloud each time the clock shows a new hour.
   Say: There are 10 hours between 9:00 p.m. and 7:00 a.m.

7. **Say:** Did you notice how the time changed from p.m. to a.m.? 12 midnight is the middle of the night. After 12 midnight, a new day begins. A.M. is used to show times after 12 midnight and before 12 noon.

8. Have students find the elapsed time between 10:00 p.m. and 3:00 a.m. and between 11:00 p.m. and 7:00 a.m. Have them pause and say "p.m.," at noon and "a.m.," at midnight to emphasize the change between a.m. and p.m.

Tips

When the hour hand reaches the 12, remind students to start over with one o'clock. Emphasize that this happens twice a day, once at noon and once at midnight.

TRY IT Show Elapsed Time

Students will practice finding elapsed time by counting the hours. Give students the paper clock model and the Show Elapsed Time activity page. Read the directions with them.

- Determine elapsed time in hours, such as 11:00 a.m. to 4:00 p.m.

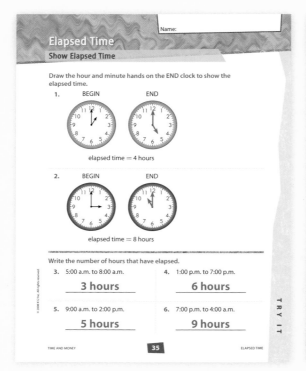

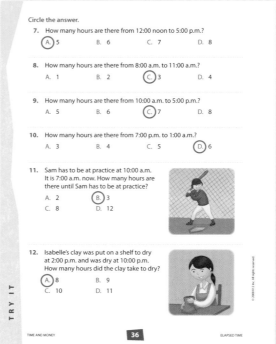

CHECKPOINT

Students will complete an online Checkpoint. Read the directions, questions, and answer choices to students. If necessary, help students with keyboard or mouse operations. Students may use their clock model.

- Determine elapsed time in hours, such as 11:00 a.m. to 4:00 p.m.

Find the Value of Coins or Bills

Lesson Overview

Skills Update	5 minutes	**ONLINE**
GET READY Same Value	10 minutes	**ONLINE**
LEARN Groups of Coins	20 minutes	**ONLINE**
LEARN Groups of Bills	15 minutes	**ONLINE**
TRY IT How Much?	10 minutes	OFFLINE

▶ Lesson Objectives

Identify the value of a combination of coins and bills.

▶ Prerequisite Skills

Show different combinations of coins that equal the same value.

▶ Content Background

In this lesson, students will find the value of groups of coins or groups of bills by counting on in order from the coin or bill with the greatest value to the coin or bill with the least value.

    For groups of coins, students will count the quarters first, then the dimes, then the nickels, and then the pennies. For groups of bills, they will count the $20 bills first, then the $10 bills, then the $5 bills, and then the $1 bills. Although it is not necessary to count on in order, this method makes finding the values easier.

Materials to Gather

SUPPLIED

How Much? activity page

ONLINE

10min

GET READY Same Value

Objectives

Students will review the value of coins and identify different combinations of coins that have the same value as a nickel, a dime, or a quarter.

- Show different combinations of coins that equal the same value.

LEARN Groups of Coins

Objectives

- Identify the value of a combination of coins and bills.

Students will learn to find the value of groups of coins by counting on in order from the coin with the greatest value to the coin with the least value. Students will then show amounts of money by counting out coins.

After they count the coins in the piggy bank, students will use the Money: Coins Learning Tool.

DIRECTIONS FOR USING THE MONEY: COINS LEARNING TOOL

1. Click Problem Type 2.
2. The top of the screen will give an amount in cents to be shown. Students should start with the coins with the higher values to begin counting out the amount shown. When they have the coins counted out, they should click Check.
3. Repeat as time permits.

LEARN Groups of Bills

Objectives

- Identify the value of a combination of coins and bills.

Students will identify bills up to the $20 bill and learn to find the value of a group of bills. Students will start with the bill with the greatest value first and count on to the bill with the least value.

Tips

Remind students to always start with the bills of the greatest value first when they are counting bills.

TRY IT How Much?

Objectives

- Identify the value of a combination of coins and bills.

Students will practice counting groups of coins and bills. Give students the How Much? activity page from their Activity Book and read the directions with them.

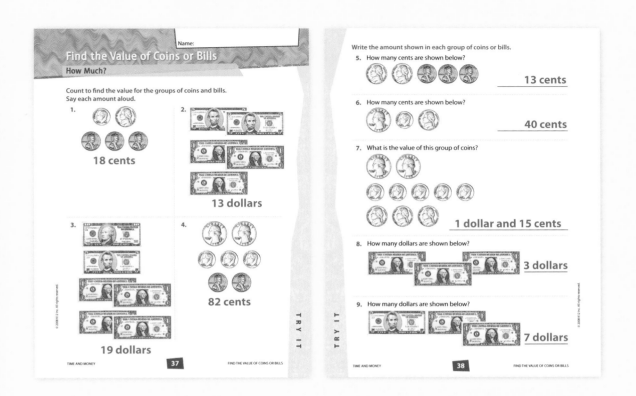

Find the Value of Coins or Bills

How Much?

Count to find the value for the groups of coins and bills.
Say each amount aloud.

1.

18 cents

2.

13 dollars

3.

19 dollars

4.

82 cents

Write the amount shown in each group of coins or bills.

5. How many cents are shown below?

13 cents

6. How many cents are shown below?

40 cents

7. What is the value of this group of coins?

1 dollar and 15 cents

8. How many dollars are shown below?

3 dollars

9. How many dollars are shown below?

7 dollars

TRY IT

TIME AND MONEY   37   FIND THE VALUE OF COINS OR BILLS

TIME AND MONEY   38   FIND THE VALUE OF COINS OR BILLS

Dollar and Cent Symbols for Money

Lesson Overview

Skills Update	5 minutes	**ONLINE**
GET READY Identify the Value of Coins or Bills	10 minutes	**ONLINE**
LEARN Cent Symbol and Dollar Symbol	15 minutes	**ONLINE**
LEARN Write Dollars and Cents	20 minutes	**OFFLINE**
TRY IT Write Money Amounts Using Symbols	10 minutes	**OFFLINE**

▶ Lesson Objectives

Use dollar and cent symbols for money.

▶ Prerequisite Skills

Identify the value of a combination of coins and bills.

▶ Content Background

In this lesson, students will write the value of a group of coins or bills using the dollar and cent symbols for money.

> **Materials to Gather**
>
> **SUPPLIED**
> Cent Symbol activity page
> Dollar Symbol activity page
> Write Money Amounts Using Symbols
>   activity page

GET READY Identify the Value of Coins or Bills

ONLINE 10min

Students will practice finding the value of bills and coins. First students will review the values of bills and coins, and practice counting. Then they will practice showing money amounts using the Money Learning Tool.

Objectives

- Identify the value of a combination of coins and bills.

DIRECTIONS FOR USING THE MONEY LEARNING TOOL

1. Click Counting Money and choose the following:
   - Coins
   - Level 1
2. Have students enter the correct money amount for each problem.
3. Continue as time allows.

LEARN Cent Symbol and Dollar Symbol

ONLINE 15min

Students will learn how to use the symbols for cents and for dollars to write the value of money.

Objectives

- Use dollar and cent symbols for money.

LEARN Write Dollars and Cents

OFFLINE
20min

Students will write money amounts using the cent symbol or the dollar symbol.
Gather the Cent Symbol activity page and the Dollar Symbol activity page.
Make sure students place the cent symbol after the value of amounts less than one dollar, and place the dollar symbol before the value of the amounts more than one dollar.

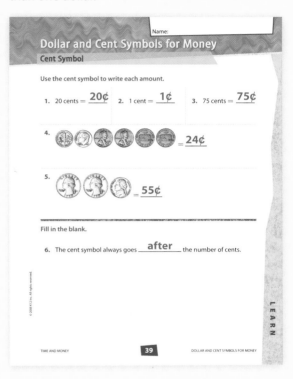

Objectives

- Use dollar and cent symbols for money.

Tips

If students have difficulty writing the cent symbol, tell them to write the lowercase letter c and place a line through it. The line should run from just above the top of the letter to just below the bottom of the letter.

Tips

If students have difficulty writing the dollar symbol, tell them to write an upper case letter S and place a line through it ($). Let them know that officially the dollar sign has two lines through it, but it's often written with just one line. With fonts on computers and in print there are times when the line doesn't appear to go all the way through the S but just appears at the top and bottom ($).

TRY IT Write Money Amounts Using Symbols

Students will practice writing money amounts using the dollar and cent symbols. Give students the Write Money Amounts Using Symbols activity page from their Activity Book and read the directions with them.

- Use dollar and cent symbols for money.

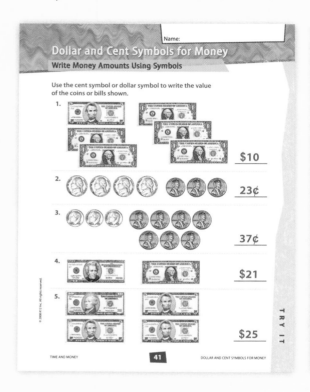

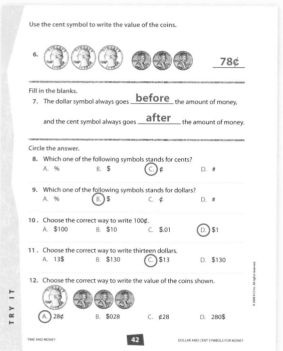

Decimal Notation for Money

Lesson Overview

Skills Update	5 minutes	**ONLINE**
GET READY Dollars and Cents	5 minutes	**ONLINE**
LEARN Combinations of Dollars and Cents	10 minutes	**OFFLINE**
LEARN Write Dollars and Cents	20 minutes	**OFFLINE**
TRY IT Money as Dollars and Cents	10 minutes	**OFFLINE**
CHECKPOINT	10 minutes	**OFFLINE**

▶ Lesson Objectives

Use decimal notation for money.

▶ Prerequisite Skills

Use dollar and cent symbols for money.

▶ Advance Preparation

Number two sets of index cards 0 through 9. Label two other index cards with the following symbols: $ and ¢.

▶ Content Background

In this lesson, students will use decimal notation to show money amounts.

Keywords

decimal notation – the display of a number by a whole number, a decimal point, and parts of a whole, such as the monetary value $1.35

Materials to Gather

SUPPLIED

Money as Dollars and Cents
  activity page

Checkpoint (printout)

ALSO NEEDED

play money – two $10 bills, two
  $5 bills, and four $1 bills

play money – 3 quarters, 3 dimes,
  3 nickels, and 12 pennies

index cards – numbered 0 through 9
  (two sets)

index cards – labeled with symbols
  $ and ¢

GET READY Dollars and Cents

ONLINE 5min

Students will find the value of a group of coins or bills and then match the value to a written amount.

Objectives

- Use dollar and cent symbols for money.

Tips

If students have trouble matching the groups of coins or bills to the correct written value, review the dollar and cent symbols and their proper placements.

LEARN Combinations of Dollars and Cents

- Use decimal notation for money.

Students will read and write decimal notation for a combination of coins and bills. Gather the play money and give students the bills and coins.

Tips

If students make an amount greater than $25 and have trouble reading it, give them the answer. Then encourage them to make another amount that is equal to or less than $25.

1. Have students use dollar bills to show 3 dollars. Then have them use a combination of coins to show 12 cents.

2. **Say:** To find the total amount, say the dollars, then the cents together: 3 dollars and 12 cents.

    As you say this, point to each amount. Stress that students should say "and" as they say the dollars and the cents.

3. Write $3.12.

    Say: You can write this amount as 3 dollars and 12 cents. The symbol between the dollars and the cents is called a decimal point. The "and" tells you where to put the decimal point.

4. Place one $5 bill, two $1 bills, and three pennies in front of students.

    Ask: What is the value of the bills?
    ANSWER: 7 dollars

    Ask: What is the value of the coins?
    ANSWER: 3 cents

    Ask: What is the value of the bills and coins together?
    ANSWER: 7 dollars and 3 cents

5. Write $7.03.

    Say: You can write this amount as 7 dollars **and** 3 cents. There are always two numbers after the decimal point. If there are fewer than 10 cents, we put a 0 first. We write seven point zero three.

6. Have students use a combination of coins and bills to make another money amount. Then have them say the amount using the words *dollars* and *cents*. Have them repeat the amounts as you write them in decimal notation. Make sure students say "and" in place of the decimal point.

7. **Ask:** When you say a money amount, how do you know whether to say "cents," "dollars," or "dollars and cents"?

    ANSWER: Say cents if the amount is less than one dollar. Say dollars if there are only bills. If the amount has both dollars and cents, say dollars and cents. (Answers will vary.)

8. Have students read each of the following amounts aloud.

    $13.02
    $ 4.00
    $28.65

LEARN Write Dollars and Cents

Objectives

- Use decimal notation for money.

Tips

Watch for students who use both a dollar symbol and a cent symbol with decimal notation. Remind students that the two symbols are never used together.

Students will use number and symbol cards to show money amounts in decimal notation. Students will also learn to write the money amount when they hear it spoken.

Gather the index cards and the play money.

1. Have students use dollar bills to show 4 dollars. Then have them use coins to show 16 cents.

   Say: When we say this amount, we say 4 dollars and 16 cents. We write money amounts with a dollar symbol and decimal point. This is called decimal notation.

   Read the amount again. As you say each word, lay down the index card with the 4, the dollar symbol, the decimal point, and the 1 and the 6. Stress the word *and* as you put the decimal point in place.

2. **Say:** The decimal point separates the dollars from the cents. The word *and* tells you where the decimal goes.

3. Have students read the amount again with you as they look at the cards, stressing *and*. Then repeat Steps 1–3 with $13.55 and $24.17.

4. **Say:** When we use a dollar symbol, we don't need a cent symbol. We only use the cent symbol when we have less than 1 dollar.

5. Have students use cards to show $3.56 in decimal notation.

6. **Ask:** What is one way to write 4 dollars that you have seen before?
   ANSWER: a 4 with a dollar symbol in front of it

   Have students show 4 dollars with cards.

7. **Say:** There is another way to write 4 dollars. Four dollars is the same as 4 dollars and 0 cents. We can use decimal notation to show the 4 dollars and 0 cents.

8. Place the number and symbol cards to show $4.00.

   Say: 4 dollars…and…zero cents. The decimal point separates the dollars from the cents. We always use two numbers to show the cents amount after the decimal point so there are two zeros. Write $4.00.

9. Repeat Steps 6–8 with $12.00.

10. Have students use coins to show 45 cents.

    Ask: What is one way that you have seen before to write 45 cents?
    ANSWER: 45 with a cent symbol after it.

    Have students show 45 cents with cards.

11. **Say:** We can use decimal notation to write 45 cents. We use a dollar symbol and a decimal point. Think of 45 cents as zero dollars **and** 45 cents.

    Place the cards to show $0.45 as you again say zero dollars and 45 cents.

    Say: Since there are zero dollars, use a 0 to show the dollars.
    Have students write $0.45 on paper.

12. Repeat Steps 10–11 with 72 cents.

13. Show $3.06 with the cards.

    Say: Suppose we had 3 dollars and only 6 cents. We said that you had to show the cents with two numbers. This is how to show 3 dollars and 6 cents in decimal notation. When you have fewer than 10 cents, use a zero between the decimal and the number of cents.

14. Have students use cards to show $11.02.

15. **Ask:** What if you had 8 cents? How many dollars are there?
ANSWER: zero

Say: Show 8 cents in decimal notation by thinking zero dollars and 8 cents.

16. As time permits, give students more combinations of bills and coins. Include at least one amount with no dollars, one amount with no cents, and one with or without dollars, but with fewer than 10 cents. Have students show the amount with the number and symbol cards and then write the amount on paper.

TRY IT Money as Dollars and Cents

OFFLINE **10 min**

Students will practice writing money amounts in decimal notation. Give students the Money as Dollars and Cents activity page from their Activity Book and read the directions with them.

For Problems 3–6, read the amounts aloud. Speak slowly and stress the word *and*.

Objectives

- Use decimal notation for money.

Tips

If students have difficulty writing the dollar symbol, have them write the uppercase letter S and place a line through it. The line should run from just above the top of the letter to just below the bottom of the letter.

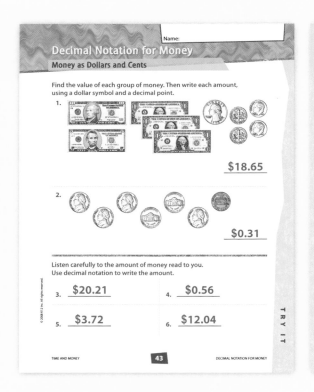

Name: _____

Decimal Notation for Money
Money as Dollars and Cents

Find the value of each group of money. Then write each amount, using a dollar symbol and a decimal point.

1. $18.65

2. $0.31

Listen carefully to the amount of money read to you. Use decimal notation to write the amount.

3. $20.21   4. $0.56

5. $3.72   6. $12.04

TIME AND MONEY   **43**   DECIMAL NOTATION FOR MONEY

TRY IT

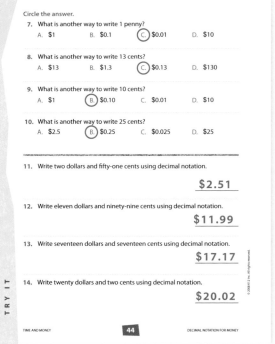

Circle the answer.

7. What is another way to write 1 penny?
   A. $1   B. $0.1   C. $0.01   D. $10

8. What is another way to write 13 cents?
   A. $13   B. $1.3   C. $0.13   D. $130

9. What is another way to write 10 cents?
   A. $1   B. $0.10   C. $0.01   D. $10

10. What is another way to write 25 cents?
   A. $2.5   B. $0.25   C. $0.025   D. $25

11. Write two dollars and fifty-one cents using decimal notation.
    $2.51

12. Write eleven dollars and ninety-nine cents using decimal notation.
    $11.99

13. Write seventeen dollars and seventeen cents using decimal notation.
    $17.17

14. Write twenty dollars and two cents using decimal notation.
    $20.02

TRY IT

TIME AND MONEY   **44**   DECIMAL NOTATION FOR MONEY

CHECKPOINT

Objectives

- Use decimal notation for money.

Print the assessment and have students complete it on their own. Read the directions, questions, and answer choices to students if necessary. Use the answer key to score the assessment, and then enter the results online.

⚙ Checkpoint

Math | Time and Money | Decimal Notation for Money

Name _____ Date _____

Checkpoint Answer Key

Circle the answer.
(1 point)
1. What is another way to write twenty-three cents?
   A. $0.023   **B. $0.23**   C. $23.00   D. $2.30

(1 point)
2. What is another way to write seventeen cents?
   A. $17   B. $1.70   **C. $0.17**   D. $0.017

(1 point)
3. What is another way to write twelve cents?
   A. $0.12   B. $12.00   C. $12   D. $0.012

(1 point)
4. What is another way to write seventy-five cents?
   A. $75   **B. $0.75**   C. $0.075   D. $7.5

(1 point)
5. Penny has two dollars and thirty-two cents. Which is the correct way to write that amount of money?
   A. $2.32   B. $2.32¢   C. $2 and 3.2¢   D. $2 and .32¢

(1 point)
6. Which is the correct way to write 1 dollar and twenty-five cents?
   A. $125¢   B. $1 and 2.5¢   C. ¢1.25   **D. $1.25**

(1 point)
7. Write numbers on the lines to write twenty-five cents. $0. **2 5**

(1 point)
8. Write numbers on the lines to write fifty-two cents. $0. **5 2**

1 of 1

Fewest Bills and Coins

▶ Lesson Objectives

- Identify the value of a combination of coins and bills.
- Find the fewest number of bills and coins to represent an amount of money.

▶ Prerequisite Skills

Show different combinations of coins that equal the same value.

▶ Content Background

Students will trade combinations of bills and coins of lesser denominations for bills and coins of greater denominations to find the fewest bills or coins to represent an amount.

Materials to Gather

SUPPLIED

You're in the Money activity page

ALSO NEEDED

play money – one $20 bill, ten $10 bills, ten $5 bills, and ten $1 bills

play money – 4 quarters, 10 dimes, 10 nickels, and 15 pennies

---

GET READY Different Coins, Equal Value

ONLINE
5 min

Objectives

- Show different combinations of coins that equal the same value.

Students will use the Money: Coins Learning Tool to see that different groups of coins may have the same value.

DIRECTIONS FOR USING THE MONEY: COINS LEARNING TOOL

1. Click Problem Type 4.
2. Drag coins onto the mat.
3. Click Show Value to check answers.
4. Clear the mat.

   Have students drag coins to show 10¢ in three ways. (1 dime; 2 nickels; 1 nickel and 5 pennies; 10 pennies)

   Then repeat the process with:

   - 12¢ (1 dime and 2 pennies; 2 nickels and 2 pennies; 1 nickel and 7 pennies; 12 pennies)
   - 15¢ (1 dime and 1 nickel; 3 nickels; 1 dime and 5 pennies; 2 nickels and 5 pennies; 1 nickel and 10 pennies; 15 pennies)

LEARN Fewest Coins

Students will use an online learning tool to trade coins of lesser value for coins of greater value to show a specific value using the fewest coins.

DIRECTIONS FOR USING THE MONEY: COINS LEARNING TOOL

1. Click Practice Mode.

2. **Say:** You can almost always show an amount of money in more than one way. For example, 1 dollar can be 4 quarters, 10 dimes, 20 nickels, 100 pennies, or any combination of coins that add up to 1 dollar. It is simpler, though, to show an amount using the fewest coins possible. In this case, that would be 4 quarters.

3. **Say:** To show a specific amount of money in different ways, we can trade coins of equal value. To find the fewest number of coins possible, we need to trade coins that have lesser values for coins that have greater values.

4. Drag 1 nickel and 6 pennies onto the mat.

   Say: Suppose you have 1 nickel and 6 pennies. That's 7 coins to make 11 cents. You could trade the 7 coins for 1 dime and 1 penny, and still have 11 cents, but only have 2 coins to carry around.

   Drag 1 dime onto the mat, and drag 1 nickel and 5 pennies off the mat to show that you are replacing them.

5. Clear the mat and drag 2 dimes, 4 nickels, and 6 pennies onto it. Ask students how many coins are in the group. (12) Have them tell you the value of the group of coins. (46 cents)

   Say: Let's make a group of coins worth 46 cents using the fewest possible coins.

6. **Ask:** Which has the greatest value: a penny, nickel, dime, or quarter? (a quarter) What is the value of a quarter? (25 cents)

   Say: To trade some coins for a quarter, we have to find a combination of coins that also makes 25 cents.

7. Have students trade 2 dimes and 1 nickel for 1 quarter. (They should drag the 2 dimes and 1 nickel off the mat, and drag a quarter on.)

8. **Ask:** Now what coins do you have? (1 quarter, 3 nickels, and 6 pennies) Do you have any other coins that you can trade for a quarter? (no)

9. **Say:** We cannot trade any more coins for quarters, let's move to the coin with the next highest value, the dime. What coins can you trade for a dime? (2 nickels)

10. Have students trade 2 nickels for 1 dime.

    Ask: Are there any other coins you can trade for 1 dime? (1 nickel and 5 pennies)

11. Have students trade 1 nickel and 5 pennies for 1 dime.

    Ask: Can you make any more trades, or is this the fewest coins that you can use to show 46 cents? Why?

12. Repeat the process using the following combinations of coins:

    - 6 dimes, 2 nickels, 8 pennies (3 quarters, 3 pennies)
    - 1 quarter, 3 dimes, 1 nickel (2 quarters, 1 dime)

Tips

If students have trouble finding the fewest number of coins, have them order the coins from greatest value to least value and trade.

LEARN Fewest Bills

Objectives

- Identify the value of a combination of coins and bills.
- Find the fewest number of bills and coins to represent an amount of money.

Students will trade bills of lesser denominations for bills of greater denominations to show a specific value using the fewest bills.
   Gather the play money.

1. **Say:** You can make different combinations of bills that equal the same amount. Although any combination of bills can be used, it is simpler to use the fewest number of bills.

2. **Say:** To show a specific amount of money, we can trade bills of equal value. To find the fewest number of bills, we need to trade bills that have lesser values for bills that have greater values. Suppose you have one $10 bill and seven $1 bills. That's 8 bills to make $17. You could trade five $1 bills for a $5 bill and still have $17 but only have 4 bills to carry around.

3. Place eight $1 bills and one $5 bill on the table. Ask students how many bills are in this group. (9) Then have them tell you the value of the bills. ($13)
   Say: Let's make a group of bills worth $13 using the fewest possible bills. Put the bills in order from greatest to least.

4. Have students trade 5 of the $1 bills for a $5 bill.
   Ask: Is that the fewest bills you could use to show $13? (no) What else can you trade? (two $5 bills for a $10 bill)

5. **Ask:** Can you make any more trades, or is this the fewest bills you can use to show $13? Why?

6. Repeat the process using the following combination of bills:
   three $5 bills, two $1 bills. (one $10 bill, one $5 bill, two $1 bills)

LEARN Fewest Bills and Coins

Objectives

- Identify the value of a combination of coins and bills.
- Find the fewest number of bills and coins to represent an amount of money.

Students will find the fewest bills and coins to represent an amount of money with both dollars and cents.
   Gather the play money.

1. Have students count out eight $1 bills and 7 pennies.
   Say: We can show 8 dollars and 7 cents using fewer coins and bills.

2. Trade five $1 bills for one $5 bill. Trade 5 pennies for 1 nickel.
   Say: Count the bills and coins now to see if we still have $8.07.

3. Place two $5 bills, two $1 bills, 4 dimes, and 2 nickels on the table. Have students count the money and tell you its value. ($12.50)

4. Have students trade to get fewer bills. Then have them trade to get fewer coins.
   Say: Count the money aloud to be sure you still have $12.50.

5. **Ask:** Can you show this amount using fewer bills and coins? Why not?

6. Repeat the activity using the following combinations of money.
   - ten $1 bills and 7 nickels (one $10 bill, 1 quarter, and 1 dime)
   - one $10 bill, two $5 bills, 1 quarter, and 13 pennies (one $20 bill, 1 quarter, 1 dime, and 3 pennies)

7. Write the following amounts, and have students make that amount with the fewest coins and bills.

- $16.06 (one $10 bill, one $5 bill, one $1 bill, 1 nickel, and 1 penny)
- $21.43 (one $20 bill, one $1 bill, 1 quarter, 1 dime, 1 nickel, and 3 pennies)

TRY IT You're in the Money

OFFLINE
15 min

Students will practice trading coins and bills to get the same amount of money using the fewest number of coins and bills. Give students the play money and the You're in the Money activity page from their Activity Book. Read the directions with them.

For Problems 1–3, give them the following combinations of coins and bills:

1. 4 dimes and 12 pennies
2. nine $1 bills
3. one $10 bill, seven $1 bills, 4 nickels, and 9 pennies

Objectives

- Identify the value of a combination of coins and bills.

Tips

If students have trouble finding the fewest number of bills and coins, have them order the bills and coins from greatest value to least and trade.

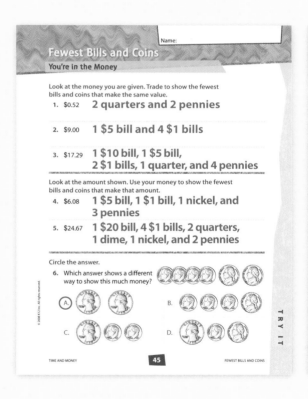

Name: _____

Fewest Bills and Coins
You're in the Money

Look at the money you are given. Trade to show the fewest bills and coins that make the same value.

1. $0.52   **2 quarters and 2 pennies**

2. $9.00   **1 $5 bill and 4 $1 bills**

3. $17.29 **1 $10 bill, 1 $5 bill, 2 $1 bills, 1 quarter, and 4 pennies**

Look at the amount shown. Use your money to show the fewest bills and coins that make that amount.

4. $6.08   **1 $5 bill, 1 $1 bill, 1 nickel, and 3 pennies**

5. $24.67 **1 $20 bill, 4 $1 bills, 2 quarters, 1 dime, 1 nickel, and 2 pennies**

Circle the answer.

6. Which answer shows a different way to show this much money?

TIME AND MONEY   45   FEWEST BILLS AND COINS

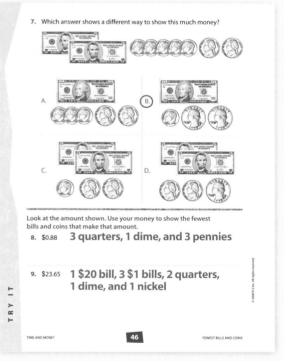

7. Which answer shows a different way to show this much money?

A.   B.

C.   D.

Look at the amount shown. Use your money to show the fewest bills and coins that make that amount.

8. $0.88   **3 quarters, 1 dime, and 3 pennies**

9. $23.65 **1 $20 bill, 3 $1 bills, 2 quarters, 1 dime, and 1 nickel**

TIME AND MONEY   46   FEWEST BILLS AND COINS

How Much Money?

Lesson Overview

Skills Update	5 minutes	ONLINE
GET READY The Value of Money	5 minutes	ONLINE
LEARN Alex's Money	10 minutes	ONLINE
LEARN Let's Go to the Store	20 minutes	OFFLINE
TRY IT Solve Money Problems	10 minutes	OFFLINE
CHECKPOINT	10 minutes	OFFLINE

▶ **Lesson Objectives**

Solve problems by using combinations of coins and bills.

▶ **Prerequisite Skills**

Identify the value of a combination of coins and bills.

▶ **Advance Preparation**

Choose items from around the house. Place prices on sticky notes on the items as if they were in a store. For example:

- game $3.49
- hat $2.85
- umbrella $12.14

Include a variety of prices. Do not price anything at more than $25.

▶ **Content Background**

Students already know how to identify the value of a combination of coins and bills. In this lesson, students will use coins and bills to solve problems.

Materials to Gather

SUPPLIED

Solve Money Problems activity page

Checkpoint (printout)

Money (printout)

ALSO NEEDED

sticky notes

household objects – 5 or 6 to "sell" at store

play money – one $20 bill, two $10 bills, four $5 bills, and ten $1 bills

play money – 4 quarters, 10 dimes, 10 nickels, and 10 pennies

---

GET READY The Value of Money

ONLINE 5 min

Students will identify the value of several combinations of bills and coins.

Objectives

- Identify the value of a combination of coins and bills.

LEARN Alex's Money

- Solve problems by using combinations of coins and bills.

Students will count groups of bills and coins. Ask students to explain their answers.

LEARN Let's Go to the Store

- Solve problems by using combinations of coins and bills.

Students will identify the value of a combination of coins and bills to play a shopping game.

Gather real or play money and the items you priced. Give students the money.

1. **Say:** I want you to shop in my store. I have the following items for sale. Show students the items.

2. Have students pick two items to buy. Show them how much each item costs.

3. Have students count their coins and bills to pay for each item. Encourage them to count the money aloud.

4. **Ask:** How can you find out how much it costs altogether for both items? **ANSWER:** Put the money for both items together and count it.

   Have students recount the bills and coins to find the total.

5. Continue until students do not have enough money left to buy any more items.

6. Switch roles and have students become the cashiers.

   Ask: What do you have for sale? How much does it cost?

7. Give students either the correct amount or the incorrect amount of money.

   Ask: Did I give you the right amount of money?

   If you gave students the incorrect amount, ask them to tell you how to make the correct amount.

8. Continue shopping. Give students a variety of different combinations of coins and bills including several incorrect amounts.

Tips

If you are using real money, encourage students to study the front and the back of each bill and coin so they can recognize them quickly. Ask them about similarities and differences.

TRY IT Solve Money Problems

Students will practice counting money and finding out if they have enough money to make a purchase. Give students the Solve Money Problems activity page and read the directions with them.

- Solve problems by using combinations of coins and bills.

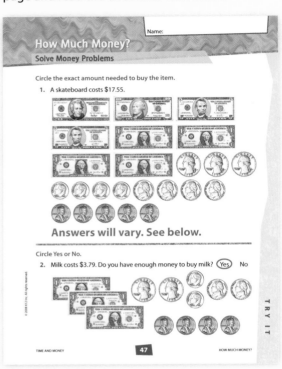

How Much Money?

Solve Money Problems

Name:

Circle the exact amount needed to buy the item.

1. A skateboard costs $17.55.

Answers will vary. See below.

Circle Yes or No.

2. Milk costs $3.79. Do you have enough money to buy milk? (Yes) No

TIME AND MONEY **47** HOW MUCH MONEY?

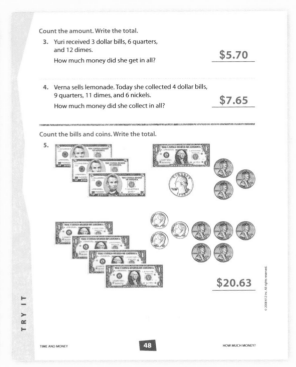

Count the amount. Write the total.

3. Yuri received 3 dollar bills, 6 quarters, and 12 dimes.
   How much money did she get in all?

   $5.70

4. Verna sells lemonade. Today she collected 4 dollar bills, 9 quarters, 11 dimes, and 6 nickels.
   How much money did she collect in all?

   $7.65

Count the bills and coins. Write the total.

5.

   $20.63

TIME AND MONEY **48** HOW MUCH MONEY?

Additional Answers

1. 1 $10 bill, 1 $5 bill, 2 $1 bills, 2 quarters, 1 nickel

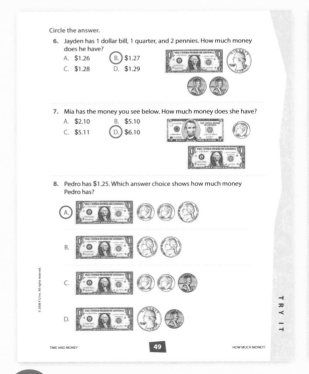

Circle the answer.

6. Jayden has 1 dollar bill, 1 quarter, and 2 pennies. How much money does he have?
   A. $1.26 (B.) $1.27
   C. $1.28 D. $1.29

7. Mia has the money you see below. How much money does she have?
   A. $2.10 B. $5.10
   C. $5.11 (D.) $6.10

8. Pedro has $1.25. Which answer choice shows how much money Pedro has?
   (A)
   B.
   C.
   D.

TIME AND MONEY **49** HOW MUCH MONEY?

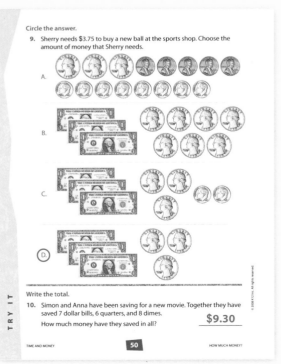

Circle the answer.

9. Sherry needs $3.75 to buy a new ball at the sports shop. Choose the amount of money that Sherry needs.
   A.
   B.
   C.
   (D.)

Write the total.

10. Simon and Anna have been saving for a new movie. Together they have saved 7 dollar bills, 6 quarters, and 8 dimes.
    How much money have they saved in all?

    $9.30

TIME AND MONEY **50** HOW MUCH MONEY?

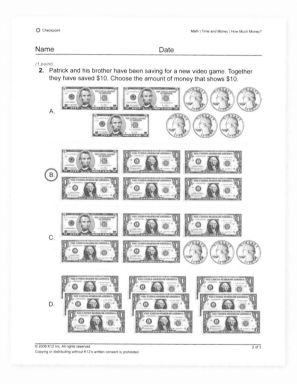

CHECKPOINT

Objectives

- Solve problems by using combinations of coins and bills.

Print the assessment and have students complete it on their own. Read the directions, questions, and answer choices to students if necessary. Students may use the Money printout during the Lesson Checkpoint. Use the answer key to score the assessment, and then enter the results online.

Checkpoint   Math | Time and Money | How Much Money?

Name _____ Date _____

Checkpoint Answer Key

(1 point)
1. Sue wants to go to the store to buy some milk. She needs $4.50. Choose the amount of money that Sue needs.

A.

B.

C.

D.

Checkpoint   Math | Time and Money | How Much Money?

Name _____ Date _____

(1 point)
2. Patrick and his brother have been saving for a new video game. Together they have saved $10. Choose the amount of money that shows $10.

A.

B.

C.

D.

Checkpoint   Math | Time and Money | How Much Money?

Name _____ Date _____

(1 point)
3. Polly looks in her piggy bank and sees she has 9 quarters, 6 dimes, 3 nickels, and 20 pennies.
   How much money does she have in all? __**$3.20**__

(1 point)
4. Jeremy has 7 nickels and 6 pennies. Which of the following shows the same amount of money?

A.

B.

C.

D.

(1 point)
5. Melissa wants to buy a book that costs $10. She has 1 five-dollar bill, 2 one-dollar bills, 6 quarters, and 7 dimes. Add up how much money she has. Does she have enough money to buy the book?
   A. Yes   B. No

Unit Review

Lesson Overview

UNIT REVIEW Look Back	20 minutes	ONLINE
UNIT REVIEW Checkpoint Practice	20 minutes	OFFLINE
⏩ **UNIT REVIEW** Prepare for the Checkpoint		

▶ Unit Objectives

This lesson assesses the following objectives:

- Tell time to the nearest quarter hour.
- Identify relationships between units of time, such as minutes in an hour, days in a month, weeks in a year.
- Determine elapsed time in hours, such as 11:00 a.m. to 4:00 p.m.
- Identify the value of a combination of coins and bills.
- Use dollar and cent symbols for money.
- Use decimal notation for money.
- Find the fewest number of bills and coins to represent an amount of money.
- Solve problems by using combinations of coins and bills.

▶ Advance Preparation

In this lesson, students will have an opportunity to review previous activities in the Time and Money unit. Look at the suggested activities in Unit Review: Prepare for the Checkpoint and gather any needed materials.

Materials to Gather

SUPPLIED

Checkpoint Practice activity page

Keywords

analog clock　　　　　　**elapsed time**
decimal notation

UNIT REVIEW Look Back

ONLINE
20min

In this unit, students learned to tell time to the nearest quarter hour and identified elapsed time and time relationships.

They also found the value of combinations of coins and bills, solved practical problems involving money, and learned to use money symbols to write decimal notation for money.

Students will review these concepts to prepare for the Unit Checkpoint.

Objectives

- Review unit objectives.

UNIT REVIEW Checkpoint Practice

Objectives

- Review unit objectives.

Students will use the Checkpoint Practice activity page to prepare for the Unit Checkpoint. If necessary, read the directions, questions, and answer choices to students. Have students answer the problems on their own. Carefully review the answers with students.

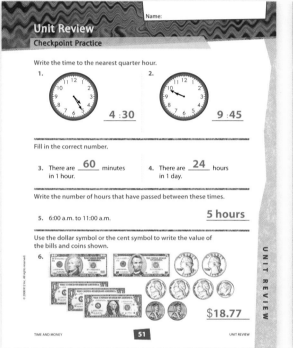

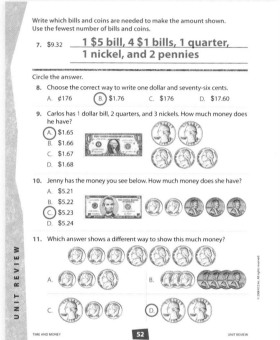

→ UNIT REVIEW Prepare for the Checkpoint

What you do next depends on how students performed in the previous activity, Unit Review: Checkpoint Practice. If students had difficulty with any of the problems, complete the appropriate review activity listed in the table online.

Unit Checkpoint

Lesson Overview

UNIT CHECKPOINT Online	30 minutes	**ONLINE**
UNIT CHECKPOINT Offline	30 minutes	**OFFLINE**

▶ Unit Objectives

This lesson assesses the following objectives:

- Tell time to the nearest quarter hour.
- Identify relationships between units of time, such as minutes in an hour, days in a month, weeks in a year.
- Determine elapsed time in hours, such as 11:00 a.m. to 4:00 p.m.
- Identify the value of a combination of coins and bills.
- Use dollar and cent symbols for money.
- Use decimal notation for money.
- Find the fewest number of bills and coins to represent an amount of money.
- Solve problems by using combinations of coins and bills.

Materials to Gather

SUPPLIED

Unit Checkpoint (printout)

UNIT CHECKPOINT Online

ONLINE 30 min

Objectives

- Assess unit objectives.

Students will complete this part of the Unit Checkpoint online. Read the directions, problems, and answer choices to students. If necessary, help students with keyboard or mouse operations.

UNIT CHECKPOINT Offline

OFFLINE 30 min

Objectives

- Assess unit objectives.

Students will complete this part of the Unit Checkpoint offline. Print the Checkpoint and have students complete it on their own. Read the directions, problems, and answer choices to students if necessary. Use the answer key to score the Checkpoint, and then enter the results online.

Name _____ Date _____

Unit Checkpoint Answer Key

For Problems 1–3, write the answer in the space provided.

(1 point)
1. Use decimal notation to write three dollars and twenty-five cents.

$ _3_ _2_ _5_

(1 point)
2. Using decimal notation, show how you would write twenty dollars.

$ _2_ _0_ . _0_ _0_

(1 point)
3. Write the amount of money, using the cent symbol.

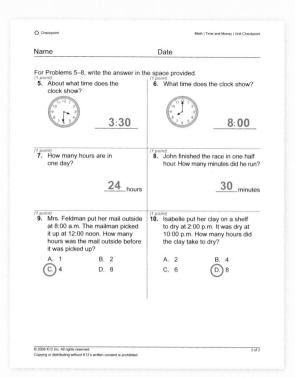

_41¢_

(1 point)
4. Which answer is a different way to show this much money? Circle the correct answer.

A.

B. (circled)

C.

D.

Name _____ Date _____

For Problems 5–8, write the answer in the space provided.

(1 point)
5. About what time does the clock show?

_3:30_

(1 point)
6. What time does the clock show?

_8:00_

(1 point)
7. How many hours are in one day?

_24_ hours

(1 point)
8. John finished the race in one half hour. How many minutes did he run?

_30_ minutes

(1 point)
9. Mrs. Feldman put her mail outside at 8:00 a.m. The mailman picked it up at 12:00 noon. How many hours was the mail outside before it was picked up?

A. 1   B. 2
C. 4 (circled)   D. 8

(1 point)
10. Isabelle put her clay on a shelf to dry at 2:00 p.m. It was dry at 10:00 p.m. How many hours did the clay take to dry?

A. 2   B. 4
C. 6   D. 8 (circled)

Add, Subtract, Number Composition

▶ Unit Objectives

- Use concrete objects or sketches to model and solve addition or subtraction computation problems with sums or minuends up through 500 with and without regrouping.

- Find the sum of two whole numbers with sums up through 500.

- Use regrouping to find the difference of two whole numbers with the minuend up through 500.

- Explain the meaning of the equals symbol.

- Demonstrate that a number can be composed of other numbers in various ways.

- Decompose numbers to solve subtraction problems, such as $213 - 12 = 200 + 13 - 12$.

▶ Big Ideas

- Models and mathematical symbols can represent addition and subtraction.

- The equals symbol denotes an equivalent relationship.

- Numbers can be created by adding other numbers together.

▶ Unit Introduction

In this unit, students will learn how to add and subtract with numbers through 500. They will use strategies for addition and subtraction, and identify and correct errors.

Students will use base-10 blocks, drawings, and place-value charts to solve addition and subtraction problems with sums or minuends up through 500 with and without regrouping. They will learn the meaning of the equals symbol and will write equivalent expressions.

Students will learn that numbers are composed of other numbers, and they will decompose numbers in various ways. They will use this knowledge to solve addition and subtraction problems.

Addition and Subtraction

Lesson Overview

Skills Update	5 minutes	**ONLINE**
GET READY Addition with Models	5 minutes	**ONLINE**
LEARN Addition	10 minutes	**ONLINE**
LEARN Subtraction	10 minutes	**ONLINE**
LEARN Add and Subtract with Blocks	10 minutes	OFFLINE
TRY IT Model Addition and Subtraction	10 minutes	OFFLINE
CHECKPOINT	10 minutes	OFFLINE

▶ ## Lesson Objectives

Use concrete objects or sketches to model and solve addition or subtraction computation problems with sums or minuends up through 500 with and without regrouping.

▶ ## Prerequisite Skills

Use concrete objects or sketches to model and solve addition or subtraction problems involving sums or minuends up through 100.

▶ ## Content Background

Students know how to add and subtract numbers through 100. In this lesson, students will use base-10 blocks and drawings to solve addition and subtraction problems with sums or minuends up through 500 with and without regrouping.

Algorithm is a mathematical term for a repeated, step-by-step mathematical procedure, such as adding or subtracting numbers. Although specific algorithms are used by convention, multiple algorithms may exist for performing any given operation. In this lesson, when students see an algorithm, the purpose is to help them model their answers, not to learn the algorithm.

The three parts of a subtraction sentence are the minuend, the subtrahend, and the difference. In the subtraction sentence $4 - 1 = 3$, the number you are subtracting from (4) is the minuend, the number you are subtracting (1) is the subtrahend, and the answer (3) is the difference.

The term *difference* is used with students and by students, but the terms *minuend* and *subtrahend* will not be formally introduced to students yet.

Materials to Gather

SUPPLIED
base-10 blocks
place-value mat
Model Addition and Subtraction
    activity page
Checkpoint (printout)

ALSO NEEDED
dry-erase marker
dry-erase eraser

addend – one of the two or more numbers that are added to determine a sum

algorithm – a repeated step-by-step mathematical procedure

base-10 blocks – a set of blocks used to model the place values of numbers; blocks include ones cubes, tens rods, hundreds flats, and thousands cubes

difference – the solution to a subtraction problem

minuend – in subtraction, the quantity or number from which another number is subtracted; 8 is the minuend in the problem $8 - 7 = ?$

model (verb) – to use physical objects, diagrams, or pictures to represent an amount, an expression, an equation, or a problem situation

place value – the value of a digit, given its position in a number; for example, 23 means 2 tens and 3 ones

place-value chart – a chart or arrangement that shows the value of each digit in a number

place-value mat – a grid with columns labeled with place values (ones, tens…), used with corresponding base-10 blocks to illustrate place value

regroup; regrouping – to use place-value concepts to rename numbers, such as one ten and 3 ones = 13 ones; often used in addition and subtraction

sum – the solution to an addition problem

ONLINE 5 min

GET READY Addition with Models

Objectives

- Use concrete objects or sketches to model and solve addition or subtraction problems involving sums or minuends up through 100.

Students will use the Place Value Addition Learning Tool to review addition with sums through 100. The learning tool models addition problems using base-10 blocks and a place-value mat.

DIRECTIONS FOR USING THE PLACE VALUE ADDITION LEARNING TOOL

1. Click Begin Setup. Choose the following:
   - Present addition problems with SUMS up to: 99
   - Allow REGROUPING in problems: NO
2. **Say:** You can solve addition problems by using blocks to represent the numbers. The numbers you add together are called addends.
3. Have students complete two problems.
4. Move the cursor over Menu and Click Setup. Choose the following:
   - Allow REGROUPING in problems: YES
5. Have students complete two problems with regrouping.

LEARN Addition

ONLINE 10 min

Students will use the Place Value Addition Learning Tool to find sums through 500 with and without regrouping. The learning tool models addition problems using base-10 blocks and a place-value mat.

DIRECTIONS FOR USING THE PLACE VALUE ADDITION LEARNING TOOL

1. Click Begin Setup. Choose the following:
   - Present addition problems with SUMS up to: 500
   - Allow REGROUPING in problems: NO
2. Have students complete problems until they are comfortable adding without regrouping.
3. Move the cursor over Menu and Click Setup. Choose the following:
   - Allow REGROUPING in problems: YES
4. Have students complete at least three problems until they are comfortable adding with regrouping. Point out that the problem in the upper left corner shows each step.

Objectives

- Use concrete objects or sketches to model and solve addition or subtraction computation problems with sums or minuends up through 500 with and without regrouping.

Tips

Review the meaning of the ones cubes, tens rods, and hundreds flats if students have trouble with the problems.

LEARN Subtraction

ONLINE 10 min

Students will use the Place Value Subtraction Learning Tool to subtract two numbers with a minuend up through 500 with and without regrouping. The learning tool models subtraction problems using base-10 blocks and a place-value mat.

DIRECTIONS FOR USING THE PLACE VALUE SUBTRACTION LEARNING TOOL

1. Click Begin Setup. Choose the following:
   - Present subtraction problems with MINUENDS up to: 500
   - Allow REGROUPING in problems: NO
2. **Say:** The subtraction symbol tells you to subtract, or take away. We take away the bottom number from the top number. The answer is called the difference. You can solve subtraction problems by using blocks to represent the numbers.
3. Have students complete problems until they are comfortable subtracting without regrouping.
4. Move the cursor over Menu and Click Setup. Choose the following:
   - Allow REGROUPING in problems: YES
5. Have students complete three problems or as many as needed to be comfortable subtracting with regrouping. Point out that the problem in the upper left corner shows each step.

Objectives

- Use concrete objects or sketches to model and solve addition or subtraction computation problems with sums or minuends up through 500 with and without regrouping.

Tips

Review the meaning of the ones cubes, tens rods, and hundreds flats if students have trouble with the problems.

Tips

Point out that regrouping a hundred to 10 tens, or a ten to 10 ones, does not change the value of the number.

LEARN Add and Subtract with Blocks

Students will use base-10 blocks to model and solve addition and subtraction problems through 500.

Gather the blocks, the place-value mat, marker, and eraser.

1. Write 372 + 129 (vertically) on the place-value mat. Ask students to model each number with the blocks. Then have them solve the problem as follows:

- Add the ones cubes and regroup. Write 1 in the ones place on the place-value mat.
- Add the tens rods and regroup. Write 0 in the tens place.
- Add the hundreds flats. Write 5 in the hundreds place.

2. Write 233 − 116 on the place-value mat. Ask students to model 233 with the blocks. Then have them solve the problem as follows:

- Regroup 1 ten to 10 ones in order to take away 6 ones cubes. Write a 7 in the ones place.
- Take away 1 ten from 2 tens. Write a 1 in the tens place.
- Take away 1 hundred.

Objectives

- Use concrete objects or sketches to model and solve addition or subtraction computation problems with sums or minuends up through 500 with and without regrouping.

Tips

You can remind students that they don't need to model 116, because they are taking away that number.

TRY IT Model Addition and Subtraction

Students will use base-10 blocks to model and solve addition and subtraction problems. Gather the base-10 blocks, place-value mat, marker, and eraser. Give students the Model Addition and Subtraction activity page from their Activity Book. Read the directions with them.

Objectives

- Use concrete objects or sketches to model and solve addition or subtraction computation problems with sums or minuends up through 500 with and without regrouping.

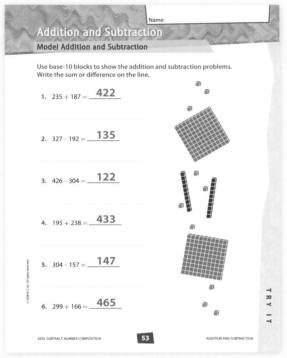

Addition and Subtraction
Model Addition and Subtraction

Use base-10 blocks to show the addition and subtraction problems. Write the sum or difference on the line.

1. 235 + 187 = __422__

2. 327 − 192 = __135__

3. 426 − 304 = __122__

4. 195 + 238 = __433__

5. 304 − 157 = __147__

6. 299 + 166 = __465__

53

ADD, SUBTRACT, NUMBER COMPOSITION   ADDITION AND SUBTRACTION

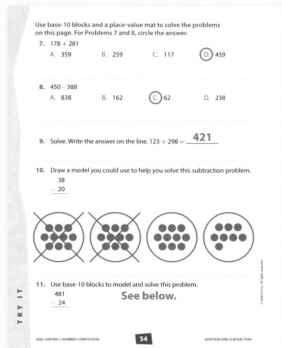

Use base-10 blocks and a place-value mat to solve the problems on this page. For Problems 7 and 8, circle the answer.

7. 178 + 281
    A. 359   B. 259   C. 117   (D.) 459

8. 450 − 388
    A. 838   B. 162   (C.) 62   D. 238

9. Solve. Write the answer on the line. 123 + 298 = __421__

10. Draw a model you could use to help you solve this subtraction problem.
     38
    − 20

11. Use base-10 blocks to model and solve this problem.
     481   **See below.**
    − 24

54

ADD, SUBTRACT, NUMBER COMPOSITION   ADDITION AND SUBTRACTION

Additional Answers

11. Use the base-10 blocks to model and solve the subtraction problem. Students should take away 24. First they will need to regroup 1 ten rod for 10 ones cubes. They can then take away 24 to get the correct answer, 457, which should be shown with 4 hundreds flats, 5 tens rods, and 7 ones cubes.

CHECKPOINT

Print the assessment and have students complete it on their own. Read the directions, questions, and answer choices to students if necessary. Use the answer key to score the assessment, and then enter the results online.

Gather the blocks and place-value mat.

- Use concrete objects or sketches to model and solve addition or subtraction computation problems with sums or minuends up through 500 with and without regrouping.

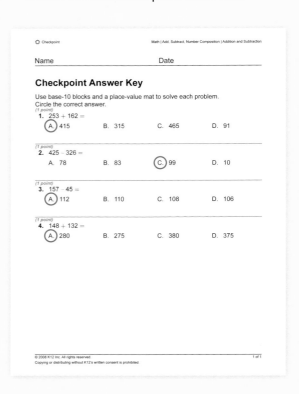

Addition Computation Through 500

Lesson Overview

Skills Update	5 minutes	**ONLINE**
GET READY Addition with Base-10 Blocks	5 minutes	**ONLINE**
LEARN Modeling Addition	15 minutes	OFFLINE
LEARN Addition with Regrouping	15 minutes	OFFLINE
TRY IT Addition Computation	10 minutes	OFFLINE
CHECKPOINT	10 minutes	OFFLINE

▶ Lesson Objectives

Find the sum of two whole numbers with sums up through 500.

▶ Prerequisite Skills

Use concrete objects or sketches to model and solve addition or subtraction computation problems with sums or minuends up through 500 with and without regrouping.

▶ Advance Preparation

Print the Place-Value Chart (Hundreds).

▶ Content Background

In this lesson, students will add two whole numbers with sums up through 500. Students will model problems and record the answer. Then they will solve problems without models using numbers only. As students add the blocks or the numbers from right to left, regrouping when necessary, they will begin to understand the algorithm for addition.

Materials to Gather

SUPPLIED

base-10 blocks

place-value mat

Modeling Addition activity page

Addition with Regrouping activity page

Addition Computation activity page

Place-Value Chart (Hundreds) printout

Checkpoint (printout)

GET READY Addition with Base-10 Blocks

ONLINE 5 min

Students will use the Place Value Addition Learning Tool to review addition with sums through 500. The learning tool models addition problems using base-10 blocks and a place-value mat.

DIRECTIONS FOR USING THE PLACE VALUE ADDITION LEARNING TOOL

1. Click Begin Setup. Choose the following:
   - Present addition problems with SUMS up to: 500
   - Allow REGROUPING in problems: YES

Objectives

- Use concrete objects or sketches to model and solve addition or subtraction computation problems with sums or minuends up through 500 with and without regrouping.

2. Show students the two addends and the models that represent them using base-10 blocks. Review the meaning of the ones cubes, tens rods, and hundred flats if necessary.

3. Have students complete 2 to 3 problems.

LEARN Modeling Addition

OFFLINE 15min

Objectives

- Find the sum of two whole numbers with sums up through 500.

Students will find the sum of two whole numbers with sums up through 500. Students will start by modeling with base-10 blocks. Then they will progress to using numbers only on a place-value chart.

Gather the Modeling Addition activity page, base-10 blocks, and the place-value mat.

1. Have students model 179 + 115 with base-10 blocks on the place-value mat.

2. Have students write the problem on the place-value chart on the activity page.

Say: This chart has a ones column, a tens column, and a hundreds column just like your place-value mat. You can write numbers on this chart instead of placing models.

Write 179 first. There is 1 hundred just like your model. There are 7 tens and 9 ones. Write 115 below 179. There is 1 hundred and 1 ten. There are 5 ones.

3. Have students add the ones cubes and regroup. Have them record the number of ones cubes that remain on the place value-chart. Point out that they would get the same number of ones by adding the numbers in the ones column and regrouping without using models.

4. Have students look at the tens in their model.

Ask: Do you still have only 7 tens and 1 ten?
ANSWER: No, there is another ten from regrouping.

Show students how to record the additional ten on the place-value chart by writing a 1 in the gray row at the top of the tens column.

5. Have students add the tens rods. Point out that they get the same answer by adding the tens column on the chart, including the 1 ten that was regrouped. Have them record the number of tens on the place-value chart.

6. Have students add the hundreds flats and record the number of hundreds on the chart.

7. Repeat this procedure for the remaining problems without the use of the models. Students may use models to help with regrouping, but they should rely on addition facts and strategies to add each column.

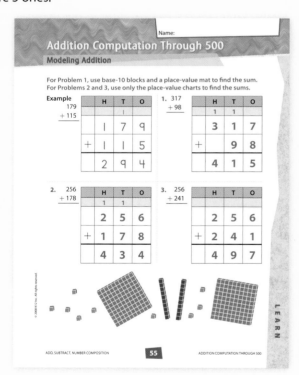

LEARN Addition with Regrouping

Students will use a place-value chart to find the sum of addends up through 500.

Gather the Addition with Regrouping activity page, which is on the back of the Modeling Addition activity page.

Have students record each addend in the place-value chart. Guide them as they add the ones, tens, and hundreds columns to find the sum. If students have trouble with regrouping, they may use base-10 blocks. They should not use the blocks to help with the addition.

- Find the sum of two whole numbers with sums up through 500.

Tips

If students have difficulty, model the problems with the base-10 blocks. Point out that the numbers represent the blocks that they are already familiar with. For additional practice problems, use graph paper to line up place values if place-value charts are not available.

Addition with Regrouping

Find the sums. First write the numbers in the place-value chart, and then add the numbers.

1. 329 + 89 = _____

	H	T	O
	1	1	
	3	2	9
+		8	9
	4	1	8

2. 315 + 164 = _____

	H	T	O
	3	1	5
+	1	6	4
	4	7	9

3. 138 + 148 = _____

	H	T	O
		1	
	1	3	8
+	1	4	8
	2	8	6

4. 275 + 149 = _____

	H	T	O
	1	1	
	2	7	5
+	1	4	9
	4	2	4

LEARN

ADD, SUBTRACT, NUMBER COMPOSITION   **56**   ADDITION COMPUTATION THROUGH 500

TRY IT Addition Computation

Students will practice adding with regrouping using place-value charts. Give students the Addition Computation activity page from their Activity Book and the Place-Value Chart (Hundreds) printout. Read the directions with them.

- Find the sum of two whole numbers with sums up through 500.

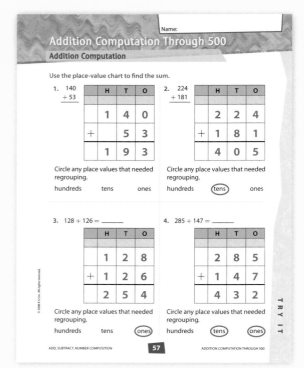

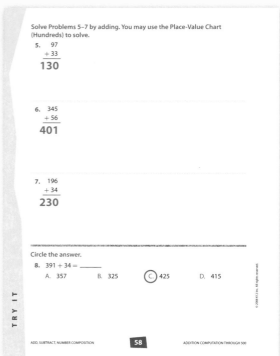

Addition Computation Through 500
Addition Computation

Use the place-value chart to find the sum.

1. 140
+ 53

H	T	O
1	4	0
+	5	3
1	9	3

Circle any place values that needed regrouping.

hundreds   tens   ones

2. 224
+ 181

H	T	O
2	2	4
+ 1	8	1
4	0	5

Circle any place values that needed regrouping.

hundreds   (tens)   ones

3. 128 + 126 = _____

H	T	O
1	2	8
+ 1	2	6
2	5	4

Circle any place values that needed regrouping.

hundreds   tens   (ones)

4. 285 + 147 = _____

H	T	O
2	8	5
+ 1	4	7
4	3	2

Circle any place values that needed regrouping.

hundreds   (tens)   (ones)

TRY IT

TRY IT

Solve Problems 5–7 by adding. You may use the Place-Value Chart (Hundreds) to solve.

5. 97
+ 33
130

6. 345
+ 56
401

7. 196
+ 34
230

Circle the answer.

8. 391 + 34 = _____

A. 357   B. 325   (C.) 425   D. 415

CHECKPOINT

OFFLINE **10 min**

Print the assessment and have students complete it on their own. Read the directions, questions, and answer choices to students if necessary. Use the answer key to score the assessment, and then enter the results online.

Objectives

- Find the sum of two whole numbers with sums up through 500.

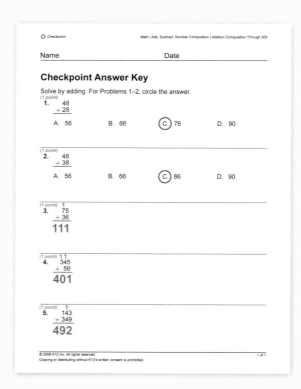

Checkpoint   Math | Add, Subtract, Number Composition | Addition Computation Through 500

Name _____   Date _____

Checkpoint Answer Key

Solve by adding. For Problems 1–2, circle the answer.

(1 point)
1. 48
+ 28

A. 56   B. 66   (C.) 76   D. 90

(1 point)
2. 48
+ 38

A. 56   B. 66   (C.) 86   D. 90

(1 point) 1
3. 75
+ 36
111

(1 point) 11
4. 345
+ 56
401

(1 point) 1
5. 143
+ 349
492

Finding the Difference

▶ ## Lesson Objectives

Use regrouping to find the difference of two whole numbers with the minuend up through 500.

▶ ## Prerequisite Skills

Use concrete objects or sketches to model and solve addition or subtraction computation problems with sums or minuends up through 500 with and without regrouping.

▶ ## Advance Preparation

Print the Place-Value Chart (Hundreds).

▶ ## Content Background

Students have learned to model regrouping in subtraction. In this lesson, students will learn to represent subtraction with regrouping on paper, and will begin to subtract without models.

Keywords   **minus symbol (−)** – the symbol that signals subtraction

Materials to Gather

SUPPLIED

base-10 blocks

place-value mat

Place-Value Chart (Hundreds) printout

Regroup and Subtract activity page

ALSO NEEDED

dry-erase marker

dry-erase eraser

ONLINE
10min

GET READY Remember Subtraction?

Students will use the Place Value Subtraction Learning Tool to review subtraction with minuends up through 500. The learning tool models subtraction problems using base-10 blocks and a place-value mat.

DIRECTIONS FOR USING THE PLACE VALUE SUBTRACTION LEARNING TOOL

1. Click Begin Setup. Choose the following:
   - Present subtraction problems with MINUENDS up to: 500
   - Allow REGROUPING in problems: YES

Objectives

- Use concrete objects or sketches to model and solve addition or subtraction computation problems with sums or minuends up through 500 with and without regrouping.

2. Show students the subtraction problem and the model of the number displayed with base-10 blocks. Review the meaning of the ones cubes, tens rods, and hundreds flats if necessary.

3. Have students complete 2 to 3 problems. Make sure students notice that each step with the base-10 blocks is also shown with numbers in the upper left corner of the screen. Understanding that the numbers and the blocks show the same steps is key to understanding subtraction. If students have difficulty with certain types of problems, such as those with zeros in the minuend, then do the following:

- Mouse over Menu in the right corner of the screen and click Setup
- Choose Problems Set by Learning Coach
- Enter a few problems for extra practice.

OFFLINE

15 min

LEARN Model Subtraction

Objectives

- Use regrouping to find the difference of two whole numbers with the minuend up through 500.

Students will subtract with minuends up through 500 using models, sketches, and a place-value chart.

Gather the Place-Value Chart (Hundreds) printout, base-10 blocks, place-value mat, marker, and eraser.

1. Write the problem 267 − 122 on the place-value chart. Have students model 267 with base-10 blocks on the place-value mat. They should place 2 hundreds flats in the hundreds column, 6 tens rods in the tens column, and 7 ones cubes in the ones column.

2. **Say:** You need to subtract, or take away 122. What should you do first?
   ANSWER: Take away 2 ones cubes.

   Have students take away the 2 ones cubes and tell you how many ones remain. Write a 5 in the ones column on the place-value chart.

3. Have students subtract the tens and record the answer in the tens column. Then have them subtract the hundreds and record the answer in the hundreds column. Point out that the modeled answer and the answer on the chart are the same.

4. Clear the place-value mat, and write the problem: 468 − 246

   Repeat Steps 1–3, having students record each part of the answer on the place-value chart.

5. **Say:** Instead of using blocks, you can use sketches to model a subtraction problem. Use a square for the hundreds flats, a line for the tens rods, and a dot or small square for the ones cubes.

6. Write the problem 395 − 142 on the place-value chart, and have students sketch the number using the marker and the place-value mat. Walk students through subtracting the ones, the tens, and then the hundreds, crossing off the number they are subtracting on their sketch.

LEARN Subtraction and Regrouping

Objectives

- Use regrouping to find the difference of two whole numbers with the minuend up through 500.

Students will use base-10 blocks and a place-value mat to solve subtraction problems with regrouping. They will also write and solve the problems on a place-value chart.

Gather the Place-Value Chart (Hundreds) printout, base-10 blocks, place-value mat, marker, and eraser.

1. Write 368 −179 on the place-value chart.

2. Have students use base-10 blocks to model 368 on the place-value mat.

   Say: You need to take away 9 ones. How many ones do you have? (8) Can you think of a way to take away 9 ones cubes?
   ANSWER: You can trade a tens rod for ten ones.

3. Have students exchange 1 tens rod for 10 ones cubes and place them in the ones column. Then have students tell you how many tens (5) and ones (18) they have.

   Ask: Now can you take away 9 ones?

4. Have student remove 9 ones.

   Ask: How many ones are left? (9)
   Write 9 in the ones place on the place-value chart.

5. Have students tell you what they did to subtract the ones. Show them each step on the place-value chart. Cross out the 6 in the tens column and write a 5 in the space above it to represent the 5 remaining tens rods. Cross out the 8 in the ones place and write 18 above it to show the 18 ones.

6. Have students subtract 9 from 18. Point out that the numbers show the same steps that students completed with the blocks.

7. **Ask:** Now you have to subtract the tens. How many tens do you have? (5) How many tens do you have to subtract? (7) Can you think of a way to take away 7 tens?
   ANSWER: You can trade a hundreds flat for 10 tens rods.

8. Have students make the trade and tell you how many hundreds (2) and tens (15) they have. Then have them complete the subtraction. The answer will be 189.

9. Repeat the same steps on the place-value chart to complete the problem.

10. Show students that if they put the blocks for 179 back together with the 189 remaining blocks, the blocks add up to 368. This is a useful way to check their work.

11. Complete the following problems the same way.
    - 83 − 47 (36)
    - 372 − 135 (237)
    - 400 − 395 (5)

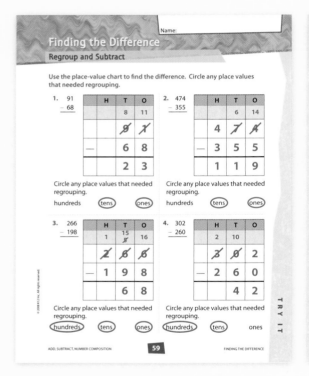

TRY IT Regroup and Subtract

OFFLINE 15 min

Students will practice solving subtraction problems with and without a place-value chart. Give students the Regroup and Subtract activity page from their Activity Book and read the directions with them.

- Use regrouping to find the difference of two whole numbers with the minuend up through 500.

Tips

Students may use the base-10 blocks and place-value mat if they have trouble regrouping.

Finding the Difference
Regroup and Subtract

Name: _____

Use the place-value chart to find the difference. Circle any place values that needed regrouping.

1.   91
      − 68

H	T	O
	8	11
	9̷	1̷
−	6	8
	2	3

Circle any place values that needed regrouping.
hundreds   (tens)   (ones)

2.   474
      − 355

H	T	O
	6	14
4	7̷	4̷
−	3	5	5
1	1	9

Circle any place values that needed regrouping.
hundreds   (tens)   (ones)

3.   266
      − 198

H	T	O
1	15 8̷	16
2̷	6̷	6̷
−	1	9	8
	6	8

Circle any place values that needed regrouping.
(hundreds)   (tens)   (ones)

4.   302
      − 260

H	T	O
	2	10
3̷	0̷	2
−	2	6	0
	4	2

Circle any place values that needed regrouping.
(hundreds)   (tens)   ones

Solve.

5.   235   1 12 15
       − 66   2̷3̷5̷
       169   − 66
                   169

Circle the answer.

6.   496
       − 37

A. 381   (B.) 459
C. 421   D. 375

7.   385
       − 126

A. 227   B. 238
(C.) 259   D. 271

TRY IT

Subtraction and the Equals Symbol

Lesson Overview

Skills Update	5 minutes	ONLINE
GET READY Subtraction Number Sentences	5 minutes	ONLINE
LEARN Subtract from 500	15 minutes	OFFLINE
LEARN The Equals Symbol	15 minutes	OFFLINE
TRY IT Equals Symbol with Subtraction	10 minutes	OFFLINE
CHECKPOINT	10 minutes	OFFLINE

▶ Lesson Objectives

- Use regrouping to find the difference of two whole numbers with the minuend up through 500.
- Explain the meaning of the equals symbol.

▶ Prerequisite Skills

- Use concrete objects or sketches to model and solve addition or subtraction computation problems with sums or minuends up through 500 with and without regrouping.
- Use the equals sign in number sentences to express equality.

▶ Advance Preparation

- Prepare index cards with the following symbols: +, −, and =.
- Prepare index cards numbered 0 through 10.
- Print the Place-Value Chart (Hundreds).

▶ Content Background

Students will continue to subtract from numbers up through 500 and regroup without the use of models or sketches. They will learn the meaning of the equals symbol.

Although *equals sign* is used often in everyday language, *equals symbol* is more accurate as a mathematical term. In math, sign specifically refers to the positive sign and negative sign that are used with numbers.

Materials to Gather

SUPPLIED

blocks – O (blue, yellow)

Place-Value Chart (Hundreds) printout

Equals Symbol with Subtraction activity page

Checkpoint (printout)

ALSO NEEDED

index cards – labeled with symbols +, −, and =

index cards – numbered 0 through 15

Keywords

equals symbol (=) – a symbol that shows the relationship between two equal values

GET READY Subtraction Number Sentences

ONLINE 5 min

Students will look at sketches of subtraction problems and write number sentences to match.

Objectives

- Use concrete objects or sketches to model and solve addition or subtraction computation problems with sums or minuends up through 500 with and without regrouping.
- Use the equals sign in number sentences to express equality.

LEARN Subtract from 500

OFFLINE 15 min

Students will subtract from numbers up through 500. They will learn to regroup without the use of models or sketches.

Gather the Place-Value Chart (Hundreds) printout.

1. **Say:** You know how to subtract with regrouping. Sometimes you need to regroup a ten into ones. Sometimes you need to regroup a hundred into tens. Now you are going to use a place-value chart to help you subtract and regroup without using a model or sketch.

2. Follow Steps 3–5 for the following problems:
   - 332 − 171 (161)
   - 458 − 263 (195)
   - 532 − 277 (255)
   - 300 − 128 (172)

3. Write the problem on the place-value chart. Have students subtract the ones, then the tens, and then the hundreds.

4. If regrouping is necessary for the ones place, have students cross off the tens and write 1 fewer ten. Then have them cross off the ones and write 10 more ones. Remind students that they are simply moving the ten—the number is still the same value.

5. If regrouping is necessary for the tens place, have students cross off the hundreds and write 1 fewer hundred, and cross off the tens and write 10 more tens.

Objectives

- Use regrouping to find the difference of two whole numbers with the minuend up through 500.

Tips

If students are struggling with regrouping, reintroduce the models or sketches to help them visualize what they are doing.

LEARN The Equals Symbol

OFFLINE 15 min

Objectives

- Explain the meaning of the equals symbol.

Students will learn the meaning of the equals symbol by creating number sentences. Gather the cubes and the index cards.

1. Have students connect 3 yellow and 7 blue cubes. Then have them connect 8 yellow and 2 blue cubes.

2. Place the 2 groups of cubes on the table with the equals symbol index card between them.

   Ask: What does the equals symbol mean?
   ANSWER: It means the two sides are the same.

3. Have students use the number and symbol cards to create expressions for each side.

   ANSWER: $3 + 7 = 8 + 2$ (If students put $10 = 10$, point out that this is a true statement, and that each ten can also be broken down by color into $3 + 7$ and $8 + 2$.)

4. Have students connect 15 yellow cubes. Then have them connect 8 blue cubes. Place the 2 trains of cubes on the table.

5. Place the 15 card below the train of 15 cubes, and the 8 card below the train of 8 cubes. Place the equals symbol in between.

   Ask: What can we do to make the two sides equal?
   ANSWER: Take away yellow cubes or add blue cubes.

   Have students remove 7 yellow cubes, and complete the number sentence with the cards. It should say $15 - 7 = 8$.

TRY IT Equals Symbol with Subtraction

OFFLINE 10 min

Objectives

- Use regrouping to find the difference of two whole numbers with the minuend up through 500.
- Explain the meaning of the equals symbol.

Students will solve subtraction problems. Give students the Equals Symbol with Subtraction activity page from their Activity Book and read the directions with them.

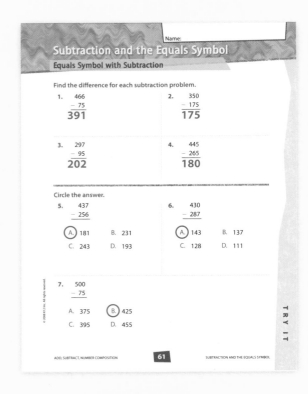

Name:

Subtraction and the Equals Symbol
Equals Symbol with Subtraction

Find the difference for each subtraction problem.

1. $\begin{array}{r} 466 \\ -\ 75 \\ \hline 391 \end{array}$
2. $\begin{array}{r} 350 \\ -\ 175 \\ \hline 175 \end{array}$

3. $\begin{array}{r} 297 \\ -\ 95 \\ \hline 202 \end{array}$
4. $\begin{array}{r} 445 \\ -\ 265 \\ \hline 180 \end{array}$

Circle the answer.

5. $\begin{array}{r} 437 \\ -\ 256 \end{array}$

   (A.) 181   B. 231
   C. 243   D. 193

6. $\begin{array}{r} 430 \\ -\ 287 \end{array}$

   (A.) 143   B. 137
   C. 128   D. 111

7. $\begin{array}{r} 500 \\ -\ 75 \end{array}$

   A. 375   (B.) 425
   C. 395   D. 455

TRY IT

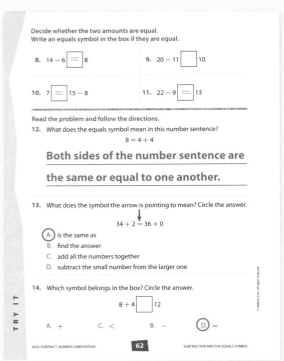

Decide whether the two amounts are equal.
Write an equals symbol in the box if they are equal.

8. $14 - 6\ \boxed{=}\ 8$
9. $20 - 11\ \boxed{}\ 10$

10. $7\ \boxed{=}\ 15 - 8$
11. $22 - 9\ \boxed{=}\ 13$

Read the problem and follow the directions.

12. What does the equals symbol mean in this number sentence?

$$8 = 4 + 4$$

Both sides of the number sentence are

the same or equal to one another.

13. What does the symbol the arrow is pointing to mean? Circle the answer.

$$34 + 2 \overset{\downarrow}{=} 36 + 0$$

  (A.) is the same as
  B. find the answer
  C. add all the numbers together
  D. subtract the small number from the larger one

14. Which symbol belongs in the box? Circle the answer.

$$8 + 4\ \boxed{}\ 12$$

  A. +   C. <   B. −   (D.) =

TRY IT

CHECKPOINT

OFFLINE 10 min

Print the assessment and have students complete it on their own. Read the directions, questions, and answer choices to students if necessary. Use the answer key to score the assessment, and then enter the results online.

Objectives

- Use regrouping to find the difference of two whole numbers with the minuend up through 500.
- Explain the meaning of the equals symbol.

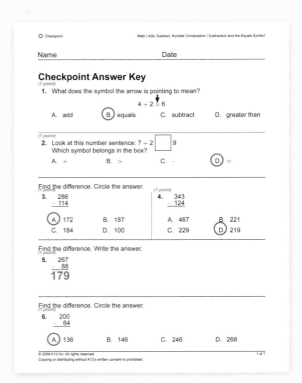

Checkpoint   Math | Add, Subtract, Number Composition | Subtraction and the Equals Symbol

Name   Date

Checkpoint Answer Key
(1 point)
1. What does the symbol the arrow is pointing to mean?

$$4 + 2 \overset{\downarrow}{=} 6$$

  A. add   (B.) equals   C. subtract   D. greater than

(1 point)
2. Look at this number sentence: $7 + 2\ \boxed{}\ 9$
   Which symbol belongs in the box?

  A. +   B. >   C. −   (D.) =

Find the difference. Circle the answer. *(1 point)*
3. $\begin{array}{r} 286 \\ -\ 114 \end{array}$

  (A.) 172   B. 187
  C. 184   D. 100

(1 point)
4. $\begin{array}{r} 343 \\ -\ 124 \end{array}$

  A. 467   B. 221
  C. 229   (D.) 219

Find the difference. Write the answer. *(1 point)*
5. $\begin{array}{r} 267 \\ -\ 88 \\ \hline 179 \end{array}$

Find the difference. Circle the answer. *(1 point)*
6. $\begin{array}{r} 200 \\ -\ 64 \end{array}$

  (A.) 136   B. 146   C. 246   D. 268

   1 of 1

Decompose Numbers

Lesson Overview

Skills Update	5 minutes	ONLINE
GET READY Why Break Numbers?	5 minutes	ONLINE
LEARN Write Numbers Different Ways	15 minutes	ONLINE
LEARN Complete the Number	25 minutes	OFFLINE
TRY IT Break Numbers	10 minutes	OFFLINE

▶ Lesson Objectives

Demonstrate that a number can be composed of other numbers in various ways.

▶ Prerequisite Skills

- Represent equivalent forms of the same number through the use of physical models such as tens rods and ones cubes through 20.
- Represent equivalent forms of the same number through the use of diagrams through 20.
- Represent equivalent forms of the same number to 20 through the use of number expressions, such as $7 = 4 + 3$, or $5 + 2$, or $1 + 2 + 4$.

▶ Advance Preparation

- Snap the cubes together in four trains of 10 and one train of 6.
- Print and cut out the Fact Family Triangles. On three of them, write 30 on the top corner. On four of them, write 46 on the top corner. On the last four, write 460 on the top corner.

▶ Content Background

In this lesson, students will learn that numbers can be decomposed, or broken apart, in various ways. The mathematical term *decomposition* describes the breaking apart of numbers into *friendly numbers* for easier computation. When talking to students, you may use the phrase *breaking apart* in place of decomposition.

In math, you will often hear the terms *nice numbers* or *friendly numbers*. Friendly numbers—numbers such as 5 and 10, or multiples of 5 and 10—are numbers that are easier to use when adding, subtracting, or operating with numbers in general. Friendly numbers are especially helpful to students in doing math problems mentally.

In this lesson students will learn how numbers can be composed of friendly numbers as a first step toward breaking apart numbers to solve addition and subtraction problems.

Materials to Gather

SUPPLIED

blocks – O (46)

Fact Family Triangles (printout)

Break Numbers activity page

compose numbers – to put numbers together in different ways to make calculations easier; for example, $3 + 4 + 7$ could be added by using 3 and 7 to compose 10 before adding 4

decompose numbers – to break apart numbers, such as $34 = 30 + 4$ or $34 = 14 + 20$; often used to make calculations easier

ONLINE
5min

GET READY Why Break Numbers?

Students will see that problems can often be solved more easily by breaking numbers apart.

Objectives

- Demonstrate that a number can be composed of other numbers in various ways.

ONLINE
15min

LEARN Write Numbers Different Ways

Students will learn that they can show the same number in different ways by breaking the number apart.

Objectives

- Demonstrate that a number can be composed of other numbers in various ways.

OFFLINE
25min

LEARN Complete the Number

Students will break numbers apart, and identify the missing pieces needed to complete the numbers.
  Gather the cubes and the fact family triangles.

Objectives

- Demonstrate that a number can be composed of other numbers in various ways.

1. Show students 3 trains of 10 cubes and the fact family triangles labeled 30. Tell students that you are going to look at different ways to break apart the number 30.

    Say: When we are finished, all of these flash cards will show a different way to make 30. I will show you one way.

2. Separate two of the cube trains from the other 10 blocks. Write a 20 in the corner of the one of the fact family triangles.

    Ask: I broke 30 apart. One of the parts is 20. What is the other part?

    Students may know the answer; if not, have them count the remaining 10 cubes. Then have students write 10 in the other corner of the fact family triangle. Explain that $20 + 10$ is one way to break apart the number 30.

3. Guide students to break 30 apart in two additional ways using the cubes to help. As they find each way to break apart 30, have them complete the fact family triangles to show their decomposition.

    ANSWERS: $15 + 15$; $5 + 25$; $2 + 28$, etc.

4. Show students 4 trains of 10 cubes, 1 train of 6 cubes, and the fact family triangles labeled 46.

Say: Now we are going to break apart the number 46. I will choose the first piece, and you will find the second piece.

5. Write the number below in the corner of one of the fact family triangles. Students will use the cubes or subtraction to find the missing piece. They will write the missing number in the third corner of the card.

- 30 (16)
- 23 (23)
- 20 (26)
- 10 (36)

6. Explain that students can use the same thinking to break apart larger numbers. Show students the fact family triangles labeled 460 and the card they made that says $30 + 16 = 46$.

Say: Since $30 + 16 = 46$, $300 + 160 = 460$.

7. Write $300 + 160$ on the first fact family triangle. Then have students complete two more fact family triangles using the cards from Step 5 to help.

TRY IT Break Numbers

Students will practice breaking apart and making numbers. Give students the Break Numbers activity page from their Activity Book and read the directions with them. Use the answer key to check students' answers, and then enter the results online.

Objectives

- Demonstrate that a number can be composed of other numbers in various ways.

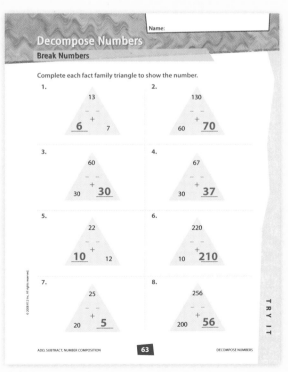

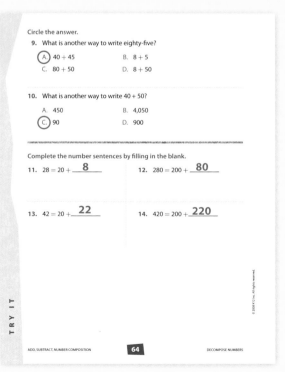

Make and Break Numbers

Skills Update	5 minutes	ONLINE
LEARN Break Numbers Apart	20 minutes	ONLINE
LEARN Model Numbers in Expanded Form	25 minutes	OFFLINE
TRY IT Use Expanded Form	10 minutes	OFFLINE

▶ Lesson Objectives

Demonstrate that a number can be composed of other numbers in various ways.

▶ Prerequisite Skills

- Represent equivalent forms of the same number through the use of physical models such as tens rods and ones cubes through 20.
- Represent equivalent forms of the same number through the use of diagrams through 20.
- Represent equivalent forms of the same number to 20 through the use of number expressions, such as $7 = 4 + 3$, or $5 + 2$, or $1 + 2 + 4$.

▶ Content Background

Students will break numbers apart into hundreds, tens, and ones. They will model numbers in equivalent forms and will write the numbers in expanded form.

Keywords	**equivalent forms** – multiple expressions of quantity that are equal; $3 + 4$, $15 - 8$, and $2 + 4 + 1$ are equivalent forms of the number 7
	expanded form – a way to write a number that shows the place value of each of its digits; for example, $428 = 400 + 20 + 8$, or 4 hundreds $+$ 2 tens $+$ 8 ones

Materials to Gather

SUPPLIED

base-10 blocks

Model Numbers in Expanded Form activity page

Use Expanded Form activity page

LEARN Break Numbers Apart

ONLINE
20min

Students will use expanded form as a way to break numbers apart. They will compare modeled numbers to determine if they show the same number.

Objectives

- Demonstrate that a number can be composed of other numbers in various ways.

LEARN Model Numbers in Expanded Form

Students will use base-10 blocks to model numbers broken into expanded form. Gather the base-10 blocks and the Model Numbers in Expanded Form activity page.

1. Have students model 184 with base-10 blocks. Then have them write the number in expanded form on the first blank line for Problem 1 on the activity page.

   ANSWER: $100 + 80 + 4$

2. Have students exchange some of the blocks in their model to show the number another way. For example, they might trade two of the tens rods for 20 ones cubes. They would then write $100 + 60 + 24$.

3. Repeat this procedure for Problems 2 and 3.

4. Tell students that they will break numbers apart in different ways without using the blocks. For Problems 4–6, have students write each number in expanded form, and then in one additional way. Remind them that they can break the number by exchanging hundreds for tens, or tens for ones.

   For example, 374 could be written as $300 + 70 + 4$. It could also be written as $200 + 174$, or $350 + 24$. Encourage students to be creative in their decomposition, but not to get too complicated.

5. Have students answer the last question on the activity page.

Objectives

- Demonstrate that a number can be composed of other numbers in various ways.

Tips

Numbers can be composed by adding numbers together. Encourage students to demonstrate multiple ways to compose numbers. Their strategies can include writing the expanded form of a number or writing an addition number expression that is equivalent to the number.

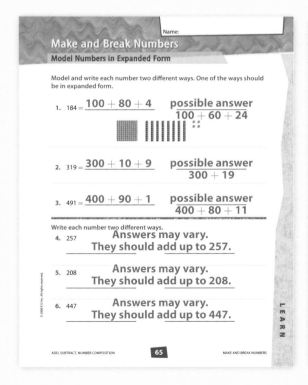

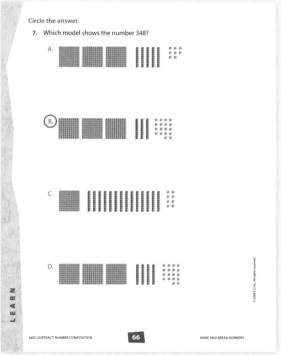

TRY IT Use Expanded Form

Students will use expanded form to break numbers apart. Give students the Use Expanded Form activity page from their Activity Book and read the directions with them. Use the answer key to check students' answers, and then enter the results online.

Objectives

- Demonstrate that a number can be composed of other numbers in various ways.

Name: _____

Make and Break Numbers
Use Expanded Form

Write each number in expanded form.

1. $283 = $ **$200 + 80 + 3$**   2. $499 = $ **$400 + 90 + 9$**

3. $132 = $ **$100 + 30 + 2$**   4. $326 = $ **$300 + 20 + 6$**

Write each expanded notation another way. **Sample answers:**

5. $219 = 200 + 10 + 9$ **$100 + 50 + 50 + 19$**

6. $162 = 100 + 60 + 2$ **$100 + 30 + 30 + 2$**

Circle Yes or No. Write the numbers in expanded notation.

7. Katie has 2 hundreds flats and 18 ones cubes. Ryan has 2 hundreds flats, 1 tens rod, and 8 ones cubes. Do they have the same number?

   (A.) Yes   B. No

   $200 + 18$ and $200 + 10 + 8$

8. Calvin has 3 hundreds flats, 6 tens rods, and 4 ones cubes. Anna has 3 hundreds flats, 4 tens rods, and 14 ones cubes. Do they have the same number?

   A. Yes   (B.) No

   $300 + 60 + 4$ and $300 + 40 + 14$

Circle the answer.

9. What is another way to write $300 + 30 + 4$?

   A. 330   (B.) 334   C. 433   D. 300

Write the answer to each question. **Sample answers:**

10. What is another way to write 323?

    $300 + 23$ or $320 + 3$

11. What is another way to write 122?

    $100 + 22$ or $120 + 2$

12. Tony has 2 hundreds flats and 14 ones cubes. David has 1 hundreds flat, 11 tens rods, and 4 ones cubes. Do their blocks model the same number? Write two number sentences to show your thinking.

    Yes. $200 + 14 = 214$ and
    $100 + 110 + 4 = 214$

TRY IT

Break Up Numbers

Lesson Overview

Skills Update	5 minutes	ONLINE
LEARN Another Way to Write a Number	10 minutes	ONLINE
LEARN Solve Addition Problems	10 minutes	ONLINE
LEARN Break Numbers Your Way	15 minutes	OFFLINE
TRY IT Break Up Numbers	10 minutes	OFFLINE
CHECKPOINT	10 minutes	OFFLINE

▶ Lesson Objectives

Demonstrate that a number can be composed of other numbers in various ways.

▶ Prerequisite Skills

- Represent equivalent forms of the same number through the use of physical models such as tens rods and ones cubes through 20.
- Represent equivalent forms of the same number through the use of diagrams through 20.
- Represent equivalent forms of the same number to 20 through the use of number expressions, such as $7 = 4 + 3$, or $5 + 2$, or $1 + 2 + 4$.

▶ Advance Preparation

- Snap 25 cubes together in two trains of 10 and one train of 5. Snap 28 other cubes together in two trains of 10 and one train of 8.
- Print two copies of the Number Line 0–100. Cut out the number lines, leaving space above each line for students to write. Attach the pieces end to end to create two number lines through 100.
- Print the Open Number Lines.

▶ Content Background

In this lesson, students will practice breaking numbers apart to make them easier to add. They will choose strategies to solve problems on their own.

Keywords	**mental math** – the process of using only the brain to solve math problems **standard form** – the conventional way of writing numbers; 348 is standard form whereas $300 + 40 + 8$ is expanded form **strategy** – a method or approach to solve a problem

Materials to Gather

SUPPLIED

Number Line 0–100 (printout)
Open Number Lines (printout)
blocks – O (all colors)
Break Up Numbers activity page
Checkpoint (printout)
base-10 blocks

LEARN Another Way to Write a Number

ONLINE 10 min

Students will learn how breaking a number into parts and rearranging their order can make it easier to add.

Objectives

- Demonstrate that a number can be composed of other numbers in various ways.

LEARN Solve Addition Problems

ONLINE 10 min

Students will watch Rosa and Alex model different ways to solve problems. Students will also practice solving problems themselves.

Objectives

- Demonstrate that a number can be composed of other numbers in various ways.

LEARN Break Numbers Your Way

OFFLINE 15 min

Students will model addition problems. Students will break numbers apart to make addition easier, and they will show their thinking on a number line.

Gather a set of 25 cubes (two trains of 10 and one train of 5) and a set of 28 cubes (two trains of 10 and one train of 8), the Number Line 0–100 printouts, and the Open Number Lines printout.

Objectives

- Demonstrate that a number can be composed of other numbers in various ways.

Part 1

1. **Say:** We are going to look at some different ways to add numbers by breaking them apart. Let's start by adding 25 + 28.

2. Circle 25 on the number line, and hand the set of 25 cubes to students.

   Say: We will start with our first number, 25, and we will add 28. There are different ways to break apart these numbers to make them easier to add. I will show you one way. I am going to count on by 10s.

3. Hand students 1 train of 10 cubes from the set of 28.

   Ask: What is 25 + 10? (35)

4. **Say:** Counting on by 10s is easy because the tens place goes up by one, and the ones place stays the same. I can show that on the number line like this.

   Draw an arc from 25 to 35, and write +10 above it.

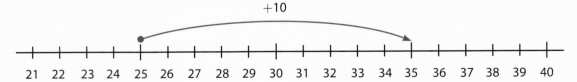

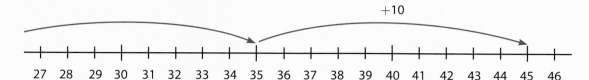

5. Have students count on another ten. Hand students another train of 10 cubes from the set of 28.

   Ask: What is 35 + 10?

6. Have students show the jump on the number line by drawing an arc from 35 to 45 and writing +10 above it.

7. Show students the remaining train of 8 cubes. Break off 5 of them and attach them to the other train of 5 cubes that students already have. Tell students that you are using 5 cubes to complete the train and make 10.

   Ask: By adding 5 to complete this 10, how many do we have now?

8. Have students show a jump of 5 on the number line. Students should draw an arc from 45 to 50 with a +5 above it.

   Ask: How many do we still need to add?

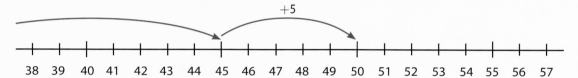

   Hand students the final 3 cubes. Have them tell you the sum (53), and add the final jump to the number line. Students should add an arc from 50 to 53 with a +3 above it.

9. Point to the arcs on the number line with the numbers above them. Draw a box around 53.

   Say: To add 25 + 28, we broke 28 into 10 + 10 + 5 + 3. The sum is 53.

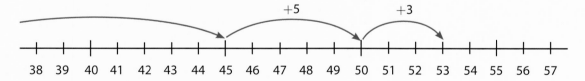

10. Have students find another sum: 18 (1 train of 10 and 1 train of 8 cubes) + 36 (3 trains of 10 and 1 train of 6 cubes). Students may choose to break the numbers apart in many different ways. Examples:

    10 + 30 + 8 + 6

    18 + 30 + 6

    18 + 10 + 10 + 10 + 2 + 4

    Have students show each step using the cubes and the number line.

Part 2

11. Show students the Open Number Lines printout.

Say: When we want to add greater numbers, we can't use a regular number line. It would be too long! We can use open number lines instead. Since there are no marks or numbers on these number lines, we can make our own marks and use them in any way we like. I'm going to add $139 + 24$.

12. Make a tick mark on the number line, near the left side. Write 139 below the mark.

Say: I will start on 139. I'll break 24 into 20 and 4. I'll add 20, and then I'll add 4.

139

13. On the number line, make an arc from left to right, starting at139. Mark the landing point, and write 159. Write +20 above the arc.

Say: $139 + 20$ is 159.

139   159

14. Make a smaller arc from 159. Mark the landing point and write 163. Write +4 above the arc.

Say: $159 + 4$ is 163.

139   159   163

15. Guide students to use the Open Number Lines printout to decompose numbers to solve the following problems. It is not important how they break the numbers apart, as long as they do it in a way that makes sense to them and gives the correct answer.

- $236 + 53$
- $412 + 79$
- $128 + 200$
- $382 + 80$

TRY IT Break Up Numbers

Students will break up numbers and practice using them to solve addition problems. Give students the Break Up Numbers activity page from their Activity Book and read the directions with them. Use the answer key to check students' answers, and then enter the results online.

Objectives

- Demonstrate that a number can be composed of other numbers in various ways.

Break Up Numbers

Break Up Numbers

Circle the answer.

1. What is another way to write one hundred thirty-six?
   - A. $100 + 3 + 6$
   - B. $1 + 3 + 6$
   - C. $100 + 30 + 6$ (circled)
   - D. $1 + 30 + 6$

2. Which of the following is another way to write 499?
   - A. $400 + 9 + 9$
   - B. $4 + 9 + 9$
   - C. $400 + 90 + 9$ (circled)
   - D. $490 + 99$

3. Which of the following is another way to write 100?
   - A. $50 + 50$ (circled)
   - B. $40 + 40 + 40$
   - C. $50 + 100$
   - D. $100 + 100$

4. Which of the following is another way to write 76?
   - A. $7 + 6$
   - B. $70 + 6$ (circled)
   - C. $76 + 2$
   - D. $76 - 6$

5. You can write 126 as $100 + 20 + 6$. What is another way to write 126?
   - A. $1 + 2 + 6$
   - B. $100 + 16 + 10$ (circled)
   - C. $100 - 16 - 10$
   - D. $100 + 26 + 1$

ADD, SUBTRACT, NUMBER COMPOSITION   **69**   BREAK UP NUMBERS

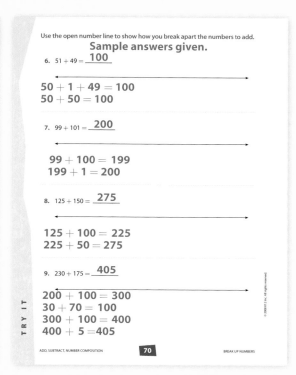

Use the open number line to show how you break apart the numbers to add.

Sample answers given.

6. $51 + 49 = \underline{100}$

$50 + 1 + 49 = 100$
$50 + 50 = 100$

7. $99 + 101 = \underline{200}$

$99 + 100 = 199$
$199 + 1 = 200$

8. $125 + 150 = \underline{275}$

$125 + 100 = 225$
$225 + 50 = 275$

9. $230 + 175 = \underline{405}$

$200 + 100 = 300$
$30 + 70 = 100$
$300 + 100 = 400$
$400 + 5 = 405$

T R Y   I T

ADD, SUBTRACT, NUMBER COMPOSITION   **70**   BREAK UP NUMBERS

CHECKPOINT

Objectives

- Demonstrate that a number can be composed of other numbers in various ways.

Students will complete a two-part assessment. In Part 1, students will take a performance-based assessment. In Part 2, students will complete the assessment on their own. Print the assessment. Read the directions, problems, and answer choices to students if necessary. Use the answer key to score the assessment, and then enter the results online.

Gather the base-10 blocks.

Name _____ Date _____

Checkpoint Answer Key

Part 1

Follow the instructions for each item. Choose the response that best describes how the student performs on the task. When you have finished, enter the results online.

1. Display 12 tens rods and 30 ones cubes.

   Say, "These base-10 blocks show the number 150. Use other blocks to show another way you can make 150."

   Examples: 15 tens rods or 11 tens rods and 40 ones cubes
   (1 point) Did the student show another way to model the number 150 with base-10 blocks?

   A. Yes   B. No

2. Display 8 tens rods and 22 ones cubes.

   Say, "These base-10 blocks show the number 102. Use other blocks to show another way you can make 102."

   Examples: 10 tens rods and 2 ones cubes or 9 tens rods and 12 ones cubes
   (1 point) Did the student show another way to model the number 102 with base-10 blocks?

   A. Yes   B. No

3. Display 3 tens rods and 12 ones cubes.

   Say, "These base-10 blocks show the number 42. Use other blocks to show another way you can make 42."

   Examples: 2 tens rods and 22 ones cubes or 4 tens rods and 2 ones cubes
   (1 point) Did the student show another way to model the number 42 with base-10 blocks?

   A. Yes   B. No

Give students Part 2 of the assessment.

Name _____ Date _____

Part 2

Circle each answer.
(1 point)
4. You can write 256 as 200 + 50 + 6. What is another way to write 256?

   A. 250 + 60
   B. 200 + 50 + 60
   C. 100 + 50 + 6
   D. 100 + 100 + 56

(1 point)
5. What is another way to write 374?

   A. 200 + 170 + 4
   B. 370 + 70 + 4
   C. 300 + 70 + 40
   D. 3 + 7 + 4

(1 point)
6. What is another way to write 499?

   A. 400 + 10 + 7
   B. 400 + 90 + 9
   C. 4 + 90 + 9
   D. 40 + 90 + 9

Breaking Numbers to Subtract

Lesson Overview

Skills Update	5 minutes	ONLINE
GET READY Build Number Sentences	5 minutes	ONLINE
LEARN Break Numbers to Subtract	20 minutes	ONLINE
LEARN Number Combinations with Cubes	10 minutes	OFFLINE
LEARN Break Apart Larger Numbers	10 minutes	OFFLINE
TRY IT Break Numbers Using Number Lines	10 minutes	OFFLINE

▶ Lesson Objectives

Decompose numbers to solve subtraction problems, such as
$213 - 12 = 200 + 13 - 12$.

▶ Prerequisite Skills

Demonstrate that a number can be composed of other numbers in various ways.

▶ Advance Preparation

Print two copies of the Open Number Lines.

▶ Content Background

In this lesson, students will break apart numbers to make subtraction problems easier to solve.

The mathematical term *decomposition* describes the breaking apart of numbers into *friendly numbers* for easier computation. When talking to students, you may use the phrase *breaking apart* in place of decomposition.

In math, you will often hear the terms *nice numbers* or *friendly numbers*. Friendly numbers—numbers such as 5 and 10, or multiples of 10—are numbers that are easier to use when adding, subtracting, or operating with numbers in general.

Friendly numbers are especially helpful to students in doing math problems mentally. The objective of this lesson is to show students how numbers can be composed of friendly numbers as a first step toward decomposing numbers to solve problems.

Materials to Gather

SUPPLIED

blocks – O (30 any color)

Open Number Lines (printout)

Break Numbers Using Number Lines activity page

GET READY Build Number Sentences

ONLINE 5min

Objectives

- Demonstrate that a number can be composed of other numbers in various ways.

Students will use the Building Expressions Learning Tool to compose a number. The learning tool has audio for the addition problems.

DIRECTIONS FOR USING THE BUILDING EXPRESSIONS LEARNING TOOL

1. Click Begin and choose the following:
   - Problem Type: Addition $(+)$
   - Problem Format: $? + ? = 4$
2. Click Next and choose the following:
   - Use Numbers: 0 – 20
   - Equals Symbol Placement: Both Ways
   - Timer Speed: Medium
3. Click Begin.
4. Have students complete the additional facts given. Continue as time allows.

LEARN Break Numbers to Subtract

ONLINE 20min

Objectives

- Decompose numbers to solve subtraction problems, such as $213 - 12 = 200 + 13 - 12$.

Students will see that it is often helpful to break numbers apart when subtracting.

LEARN Number Combinations with Cubes

OFFLINE 10min

Objectives

- Decompose numbers to solve subtraction problems, such as $213 - 12 = 200 + 13 - 12$.

Students will break apart numbers different ways to solve subtraction problems. They will count back and model numbers to show how they are breaking the numbers apart.

Gather the cubes and Open Number Lines printouts.

1. **Say:** Just like we broke apart numbers to make addition easier, we can also break apart numbers to make subtraction easier.

   Write $40 - 16 = ?$

   Have students use 4 trains of 10 cubes to model 40. Have them remove 10 cubes and set them aside.

   Write 40 on an open number line on the right hand side. Show a jump of 10 to the left, and write –10 above it.

Tips

Ask students to write various ways to break up the number 10 into other numbers. Becoming fluent at creating combinations of numbers that add to 10 will help students with mental math.

Ask: We started with 40 and took away 10. How many do we have left?
ANSWER: 30

2. **Ask:** How many more do we need to take away?
   ANSWER: 6

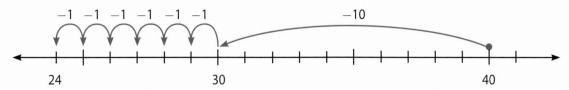

Have students take away 6 more cubes and set them aside, counting back as they do (29, 28, 27, 26, 25, 24).

Show 6 small jumps to the left on the number line. Write −1 above each jump. Write 24 below the landing point.

3. Follow these steps with the remaining problems, having students record their subtraction on an open number line each time. Allow students to decide how to break apart the numbers. You may offer ideas if they don't have one.

   - $28 - 19 =$
   - $23 - 16 =$
   - $30 - 12 =$
   - $13 - 5 =$

OFFLINE
10min

LEARN Break Apart Larger Numbers

Objectives

- Decompose numbers to solve subtraction problems, such as $213 - 12 = 200 + 13 - 12.$

Students will break apart numbers to make them easier to subtract without the use of models. They will record their subtraction on open number lines.
   Gather the Open Number Lines printout.

1. **Say:** We are going to subtract larger numbers by breaking them apart. Since the numbers are so big, we will not use models. We will still use a number line to keep track.

2. Write $219 - 56 = ?$

   Say: We are going to count back to subtract, so make a mark for the starting number, 219.

3. Have students explain a strategy to break apart 56 to subtract from 219. If they do not have an idea, suggest they count back by 10s through 50, and then count back 6 more.

4. Follow these steps with the remaining problems, encouraging students to break the numbers apart to make them easier to subtract.

   - $245 - 18 =$
   - $461 - 23 =$
   - $274 - 39 =$
   - $192 - 15 =$

Tips

Review modeling numbers with base-10 blocks to help students break apart numbers into friendly numbers.

TRY IT Break Numbers Using Number Lines

Students will practice using number lines to break apart numbers and solve subtraction problems. Give students the Break Numbers Using Number Lines activity page from their Activity Book. Read the directions with them. Use the answer key to check students' answers, and then enter the results online.

Objectives

- Decompose numbers to solve subtraction problems, such as $213 - 12 = 200 + 13 - 12$.

Tips

Students may use base-10 blocks to model the numbers.

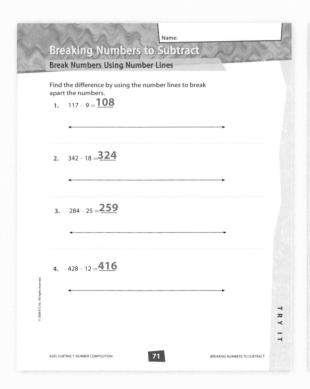

Name:

Breaking Numbers to Subtract
Break Numbers Using Number Lines

Find the difference by using the number lines to break apart the numbers.

1. $117 - 9 = \underline{108}$

2. $342 - 18 = \underline{324}$

3. $284 - 25 = \underline{259}$

4. $428 - 12 = \underline{416}$

5. $165 - 29 = \underline{136}$

6. $353 - 7 = \underline{346}$

7. $220 - 19 = \underline{201}$

8. $356 - 52 = \underline{304}$

9. $245 - 17 = \underline{228}$

10. $78 - 13 = \underline{65}$

TRY IT

Decompose to Subtract

▶ ## Lesson Objectives

Decompose numbers to solve subtraction problems, such as $213 - 12 = 200 + 13 - 12$.

▶ ## Prerequisite Skills

Demonstrate that a number can be composed of other numbers in various ways.

▶ ## Advance Preparation

Print the Open Number Lines.

▶ ## Content Background

In this lesson students will break apart numbers , use number lines, and write number sentences to find an easier way to subtract.

The mathematical term *decomposition* describes the breaking apart of numbers into *friendly numbers* for easier computation. When talking to students, you may use the phrase *breaking apart* in place of decomposition.

In math, you will often hear the terms *nice numbers* or *friendly numbers*. Friendly numbers—numbers such as 5 and 10, or multiples of 10—are numbers that are easier to use when adding, subtracting, or operating with numbers in general.

Materials to Gather

SUPPLIED

Subtract by Breaking Numbers activity page

Write Number Sentences activity page

Break Apart Numbers to Subtract activity page

Open Number Lines (printout)

ONLINE
10 min

GET READY Put Together Numbers

Objectives

- Demonstrate that a number can be composed of other numbers in various ways.

Students will use the Building Expressions Learning Tool to practice building numbers from 3 addends. The learning tool has audio for the addition problems.

DIRECTIONS FOR USING THE BUILDING EXPRESSIONS LEARNING TOOL

1. Click Begin and choose the following:
   - Problem Type: Addition ($+$)
   - Problem Format: $? + ? + ? = 6$

2. Click Next and choose the following:
   - Use Numbers: 0–20
   - Equals Symbol Placement: Both Ways
   - Timer Speed: Medium
3. Click Begin.
4. Have students complete the addition facts given. Continue as time allows.

LEARN Break Numbers Different Ways

Students will learn how to subtract by counting up from the lesser number to the greater number. They will break apart numbers and put them back together as they count up.

Objectives

- Decompose numbers to solve subtraction problems, such as $213 - 12 = 200 + 13 - 12$.

LEARN Subtract by Breaking Numbers

Students will use open number lines to help them subtract. Allow students to choose any strategy they prefer to break apart numbers.

Gather the Subtract by Breaking Numbers activity page, and read the instructions.

Objectives

- Decompose numbers to solve subtraction problems, such as $213 - 12 = 200 + 13 - 12$.

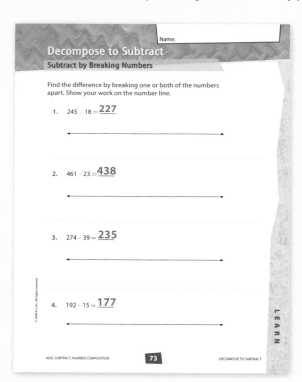

Name:

Decompose to Subtract
Subtract by Breaking Numbers

Find the difference by breaking one or both of the numbers apart. Show your work on the number line.

1. $245 - 18 = \underline{227}$

2. $461 - 23 = \underline{438}$

3. $274 - 39 = \underline{235}$

4. $192 - 15 = \underline{177}$

ADD, SUBTRACT, NUMBER COMPOSITION   73   DECOMPOSE TO SUBTRACT

LEARN

LEARN Write Number Sentences

Objectives

- Decompose numbers to solve subtraction problems, such as $213 - 12 = 200 + 13 - 12$.

Students will write number sentences to show how they break apart numbers to subtract.

Gather the Write Number Sentences activity page and the Open Number Lines printout.

1. **Say:** One way to show how you solved a subtraction problem is by writing number sentences. A number sentence shows how you broke apart the numbers. I'll show you.

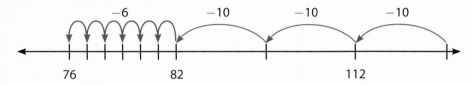

2. Write the problem $112 - 36$. Solve the problem on the open number line, explaining your steps.

   First mark 112 near the right side of the line.

   Show a hop to the left of 3 tens, landing on 82. Write "-10" above each hop.

   Show a hop to the left of 6 ones, landing on 76. Write "-6" above this hop. Draw a box around 76 to show your answer.

3. **Ask:** Now let's show my subtraction with a number sentence. What number did we start with?
   ANSWER: 112

   Write 112 below your original subtraction problem.

   Ask: What number did I subtract first?
   ANSWER: 10

   Write -10

4. Have students tell you each step of the subtraction by looking at the number line as you write the number sentence.
   $112 - 10 - 10 - 10 - 6 = 76$

5. Walk students through the first problem or two on the Write Number Sentences activity page. When students are comfortable using the number line to write number sentences, have them complete the remaining problems on their own.

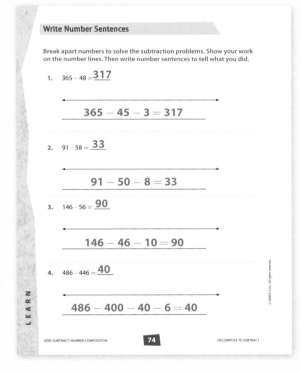

Write Number Sentences

Break apart numbers to solve the subtraction problems. Show your work on the number lines. Then write number sentences to tell what you did.

1. $365 - 48 = \underline{317}$

   $365 - 45 - 3 = 317$

2. $91 - 58 = \underline{33}$

   $91 - 50 - 8 = 33$

3. $146 - 56 = \underline{90}$

   $146 - 46 - 10 = 90$

4. $486 - 446 = \underline{40}$

   $486 - 400 - 40 - 6 = 40$

ADD, SUBTRACT, NUMBER COMPOSITION   74   DECOMPOSE TO SUBTRACT

TRY IT Break Apart Numbers to Subtract

Students will practice breaking apart numbers and use number lines to show their steps. They will also practice solving problems with number sentences. Give students the Break Apart Numbers to Subtract activity page from their Activity Book. Read the directions with them.

Objectives

- Decompose numbers to solve subtraction problems, such as $213 - 12 = 200 + 13 - 12$.

Name:

Decompose to Subtract
Break Apart Numbers to Subtract

Break apart numbers to find each difference.

1. $81 - 17 = $ __64__

2. $147 - 9 = $ __138__

3. $352 - 27 = $ __325__

4. $445 - 16 = $ __429__

T R Y   I T

---

5. $93 - 25 = $ __68__

6. $130 - 14 = $ __116__

Choose the number sentence that can be used to solve each problem.

7. $47 - 28 = $ _____
    A. $47 + 26 + 26$
    B. $47 - 27 - 1$ (circled)
    C. $20 + 27 + 26$
    D. $47 + 26 + 27$

8. $510 - 11 = $ _____
    A. $510 - 10 - 1$ (circled)
    B. $500 - 11$
    C. $510 + 10 - 11$
    D. $500 - 10 - 1$

Write a number sentence that could help you solve each problem, and then solve each problem. **Answers will vary.**

Examples:

9. $108 - 14 = $ _____
    $90 + 18 - 14 = $ __94__

10. $209 - 16 = $ _____
    $190 + 19 - 16 = $ __193__

T R Y   I T

Choose Friendly Numbers

Lesson Overview

Skills Update	5 minutes	ONLINE
LEARN Make Numbers Friendly	10 minutes	ONLINE
LEARN Mental Math	15 minutes	ONLINE
LEARN Break Numbers in Your Head	10 minutes	ONLINE
TRY IT Choose a Way to Subtract	10 minutes	OFFLINE
CHECKPOINT	10 minutes	OFFLINE

▶ Lesson Objectives

Decompose numbers to solve subtraction problems, such as
$213 - 12 = 200 + 13 - 12$.

▶ Prerequisite Skills

Demonstrate that a number can be composed of other numbers in various ways.

▶ Advance Preparation

Print the Open Number Lines.

Write the following subtraction problems on a sheet of paper. Leave room for students to solve the problems and show their work.

- $212 - 18 = (194)$
- $96 - 24 = (72)$
- $350 - 55 = (295)$
- $169 - 80 = (89)$
- $435 - 40 = (395)$

▶ Content Background

In this lesson, students learn to recognize opportunities for breaking numbers and to do mental calculations.

The mathematical term *decomposition* describes the breaking apart of numbers into *friendly numbers* for easier computation. When talking to students, you may use the phrase *breaking apart* in place of decomposition.

In math, you will often hear the terms *nice numbers* or *friendly numbers*. Friendly numbers—numbers such as 5 and 10, or multiples of 10—are numbers that are easier to use when adding, subtracting, or operating with numbers in general

Decomposing numbers to solve problems quickly in your head is easy. Explaining the steps with notation is more difficult. This lesson does not focus on notation. Instead, the goal is to help students develop an agile mind that can easily break numbers apart in different ways to do mental calculations.

Materials to Gather

SUPPLIED

Open Number Lines (printout)

Checkpoint (printout)

LEARN Make Numbers Friendly

Students will see how different strategies can be used to solve the same problem. Students should learn to choose the strategy that makes the most sense to them.

Objectives

- Decompose numbers to solve subtraction problems, such as $213 - 12 = 200 + 13 - 12$.

Tips

Allow students to review number decomposition with base-10 blocks. Encourage students to find various ways to break up numbers to do mental math.

LEARN Mental Math

ONLINE 15 min

Students will practice breaking apart numbers to solve addition and subtraction problems mentally.

Objectives

- Decompose numbers to solve subtraction problems, such as $213 - 12 = 200 + 13 - 12$.

LEARN Break Numbers in Your Head

ONLINE 10 min

Students will practice solving addition and subtraction problems mentally by playing a game.

Objectives

- Decompose numbers to solve subtraction problems, such as $213 - 12 = 200 + 13 - 12$.

TRY IT Choose a Way to Subtract

OFFLINE 10 min

Students will solve subtraction problems by choosing an appropriate way to break numbers. They can use open number lines, number sentences, or mental math to solve each problem. Give students the problems you prepared and the Open Number Lines printout. Use the answer key to check students' answers, and then enter the results online.

Objectives

- Decompose numbers to solve subtraction problems, such as $213 - 12 = 200 + 13 - 12$.

CHECKPOINT

Objectives

- Decompose numbers to solve subtraction problems, such as $213 - 12 = 200 + 13 - 12$.

Print the assessment and have students complete it on their own. Read the directions, questions, and answer choices to students if necessary. Use the answer key to score the assessment, and then enter the results online.

Checkpoint   Math | Add, Subtract, Number Composition | Choose Friendly Numbers

Name _____   Date _____

Checkpoint Answer Key

Choose the number sentence that can be used to solve each problem.

(1 point)
1. $410 - 9 =$ _____

   Ⓐ $400 + 10 - 9$
   B. $410 - 10 - 9$
   C. $410 + 10 - 9$
   D. $400 - 10 - 9$

(1 point)
2. $123 - 8 =$ _____

   A. $123 + 23 - 8$
   Ⓑ $100 + 23 - 8$
   C. $100 - 23 + 8$
   D. $123 + 8 + 8$

Write a number sentence that could help you solve each problem and then solve each problem. **Answers may vary.**

(1 point)
3. $146 - 13 = \underline{133}$

    Example:
    $130 + 16 - 13 = 133$

(1 point)
4. $489 - 19 = \underline{470}$

    Example:
    $470 + 19 - 19 = 470$

1 of 1

Unit Review

Lesson Overview

UNIT REVIEW Look Back	20 minutes	**ONLINE**
UNIT REVIEW Checkpoint Practice	20 minutes	**OFFLINE**
⤐ UNIT REVIEW Prepare for the Checkpoint		

▶ Unit Objectives

- Use concrete objects or sketches to model and solve addition or subtraction computation problems with sums or minuends up through 500 with and without regrouping.
- Find the sum of two whole numbers with sums up through 500.
- Use regrouping to find the difference of two whole numbers with the minuend up through 500.
- Explain the meaning of the equals symbol.
- Demonstrate that a number can be composed of other numbers in various ways.
- Decompose numbers to solve subtraction problems, such as $213 - 12 = 200 + 13 - 12$.

▶ Advance Preparation

In this lesson, students will have an opportunity to review previous activities in the Add, Subtract, Number Composition unit. Look at the suggested activities in Unit Review: Prepare for the Checkpoint online and gather any needed materials.

Materials to Gather

SUPPLIED

base-10 blocks

place-value mat

Checkpoint Practice activity page

Keywords

addend	minuend
algorithm	minus symbol ($-$)
base-10 blocks	model (verb)
compose numbers	place value
decompose numbers	place-value chart
difference	place-value mat
equals symbol ($=$)	regroup; regrouping
equivalent form	standard form
expanded form	strategy
mental math	sum

UNIT REVIEW Look Back

- Review unit objectives.

In this unit, students have learned to solve addition and subtraction with regrouping and by decomposing numbers. Students will review these concepts to prepare for the Unit Checkpoint.

UNIT REVIEW Checkpoint Practice

Objectives

- Review unit objectives.

Students will complete a Checkpoint Practice activity page to prepare for the Unit Checkpoint. If necessary, read the directions, questions, and answer choices to students. Have students answer the problems on their own. Carefully review the answers with students.

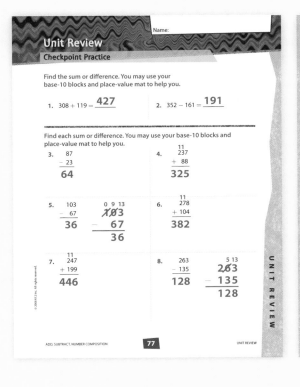

Name: _____

Unit Review

Checkpoint Practice

Find the sum or difference. You may use your base-10 blocks and place-value mat to help you.

1. $308 + 119 = \underline{427}$ 2. $352 - 161 = \underline{191}$

Find each sum or difference. You may use your base-10 blocks and place-value mat to help you.

3. $\begin{array}{r} 87 \\ -23 \\ \hline 64 \end{array}$ 4. $\begin{array}{r} {}^{11}237 \\ +88 \\ \hline 325 \end{array}$

5. $\begin{array}{r} 103 \\ -67 \\ \hline 36 \end{array}$ $\begin{array}{r} {}^{0\ 9\ 13}\cancel{1}\cancel{0}3 \\ -67 \\ \hline 36 \end{array}$ 6. $\begin{array}{r} {}^{11}278 \\ +104 \\ \hline 382 \end{array}$

7. $\begin{array}{r} {}^{11}247 \\ +199 \\ \hline 446 \end{array}$ 8. $\begin{array}{r} 263 \\ -135 \\ \hline 128 \end{array}$ $\begin{array}{r} {}^{5\ 13}2\cancel{6}3 \\ -135 \\ \hline 128 \end{array}$

ADD, SUBTRACT, NUMBER COMPOSITION **77** UNIT REVIEW

Break apart the numbers to make them easier to add or subtract. Then find each sum or difference. Show your work.

9. $160 - 45 = \underline{115}$

10. $145 + 220 = \underline{365}$

11. $300 + 125 = \underline{425}$

12. $471 - 67 = \underline{404}$

Decide whether the two amounts are equal. Write = in the box if the amounts are equal, and ≠ in the box if they are not equal.

13. $17 - 8 \;\boxed{\neq}\; 8$ 14. $16 + 12 \;\boxed{=}\; 28$

15. $7 \;\boxed{\neq}\; 19 - 7$ 16. $16 \;\boxed{=}\; 16 + 0$

ADD, SUBTRACT, NUMBER COMPOSITION **78** UNIT REVIEW

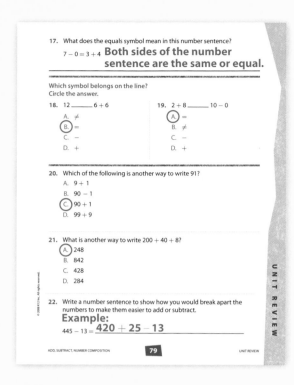

17. What does the equals symbol mean in this number sentence?

$7 - 0 = 3 + 4$ **Both sides of the number sentence are the same or equal.**

Which symbol belongs on the line?
Circle the answer.

18. 12 _____ 6 + 6
   - A. ≠
   - (B.) =
   - C. −
   - D. +

19. 2 + 8 _____ 10 − 0
   - (A.) =
   - B. ≠
   - C. −
   - D. +

20. Which of the following is another way to write 91?
   - A. 9 + 1
   - B. 90 − 1
   - (C.) 90 + 1
   - D. 99 + 9

21. What is another way to write 200 + 40 + 8?
   - (A.) 248
   - B. 842
   - C. 428
   - D. 284

22. Write a number sentence to show how you would break apart the numbers to make them easier to add or subtract.
   Example:
   $445 - 13 = $ **420 + 25 − 13**

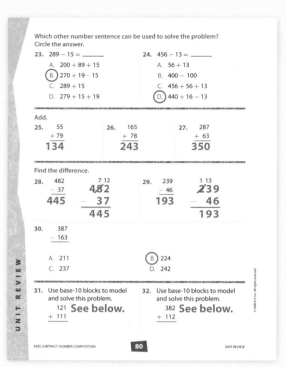

Which other number sentence can be used to solve the problem?
Circle the answer.

23. 289 − 15 = _____
   - A. 200 + 89 + 15
   - (B.) 270 + 19 − 15
   - C. 289 + 15
   - D. 279 + 15 + 19

24. 456 − 13 = _____
   - A. 56 + 13
   - B. 400 − 100
   - C. 456 + 56 + 13
   - (D.) 440 + 16 − 13

Add.

25.   55
    + 79
    134

26.   165
    + 78
    243

27.   287
    + 63
    350

Find the difference.

28.   482   7 12
    − 37   4 8̸ 2
    445   − 37
               445

29.   239   1 13
    − 46   2̸ 3 9
    193   − 46
               193

30.   387
    − 163
   - A. 211
   - (B.) 224
   - C. 237
   - D. 242

31. Use base-10 blocks to model and solve this problem.
      121   **See below.**
    + 111

32. Use base-10 blocks to model and solve this problem.
      382   **See below.**
    + 112

Additional Answers

31. Show 1 hundreds flat, 2 tens rods, and 1 ones cube. Below that is 1 hundreds flat, 1 tens rod, and 1 ones cube. The answer is 232.

32. Show 3 hundreds flats, 8 tens rods, and 2 ones cubes. Below that is 1 hundreds flat, 1 tens rod, and 2 ones cubes. The answer is 494.

➡ UNIT REVIEW Prepare for the Checkpoint

What you do next depends on how students performed in the previous activity, Unit Review: Checkpoint Practice. If students had difficulty with any of the problems, complete the appropriate review activity listed in the table online.

Unit Checkpoint

UNIT CHECKPOINT Online	20 minutes	**ONLINE**
UNIT CHECKPOINT Offline	35 minutes	**OFFLINE**

▶ Unit Objectives

This lesson reviews the following objectives:

- Use concrete objects or sketches to model and solve addition or subtraction computation problems with sums or minuends up through 500 with and without regrouping.
- Find the sum of two whole numbers with sums up through 500.
- Use regrouping to find the difference of two whole numbers with the minuend up through 500.
- Explain the meaning of the equals symbol.
- Demonstrate that a number can be composed of other numbers in various ways.
- Decompose numbers to solve subtraction problems, such as $213 - 12 = 200 + 13 - 12$.

Materials to Gather

SUPPLIED

base-10 blocks (optional)

place-value mat (optional)

Unit Checkpoint (printout)

UNIT CHECKPOINT Online

ONLINE 20 min

Students will complete this part of the Unit Checkpoint online. Read the directions, problems, and answer choices to students. If necessary, help students with keyboard or mouse operations.

Objectives

- Assess unit objectives.

OFFLINE
35min

Objectives

- Assess unit objectives.

Students will complete this part of the Unit Checkpoint offline. Print the Checkpoint and have students complete it on their own. Read the directions, problems, and answer choices to students if necessary. Use the answer key to score the Checkpoint, and then enter the results online.

Name _____ Date _____

Unit Checkpoint Answer Key

(1 point)
1. You look in a math book and see this number sentence: 5 = 3 + 2.
What does the equals symbol mean in this number sentence?

The equals symbol means that 5 is the same as 3 + 2; or that the two sides are the same or equal.

(1 point)
2. What does the symbol the arrow is pointing to mean?

$$10 + 3 \overset{\downarrow}{=} 13$$

- (A.) equals
- B. subtract
- C. add
- D. greater than

(1 point)
3. What is another way to write 200?

- A. 100 + 20
- (B.) 100 + 100
- C. 20 + 20
- D. 100 + 100 + 100

Write a number sentence that could help you solve the problem, and then solve it. **Answers will vary.**

(1 point)
4. 267 − 23 = **244**

$$240 + 27 − 23 = 244$$

(1 point)
5. 499 − 22 = **477**

$$470 + 29 − 22 = 477$$

(1 point)
Add.

6.
$$\begin{array}{r} 196 \\ + 134 \\ \hline \textbf{330} \end{array}$$

Name _____ Date _____

Choose the answer for the problem below.
(1 point)
7. 391 + 34 = _____

- A. 357
- B. 325
- (C.) 425
- D. 415

Circle the difference. *(1 point)*	Write the difference. *(1 point)*
8. $\begin{array}{r} 400 \\ - \ 72 \\ \hline \end{array}$ A. 357 (B.) 328 C. 425 D. 415	**9.** $\begin{array}{r} 288 \\ - \ 69 \\ \hline \textbf{219} \end{array}$

(1 point)
10. Draw a sketch of a model you could use to help you solve this subtraction problem.

$$\begin{array}{r} 88 \\ - 36 \\ \hline \end{array}$$

Students should model 88 as 8 tens and 8 ones. These can be drawn as lines or dots. Students should then cross out 6 ones and 3 tens to leave 5 tens and 2 ones, or 52.

Use base-10 blocks and the place-value mat, if needed, to model and solve these problems.

(1 point) **11.** $\begin{array}{r} 301 \\ - 120 \\ \hline \textbf{181} \end{array}$	*(1 point)* **12.** $\begin{array}{r} 455 \\ - \ 66 \\ \hline \textbf{389} \end{array}$	*(1 point)* **13.** $\begin{array}{r} 85 \\ + 95 \\ \hline \textbf{180} \end{array}$

See below.

Additional Answers

11. Students should model 301 as 3 hundreds flats and 1 ones cube. Students should trade 1 hundreds flat for 10 tens rods. Then they should subtract 0 ones cubes, 2 tens rods, and 1 hundreds flat, leaving 1 hundreds flat, 8 tens rods, and 1 ones cube, or 181.

12. Students should model 455 as 4 hundreds flats, 5 tens rods, and 5 ones cubes. Students should trade 1 hundreds flat for 10 tens rods, and 1 tens rod for 10 ones cubes. Then they should subtract 6 ones cubes, 6 tens rods, and 0 hundreds flats, leaving 3 hundreds flats, 8 tens rods, and 9 ones cubes, or 389.

13. Students should model 85 as 8 tens rods and 5 ones cubes. Below that are 9 tens rods and 5 ones cubes with tens and ones in the same columns respectively. Students should add 5 + 5 in the ones column to get 10 ones cubes. The 10 ones cubes can be traded for 1 tens rod. Students should add 8 + 9 + 1 tens to get 18 tens rods. They should trade 10 tens rods for 1 hundreds flat.

Inverse Operations: Add and Subtract

2 + ? = 5

2 + 3 = 5

5

−　−

2　+　3

5 − ? = 3

5 − 2 = 3

▶ Unit Objectives

- Use models or drawings to show how addition and subtraction are inversely related.
- Use the inverse relationship between addition and subtraction to solve problems.
- Use mental math to find the sum or difference of two 2-digit numbers.
- Identify and explain the approach and strategies for solving addition or subtraction computation problems with sums or minuends up through 500.
- Demonstrate an understanding of connections between similar addition or subtraction computation problems, involving sums and minuends up through 500.

▶ Big Ideas

- Models and mathematical symbols can represent addition and subtraction.
- An inverse operation undoes another operation. Addition and subtraction are inverse operations.

▶ Unit Introduction

Students will observe and use models to explore how addition and subtraction are related. They will learn that the two operations are the inverse of each other and will use fact triangles to show the inverse relationship. They will use that knowledge to solve missing addend or missing subtrahend problems.

Students will learn strategies for using mental math to calculate sums and differences of 2-digit numbers. They will learn strategies for computing sums and differences of numbers through 500. They will explain the strategies that they use.

Opposite Operations: + and −

Lesson Overview

Skills Update	5 minutes	ONLINE
GET READY Connections: Add and Subtract	5 minutes	ONLINE
LEARN Show Opposite Operations	20 minutes	OFFLINE
LEARN How Are They Related?	15 minutes	OFFLINE
TRY IT Addition and Subtraction Are Opposites	10 minutes	OFFLINE
CHECKPOINT	5 minutes	OFFLINE

▶ Lesson Objectives

- Use models or drawings to show how addition and subtraction are inversely related.
- Use the inverse relationship between addition and subtraction to solve problems.

▶ Prerequisite Skills

Given concrete objects, show how two sets can be added together, and then reverse the operation to show how a number can be subtracted from the whole.

▶ Common Errors and Misconceptions

Students might have difficulty understanding that addition and subtraction are opposite, or inverse, operations. It might not be obvious to them that addition "undoes" subtraction.

▶ Advance Preparation

Print and cut out the Fact Family Triangles. On one of them, write 16 on the top corner, and 9 and 7 on the bottom two corners. Leave the rest of the triangles blank.

▶ Content Background

Students will learn how addition and subtraction are related.

Inverse operations are operations that undo each other. Addition and subtraction are inverse operations. For example, if you add 4 to 3, the sum is 7 ($3 + 4 = 7$). If you subtract 4 from 7, the difference is 3 ($7 − 4 = 3$). First you add 4, and then you undo the addition by subtracting 4. The operations are inverse because the amounts you began with and ended with are both 3.

Materials to Gather

SUPPLIED

blocks – B (7 red and 9 blue)

Show Opposite Operations activity page

Fact Family Triangles (printout)

How Are They Related activity page

Addition and Subtraction Are Opposites activity page

Checkpoint (printout)

ONLINE 5 min

GET READY Connections: Add and Subtract

Students will see how addition and subtraction reverse each other.

Objectives

• Given concrete objects, show how two sets can be added together, and then reverse the operation to show how a number can be subtracted from the whole.

OFFLINE 20 min

LEARN Show Opposite Operations

Students will use models to show that addition and subtraction are opposite operations that undo each other.

Gather the red and blue circles, the 16 fact family triangle, and Show Opposite Operations activity page.

1. Display the sum $7 + 9$ using 7 red circles and 9 blue circles. Have students write the number sentence on the paper. ($7 + 9 = 16$)

   Ask: If I wanted to undo my addition, what would I do?
   ANSWER: Take away 9.

2. Slide the 9 blue circles away from the 7 red circles to show that you are subtracting them.

   Say: I started with 7 and added 9. The total was 16. To undo the addition, I will subtract 9 from 16. Write a number sentence to show my subtraction. ($16 - 9 = 7$)

3. **Ask:** Look at the two number sentences you wrote. What do you notice about them?
   ANSWER: They have the same numbers in them.

4. Show students the 16 fact family triangle.

   Say: 16 is the whole. 9 and 7 are parts of 16. If you add the two parts, the answer is the whole. If you subtract one of the parts from the whole, the answer is the other part.

Objectives

• Use models or drawings to show how addition and subtraction are inversely related.

• Use the inverse relationship between addition and subtraction to solve problems.

5. Have students complete the Show Opposite Operations activity page. For Problems 4 and 5, have students create fact family triangles using the numbers in the problem. Then have them use the triangle to write the number sentences. (Note: Be sure students only use the front side of the activity page for this activity.)

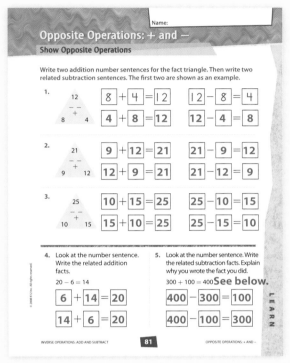

Additional Answers:

5. Students should explain that addition and subtraction are opposite operations, and that they subtracted to undo the addition.

OFFLINE
15min

LEARN How Are They Related?

Objectives

Students will use fact family triangles to show the inverse relationship between addition and subtraction.

Gather the red and blue circles, the blank fact family triangles, and How Are They Related? activity page (on the back of previous page).

1. Say: Addition and subtraction are opposite, or inverse, operations. They undo each other. You can write related addition number sentences to check subtraction problems. You can write related subtraction sentences to check addition problems. In an addition number sentence, the numbers you add are the parts. The sum is the whole.

2. Point to the example on the activity page.

   Say: The first number sentence is $14 - 5 = 9$. To check that answer, you can use two different addition number sentences.

3. Have students complete fact family triangles for Problems 1 and 2 before filling in the number sentences. Then have students complete the activity page.

- Use models or drawings to show how addition and subtraction are inversely related.

- Use the inverse relationship between addition and subtraction to solve problems.

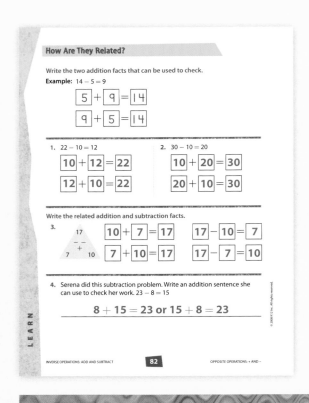

How Are They Related?

Write the two addition facts that can be used to check.

Example: 14 − 5 = 9

$$\boxed{5} + \boxed{9} = \boxed{14}$$
$$\boxed{9} + \boxed{5} = \boxed{14}$$

1. 22 − 10 = 12

$$\boxed{10} + \boxed{12} = \boxed{22}$$
$$\boxed{12} + \boxed{10} = \boxed{22}$$

2. 30 − 10 = 20

$$\boxed{10} + \boxed{20} = \boxed{30}$$
$$\boxed{20} + \boxed{10} = \boxed{30}$$

Write the related addition and subtraction facts.

3.

$$\boxed{10} + \boxed{7} = \boxed{17} \qquad \boxed{17} - \boxed{10} = \boxed{7}$$
$$\boxed{7} + \boxed{10} = \boxed{17} \qquad \boxed{17} - \boxed{7} = \boxed{10}$$

4. Serena did this subtraction problem. Write an addition sentence she can use to check her work. 23 − 8 = 15

$$8 + 15 = 23 \text{ or } 15 + 8 = 23$$

LEARN

TRY IT Addition and Subtraction Are Opposites

OFFLINE **10** min

Students will practice using related addition and subtraction facts to solve and check problems. They may use fact family triangles or models to show the sum or difference. Give students the Addition and Subtraction Are Opposites activity page from their Activity Book and read directions with them.

Objectives

- Use models or drawings to show how addition and subtraction are inversely related.
- Use the inverse relationship between addition and subtraction to solve problems.

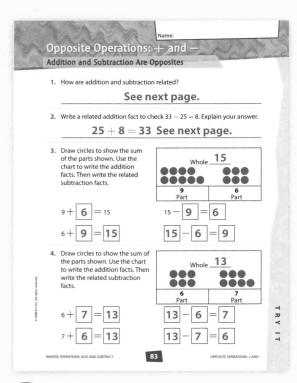

Name: _____

Opposite Operations: + and −

Addition and Subtraction Are Opposites

1. How are addition and subtraction related?

   See next page.

2. Write a related addition fact to check 33 − 25 = 8. Explain your answer.

   25 + 8 = 33 See next page.

3. Draw circles to show the sum of the parts shown. Use the chart to write the addition facts. Then write the related subtraction facts.

   Whole __15__

   | **9** Part | **6** Part |

   $9 + \boxed{6} = 15$ $15 - \boxed{9} = \boxed{6}$

   $6 + \boxed{9} = \boxed{15}$ $15 - \boxed{6} = \boxed{9}$

4. Draw circles to show the sum of the parts shown. Use the chart to write the addition facts. Then write the related subtraction facts.

   Whole __13__

   | **6** Part | **7** Part |

   $6 + \boxed{7} = \boxed{13}$ $13 - \boxed{6} = \boxed{7}$

   $7 + \boxed{6} = \boxed{13}$ $13 - \boxed{7} = \boxed{6}$

TRY IT

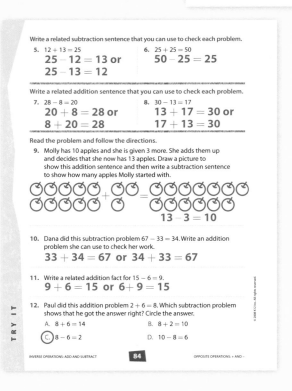

Write a related subtraction sentence that you can use to check each problem.

5. 12 + 13 = 25
   25 − 12 = 13 or
   25 − 13 = 12

6. 25 + 25 = 50
   50 − 25 = 25

Write a related addition sentence that you can use to check each problem.

7. 28 − 8 = 20
   20 + 8 = 28 or
   8 + 20 = 28

8. 30 − 13 = 17
   13 + 17 = 30 or
   17 + 13 = 30

Read the problem and follow the directions.

9. Molly has 10 apples and she is given 3 more. She adds them up and decides that she now has 13 apples. Draw a picture to show this addition sentence and then write a subtraction sentence to show how many apples Molly started with.

   13 − 3 = 10

10. Dana did this subtraction problem 67 − 33 = 34. Write an addition problem she can use to check her work.

    33 + 34 = 67 or 34 + 33 = 67

11. Write a related addition fact for 15 − 6 = 9.
    9 + 6 = 15 or 6 + 9 = 15

12. Paul did this addition problem 2 + 6 = 8. Which subtraction problem shows that he got the answer right? Circle the answer.

    A. 8 + 6 = 14
    B. 8 + 2 = 10
    C. 8 − 6 = 2
    D. 10 − 8 = 6

TRY IT

Additional Answers:

1. Addition and subtraction are opposite because they undo each other.

2. The addition number sentence undoes the subtraction sentence.

CHECKPOINT

OFFLINE
5 min

Print the assessment and have students complete it on their own. Read the directions, questions, and answer choices to students if necessary. Use the answer key to score the assessment, and then enter the results online.

Objectives

- Use models or drawings to show how addition and subtraction are inversely related.
- Use the inverse relationship between addition and subtraction to solve problems.

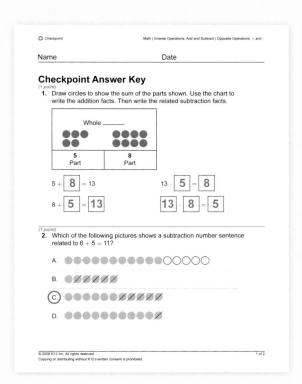

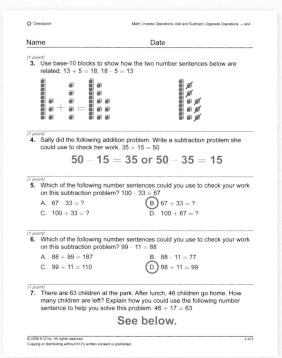

Additional Answers

7. Students should answer that there are 17 children left at the park. They should explain that they can use the number sentence 46 + 17 = 63 to find out how many are left when you take away 46 from 63. This is because addition and subtraction are opposites and they undo one another.

Mental Math: Addition and Subtraction

Lesson Overview

Skills Update	5 minutes	ONLINE
GET READY Bouncy Ball Math	10 minutes	ONLINE
LEARN Mental Math Strategies	10 minutes	ONLINE
LEARN Add and Subtract Mentally	20 minutes	ONLINE
TRY IT Find the Answer Mentally	10 minutes	OFFLINE
CHECKPOINT	5 minutes	OFFLINE

▶ Lesson Objectives

Use mental math to find the sum or difference of two 2-digit numbers.

▶ Prerequisite Skills

- Find the sum of two whole numbers with sums up through 500.
- Use regrouping to find the difference of two whole numbers with minuends up through 500.

▶ Content Background

In this lesson, students will use mental math strategies to find the sums and differences of 2-digit numbers.

In math, you will often hear the terms *nice numbers* or *friendly numbers*. Friendly numbers—numbers such as 5 and 10, or multiples of 10—are numbers that are easier to use when adding, subtracting, or operating with numbers in general. Friendly numbers are especially helpful to students in doing math problems mentally. The objective of this lesson is to decompose—or break apart—numbers that are less friendly into numbers that are more friendly to make it easier to subtract.

Keywords

mental math – the process of using only the brain to solve math problems
strategy – a method or approach to solve a problem

Materials to Gather

SUPPLIED
Find the Answer Mentally activity page
Checkpoint (printout)

GET READY Bouncy Ball Math

ONLINE
10 min

Students will practice adding and subtracting 2-digit and 3-digit numbers.

Objectives

- Find the sum of two whole numbers with sums up through 500.
- Use regrouping to find the difference of two whole numbers with the minuend up through 500.

LEARN Mental Math Strategies

Students will practice adding and subtracting mentally. They will apply and explain mental math strategies to find sums and differences of two 2-digit numbers.

Objectives

- Use mental math to find the sum or difference of two 2-digit numbers.

LEARN Add and Subtract Mentally

Students will practice solving addition and subtraction problems mentally by playing a game. Have students describe their mental math strategies. Remind them that there is more than one way to solve each problem.

Objectives

- Use mental math to find the sum or difference of two 2-digit numbers.

TRY IT Find the Answer Mentally

Students will practice using mental math strategies to solve addition and subtraction problems. Give students the Find the Answer Mentally activity page from their Activity Book and read the directions with them.

Objectives

- Use mental math to find the sum or difference of two 2-digit numbers.

Name: _____

Mental Math: Addition and Subtraction

Find the Answer Mentally

Use mental math to find each sum.

1. $60 + 37 = \underline{97}$
2. $71 + 18 = \underline{89}$
3. $15 + 24 = \underline{39}$
4. $94 + 13 = \underline{107}$
5. $39 + 42 = \underline{81}$
6. $55 + 27 = \underline{82}$

Use mental math to find each difference.

7. $80 - 50 = \underline{30}$
8. $65 - 12 = \underline{53}$
9. $90 - 44 = \underline{46}$
10. $77 - 20 = \underline{57}$
11. $58 - 34 = \underline{24}$
12. $46 - 19 = \underline{27}$

T R Y I T

INVERSE OPERATIONS: ADD AND SUBTRACT   **85**   MENTAL MATH: ADDITION AND SUBTRACTION

Use mental math to find each sum or difference.
Circle the answer.

13. $22 + 10 = \underline{\quad}$
 A. 23 (B.) 32
 C. 33 D. 26

14. $47 + 12 = \underline{\quad}$
 A. 35 B. 51
 (C.) 59 D. 62

15. $35 + 7 = \underline{\quad}$
 A. 30 B. 32
 C. 40 (D.) 42

16. $54 + 55 = \underline{\quad}$
 A. 59 B. 106
 (C.) 109 D. 119

17. $64 - 24 = \underline{\quad}$
 A. 88 B. 52
 (C.) 40 D. 30

18. $35 - 22 = \underline{\quad}$
 (A.) 13 B. 17
 C. 21 D. 23

19. $45 - 17 = \underline{\quad}$
 (A.) 28 B. 35
 C. 38 D. 40

20. $120 - 19 = \underline{\quad}$
 A. 80 B. 91
 C. 100 (D.) 101

T R Y I T

INVERSE OPERATIONS: ADD AND SUBTRACT   **86**   MENTAL MATH: ADDITION AND SUBTRACTION

Print the assessment and have students complete it on their own. Read the directions, problems, and answer choices to students if necessary. Use the answer key to score the assessment, and then enter the results online.

⚙ Checkpoint   Math | Inverse Operations: Add and Subtract | Mental Math: Addition and Subtraction

Name _____   Date _____

Checkpoint Answer Key

Add or subtract mentally. Circle the answer.

(1 point)
1. 57 + 10 = _____

    (A.) 67   B. 47

    C. 62   D. 42

(1 point)
2. 32 + 46 = _____

    (A.) 78   B. 76

    C. 74   D. 72

(1 point)
3. 87 − 67 = _____

    A. 19   (B.) 20

    C. 22   D. 23

(1 point)
4. 72 − 12 = _____

    A. 51   B. 57

    (C.) 60   D. 61

Add or subtract mentally. Write the answer.

(1 point)
5. 40 + 20 = **60**

(1 point)
6. 71 + 22 = **93**

(1 point)
7. 45 − 11 = **34**

(1 point)
8. 35 − 22 = **13**

1 of 1

Strategies to Add & Subtract Through 500

Skills Update	5 minutes	ONLINE
GET READY Different Ways to Add	5 minutes	ONLINE
LEARN Addition Strategies	15 minutes	ONLINE
TRY IT Use Addition Strategies	10 minutes	OFFLINE
LEARN Subtraction Strategies	15 minutes	OFFLINE
TRY IT Subtraction Strategies	10 minutes	ONLINE

▶ Lesson Objectives

Identify and explain the approach and strategies for solving addition or subtraction computation problems with sums or minuends up through 500.

▶ Prerequisite Skills

Identify and explain the approach for addition or subtraction computation problems with sums or minuends up through 100.

▶ Content Background

Students will learn to identify and explain strategies for solving addition and subtraction computation problems. For example, they will regroup to solve problems or break apart numbers to make them easier to add or subtract.

The strategy a student uses is not important, as long as it is a strategy that works. What matters is that students are able to choose a strategy and explain to you what they are doing.

Keywords	**count on** – to add two groups by starting with the number of objects in one group and then counting up, in order, the number of objects in the other group

Materials to Gather

SUPPLIED

Use Addition Strategies activity page

Subtraction Strategies activity page

Open Number Lines (printout)

base-10 blocks (optional)

GET READY Different Ways to Add

Objectives

Students will review three strategies for solving addition problems with sums through 100: modeling the numbers, counting on with a number line, and using a place-value chart.

- Identify and explain the approach for addition or subtraction computation problems with sums or minuends up through 100.

LEARN Addition Strategies

Objectives

Students will learn different strategies for solving addition problems with sums up through 500. They will see that they can find the correct answer in more than one way.

- Identify and explain the approach and strategies for solving addition or subtraction computation problems with sums or minuends up through 500.

TRY IT Use Addition Strategies

Objectives

Students will practice choosing and applying strategies to solve addition problems. Give students the Use Addition Strategies activity page from their Activity Book and read the directions with them.

Enter students' results online when they complete the activity page.

- Identify and explain the approach and strategies for solving addition computation problems with sums or minuends up through 500.

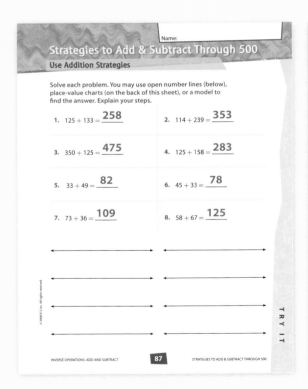

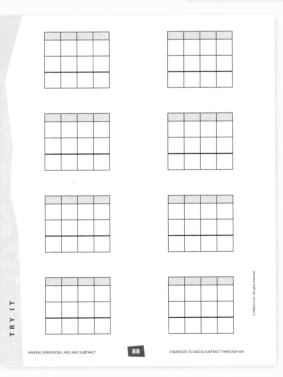

Tips

If necessary, students may use base-10 blocks to help solve the problems.

LEARN Subtraction Strategies

OFFLINE
15 min

Objectives

- Identify and explain the approach and strategies for solving addition or subtraction computation problems with sums or minuends up through 500.

Students will solve subtraction problems by breaking up the smaller number into tens and ones and then counting back.
  Gather the Subtraction Strategies activity page.

1. **Say:** One strategy you can use to solve a subtraction problem is to break the smaller number apart. To subtract, you start at the larger number, and then count back by the smaller number. The number you land on is the difference.

2. Point to the first subtraction problem on the Subtraction Strategies activity page. Draw a mark at the right end of the number line, and write 250 below it.

Tips

If necessary, students may use base-10 blocks to help them solve the problems.

250

Say: I am going to solve the problem 250 − 44. First, I will break up 44 into 40 + 4. Then I will count back 40, or 4 tens.

3. Draw 4 jumps of 10, counting back by 10s as you draw each jump. Label each jump with the number 10. Label the four jumps −40. Label the landing point with the number 210, as shown.

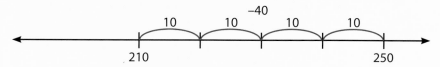

4. **Say:** I have counted back 40. Now I will count back 4 more to make 44.

5. Draw 4 jumps of 1, counting back by 1s as you draw each jump. Label each jump with the number 1. Label the 4 jumps −4, and label the landing point 206.

Say: I counted back to find the difference. 250 − 44 = 206.

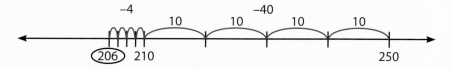

6. Follow Steps 1–5 for Problems 2 and 3 on the activity page. Guide students to write the numbers and to draw the jumps as you count together.

The key below is one way to show the solutions.

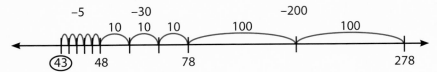

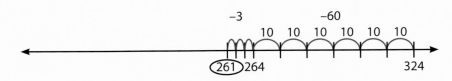

7. Have students complete the subtraction Problems 4–6 by counting back. Assist them when necessary.

Name:

Strategies to Add & Subtract Through 500

Subtraction Strategies

Follow the instructions in the Lesson Guide as you complete this activity page.

1. $250 - 44 =$ **206**

2. $278 - 235 =$ **43**

3. $324 - 63 =$ **261**

INVERSE OPERATIONS: ADD AND SUBTRACT **89** STRATEGIES TO ADD & SUBTRACT THROUGH 500

L E A R N

L E A R N

Solve each problem by breaking apart the smaller number and counting back. Show your work on the open number line.

4. $419 - 94 =$ **325**

5. $205 - 174 =$ **31**

6. $500 - 112 =$ **388**

INVERSE OPERATIONS: ADD AND SUBTRACT **90** STRATEGIES TO ADD & SUBTRACT THROUGH 500

ONLINE

10 min

TRY IT Subtraction Strategies

Objectives

Students will practice counting back to solve subtraction problems.

- Identify and explain the approach and strategies for solving addition computation problems with sums or minuends up through 500.

Subtraction Strategies Up Through 500

Lesson Overview

Skills Update	5 minutes	ONLINE
GET READY Different Ways to Subtract	5 minutes	ONLINE
LEARN So Many Ways to Subtract	15 minutes	ONLINE
LEARN Practice Ways to Subtract	10 minutes	OFFLINE
TRY IT Explain Subtraction Strategies	5 minutes	OFFLINE
TRY IT Use Subtraction Strategies	10 minutes	OFFLINE
CHECKPOINT	10 minutes	OFFLINE

▶ Lesson Objectives

Identify and explain the approach and strategies for solving addition or subtraction computation problems with sums or minuends up through 500.

▶ Prerequisite Skills

Identify and explain the approach for addition or subtraction computation problems with sums or minuends up through 100.

▶ Advance Preparation

Print the Open Number Lines printout and Place-Value Chart (Hundreds).

▶ Content Background

Students will learn to identify and explain strategies for solving subtraction problems up through 500. The goal is to help students gain fluency and confidence, so they can solve problems efficiently using a variety of approaches.

When students have developed different strategies for solving subtraction problems, they will be able to look carefully at a problem and choose an approach to solve it. Strategies include counting back from the first number to the second, counting on from the second number to the first, breaking numbers apart, and writing out the traditional vertical subtraction process with or without regrouping. Students may also invent another strategy.

Encourage students to solve problems in the way that is easiest for them.

Materials to Gather

SUPPLIED

Practice Ways to Subtract activity page
Using Subtraction Strategies activity page
Checkpoint (printout)
Open Number Lines (printout)
Place-Value Chart (Hundreds) (printout)

GET READY Different Ways to Subtract

ONLINE
5 min

Students will review strategies for solving subtraction problems up through 100.

Objectives

- Identify and explain the approach for addition or subtraction computation problems with sums or minuends up through 100.

LEARN So Many Ways to Subtract

ONLINE 15 min

Students will learn strategies for solving subtraction problems up through 500. Students will see the following subtraction strategies:

- Align the problem vertically and then subtract the ones, tens, and hundreds.
- Use base-10 blocks.
- Break numbers apart.

Objectives

- Identify and explain the approach and strategies for solving addition or subtraction computation problems with sums or minuends up through 500.

LEARN Practice Ways to Subtract

OFFLINE 10 min

Students will practice choosing strategies to solve subtraction problems with minuends up through 500. The goal is to help students gain confidence to solve problems efficiently with a variety of approaches.

Have students look carefully at each problem and decide the best approach:

- Counting up or counting back are often best when the numbers are close to each other.
- Break numbers apart to subtract is often best when the second number has just a few hundreds, tens, or ones.
- Using the traditional algorithm is often best when another approach doesn't come to mind.

Observe whether students notice the most efficient methods, but allow them to solve the problems with their own strategy. Give students the Practice Ways to Subtract activity page from their Activity Book, an Open Number Lines printout, and a Place-Value Chart (Hundreds) printout. Read the directions to students.

Objectives

- Identify and explain the approach and strategies for solving addition or subtraction computation problems with sums or minuends up through 500.

Name:

Subtraction Strategies Up Through 500

Practice Ways to Subtract

Solve the subtraction problems the easiest way you can.

1. $375 - 75 = \underline{300}$

2. $435 - 389 = \underline{46}$

3. $500 - 499 = \underline{1}$

4. $375 - 76 = \underline{299}$

5. $888 - 234 = \underline{654}$

6. $375 - 50 = \underline{325}$

7. $422 - 20 = \underline{402}$

8. $462 - 252 = \underline{210}$

INVERSE OPERATIONS: ADD AND SUBTRACT   **91**   SUBTRACTION STRATEGIES UP THROUGH 500

TRY IT Explain Subtraction Strategies

- Identify and explain the approach and strategies for solving addition or subtraction computation problems with sums or minuends up through 500.

Students will solve subtraction problems and explain their strategies. Give students the Open Number Lines printout and the Place-Value Chart (Hundreds).
 Pay attention to how well students explain their strategies during this activity, and enter the results online.

Students will solve two subtraction problems.

- $158 - 20$
- $299 - 98$

1. Write the problem. Have students choose a strategy and solve the problem.
2. Have students explain how they solved the problem. The strategy students choose is not important. They only need to choose a strategy, explain their work, and find the correct answer.

TRY IT Use Subtraction Strategies

- Identify and explain the approach and strategies for solving addition or subtraction computation problems with sums or minuends up through 500.

Students will practice choosing strategies to solve subtraction problems. Give students the Use Subtraction Strategies activity page and the Open Number Lines printout and Place-Value Chart (Hundreds). Use the answer key to check students' answers, and then enter the results online.

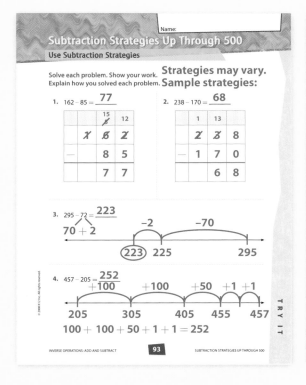

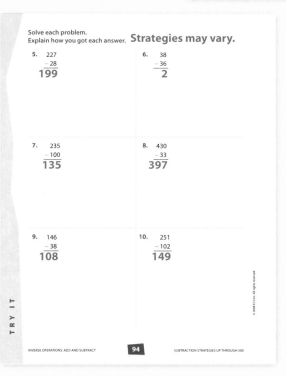

CHECKPOINT

Students will take a performance-based assessment. Print the assessment and follow the instructions for each item. Enter the results online.

Allow students to use base-10 blocks if necessary.

- Identify and explain the approach and strategies for solving addition or subtraction computation problems with sums or minuends up through 500.

Name   Date

Checkpoint Answer Key

Follow the instructions for each item. Choose the response that best describes how the student performs on the task. When you have finished, enter the results online.

1. Write "71 − 46 = " on a sheet of paper.
   Say, "Solve this problem and explain how you got your answer."

   Accept any reasonable explanation. Example explanation: I took one away from 71 to make 70. Then I subtracted 46 from 70 to get 24, and then added 1 to make 25.
   (1 point)
   Did the student give 25 as the answer to the problem?

   A. Yes   B. No
   (1 point)
   Did the student give a reasonable explanation for how he or she solved the problem?

   A. Yes   B. No

---

2. Write "246 + 138 = " on a sheet of paper.
   Say, "Solve this problem and explain how you got your answer."

   Accept any reasonable explanation. Example explanation: I first added the hundreds to get 300. Then I added the tens to get 70, and then added the ones to get 14. Finally, I added these three numbers together to find 300 + 70 + 14 = 384.
   (1 point)
   Did the student give 384 as the answer to the problem?

   A. Yes   B. No
   (1 point)
   Did the student give a reasonable explanation for how he or she solved the problem?

   A. Yes   B. No

Name   Date

3. Write the following problem on a sheet of paper:

   $$\begin{array}{r} 100 \\ -\ 90 \\ \hline \end{array}$$

   Say, "Solve this problem and explain how you got your answer."

   Accept any reasonable explanation. Example explanation: I subtracted 9 tens from 10 tens to get 1 ten.
   (1 point)
   Did the student give 10 as the answer to the problem?

   A. Yes   B. No
   (1 point)
   Did the student give a reasonable explanation for how he or she solved the problem?

   A. Yes   B. No

---

4. Write the following problem on a sheet of paper:

   $$\begin{array}{r} 49 \\ +\ 50 \\ \hline \end{array}$$

   Say, "Solve this problem and explain how you got your answer."

   Accept any reasonable explanation. Example explanation: I made 49 into 50 − 1, and I added 50 + 50 − 1, which equals 100 − 1, which is 99.
   (1 point)
   Did the student give 99 as the answer to the problem?

   A. Yes   B. No
   (1 point)
   Did the student give a reasonable explanation for how he or she solved the problem?

   A. Yes   B. No

Addition and Subtraction Are Related

Lesson Overview

Skills Update	5 minutes	ONLINE
LEARN Opposite Operations	15 minutes	ONLINE
TRY IT Addition and Subtraction	5 minutes	ONLINE
LEARN Make Addition Simple	15 minutes	ONLINE
TRY IT Use Simple Addition	5 minutes	ONLINE
TRY IT Make Addition and Subtraction Simple	10 minutes	OFFLINE
CHECKPOINT	5 minutes	OFFLINE

▶ Lesson Objectives

Demonstrate an understanding of connections between similar addition or subtraction computation problems, involving sums and minuends up through 500.

▶ Prerequisite Skills

Use models or drawings to show how addition and subtraction are inversely related.

▶ Common Errors and Misconceptions

Students might have difficulty understanding that addition and subtraction are opposite, or inverse, operations. It might not be obvious to them that addition "undoes" subtraction.

▶ Content Background

Inverse operations are operations that undo each other. Addition and subtraction are inverse operations, as are multiplication and division. In addition and subtraction, for example, if you add 4 to 3, the sum is 7 ($3 + 4 = 7$). If you subtract 4 from 7, the difference is 3. They are inverse operations because you begin with 3 and end with 3. For simplicity, you may call inverse operations *opposite operations* when you talk to students.

In this lesson, students will use fact family triangles to learn about the inverse relationship of addition and subtraction. Fact families are related number sentences. Every addition sentence has a related addition number sentence. For example, $5 + 3 = 8$ and $3 + 5 = 8$ are related. Every addition sentence also has two related subtraction number sentences. For example, $5 + 3 = 8$ and $8 - 3 = 5$ are related. $5 + 3 = 8$ and $8 - 5 = 3$ are also related. The related number sentences make up the fact family for 3, 5, and 8. A fact family triangle for 3, 5, and 8 enables a student to see all the related facts at one time.

LEARN Opposite Operations

ONLINE 15min

Objectives

Students will use inverse operations to learn the relationship between addition and subtraction problems.

- Demonstrate an understanding of connections between similar addition or subtraction computation problems, involving sums and minuends up through 500.

TRY IT Addition and Subtraction

ONLINE 5min

Objectives

Students will answer questions online to demonstrate what they know about using addition and subtraction strategies.

- Demonstrate an understanding of connections between similar addition or subtraction computation problems, involving sums and minuends up through 500.

LEARN Make Addition Simple

ONLINE 15min

Objectives

Students will see how to solve difficult addition problems by identifying similar, easier addition problems.

- Demonstrate an understanding of connections between similar addition or subtraction computation problems, involving sums and minuends up through 500.

Tips

Point out that students can change the problems in different ways, not just the solutions shown online.

TRY IT Use Simple Addition

ONLINE 5min

Objectives

Students will answer questions online to demonstrate what they know about using simpler problems to help solve more difficult addition problems.

- Demonstrate an understanding of connections between similar addition or subtraction computation problems, involving sums and minuends up through 500.

TRY IT Make Addition and Subtraction Simple

OFFLINE 10 min

Objectives

- Demonstrate an understanding of connections between similar addition or subtraction computation problems, involving sums and minuends up through 500.

Students will choose and apply strategies to solve addition and subtraction problems. Give students the Make Addition and Subtraction Simple activity page from their Activity Book and read the directions with them. Use the answer key to check students' answers, and then enter the results online.

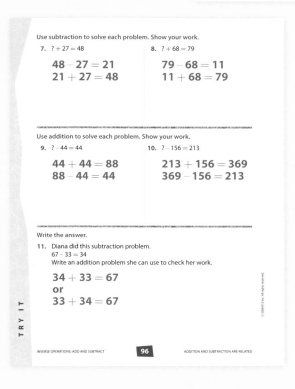

Addition and Subtraction Are Related
Make Addition and Subtraction Simple

Name:

Use subtraction to solve each problem. Show your work.

1. ? + 45 = 75

75 − 45 = 30
30 + 45 = 75

2. ? + 31 = 55

55 − 31 = 24
24 + 31 = 55

Use addition to solve each problem. Show your work.

3. ? − 24 = 33

33 + 24 = 57
57 − 24 = 33

4. ? − 72 = 275

275 + 72 = 347
347 − 72 = 275

Solve each problem. Show your work.

5. If you know that 25 + 25 = 50, how could you solve 24 + 25?

24 + 25 is like 25 + 25 − 1 = 49
24 + 25 = 49

6. If you know that 20 + 20 = 40, how could you solve 22 + 21?

22 + 21 = 20 + 20 + 2 + 1 = 43
22 + 21 = 43

Use subtraction to solve each problem. Show your work.

7. ? + 27 = 48

48 − 27 = 21
21 + 27 = 48

8. ? + 68 = 79

79 − 68 = 11
11 + 68 = 79

Use addition to solve each problem. Show your work.

9. ? − 44 = 44

44 + 44 = 88
88 − 44 = 44

10. ? − 156 = 213

213 + 156 = 369
369 − 156 = 213

Write the answer.

11. Diana did this subtraction problem.
67 − 33 = 34
Write an addition problem she can use to check her work.

34 + 33 = 67
or
33 + 34 = 67

TRY IT

INVERSE OPERATIONS: ADD AND SUBTRACT **95** ADDITION AND SUBTRACTION ARE RELATED

INVERSE OPERATIONS: ADD AND SUBTRACT **96** ADDITION AND SUBTRACTION ARE RELATED

CHECKPOINT

Print the assessment and have students complete it on their own. Read the directions, questions, and answer choices to students if necessary. Use the answer key to score the assessment, and then enter the results online.

Objectives

- Demonstrate an understanding of connections between similar addition or subtraction computation problems, involving sums and minuends up through 500.

Tips

Make sure students are able to choose an appropriate strategy to solve the problems. Allow students to use base-10 blocks if necessary.

☼ Checkpoint   Math | Inverse Operations: Add and Subtract | Addition and Subtraction Are Related

Name _____ Date _____

Checkpoint Answer Key

Complete each problem.
(1 point)
1. _____ − 35 = 72 is similar to which number sentence?

  A. 35 + 35 = _____
  B. 72 + 45 = _____
  C. 72 + 35 = _____
  D. 72 + 53 = _____

(1 point)
2. Quemars needs to solve this addition problem: _____ + 68 = 129. Write a subtraction problem he could use to help him solve the addition problem.

  129 − 68 = 61

(1 point)
3. Daniel needs to solve this addition problem: _____ + 299 = 400. Write a subtraction problem he could use to help him solve the addition problem.

  400 − 299 = 101

(1 point)
4. Tina needs to solve this addition problem: _____ + 199 = 301. Write a subtraction problem she could use to help her solve the addition problem.

  301 − 199 = 102

© 2008 K12 Inc. All rights reserved.   1 of 1
Copying or distributing without K12's written consent is prohibited.

Unit Review

Lesson Overview

UNIT REVIEW Look Back	20 minutes	ONLINE
UNIT REVIEW Checkpoint Practice	20 minutes	OFFLINE
⇥ **UNIT REVIEW** Prepare for the Checkpoint		

▶ Unit Objectives

This lesson reviews the following objectives:

- Use models or drawings to show how addition and subtraction are inversely related.
- Use the inverse relationship between addition and subtraction to solve problems.
- Use mental math to find the sum or difference of two 2-digit numbers.
- Identify and explain the approach and strategies for solving addition or subtraction computation problems with sums or minuends up through 500.
- Demonstrate an understanding of connections between similar addition or subtraction computation problems, involving sums and minuends up through 500.

Materials to Gather

SUPPLIED

Checkpoint Practice activity page

base-10 blocks

▶ Advance Preparation

In this lesson, students will have an opportunity to review previous activities in the Inverse Operations: Add and Subtract unit. Look at the suggested activities in Unit Review: Prepare for the Checkpoint online and gather any needed materials.

Keywords

count on	**mental math**
fact triangle	**number sentence**
inverse operations	**strategy**

UNIT REVIEW Look Back

In this unit, students have used used models and place-value charts to learn how addition and subtraction are inversely related. They have used mental math to add and subtract 2-digit numbers. Students have also learned how to identify and explain different strategies for solving addition and subtraction computation problems. Students will review these concepts to prepare for Unit Checkpoint.

Objectives

- Review unit objectives.

UNIT REVIEW Checkpoint Practice

Students will complete a Checkpoint Practice activity page to prepare for the Unit Checkpoint. If necessary, read the directions, questions, and answer choices to students. Have students answer the problems on their own. Carefully review the answers with students. For Problem 9, give students the ones cubes.

Objectives

- Review unit objectives.

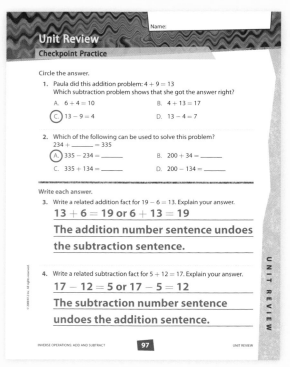

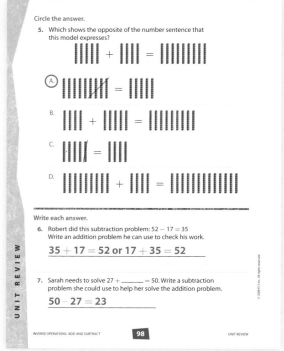

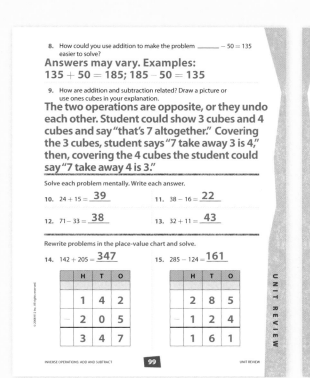

8. How could you use addition to make the problem _____ − 50 = 135 easier to solve?

Answers may vary. Examples:
135 + 50 = 185; 185 − 50 = 135

9. How are addition and subtraction related? Draw a picture or use ones cubes in your explanation.

The two operations are opposite, or they undo each other. Student could show 3 cubes and 4 cubes and say "that's 7 altogether." Covering the 3 cubes, student says "7 take away 3 is 4," then, covering the 4 cubes the student could say "7 take away 4 is 3."

Solve each problem mentally. Write each answer.

10. 24 + 15 = **39**   **11.** 38 − 16 = **22**

12. 71 − 33 = **38**   **13.** 32 + 11 = **43**

Rewrite problems in the place-value chart and solve.

14. 142 + 205 = **347**

H	T	O
1	4	2
− 2	0	5
3	4	7

15. 285 − 124 = **161**

H	T	O
2	8	5
− 1	2	4
1	6	1

Choose a way to solve each problem. Show your work.

16. 360 + 125 = **485**   **17.** 358 − 40 = **318**

Examples:
(360+100)+25 = ___   300 + 58 − 40 = ___
460 + 25 = 485   300 + (58 − 40)
360 + 125 = 485   300 + 18 = 318

Choose a way to solve each problem. Explain how you got your answer.

Answers may vary.

18. 200 + 165 = **365**   **19.** 83
                                          − 46
                                          ____
                                           37

Write each answer.   **Answers may vary. Examples:**

20. If you know that 25 + 75 = 100, show how you could use that to solve 27 + 74.

27 + 74 is like 25 + 75 + 2 − 1 = 101;
27 + 74 = 101

21. Frank solved the addition problem 26 + 28 in the following way:

Step 1: 26 + 30 = 56
Step 2: 56 − 2 = 54

Explain how he solved the problem.   **Frank added 2 to 28 to make it 30, which is an easier number to add. He added 26 to 30 to get 56, and then he subtracted the 2 that he had used to make the 30.**

→ UNIT REVIEW Prepare for the Checkpoint

What you do next depends on how students performed in the previous activity, Unit Review: Checkpoint Practice. If students had difficulty with any of the problems, complete the appropriate review activity listed in the table online.

Unit Checkpoint

UNIT CHECKPOINT Offline .... 60 minutes : **OFFLINE**

▶ Unit Objectives

This lesson assesses the following objectives:

- Use models or drawings to show how addition and subtraction are inversely related.
- Use the inverse relationship between addition and subtraction to solve problems.
- Use mental math to find the sum or difference of two 2-digit numbers.
- Identify and explain the approach and strategies for solving addition or subtraction computation problems with sums or minuends up through 500.
- Demonstrate an understanding of connections between similar addition or subtraction computation problems, involving sums and minuends up through 500.

Materials to Gather

SUPPLIED

base-10 blocks

Fact Family Triangles (printout) (optional)

Unit Checkpoint (printout)

UNIT CHECKPOINT Offline

OFFLINE
60min

Students will complete the Unit Checkpoint offline. In Part 1, students will take a performance-based assessment. In Part 2, students will complete the problems on their own. Print the Checkpoint. Read the directions, problems, and answer choices to students if necessary. Use the answer key to score the Checkpoint, and then enter the results online.

Objectives

- Assess unit objectives.

Tips

If necessary, students may use or fact family triangles to help solve the problems.

◯ Checkpoint   Math | Inverse Operations: Add and Subtract | Unit Checkpoint

Name _____   Date _____

Unit Checkpoint Answer Key

Part 1
Follow the instructions for each item. Choose the response that best describes how the student performs on the task. When you have finished, enter the results online.

1. Write the following number sentences on a piece of paper:

   $6 + 9 = 15$ $15 - 9 = 6$

   Say: Use ones cubes to show how these two number sentences are related.

   ANSWER: Students should use ones cubes to show that these facts are related because they are opposite, or because they undo each other.
   (1 point)
   Did the student use ones cubes to show how the two number sentences are related?

   A. Yes   B. No

2. **Ask:** How are addition and subtraction related? Draw a picture or use ones cubes in your explanation.

   ANSWER: Students should draw a picture or use ones cubes to explain that the two operations are opposite, or they undo each other.
   (1 point)
   Did the student draw a picture or use ones cubes to explain how addition and subtraction are related?

   A. Yes   B. No

3. **Say:** Your friend tells you that $7 + 7 = 14$. Explain how you can use this information to figure out what $14 - 7$ is.

   ANSWER: Students should explain that subtraction is the opposite of addition. If you know that $7 + 7 = 14$, you can solve $14 - 7$ to find 7.
   (1 point)
   Did the student explain how to use $7 + 7 = 14$ to figure out $14 - 7$?

   A. Yes   B. No

© 2008 K12 Inc. All rights reserved.   1 of 5
Copying or distributing without K12's written consent is prohibited.

Name _____   Date _____

4. Write the following number sentence on a piece of paper: 144 − 29 = ?
    Say: Explain one way to solve this problem.
    EXAMPLE: 29 is 30 − 1. 144 − 30 = 114. 114 + 1 = 115.
    (1 point)
    Did the student explain one way to solve 144 − 29?

    A. Yes   B. No

5. Write the following number sentence on a piece of paper: 99 + 39 = ?
    Say: Explain one way to solve this problem.
    EXAMPLE: 99 is 100 − 1, and 39 is 40 − 1. 100 + 40 = 140. 140 − 2 = 138.
    (1 point)
    Did the student explain one way to solve 99 + 39?

    A. Yes   B. No

6. **Say:** Show how you could use the strategies you've learned to change
    47 − 32 into a problem that is easier to solve.
    EXAMPLE: Subtract 2 from 47 to make 45. Then subtract 2 from 32 to
    make 30. Subtract 30 from 45 to get 15.
    (1 point)
    Did the student show how to change 47 − 32 into a problem that is easier
    to solve?

    A. Yes   B. No

7. **Say:** Show how you could use the strategies you've learned to change
    66 + 34 into a problem that is easier to solve.
    EXAMPLE: Subtract 1 from 66 to get 65 and add 1 to 34 to make 35. Then
    add 65 + 35 = 100.
    (1 point)
    Did the student show how to change 66 + 34 into a problem that is easier
    to solve?

    A. Yes   B. No

Name _____   Date _____

8. Write the following number sentence on a piece of paper: 72 − 49 = ?
    SAY: Explain one way to solve this problem.
    EXAMPLE: 49 is 50 − 1. 72 − 50 = 22. Add 1 back on to get 23.
    (1 point)
    Did the student explain one way to solve 72 − 49?

    A. Yes   B. No

9. Write the following number sentences on a piece of paper:

    144 = 56 + 88

    144 − 56 = ?
    Draw a box around 144 − 56 = ?

    Say: Explain how you would use the first number sentence to solve the
    number sentence in the box."

    ANSWER: Students should explain that addition and subtraction are
    opposites and they undo one another. If you know that 56 + 88 = 144, you
    can solve 144 − 56 to find 88.
    (1 point)
    Did the student explain how to use the first number sentence to solve the
    number sentence in the box?

    A. Yes   B. No

Give students Part 2 of the assessment.

Name _____   Date _____

Part 2
Circle the answer.

10. Which drawing shows the opposite of the number sentence in the
     drawing below?

     ●●● + ●●●● = ●●●●●●●

     A. ●●● + ●●●●●●● = ●●●●●●●●●●

     B. ●─●─●─● = ●

     C. ●●●● + ●●● = ●●●●●●●

     D. (circled) ●●●●─●─● = ●●●

(1 point)
11. Add mentally.

     66 + 28 = _____

     A. 84   B. 95
     C. (circled) 94   D. 92

(1 point)
12. Which of the following number sentences could you use to check your work
     on this subtraction problem?

     101 − 50 = 51

     A. 101 − 1 = 100   B. (circled) 50 + 51 = 101
     C. 50 − 51 = 1   D. 51 + 101 = 152

(1 point)
13. Add mentally.

     43 + 16 = _____

     A. 60   B. 69
     C. (circled) 59   D. 53

Name _____   Date _____

(1 point)
14. Which problem is similar to the one below?

     199 + 51 = _____

     A. 199 + 50 + 11 = _____   B. (circled) 199 + 1 + 50 = _____
     C. 200 + 50 + 11 = _____   D. 199 + 40 + 31 = _____

Write the answer.
(1 point)
15. Write a related addition number sentence for 20 − 6 = 14.

     14 + 6 = 20, or 6 + 14 = 20

Add mentally.
(1 point)   *(1 point)*
16. 67 + 23 = **90**   17. 50 + 20 = **70**

(1 point)
18. Kathie did the following addition problem. Write a subtraction problem that
     she could use to check her work.

     46 + 11 = 57

     57 − 11 = 46 or 57 − 46 = 11

Measurement

▶ Unit Objectives

- Identify inches on a ruler and measure the length of an object to the nearest inch.
- Measure the length of objects by repeating a standard unit.
- Identify centimeters on a ruler and measure the length of an object to the nearest centimeter.
- Estimate the length of an object to the nearest inch or centimeter.
- Recognize when a measurement estimate is reasonable.

- Measure the same object with different units, and predict whether the number of units will be greater or less when a larger or smaller unit is used.
- Understand that quantities may be compared, added, or subtracted if they have been measured by the same unit.
- Compare, add, or subtract quantities that have been measured by the same unit.
- Measure and compare volumes by using a standard unit (for example, use a measuring cup to measure contents of a water bottle).

▶ Big Ideas

- A quantity can be measured by identifying a unit of measure and repeating that unit over the quantity.
- Estimation is a useful tool in problem solving.
- The size of the unit used in measurement does not affect the quantity measured, but the larger the unit, the smaller the total number of units will be.
- Quantities can be compared, added, or subtracted if they have been measured by the same unit.

▶ Unit Introduction

Students will build on their understanding of the concepts of length and volume, as well as measurement with nonstandard units. Students will use three standard units—inch, centimeter, and cup—to measure, compare, and estimate length and capacity. This work will lay the foundation for more complex operations and conversions of customary and metric units in later grades.

Inches

▶ ## Lesson Objectives

- Identify inches on a ruler and measure the length of an object to the nearest inch.
- Measure the length of objects by repeating a standard unit.

▶ ## Prerequisite Skills

Describe the length of objects by using nonstandard units (for example, length of a page = 10 paper clips; width of a desk = 3 pencils).

▶ ## Common Errors and Misconceptions

Students might measure an object incorrectly if the object is not aligned with the end of the ruler. That is because there is a difference between using a measuring device and understanding how it works. Using nonstandard objects that students are familiar with will help them understand how an instrument actually measures. For example, if students line up physical units along a sheet of paper and mark them off, they can see that the spaces on rulers—and not the marks or numbers—are the important thing.

▶ ## Advance Preparation

- Cut pipe cleaners to different lengths. Be sure none of the lengths fall exactly at a half-inch mark. Save the cut pipe cleaners for use in other measuring activities. Instead of pipe cleaners, you can also use drinking straws or strips of cardboard.
- Gather 6–8 objects that are 12 inches long or shorter (examples: pencil, marker, crayon, stapler, book, spoon, fork, and shoe).

Materials to Gather

SUPPLIED

blocks – E
blocks – O (10 any color)
base-10 blocks
Measure It activity page
Checkpoint (printout)

ALSO NEEDED

ruler – inches
pipe cleaners – 7
household objects – 6 to 8 for students to measure
sheet of paper

▶ Content Background

Measuring with nonstandard units, such as paper clips, develops students' sense of length. Nonstandard units can be of any size and allow students to count to find the length of objects. When students use paper clips, cubes, or fingers to measure similar objects, they come to realize that the number of units differs depending on the size of the nonstandard unit.

In this lesson, students will use an inch ruler to measure length. Students will learn that when they use a standard unit, such as an inch, the measurements are the same. Inches, feet, and yards are standard units used to measure length.

When we write the abbreviation for inch (in.), we use a period. This ensures that it will not be confused with the word *in*. All other measurements, such as centimeter (cm), have no period.

Keywords

English system of measurement – a system of measurement using such units as inches, feet, and miles for length; quarts and gallons for capacity; and ounces and pounds for weight

inch (in.) – the basic English unit for measuring length

measure (verb) – to use standard units to find a distance, area, volume, capacity, temperature, or interval of time

measurement – the process of using units to find a quantity or size

nonstandard unit – any unit chosen to be used repeatedly to measure, such as a paper clip or triangular tile

ruler – a tool for measuring length, typically in inches or centimeters

standard unit – a universally defined unit of measure, such as foot or meter

unit of measure – an amount or quantity used to measure, such as 1 ounce, where ounce is the unit of measure

GET READY Nonstandard Units

ONLINE
5 min

Students will practice using nonstandard units to measure the length of various objects. They will choose objects to measure and nonstandard units with which to measure the objects.

Objectives

- Describe the length of objects by using nonstandard units (for example, length of a page = 10 paper clips; width of a desk = 3 pencils).

Tips

Remind students to align the nonstandard units end to end as they measure, without overlapping units or leaving spaces between them.

LEARN The Inch Ruler

Students will use a ruler to measure the length of pipe cleaner pieces to the nearest inch. They will learn that we use standard measuring units to make sure that we get the same, correct measurement every time.

Gather the ruler and cut pipe cleaners.

1. Give students a 12-inch ruler. Explain that you can use a ruler to measure length. Point to the numbers 1 and 2.

   Say: The distance between one number and the next is 1 inch. An inch is a standard unit of measure.

2. **Ask:** How many inches are shown on your ruler?

3. **Say:** Your ruler is 12 inches long. Let's practice measuring with a ruler.

4. Have students measure several pipe cleaners of varying lengths to the nearest inch.

Objectives

- Identify inches on a ruler and measure the length of an object to the nearest inch.

Tips

Check that students are aligning the 0 mark on the ruler with one end of the pipe cleaner and reading the number at the mark that aligns with the other end of the pipe cleaner.

LEARN How Long Is It?

Students will use a square (1 in.) as a standard unit. They will move it along the length of an object to measure the object's length. Students will also measure items with a 12-inch ruler.

Gather the squares, ruler, household objects, and sheet of paper.

1. Give students a square and the ruler. Explain that an inch is a standard unit.

   Ask: How many inches long is the square?

2. Place 3 squares side by side.

   Ask: How many squares are there? How many inches long are the 3 squares?

3. Give students one square and an object to measure. Explain that they will need to move the square along the length of the object. Show students how to mark the end of the square with a finger, and then slide the square so that the beginning side aligns with their finger.

4. Have students measure the length of several household objects, measuring shorter objects first and moving on to longer objects. Have students tell you how many inches long each object is.

   Say: Each time you move the square, make sure it lines up to where you left off.

5. Place the sheet of paper horizontally on a table. Have students line up squares along the length of the paper to measure its length.

   Ask: How many squares equal the length of the paper? How many inches long is the paper?

6. Have students check the length of the paper with a ruler.

7. Lay 12 squares on the ruler so that students can see that 12 squares are the same as a 12-inch ruler.

   Say: You don't need the square to measure an inch. You can use the ruler instead, because it has 12 inches marked on it.

8. Have students use the ruler to measure a few objects again.

   Ask: Which way did you find it easier to measure—by using a 12-inch ruler or by repeating an inch unit?

Objectives

- Measure the length of objects by repeating a standard unit.

Tips

Students can use thin strips of tape to mark where the tile ends before moving it along the length of the object. When students reach the end of an object, the total number of tiles or inches will be shown by the number of pieces of tape. This is especially helpful when measuring long lengths.

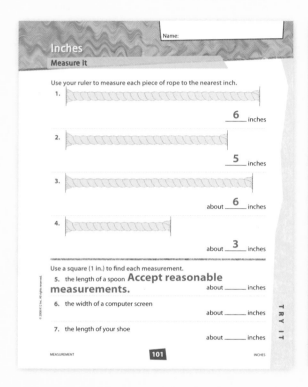

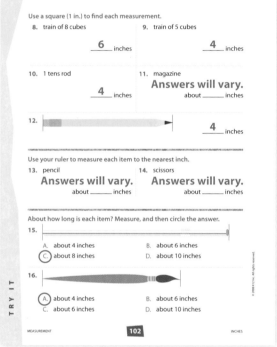

TRY IT Measure It

OFFLINE 10 min

Students will practice measuring length using tiles and a 12-inch ruler. Give students the tiles, cubes, ruler, and the Measure It activity page from their Activity Book. Read the directions with them.

Remind students when measuring to the nearest inch they should always align one end of the item being measured with the zero mark on the ruler. When repeating the 1-inch unit to measure, have students use a finger to mark where the tile ends before moving it along the length.

Objectives

- Identify inches on a ruler and measure the length of an object to the nearest inch.

- Measure the length of objects by repeating a standard unit.

Name: _____

Inches
Measure It

Use your ruler to measure each piece of rope to the nearest inch.

1. _____ 6 inches

2. _____ 5 inches

3. about _6_ inches

4. about _3_ inches

Use a square (1 in.) to find each measurement.

5. the length of a spoon **Accept reasonable measurements.** about _____ inches

6. the width of a computer screen about _____ inches

7. the length of your shoe about _____ inches

MEASUREMENT **101** INCHES

TRY IT

Use a square (1 in.) to find each measurement.

8. train of 8 cubes _6_ inches

9. train of 5 cubes _4_ inches

10. 1 tens rod _4_ inches

11. magazine **Answers will vary.** about _____ inches

12. _4_ inches

Use your ruler to measure each item to the nearest inch.

13. pencil **Answers will vary.** about _____ inches

14. scissors **Answers will vary.** about _____ inches

About how long is each item? Measure, and then circle the answer.

15.
A. about 4 inches B. about 6 inches
(C.) about 8 inches D. about 10 inches

16.
(A.) about 4 inches B. about 6 inches
C. about 6 inches D. about 10 inches

MEASUREMENT **102** INCHES

TRY IT

CHECKPOINT

Objectives

- Identify inches on a ruler and measure the length of an object to the nearest inch.
- Measure the length of objects by repeating a standard unit.

Print the assessment and have students complete it on their own. Read the directions, questions, and answer choices to students if necessary. Use the answer key to score the assessment, and then enter the results online.

Page 1

Name   Date

Checkpoint Answer Key

Use a square (1 in.) to measure the length of the items below to the nearest inch.
(1 point)

1. train of 10 cubes

about __8__ inches

(1 point)
2. train of 6 cubes

about __5__ inches

(1 point)
3.

about __6__ inches

(1 point)
4.

about __4__ inches

Page 2

Name   Date

Use your ruler to measure the length of each item to the nearest inch.
(1 point)

5.

about __3__ inches

(1 point)
6.

about __6__ inches

(1 point)
7.

about __4__ inches

(1 point)
8.

about __1__ inches

Centimeters

Skills Update	5 minutes	ONLINE
GET READY Measure with Paper Clips	5 minutes	OFFLINE
LEARN The Centimeter Ruler	15 minutes	OFFLINE
LEARN How Many Centimeters?	15 minutes	OFFLINE
TRY IT Measure Length	10 minutes	OFFLINE
CHECKPOINT	10 minutes	OFFLINE

▶ Lesson Objectives

- Identify centimeters on a ruler and measure the length of an object to the nearest centimeter.
- Measure the length of objects by repeating a standard unit.

▶ Prerequisite Skills

Describe the length of objects by using nonstandard units (for example, length of a page = 10 paper clips; width of a desk = 3 pencils).

▶ Common Errors and Misconceptions

Students might measure an object incorrectly if the object is not aligned with the end of the ruler. That is because there is a difference between using a measuring device and understanding how it works. Using nonstandard objects that students are familiar with will help them understand how an instrument actually measures. For example, if students line up physical units along a sheet of paper and mark them off, they can see that the spaces on rulers—and not the marks or numbers—are the important thing.

▶ Advance Preparation

- Cut pipe cleaners to different lengths. Be sure none of the lengths fall exactly at a half-centimeter mark. Save the cut pipe cleaners for use in other measuring activities.
- Gather 6–8 objects that are 30 centimeters long or less (examples: pencils, pens, markers, crayons, baskets, boxes, stapler, book, spoon, and fork).

▶ Content Background

Measuring with nonstandard units, such as paper clips, develops students' sense of length. Nonstandard units can be of any size and allow students to count to find the length of objects. When students use paper clips, cubes, or fingers to measure similar objects, they come to realize that the number of units differs depending on the size of the nonstandard unit.

Materials to Gather

SUPPLIED

blocks – E

base-10 blocks

Measure Length activity page

Checkpoint (printout)

ALSO NEEDED

household objects – 6 to 8 for students to measure

ruler – centimeters

sheet of paper

paper clips, small – 15

pipe cleaners – 7

fork

crayon

scissors

pencil

In this lesson, students will use ruler to measure length in centimeters. Students will learn that when they use a standard unit, such as an inch, the measurements are the same. Inches, feet, and yards are standard units used to measure length.

When we write the abbreviation for inch (in.), we use a period. This ensures that it will not be confused with the word *in*. All other measurements, such as centimeter (cm), have no period.

centimeter (cm) – a metric unit used to measure length;
1 centimeter = 1/100 of a meter

metric system – a measurement system with units based on powers of 10

OFFLINE
5min

GET READY Measure with Paper Clips

Objectives

Students will use nonstandard units to measure the length of objects.
  Gather the paper clips and household objects.

1. Explain that you can use nonstandard units, such as paper clips, to measure the length of an object. Show students how to measure one object with paper clips.

   Say: When measuring with nonstandard units, make sure to align the units end to end to get the correct measurement. Watch how I measure an object with paper clips.

2. Have students count the number of paper clips you used to measure the object and tell you how many paper clips long the object is.

3. Have students choose an object to measure with paper clips.

   Ask: How many paper clips long is the object?

4. Repeat the steps with the remaining objects.

- Describe the length of objects by using nonstandard units (for example, length of a page = 10 paper clips; width of a desk = 3 pencils).

LEARN The Centimeter Ruler

Students will examine a ruler with centimeter marks. They will use the ruler to measure length of objects to the nearest centimeter. Gather your centimter ruler and pipe cleaners and start the activity. Help students identify a centimeter on the centimeter ruler. Help them use the ruler to measure length of objects. Next allow students to measure pipe cleaners. Assist students as needed and continue until activity time is over.

1. Give students a ruler with centimeters. Point to the numbers 1 and 2.

   Say: The distance between one number and the next is 1 centimeter. A centimeter is a standard unit of measure.

2. **Say:** Show me with your fingers how big a centimeter is.

   Students should use thumb and first finger to indicate a space of 1 centimeter. (The illustration shows a real-life example of about how long a centimeter is.)

3. **Ask:** How many centimeters are shown on your ruler? (There are usually 30 centimeters.)

4. Have students measure several pipe cleaners of varying lengths to the nearest centimeter.

Objectives

- Identify centimeters on a ruler and measure the length of an object to the nearest centimeter.

Tips

Check that students are aligning the 0 mark on the ruler with one end of the pipe cleaner and reading the number at the mark that aligns with the other end of the pipe cleaner.

centimeters

LEARN How Many Centimeters?

Students will use a standard unit to measure objects in centimeters. Students will also measure items in centimeters with a ruler.

Gather the base-10 blocks, ruler, household objects, and sheet of paper.

1. Give students a ones cube (1 cm) and the ruler. Explain that a centimeter is a standard unit.

   Ask: How many centimeters long is the cube?

2. Place 7 ones cubes side by side in a row.

   Ask: How many cubes are there? How many centimeters long are the 7 cubes?

3. Give students a small object to measure, such as an eraser or a crayon. Explain that they will need to move the ones cube along the length of the object. Show students how to mark the end of the cube with a finger, and then slide the cube so that the beginning side aligns with their finger.

4. Give students a tens rod (10 cm). Have them line up 10 ones cubes next to the tens rod.

   Ask: What do you notice? (1 tens rod is the same length as 10 ones cubes.)

5. Have students use the tens rod to measure the length of several household objects, measuring shorter objects first. Have students tell you how many centimeters long each object is. Encourage them to select other objects in the room to measure.

6. Place the sheet of paper horizontally on a table. Have students line up tens rods along the length of the paper to measure its length.

   Ask: How many tens rods equal the length of the paper? (almost 3)

Objectives

- Measure the length of objects by repeating a standard unit.

Tips

Be sure students line up the proper end of the ruler with one end of the objects to get an accurate measure.

7. Have students count the ones cubes on the tens rods.

   Ask: About how many centimeters long is the paper?
   ANSWER: 28 centimeters

8. Lay the tens rods on the ruler from end to end.

   Say: You don't need a tens rod to measure in centimeters. You can use the ruler instead because it has centimeters marked on it.

9. Have students measure a few objects again using the ruler.

   Ask: Which way did you find it easier to measure—by using a centimeter ruler or the tens rods?

OFFLINE
10 min

TRY IT Measure Length

Students will practice measuring objects using a tens rod (10 cm) rod and a ruler. Give students the pencil, a paper clip, fork, base-10 blocks, and the Measure Length activity page. Read the directions with them.

Objectives

- Identify centimeters on a ruler and measure the length of an object to the nearest centimeter.

- Measure the length of objects by repeating a standard unit.

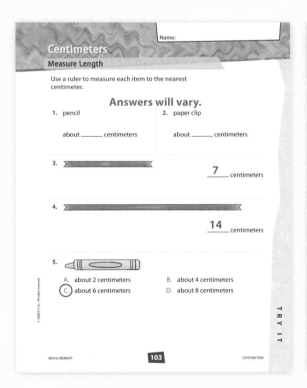

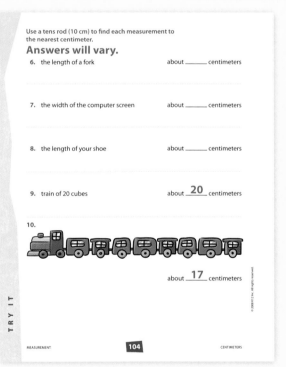

Objectives

- Identify centimeters on a ruler and measure the length of an object to the nearest centimeter.
- Measure the length of objects by repeating a standard unit.

Print the assessment and have students complete it on their own. Read the directions, questions, and answer choices to students if necessary. Use the answer key to score the assessment, and then enter the results online.

Give students the ruler, base-10 blocks, and tiles.

○ Checkpoint   Math | Measurement | Centimeters

Name   Date

Checkpoint Answer Key

Use your ruler to measure the length of one of your crayons to the nearest centimeter.
(1 point)

1. crayon   **Answers will vary.**   about _____ centimeters

(1 point)
Use your ruler to measure the length of the line below to the nearest centimeter.

2. —————————   about __7__ centimeters

(1 point)
Use a tens rod to measure the length of the rectangle.

3. [rectangle]   about __10__ centimeters

Line up 2 tens rods (10 cm each) so they make one long line. Use tiles (1 in.) to measure the length of the tens rods together to the nearest inch.

(1 point)
4. __8__ inches

Use ten rods (10 cm each) to measure the long side of this piece of paper to the nearest centimeter.

(1 point)
5. about __28__ centimeters

© 2008 K12 Inc. All rights reserved.   1 of 1
Copying or distributing without K12's written consent is prohibited.

Estimate Length

Lesson Overview

Skills Update	5 minutes	ONLINE
GET READY Measure to the Nearest Inch	5 minutes	OFFLINE
LEARN Estimate to the Nearest Inch	15 minutes	OFFLINE
LEARN Estimate in Centimeters	15 minutes	OFFLINE
TRY IT Make Length Estimates	10 minutes	OFFLINE
CHECKPOINT	10 minutes	OFFLINE

▶ Lesson Objectives

- Estimate the length of an object to the nearest inch or centimeter.
- Recognize when a measurement estimate is reasonable.

▶ Prerequisite Skills

- Identify inches on a ruler and measure the length of an object to the nearest inch.
- Measure the length of objects by repeating a standard unit.

▶ Content Background

In this lesson, students will learn how to estimate the length of an object to the nearest inch and centimeter. Students will also learn to choose the most reasonable estimate.

Materials to Gather

SUPPLIED
blocks – E (1)
Estimate in Centimeters activity page
Make Length Estimates activity page
Checkpoint (printout)

ALSO NEEDED
ruler – inches and centimeters
household objects – CD, pen, pencil, toothpick, safety pin, spoon, and fork

Keywords

estimate (verb) – to approximate or perform a rough calculation

reasonable estimate or answer – a solution that makes sense on the basis of available data

GET READY Measure to the Nearest Inch

OFFLINE
5 min

Students will use a 12-inch ruler to measure objects in inches.
   Gather the ruler and household objects. Have students measure each object to the nearest inch.

Objectives

- Identify inches on a ruler and measure the length of an object to the nearest inch.

LEARN Estimate to the Nearest Inch

- Estimate the length of an object to the nearest inch or centimeter.
- Recognize when a measurement estimate is reasonable.

Students will estimate the length of objects to the nearest inch. Then they will practice choosing the most reasonable estimate from three possible choices. Students will use a ruler to check their estimates.

Gather the ruler and household objects.

Tips

If the estimates are more than an inch from the actual measurements, guide students in visually marking and counting the inches along the objects.

1. Have students put their forefinger and middle finger together to estimate an inch. Show them how to align their fingers along the length of an object and repeatedly move them along the length to estimate.

2. Give students an object.

   Ask: About how many inches long is the object?

   Say: An estimate is not an exact measurement, but it should be as close as possible to the actual measurement.

3. Have students use the ruler to measure the length of the object in inches. Remind students to align the zero end of the ruler with the left edge of the object.

   Say: On the ruler, the inch number that is closest to the end of the object tells about how long it is.

4. Have students continue to estimate and measure the rest of the objects.

5. **Say:** Now you will choose a reasonable estimate for the length in inches of different objects. *Reasonable* means the answer is close to the actual measurement.

6. Give students an object that is about 12 inches long.

   Ask: What is a reasonable estimate for the object's length? Is it about 1 inch, about 4 inches, or about 12 inches?

   Hold up a ruler. Show students how to use the process of elimination to find the correct answer without actually measuring.

7. Continue with objects students have not already measured. Give three estimated lengths in inches from which they can choose. Have them first eliminate estimates that are not reasonable.

8. **Ask:** How do you know which answer is most reasonable?
   ANSWER: I can imagine the object next to the ruler and decide which answer is closest to the object's length.

LEARN Estimate in Centimeters

- Estimate the length of an object to the nearest inch or centimeter.
- Recognize when a measurement estimate is reasonable.

Students will estimate the length of objects to the nearest centimeter. Then they will practice choosing the most reasonable estimate from three possible choices. Students will use a ruler to check their estimates.

Gather the ruler and the Estimate in Centimeters activity page.

1. Point to one centimeter on the ruler. Help students find a finger width or fingernail length that is about one centimeter.

2. Point to Problem 1.

   Ask: About how many centimeters long is the zipper?

   Say: An estimate is not an exact measurement, but it should be as close as possible to the actual measurement.

3. Help students use their finger width or fingernail length to estimate the length of the zipper. Have students write their estimate on the activity page.

4. Have students use the ruler to measure the length of the zipper. Remind students to align the zero end of the ruler with the left edge of the zipper. Have students write the measurement in the appropriate space.

   Say: The number that is closest to the end of the zipper tells about how long the zipper is.

5. Have students solve Problems 2–5.

6. Have students solve Problem 6. Ask students to show you each of the three answer choices on the ruler.

   Ask: Think about how long a pen is. Can you find one answer choice that seems too small and one that seems too large? Is there one answer that seems closest to the length of a pen?
   ANSWER: 2 centimeters seems too small. 50 centimeters seems too large. 15 centimeters seems closest to the length of a pen.

7. Give students a pen and have them measure it to check their answers. If it is not exactly 15 centimeters long, discuss with students why their answer is still correct.

8. Have students solve Problems 7–10. If necessary, give students the items listed and have them find the actual measurements.

   Ask: How do you know which answer is most reasonable?
   ANSWER: I can imagine the object next to the ruler and decide which answer is closest to the object's length.

Tips

If necessary, have students mark the centimeter lengths on the objects in Problems 1–5 to help with their estimates.

Encourage students to cross out unreasonable estimates in Problems 6–10.

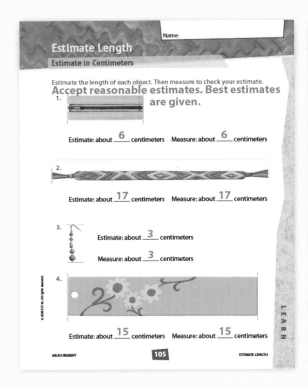

Estimate Length
Estimate in Centimeters

Estimate the length of each object. Then measure to check your estimate.

Accept reasonable estimates. Best estimates are given.

1.

Estimate: about __6__ centimeters Measure: about __6__ centimeters

2.

Estimate: about __17__ centimeters Measure: about __17__ centimeters

3.

Estimate: about __3__ centimeters

Measure: about __3__ centimeters

4.

Estimate: about __15__ centimeters Measure: about __15__ centimeters

MEASUREMENT **105** ESTIMATE LENGTH

5. Estimate the length of an object of your choice.
   Answers will vary.
   Name of object: _____

   Estimate: about _____ centimeters Measure: about _____ centimeters

Circle the most reasonable estimate.

6. About how long is a pen?
   A. 2 centimeters   (B.) 15 centimeters   C. 50 centimeters

7. About how long is a toothpick?
   (A.) 5 centimeters   B. 50 centimeters   C. 100 centimeters

8. About how long is the space bar on a computer keyboard?
   A. 1 centimeter   (B.) 10 centimeters   C. 90 centimeters

9. About how long is a safety pin?
   (A.) 2 centimeters   B. 20 centimeters   C. 40 centimeters

10. About how long is a spoon?
    A. 2 centimeters   (B.) 18 centimeters   C. 80 centimeters

MEASUREMENT **106** ESTIMATE LENGTH

TRY IT Make Length Estimates

OFFLINE
10 min

Students will practice estimating length in inches and centimeters. Give students the Make Length Estimates activity page from their Activity Book and read the directions with them. Give them the CD, fork, and pencil if needed.

Objectives

- Estimate the length of an object to the nearest inch or centimeter.
- Recognize when a measurement estimate is reasonable.

Tips

If necessary, highlight the unit of measure (inches or centimeters) for each problem.

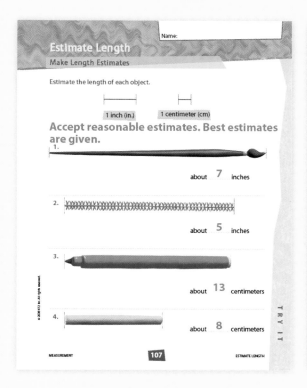

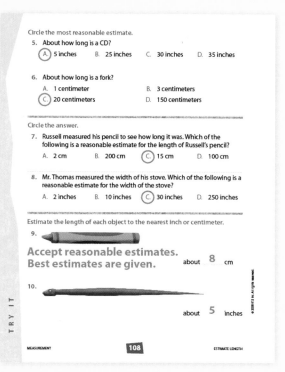

CHECKPOINT

Print the assessment and have students complete it on their own. Read the directions, questions, and answer choices to students if necessary. Use the answer key to score the assessment, and then enter the results online.

Objectives

- Estimate the length of an object to the nearest inch or centimeter.
- Recognize when a measurement estimate is reasonable.

Checkpoint   Math | Measurement | Estimate Length

Name _____   Date _____

Checkpoint Answer Key

Circle the answer.
(1 point)
1. Which is the best estimate for the length of a banana?

   A. 1 inch   (B.) 7 inches   C. 20 inches   D. 30 inches

(1 point)
2. Which is the best estimate for the height of a drinking glass?

   A. 75 cm   (B.) 15 cm   C. 3 cm   D. 1 cm

(1 point)
3. Which is the best estimate for the length of the eraser?

   A. 1 in.   (B.) 3 in.   C. 7 in.   D. 10 in.

Estimate the length of each object to the nearest inch or centimeter.
(1 point)
4.
Accept reasonable estimates.   about __12__ cm
Best estimates are given.

(1 point)
5.
about __5__ inches

(1 point)
6.
about __10__ cm

© 2008 K12 Inc. All rights reserved.   1 of 1
Copying or distributing without K12's written consent is prohibited.

Compare Measurements

Lesson Overview

Skills Update	5 minutes	ONLINE
GET READY Measure with Tiles	5 minutes	OFFLINE
LEARN Different Unit Measurements	10 minutes	OFFLINE
LEARN Compare Same Units	10 minutes	OFFLINE
LEARN Add and Subtract Measurements	10 minutes	OFFLINE
TRY IT Use Measurements	10 minutes	OFFLINE
CHECKPOINT	10 minutes	OFFLINE

▶ Lesson Objectives

- Measure the same object with different units, and predict whether the number of units will be greater or less when a larger or smaller unit is used.
- Understand that quantities may be compared, added, or subtracted if they have been measured by the same unit.

▶ Prerequisite Skills

Measure the length of objects by repeating a standard unit.

▶ Advance Preparation

Measure a pen to the nearest inch. Hide the pen so that the students can't see it.

▶ Content Background

Students will predict and compare the measurement of objects. They will also add and subtract measurements using the same units.

Materials to Gather

SUPPLIED

blocks – E (20)

base-10 blocks – ones cubes

Compare Same Units activity page

Add and Subtract Measurements activity page

Use Measurements activity page

Checkpoint (printout)

ALSO NEEDED

household objects – 8, including a pen, pencil, 10 pennies, and a paper clip

---

GET READY Measure with Tiles

OFFLINE
5 min

Objectives

- Measure the length of objects by repeating a standard unit.

Students will estimate the length of two objects. They will measure the length of each object to check the results.

Gather the household objects and the tiles.

1. Have students choose two household objects.
2. Ask them to estimate the length in tiles of each object.
3. Have them measure each object with tiles and compare the measurements with their estimates.
4. Discuss the results:
   - Were students' estimates close to the actual lengths?
   - How did students make their estimates?
   - Will they do anything different next time they estimate?

LEARN Different Unit Measurements

- Measure the same object with different units, and predict whether the number of units will be greater or less when a larger or smaller unit is used.

Students will measure the same object with different units and will determine whether the total number of units is greater or less when a larger or smaller unit is used. Students may choose the objects they want to measure.

Gather the household objects, blocks, and the ones cubes.

1. Explain that a square is 1 inch long. Show students an object.

   Ask: How many squares long do you think the object is?

2. Have students use squares to measure the object. Discuss whether their estimate was reasonable.

3. Explain that a ones cube is 1 centimeter long.

   Ask: How many cubes long do you think the object is?

4. Have students use ones cubes to measure the object. Discuss whether their estimate was reasonable.

5. **Ask:** When you measured the object, did you use more squares or cubes?
   ANSWER: more cubes

6. Repeat Steps 1–5 with a different object.

   Ask: Why do you think it took more cubes than squares to measure both objects?
   ANSWER: The cubes are smaller, so I needed more of them.

LEARN Compare Same Units

- Understand that quantities may be compared, added, or subtracted if they have been measured by the same unit.

- Compare, add, or subtract quantities that have been measured by the same unit.

Students will compare measurements and will learn that measurements must be in the same unit to be able to compare them.

Gather the household objects, blocks, and the Compare Same Units activity page.

1. Give students a pencil that is at least 1 inch longer than the pen you measured and hid. Have the students measure the pencil to the nearest inch with squares.

2. Tell students that you have a pen that is ___ inches long.

   Ask: Which is longer: my pen or your pencil? How do you know?
   ANSWER: The pencil is longer. The number of inches is greater.

3. **Say:** We knew which object was longer by measuring them both in inches and then comparing our measures.

4. Give students the pen that you hid. Have them compare the pen and pencil by placing them next to each other. Then have students measure the pen in centimeters with ones cubes.

   Ask: How long is your pen in centimeters?

5. Measure in inches an object that is just a little longer than the pen.

   Say: My object is ___ inches long.

6. **Ask:** Can you tell which object is longer without looking?
   ANSWER: I can't tell because yours is in inches and mine is in centimeters.

   Explain that you can compare measurements only if they use the same unit of measurement.

Tips

In Step 6, students might say their pen is longer because their measure is a larger number. Help students see that if you measure with a bigger unit, like the inch, it takes fewer of them to make a given length.

7. Ask: If you have a comb that is 11 inches long and a brush that is 15 inches long, which one is shorter?
ANSWER: the comb

Tell students that you were able to compare the measurements because they were both in inches. They used the same unit of measurement. Write 11 in. < 15 in.

8. Explain that when different units of measurement are used, you cannot use the numbers to compare them.

Ask: Imagine you have a napkin that is 15 centimeters long and a plate that is 11 inches long. Can you compare 11 inches and 15 centimeters to find which is longer?
ANSWER: No, because one is measured in centimeters and one is measured in inches.

LEARN Add and Subtract Measurements

OFFLINE 10 min

Students will add and subtract measurements. Students will learn that they cannot add or subtract measurements that are in different units.
Gather the Add and Subtract Measurements activity page. (This is on the back of the Compare Same Units activity page.)

1. Explain that you can add and subtract measurements that use the same unit of measurement.

Say: If there is a ribbon that is 4 inches long and a second ribbon that is 5 inches long, we can add these two measurements because they are both in inches.

2. Ask: How many inches long are the two ribbons together?
ANSWER: 9 inches

3. Ask: If you have a string that is 10 centimeters long and you cut off 3 centimeters, what can you do to find the number of centimeters left?
ANSWER: I can subtract 3 from 10.

Ask: How many centimeters will be left?
ANSWER: 7 centimeters

4. Say: Adding and subtracting measures is just like adding and subtracting other things. But to get an answer that makes sense, the measures have to be in the same unit, such as all inches or all centimeters. Be sure to notice if the units are the same before you add or subtract.

5. Ask: Janet has a paper that is 8 inches long. Paul has a paper that is 12 centimeters long. How long are their two papers together?
ANSWER: I can't add these because they are measured in different units.

Objectives

- Understand that quantities may be compared, added, or subtracted if they have been measured by the same unit.

- Compare, add, or subtract quantities that have been measured by the same unit.

- Measure the same object with different units, and predict whether the number of units will be greater or less when a larger or smaller unit is used.

Tips

If necessary, have students highlight or circle each measurement unit and make sure the units are the same before trying to solve the problem.

6. Repeat Step 5 with three more scenarios, using the same unit of measurement for two problems and different units for one problem. Make sure students understand that they cannot simply add or subtract the numerals if the units are different.

7. Have students complete the Add and Subtract Measurements activity page.

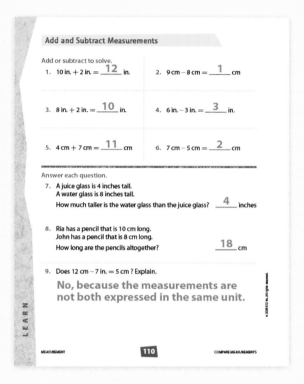

OFFLINE
10 min

TRY IT Use Measurements

Students will practice deciding if they can compare measurements and comparing quantities that have measured by the same unit. Give students the Use Measurements activity page from their Activity Book and read the directions with them.

Objectives

- Understand that quantities may be compared, added, or subtracted if they have been measured by the same unit.

- Compare, add, or subtract quantities that have been measured by the same unit.

- Measure the same object with different units, and predict whether the number of units will be greater or less when a larger or smaller unit is used.

Compare Measurements
Use Measurements

Underline the nonstandard unit that you will need more of to measure each vegetable. Circle the nonstandard unit you will need fewer of to measure each vegetable.

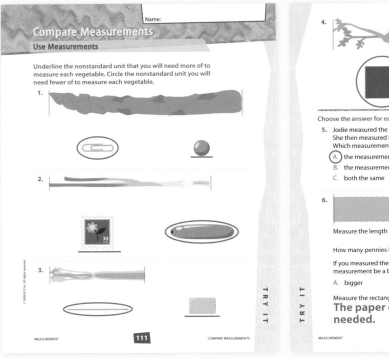

1.

2.

3.

T R Y I T

MEASUREMENT **111** COMPARE MEASUREMENTS

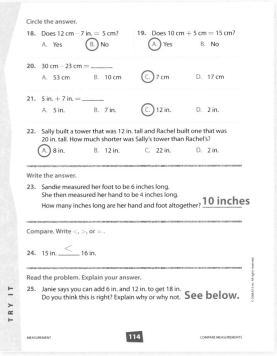

4.

Choose the answer for each problem.

5. Jodie measured the width of her bed using centimeters. She then measured her bed again, this time using inches. Which measurement do you think was the bigger number?
   - (A.) the measurement using centimeters
   - B. the measurement using inches
   - C. both the same

6.

Measure the length of the rectangle with a penny.

How many pennies long is it? __8__

If you measured the rectangle with a paper clip, would the measurement be a bigger or smaller number? Why?
   - A. bigger
   - (B.) smaller

Measure the rectangle with the paper clip to see if you are right.

The paper clip is larger, so fewer are needed.

T R Y I T

MEASUREMENT **112** COMPARE MEASUREMENTS

Circle Yes if the measures can be compared to each other in the units shown. Circle No if they cannot be compared to each other in the units shown.

7. 6 in. and 8 in.
   (A.) Yes   B. No

8. 12 cm and 7 in.
   A. Yes   (B.) No

9. 5 cm and 5 cm
   (A.) Yes   B. No

Compare. Write <, >, or =.

10. 16 cm __>__ 10 cm

11. 25 cm __=__ 25 cm

12. 9 in. __<__ 33 in.

Add or subtract.

13. 9 cm − 5 cm = __4__ cm

14. 5 cm + 6 cm = __11__ cm

Answer each question.

15. Brian has a frame that is 25 in. long. Dee has a frame that is 18 in. long. Who has the longer frame? __Brian__

16. John has a card that is 6 in. long. Jean has a card that is 8 in. long. How much longer is Jean's card than John's? __2 in.__

17. Chris says that 9 in. is equal to 9 cm. Is Chris correct? Why or why not?

No, because they are not the same units of measurement.

T R Y I T

MEASUREMENT **113** COMPARE MEASUREMENTS

Circle the answer.

18. Does 12 cm − 7 in. = 5 cm?
    A. Yes   (B.) No

19. Does 10 cm + 5 cm = 15 cm?
    (A.) Yes   B. No

20. 30 cm − 23 cm = _____
    A. 53 cm   B. 10 cm   (C.) 7 cm   D. 17 cm

21. 5 in. + 7 in. = _____
    A. 5 in.   B. 7 in.   (C.) 12 in.   D. 2 in.

22. Sally built a tower that was 12 in. tall and Rachel built one that was 20 in. tall. How much shorter was Sally's tower than Rachel's?
    (A.) 8 in.   B. 12 in.   C. 22 in.   D. 2 in.

Write the answer.

23. Sandie measured her foot to be 6 inches long. She then measured her hand to be 4 inches long. How many inches long are her hand and foot altogether? __10 inches__

Compare. Write <, >, or =.

24. 15 in. __<__ 16 in.

Read the problem. Explain your answer.

25. Janie says you can add 6 in. and 12 in. to get 18 in. Do you think this is right? Explain why or why not. **See below.**

T R Y I T

MEASUREMENT **114** COMPARE MEASUREMENTS

Additional Answers

25. Students should say yes, you can add 6 in. + 12 in. to get 18 in. They should explain that you can add the two measurements because they have been measured using the same unit (inches).

OFFLINE
10 min

Print the assessment and have students complete it on their own. Read the directions, questions, and answer choices to students if necessary. Use the answer key to score the assessment, and then enter the results online.

- Understand that quantities may be compared, added, or subtracted if they have been measured by the same unit.

- Compare, add, or subtract quantities that have been measured by the same unit.

- Measure the same object with different units, and predict whether the number of units will be greater or less when a larger or smaller unit is used.

Checkpoint   Math | Measurement | Compare Measurements

Name _____ Date _____

Checkpoint Answer Key

Circle the answer.
(1 point)
1. If you measured the height of a flower by using a paper clip and then measured the height of the flower with a crayon, which measurement would be the smaller number?

(A.) the measurement using the crayon

B. They would both be the same.

C. the measurement using the paper clip

(1 point)
2. Hannah's stove measures 30 inches across. If she measures it again by using centimeters, will the number of centimeters be bigger or smaller than the number of inches?

(A.) bigger

B. the same

C. smaller

(1 point)
3. If you measured the height of a tree by using inches and then measured the same tree by using centimeters, which measurement would be the larger number?

(A.) the measurement in centimeters

B. They would both be the same.

C. the measurement in inches

(1 point)
4. If you measured your hand by using a penny and then measured it again with a crayon, which measurement would be the larger number?

(A.) the measurement using the penny

B. They would both be the same.

C. the measurement using the crayon

1 of 3

Checkpoint   Math | Measurement | Compare Measurements

Name _____ Date _____

(1 point)
5. Rosa measured a shell that was 3 inches long and then she measured a shell that was 2 centimeters long. Can she add the 3 and the 2 together to find out how long the shells are altogether?

A. Yes   (B.) No

(1 point)
6. Choose the set of measurements that can be subtracted.

A. 7 cm − 6 in.   (B.) 24 in. − 12 in.

C. 20 cm − 12 in.   D. 8 cm − 8 in.

(1 point)
7. Ellie has a piece of string that is 6 inches long. Sammie has a piece of string that is 7 inches long. Tina has a piece of string that is 15 centimeters long. Which two lengths can be added together?

A. Tina's and Ellie's   (B.) Ellie's and Sammie's

C. Sammie's and Tina's   D. They can all be added together.

(1 point)
8. Which of the following measures can be added together?

A. 5 cm and 7 in.   B. 8 in. and 6 cm

C. 5 in. and 5 cm   (D.) 7 in. and 9 in.

(1 point)
9. Sanje says that 8 cm is equal to 8 in. because 8 = 8. Is Sanje right? Why or why not?

A. Yes   (B.) No

Sanje is not right because the measurements don't use the same units.

2 of 3

Checkpoint   Math | Measurement | Compare Measurements

Name _____ Date _____

(1 point)
10. Choose the set of measurements that can be added together.

(A.) 2 cm + 4 cm + 6 cm   B. 6 cm + 7 in. + 5 in.

C. 8 cm + 7 in. + 4 cm   D. 8 cm + 9 cm + 8 in.

(1 point)
11. Sam has a toy truck that is 21 cm long. Marcus has a toy truck that is 19 cm long. Which boy's truck is longer?

(A.) Sam's   B. Marcus's

(1 point)
Add.

12. 12 in. + 9 in. = _____ in.

A. 3   (B.) 21   C. 13   D. 10

(1 point)
Subtract.

13. 19 cm − 8 cm = _____ cm

(A.) 11   B. 12   C. 6   D. 7

(1 point)
Compare. Choose <, >, or =.

14. 15 in. _____ 16 in.

(A.) <   B. >   C. =

Write each answer.
(1 point)
15. Jeanelle has a comb that is 5 inches long. Patsy has a comb that is 8 inches long.

How long are the combs altogether? **13** in.

(1 point)
16. A rose grew to be 13 inches tall. A daisy grew to be 6 inches tall.

How much taller is the rose than the daisy? **7** in.

3 of 3

Capacity

Skills Update	5 minutes	**ONLINE**
GET READY Nonstandard Units for Capacity	5 minutes	OFFLINE
LEARN Measure Capacity	15 minutes	OFFLINE
LEARN Compare Capacity	15 minutes	OFFLINE
TRY IT Measure and Compare Capacity	10 minutes	OFFLINE
CHECKPOINT	10 minutes	OFFLINE

▶ Lesson Objectives

Measure and compare capacities by using a standard unit (for example, use a measuring cup to measure contents of a water bottle).

▶ Prerequisite Skills

Compare the capacities of objects (for example, the pail holds more water than the cup).

▶ Advance Preparation

In this lesson, students will pour water from one container to another. You may want to do this near a sink or tub, or outdoors near a water supply. You may use rice or sand in place of water, if you choose. Use a flat container (example: tray or cookie sheet) or a layer of plastic to catch any spills.

▶ Safety

If students will use any glass containers, supervise them carefully, because the glass may become slippery while students are pouring. Try to use shatterproof containers.

▶ Content Background

All measurement involves a number of a specific unit, such as 3 cups. Units can be nonstandard or standard. Standard units are ones that everyone knows and agrees are specific sizes, such as cups, liters, inches, centimeters, pounds, or kilograms.

Nonstandard units can be anything we choose to use, but they must each be the same size. For example, some people use a coffee cup to measure how much a vacuum flask will hold.

A standard measuring cup is equivalent to 8 fluid ounces (8 fl oz). The labels on drink containers often state how many fluid ounces are in the container. Since the containers usually are not filled to the top, they generally hold a little more than the amount shown on the label.

In this lesson, students will use different containers to measure capacity in nonstandard units and then will use a measuring cup to measure in a standard unit.

Materials to Gather

SUPPLIED

Checkpoint (printout)

ALSO NEEDED

water

mug

standard measuring cup – 1 cup

containers – 1 quart, 1 half-gallon, and 1 gallon

containers – 7 (large coffee mug, cereal bowl, small cooking pot, serving bowl, frying pan, small drinking glass, and larger drinking glass)

full water bottle

---

capacity – a measure indicating an amount a container can hold

cup (c) – a unit for measuring capacity in the English system of measurement; 1 cup = 8 ounces

gallon (gal) – a unit for measuring capacity in the English system of measurement; 1 gallon = 4 quarts

quart (qt) – a unit for measuring capacity in the English system of measurement; 1 quart = 4 cups

GET READY Nonstandard Units for Capacity

OFFLINE 5 min

Students will use nonstandard units to compare the capacities of two containers. Gather the mug and two containers.

1. Have students fill two containers with water using the mug. Students should count each cup as they pour the water into the container.

2. **Ask:** Which container holds more water?

Objectives

- Compare the capacities of objects (for example, the pail holds more water than the cup).

LEARN Measure Capacity

OFFLINE 15 min

Students will estimate and measure how many cups of water different containers can hold. Students are not expected to identify the other containers or convert measurements.

Gather the standard measuring cup and the 1-quart, 1-half-gallon and 1-gallon containers.

1. Have students use the standard measuring cup to fill the 1-quart container. Students should count each cup.

2. Have students estimate the number of cups it will take to fill the half-gallon container. Then have them count the cups as they fill the container.

3. Repeat these steps with the 1-gallon container.

Objectives

- Measure and compare capacities by using a standard unit (for example, use a measuring cup to measure contents of a water bottle).

LEARN Compare Capacity

OFFLINE 15 min

Students will compare capacities of different containers.

Gather the standard measuring cup and the 7 containers of varying shapes and sizes.

1. Show students 2 containers. Ask them to decide which one holds more or less.

2. Have students fill each container using the 1-cup measuring cup to see which one holds more.

3. Continue with at least five more pairs of containers. At least one pair should consist of a short, wide container and a tall, thin container. Discuss the results with students. Continue as time allows.

Objectives

- Measure and compare capacities by using a standard unit (for example, use a measuring cup to measure contents of a water bottle).

TRY IT Measure and Compare Capacity

Objectives

- Measure and compare capacities by using a standard unit (for example, use a measuring cup to measure contents of a water bottle).

Students will estimate, measure, and compare the capacity of different containers.

Gather the standard measuring cup, large coffee mug, cereal bowl, small cooking pot, serving bowl, frying pan, small drinking glass, large drinking glass, and full water bottle.

Help students select the correct containers to use with each problem. Round measurements to the nearest cup, and explain to students that students should use the word *about*. For example, a container that holds a little less than 3 cups can be said to hold about 3 cups. Record answers on a piece of paper.

1. How many cups of water can the coffee mug hold?
2. Estimate which holds more, the coffee mug or the cereal bowl? Use a measuring cup and water to check your answer.
3. Estimate which holds more, the pot or the serving bowl. How many more cups does the bigger one hold?
4. How many cups of water are in the water bottle?

Tips

For most containers, you can pour from the cup into the container. To measure the capacity of water bottles or containers with small openings, you can pour from the container into the cup.

CHECKPOINT

Objectives

- Measure and compare capacities by using a standard unit (for example, use a measuring cup to measure contents of a water bottle).

Students will take a performance-based assessment. Print the assessment and follow the instructions for each item. Enter the results online.

Gather the standard measuring cup, large coffee mug, cereal bowl, small cooking pot, serving bowl, frying pan, small drinking glass, and large drinking glass.

Unit Review

Lesson Overview

UNIT REVIEW Look Back	20 minutes	ONLINE
UNIT REVIEW Checkpoint Practice	20 minutes	OFFLINE
▶ UNIT REVIEW Prepare for the Checkpoint		

▶ Unit Objectives

This lesson reviews the following objectives:

- Identify inches on a ruler and measure the length of an object to the nearest inch.
- Measure the length of objects by repeating a standard unit.
- Identify centimeters on a ruler and measure the length of an object to the nearest centimeter.
- Estimate the length of an object to the nearest inch or centimeter.
- Recognize when a measurement estimate is reasonable.
- Measure the same object with different units, and predict whether the number of units will be greater or less when a larger or smaller unit is used.
- Understand that quantities may be compared, added, or subtracted if they have been measured by the same unit.
- Measure and compare by using a standard unit (for example, use a measuring cup to measure contents of a water bottle).

▶ Advance Preparation

- In this lesson, students will have an opportunity to review previous activities in the Measurement unit. Look at the suggested activities in Unit Review: Prepare for Checkpoint online and gather any needed materials.
- Make a train of 12 cubes of one color. Make a train of 10 cubes of another color.

Materials to Gather

SUPPLIED

base-10 blocks

blocks – E

blocks – O (two colors)

Checkpoint Practice activity page

ALSO NEEDED

ruler – inches and centimeters

household objects – paper clips (10), pennies (10), fork

Keywords		
	capacity	measurement
	centimeter (cm)	metric system
	cup (c)	nonstandard unit
	English system of measurement	quart (qt)
	estimate (verb)	reasonable estimate or answer
	gallon (gal)	ruler
	inch (in.)	standard unit
	measure (verb)	unit of measure

UNIT REVIEW Look Back

Objectives

- Review unit objectives.

In this unit, students have learned to estimate and measure the length of objects using nonstandard units and rulers. They have learned to add and subtract measurements of the same unit. Students have also learned to estimate, measure, and compare the capacity of different containers. Students will review these concepts to prepare for the Unit Checkpoint.

UNIT REVIEW Checkpoint Practice

Objectives

- Review unit objectives.

Students will complete a Checkpoint Practice activity page to prepare for the Unit Checkpoint. If necessary, read the directions, questions, and answer choices to students. Have students answer the problems on their own. Carefully review the answers with students.

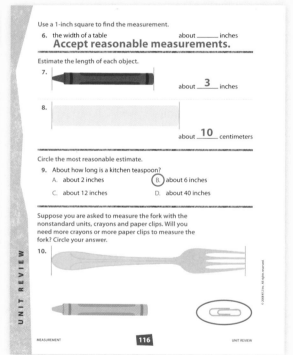

Unit Review
Checkpoint Practice

Name: _____

Use your ruler to measure each pencil to the nearest inch.

1.
about __4__ inches

2.
about __6__ inches

Use ones cubes to measure the length of the items.

3.
about __15__ centimeters

4.
about __8__ centimeters

Use the centimeter ruler to find each measurement.

5. the length of a fork   about _____ centimeters
Accept reasonable measurements.

MEASUREMENT   115   UNIT REVIEW

Use a 1-inch square to find the measurement.

6. the width of a table   about _____ inches
Accept reasonable measurements.

Estimate the length of each object.

7.
about __3__ inches

8.
about __10__ centimeters

Circle the most reasonable estimate.

9. About how long is a kitchen teaspoon?
   A. about 2 inches   B. about 6 inches
   C. about 12 inches   D. about 40 inches

Suppose you are asked to measure the fork with the nonstandard units, crayons and paper clips. Will you need more crayons or more paper clips to measure the fork? Circle your answer.

10.

MEASUREMENT   116   UNIT REVIEW

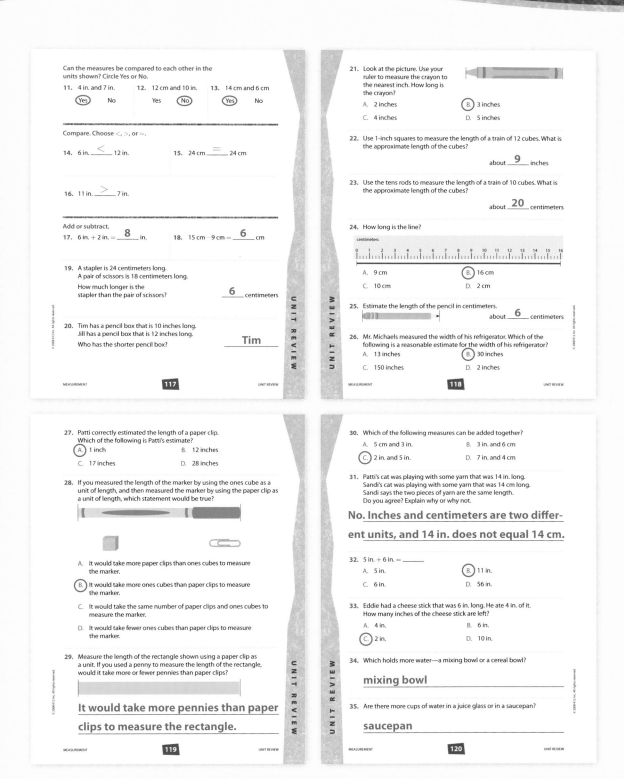

Can the measures be compared to each other in the units shown? Circle Yes or No.

11. 4 in. and 7 in. **(Yes)** No
12. 12 cm and 10 in. Yes **(No)**
13. 14 cm and 6 cm **(Yes)** No

Compare. Choose <, >, or =.

14. 6 in. __<__ 12 in.
15. 24 cm __=__ 24 cm

16. 11 in. __>__ 7 in.

Add or subtract.

17. 6 in. + 2 in. = __8__ in.
18. 15 cm – 9 cm = __6__ cm

19. A stapler is 24 centimeters long.
A pair of scissors is 18 centimeters long.
How much longer is the stapler than the pair of scissors? __6__ centimeters

20. Tim has a pencil box that is 10 inches long.
Jill has a pencil box that is 12 inches long.
Who has the shorter pencil box? __Tim__

21. Look at the picture. Use your ruler to measure the crayon to the nearest inch. How long is the crayon?
A. 2 inches **(B.)** 3 inches
C. 4 inches D. 5 inches

22. Use 1-inch squares to measure the length of a train of 12 cubes. What is the approximate length of the cubes?
about __9__ inches

23. Use the tens rods to measure the length of a train of 10 cubes. What is the approximate length of the cubes?
about __20__ centimeters

24. How long is the line?

centimeters
0 1 2 3 4 5 6 7 8 9 10 11 12 13 14 15 16

A. 9 cm **(B.)** 16 cm
C. 10 cm D. 2 cm

25. Estimate the length of the pencil in centimeters.
about __6__ centimeters

26. Mr. Michaels measured the width of his refrigerator. Which of the following is a reasonable estimate for the width of his refrigerator?
A. 13 inches **(B.)** 30 inches
C. 150 inches D. 2 inches

27. Patti correctly estimated the length of a paper clip. Which of the following is Patti's estimate?
(A.) 1 inch B. 12 inches
C. 17 inches D. 28 inches

28. If you measured the length of the marker by using the ones cube as a unit of length, and then measured the marker by using the paper clip as a unit of length, which statement would be true?

A. It would take more paper clips than ones cubes to measure the marker.
(B.) It would take more ones cubes than paper clips to measure the marker.
C. It would take the same number of paper clips and ones cubes to measure the marker.
D. It would take fewer ones cubes than paper clips to measure the marker.

29. Measure the length of the rectangle shown using a paper clip as a unit. If you used a penny to measure the length of the rectangle, would it take more or fewer pennies than paper clips?

It would take more pennies than paper clips to measure the rectangle.

30. Which of the following measures can be added together?
A. 5 cm and 3 in. B. 3 in. and 6 cm
(C.) 2 in. and 5 in. D. 7 in. and 4 cm

31. Patti's cat was playing with some yarn that was 14 in. long. Sandi's cat was playing with some yarn that was 14 cm long. Sandi says the two pieces of yarn are the same length. Do you agree? Explain why or why not.

No. Inches and centimeters are two different units, and 14 in. does not equal 14 cm.

32. 5 in. + 6 in. = _____
A. 5 in. **(B.)** 11 in.
C. 6 in. D. 56 in.

33. Eddie had a cheese stick that was 6 in. long. He ate 4 in. of it. How many inches of the cheese stick are left?
A. 4 in. B. 6 in.
(C.) 2 in. D. 10 in.

34. Which holds more water—a mixing bowl or a cereal bowl?
mixing bowl

35. Are there more cups of water in a juice glass or in a saucepan?
saucepan

⇨ UNIT REVIEW Prepare for the Checkpoint

What you do next depends on how students performed in the previous activity, Unit Review: Checkpoint Practice. If students had difficulty with any of the problems, complete the appropriate review activity listed in the table online.

Unit Checkpoint

UNIT CHECKPOINT ⋯⋯⋯⋯ 45 minutes ⋮ OFFLINE

▶ Unit Objectives

This lesson assesses the following objectives:

- Identify inches on a ruler and measure the length of an object to the nearest inch.
- Measure the length of objects by repeating a standard unit.
- Identify centimeters on a ruler and measure the length of an object to the nearest centimeter.
- Estimate the length of an object to the nearest inch or centimeter.
- Recognize when a measurement estimate is reasonable.
- Measure the same object with different units, and predict whether the number of units will be greater or less when a larger or smaller unit is used.
- Understand that quantities may be compared, added, or subtracted if they have been measured by the same unit.
- Compare, add, or subtract quantities that have been measured by the same unit.
- Measure and compare volumes by using a standard unit (for example, use a measuring cup to measure contents of a water bottle).

Materials to Gather

SUPPLIED

blocks – E (10)

blocks – O (10)

base-10 blocks

Checkpoint (printout)

ALSO NEEDED

ruler

standard measuring cup (1 cup)

soup bowl (any size)

water bottle (half-filled with water)

water pitcher (any size)

UNIT CHECKPOINT
OFFLINE
45 min

Objectives

- Assess unit objectives.

Students will complete the Unit Checkpoint offline. For Problems 1–12, students will complete the problems on their own. For Problems 13–15, students will take a performance-based assessment. Print the Checkpoint. Read the directions, problems, and answer choices to students if necessary. Use the answer key to score the Checkpoint, and then enter the results online.

Gather the measuring cup, soup bowl, water bottle, and water pitcher for Problems 13–15.

Name _____ Date _____

Unit Checkpoint Answer Key

Use an inch ruler to measure each item to the nearest inch.

(1 point)
1.

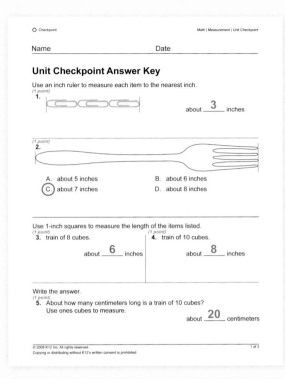

about __3__ inches

(1 point)
2.

A. about 5 inches   B. about 6 inches
(C.) about 7 inches   D. about 8 inches

Use 1-inch squares to measure the length of the items listed.

(1 point)
3. train of 8 cubes.

about __6__ inches

(1 point)
4. train of 10 cubes.

about __8__ inches

Write the answer.

(1 point)
5. About how many centimeters long is a train of 10 cubes? Use ones cubes to measure.

about __20__ centimeters

Name _____ Date _____

Use a centimeter ruler to measure each item to the nearest centimeter.

(1 point)
6.

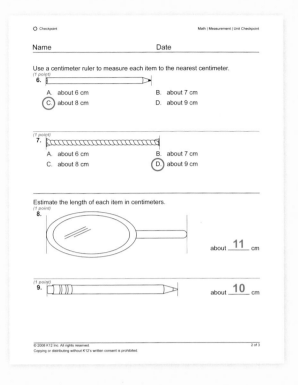

A. about 6 cm   B. about 7 cm
(C.) about 8 cm   D. about 9 cm

(1 point)
7.

A. about 6 cm   B. about 7 cm
C. about 8 cm   (D.) about 9 cm

Estimate the length of each item in centimeters.

(1 point)
8.

about __11__ cm

(1 point)
9.

about __10__ cm

Name _____ Date _____

Estimate the length of each item in inches.

(1 point)
10.

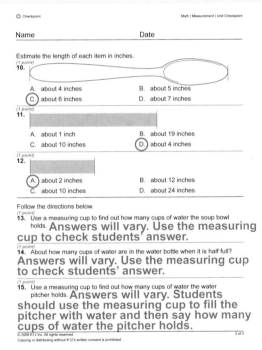

A. about 4 inches   B. about 5 inches
(C.) about 6 inches   D. about 7 inches

(1 point)
11.

A. about 1 inch   B. about 19 inches
C. about 10 inches   (D.) about 4 inches

(1 point)
12.

(A.) about 2 inches   B. about 12 inches
C. about 10 inches   D. about 24 inches

Follow the directions below.

(1 point)
13. Use a measuring cup to find out how many cups of water the soup bowl holds. **Answers will vary. Use the measuring cup to check students' answer.**

(1 point)
14. About how many cups of water are in the water bottle when it is half full? **Answers will vary. Use the measuring cup to check students' answer.**

(1 point)
15. Use a measuring cup to find out how many cups of water the water pitcher holds. **Answers will vary. Students should use the measuring cup to fill the pitcher with water and then say how many cups of water the pitcher holds.**

Add or Subtract: Problem Solving

Alex gathered 27 tennis balls. Rosa gathered 31 tennis balls. How many did they gather in all?

I can solve this problem by using models or drawing a sketch.

▶ Unit Objectives

- Use concrete objects or sketches to model and solve addition or subtraction problem-solving situations with sums or minuends up through 500.

- Recognize and solve word problems involving sums up through 500 in which two quantities are combined.

- Recognize and solve word problems involving sums or minuends up through 500 in which one quantity changes by addition or subtraction.

- Recognize and solve word problems involving numbers up to 500 in which two quantities are compared by the use of addition or subtraction.

- Recognize and solve word problems involving numbers up to 500 in which one quantity must be changed to equal another quantity.

▶ Big Ideas

- Models and mathematical symbols can represent addition and subtraction.

- The use of letters, numbers, and mathematical symbols makes it possible to translate complex situations or long word statements into concise mathematical sentences or expressions.

▶ Unit Introduction

Students will use objects and sketches to model and solve addition and subtraction problem-solving situations. The problems include the following: combine problems (two quantities are put together to find the sum); compare problems (two quantities are compared to find the difference); change problems (one quantity changes when another quantity is added to it or taken away from it); and equalize problems (one quantity is changed to equal another quantity).

Addition Problem-Solving Strategies

Lesson Overview

Skills Update	5 minutes	ONLINE
GET READY Model Match	10 minutes	ONLINE
LEARN Model Addition Problems	15 minutes	ONLINE
LEARN More Combine Problems	15 minutes	ONLINE
TRY IT Model and Sketch to Add	10 minutes	OFFLINE
LEARN Model to Add	10 minutes	OFFLINE
TRY IT Addition Sketches	10 minutes	OFFLINE

▶ Lesson Objectives

Use concrete objects or sketches to model and solve addition or subtraction problem-solving situations with sums or minuends up through 500.

▶ Prerequisite Skills

Use concrete objects or sketches to model and solve addition computation problems with sums up through 500 with and without regrouping.

▶ Content Background

Students know how to add with sums up through 500. In this lesson, they will use models and sketches to solve addition story problems.

Models and sketches are tools that will help students translate and see the problems they are to solve. This is a critical step in preparing students to solve more complex problems in the future.

Read the problem with students and look at the sketch. Make sure that students understand how the sketch shows the way to solve the problem.

Materials to Gather

SUPPLIED

base-10 blocks

place-value mat

Model and Sketch to Add activity page

Addition Sketches activity page

addend – one of the two or more numbers that are added to determine a sum

addition – the process of combining, or putting together, groups of objects or numbers; a mathematical operation

combine problem – an addition problem in which two quantities are put together to find a sum

model (noun) – a physical object, diagram, or picture that represents an amount, an expression, an equation, or a problem situation

model (verb) – to use physical objects, diagrams, or pictures to represent an amount, an expression, an equation, or a problem situation

number sentence – two expressions related by an equals symbol ($=$), a not-equal-to symbol ($\neq$), or an inequality symbol; for example, $7 - 2 = 4 + 1$; $5 \neq 4 + 2$; $6 + 2 > 1 + 4$

regroup; regrouping – to use place-value concepts to rename numbers, such as 1 ten and 3 ones $=$ 13 ones; often used in addition and subtraction

sum – the solution to an addition problem

GET READY Model Match

ONLINE 10 min

Students will practice matching addition expressions and models.

Objectives

- Use concrete objects or sketches to model and solve addition computation problems with sums up through 500 with and without regrouping.

LEARN Model Addition Problems

ONLINE 15 min

Students will watch Alexander solve story problems about his stamp collection. They will learn how to use models or sketches to solve problems that combine groups. The focus is on representing problems with models as a tool for solving more difficult problems.

Objectives

- Use concrete objects or sketches to model and solve addition problem-solving situations with sums or minuends up through 500.

LEARN More Combine Problems

ONLINE 15 min

Students will watch Winnie solve a story problem about soccer. Students will learn how to use models to represent addition with regrouping in problem-solving situations.

Objectives

- Use concrete objects or sketches to model and solve addition problem-solving situations with sums or minuends up through 500.

TRY IT Model and Sketch to Add

Students will practice drawing sketches and using base-10 blocks to model and solve addition story problems. Students may use base-10 blocks to help them add and regroup numbers for Problems 3 and 4.

Give students the base-10 blocks, place-value mat, and Model and Sketch to Add activity page. Use the answer key to check students' work, and enter the results online.

Objectives

- Use concrete objects or sketches to model and solve addition problem-solving situations with sums or minuends up through 500.

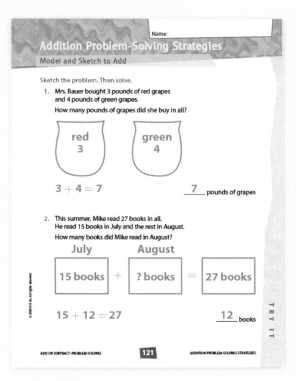

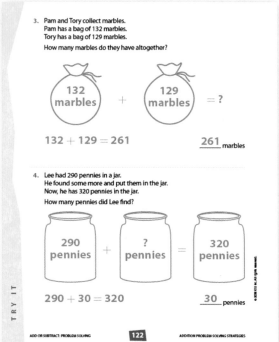

LEARN Model to Add

Objectives

- Use concrete objects or sketches to model and solve addition problem-solving situations with sums or minuends up through 500.

Students will use sketches and base-10 blocks to solve addition story problems.
Give students the base-10 blocks and place-value mat.

1. Read the following problem to students. Have them draw a sketch to show how they would solve the problem.

   Ask: Ramona went to the craft store and bought 45 gold stickers and 55 silver stickers. How many stickers did she buy in all?
   ANSWER: Sketches may vary. Example: 4 packages labeled with the number 10 and 5 small squares would show 45. Below that, 5 packages labeled with the number 10 and 5 small squares would show 55. Students might draw a circle around the 9 packages and another around the 10 small squares. Below the sketch they might write $90 + 10 = 100$.

2. Read the following problem to students. Have them use base-10 blocks and a place-value mat to model and solve the problem.

Ask: Rachel had 168 marbles in her collection and Rebecca had 121. How many marbles do they have altogether? (289)
ANSWER: Student should show 1 hundreds flat, 6 tens rods, and 8 ones cubes. Below that should be 1 hundreds flat, 2 tens rods and 1 ones cube, with an addition sign to the left.

TRY IT Addition Sketches

Students will practice using base-10 blocks and sketches to model and solve addition problems. Give students the base-10 blocks, place-value mat, and Addition Sketches activity page. Use the answer key to check students' answers, and enter the results online.

Objectives

- Use concrete objects or sketches to model and solve addition problem-solving situations with sums or minuends up through 500.

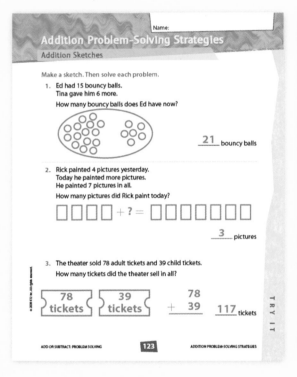

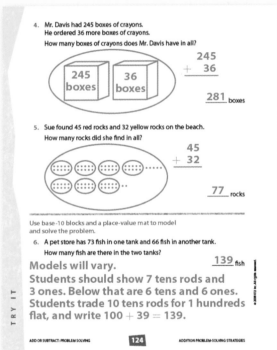

Subtraction Problem Solving

Lesson Overview

Skills Update	5 minutes	**ONLINE**
GET READY Model Subtraction	5 minutes	**ONLINE**
LEARN Subtraction Story Problems	10 minutes	**ONLINE**
LEARN Subtract to Solve	10 minutes	**ONLINE**
TRY IT Subtraction Problem Solving	10 minutes	**OFFLINE**
LEARN Sketch and Subtract	15 minutes	**OFFLINE**
TRY IT Draw and Solve	15 minutes	**OFFLINE**

Lesson Objectives

Use concrete objects or sketches to model and solve addition or subtraction problem-solving situations with sums or minuends up through 500.

Prerequisite Skills

Use concrete objects or sketches to model and solve addition or subtraction computation problems with sums or minuends up through 500 with and without regrouping.

Content Background

Students know how to subtract numbers with minuends through 500 and solve addition story problems. In this lesson, students will use models and sketches to solve subtraction story problems.

Models and sketches are tools that will help students translate and see the problems they need to solve. This is a critical step in preparing students to solve more complex problems in the future.

Read the problem with students and look at the sketch. Make sure that students understand how their sketch shows the way to solve the problem.

Materials to Gather

SUPPLIED

base-10 blocks

place-value mat

Sketch and Subtract activity page

Draw and Solve activity page

Keywords

difference – the solution to a subtraction problem

minuend – in subtraction, the quantity or number from which another number is subtracted; 8 is the minuend in the problem $8 - 7 = ?$

operation – a process or action, such as addition, subtraction, multiplication, or division, performed in a specified sequence and in accordance with specific rules; also called a mathematical operation

GET READY Model Subtraction

ONLINE 5min

Objectives

Students will practice modeling subtraction problems by matching illustrations of cubes with a number sentence.

- Use concrete objects or sketches to model and solve addition or subtraction computation problems with sums or minuends up through 500 with and without regrouping.

LEARN Subtraction Story Problems

ONLINE 10min

Objectives

Students will learn how to use models to solve subtraction problems by watching Serena solve a story problem about mystery books. The focus is on representing problems with models as a tool for solving more difficult problems.

Emphasize that students can use subtraction to solve problems in which you take away one amount from another. The amount remaining is the difference.

- Use concrete objects or sketches to model and solve addition or subtraction problem-solving situations with sums or minuends up through 500.

LEARN Subtract to Solve

ONLINE 10min

Objectives

Students will learn how to use models to represent subtraction problems with regrouping. They will model problems and solve them by using the algorithm.

- Use concrete objects or sketches to model and solve addition or subtraction problem-solving situations with sums or minuends up through 500.

TRY IT Subtraction Problem Solving

OFFLINE 10min

Objectives

Students will use base-10 blocks to model and solve subtraction story problems.

1. Read the following to students and have them use base-10 blocks to show the answer.

    Ask: Keith has 41 rocks in his collection. He gave Matt 8 of his rocks. How many rocks does Keith have left?
    ANSWER: Models will vary. Students should show 4 tens rods and 1 ones cube. Then students should remove 8 ones cubes (1 tens rod will need to be regrouped into 10 ones to provide enough ones to subtract). Answer is 33.

2. Read the following problem to students and have them use base-10 blocks and a place-value mat to model and solve the problem.

    Ask: There are 57 books on the shelf. Linda takes 41 books off the shelf. How many books are left on the shelf?
    ANSWER: Models will vary. Students should show 5 tens rods and 7 ones cubes. Then students should remove 4 tens rods and 1 ones cube. Answer is 16.

3. Enter students' results online.

- Use concrete objects or sketches to model and solve addition or subtraction problem-solving situations with sums or minuends up through 500.

LEARN Sketch and Subtract

Students will learn how to draw pictures to model and solve problems that involve taking away. Give students the Sketch and Subtract activity page from their Activity Book and read the directions with them. Help students organize the objects in their drawings into groups of tens and ones so they will be able to take away groups of objects at one time.

Students might draw sketches that show both numbers in the problem. Make sure they model the minuend (first number) and then cross out the amount being subtracted.

Objectives

- Use concrete objects or sketches to model and solve addition or subtraction problem-solving situations with sums or minuends up through 500.

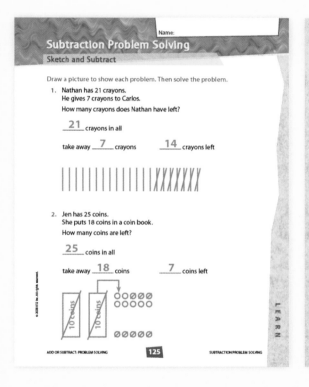

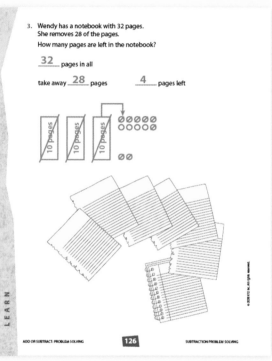

TRY IT Draw and Solve

Objectives

Students will practice solving subtraction story problems by drawing a sketch or using base-10 blocks to model the problem.

Give students the base-10 blocks, place-value mat, and the Draw and Solve activity page from their Activity Book. Read the directions with them. Use the answer key to check students' answers, and then enter the results online.

- Use concrete objects or sketches to model and solve addition or subtraction problem-solving situations with sums or minuends up through 500.

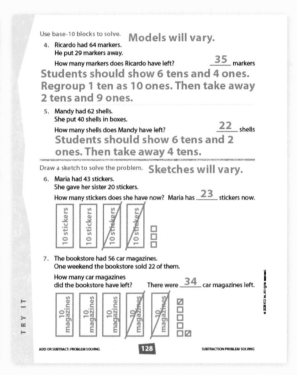

Name:

Subtraction Problem Solving
Draw and Solve

Draw a picture. Then solve each problem.

1. Courtney had 9 stickers.
   She gave away 7 stickers.
   How many stickers does Courtney have now?

   __9__ stickers in all   ☐☐/☐/☐/☐/☐/☐/☐/☐

   take away __7__ stickers   __2__ stickers left

2. There were 23 bagels in the box.
   The children ate 16 bagels.
   How many bagels were left?

   __23__ bagels in all

   take away __16__ bagels   __7__ bagels left

Use base-10 blocks to solve.

3. Mandy has 25 postcards.
   She sent 7 postcards to friends.
   How many postcards does Mandy have left?   __18__ postcards

   Students should show 2 tens and 5 ones. Regroup 1 ten as 10 ones. Then take away 7 ones.

ADD OR SUBTRACT: PROBLEM SOLVING   **127**   SUBTRACTION PROBLEM SOLVING

Use base-10 blocks to solve.   **Models will vary.**

4. Ricardo had 64 markers.
   He put 29 markers away.
   How many markers does Ricardo have left?   __35__ markers

   Students should show 6 tens and 4 ones. Regroup 1 ten as 10 ones. Then take away 2 tens and 9 ones.

5. Mandy had 62 shells.
   She put 40 shells in boxes.
   How many shells does Mandy have left?   __22__ shells

   Students should show 6 tens and 2 ones. Then take away 4 tens.

Draw a sketch to solve the problem.   **Sketches will vary.**

6. Maria had 43 stickers.
   She gave her sister 20 stickers.
   How many stickers does she have now? Maria has __23__ stickers now.

7. The bookstore had 56 car magazines.
   One weekend the bookstore sold 22 of them.
   How many car magazines did the bookstore have left?   There were __34__ car magazines left.

ADD OR SUBTRACT: PROBLEM SOLVING   **128**   SUBTRACTION PROBLEM SOLVING

Modeling Story Problems

Lesson Overview

Skills Update	5 minutes	**ONLINE**
GET READY Model Numbers	10 minutes	**ONLINE**
LEARN Think About Models	10 minutes	**ONLINE**
LEARN Visualize Taking Away	10 minutes	**ONLINE**
TRY IT Solve Story Problems	10 minutes	**OFFLINE**
CHECKPOINT	10 minutes	**OFFLINE**

▶ Lesson Objectives

Use concrete objects or sketches to model and solve addition or subtraction problem-solving situations with sums or minuends up through 500.

▶ Prerequisite Skills

Use concrete objects or sketches to model and solve addition or subtraction computation problems with sums or minuends up through 500 with and without regrouping.

▶ Content Background

Students know how to add and subtract numbers through 500 and to solve addition and subtraction story problems. In this lesson, they will use mental models to visualize and solve two types of story problems: combine problems and take-away change problems.

Materials to Gather

SUPPLIED
base-10 blocks
Checkpoint (printout)

ALSO NEEDED
crayons

GET READY Model Numbers

ONLINE
10 min

Objectives

- Use concrete objects or sketches to model and solve addition or subtraction computation problems with sums or minuends up through 500 with and without regrouping.

Students will use the Place Value Learning Tool to practice modeling numbers.

DIRECTIONS FOR USING THE PLACE VALUE LEARNING TOOL

1. Click Begin Setup and choose the following:
   - Work with NUMBERS up to: 500
   - Use regrouping: YES
   - Computer makes questions
2. As students proceed through the activity, ask questions such as the following:
   - How many hundreds are in the number?
   - How many tens are in the number?
   - How many ones are in the number?
3. Continue as time allows.

LEARN Think About Models

Students will practice using mental models to help them solve addition story problems. Students will solve problems by following these steps:

1. Think of a model in your mind.
2. Use the model to decide how to solve the problem.
3. Write a number sentence.
4. Use the number sentence to find the answer.
5. Record the answer.

- Use concrete objects or sketches to model and solve addition or subtraction problem-solving situations with sums or minuends up through 500.

Tips

If students have difficulty with the story problems, review how to add and subtract two-digit numbers. Focus on regrouping 10 ones as 1 ten, and 10 tens as 1 hundred.

LEARN Visualize Taking Away

Students will practice using mental models to help them solve subtraction story problems.

- Use concrete objects or sketches to model and solve addition or subtraction problem-solving situations with sums and minuends up through 500.

TRY IT Solve Story Problems

Students will practice drawing sketches to solve addition and subtraction story problems.

Read the problems to students and have them draw sketches.

1. **Ask:** The party store had 124 red balloons and 133 green balloons. How many balloons did they have in all?
   ANSWER: 124 is 1 bag of balloons with the number 100 on it, 2 bags of balloons with the number 10, and 4 single balloons. 133 is 1 bag of balloons with the number 100, 3 bags of balloons with the number 10, and 3 single balloons. Students should put a plus symbol between the two numbers. Answer is 257.

2. **Ask:** Alec has 276 comics in his collection. Fifty of the comics are rare and the rest are not rare. How many comics are not rare?
   ANSWER: Students should show 2 stacks of comics labeled with the number 100, 7 stacks of comics labeled with the number 10, and 6 single comics. Students should cross out 5 stacks of comics labeled 10. Answer is 226.

3. Enter students' results online.

- Use concrete objects or sketches to model and solve addition or subtraction problem-solving situations with sums or minuends up through 500.

CHECKPOINT

Print the assessment and have students complete it on their own. Read the directions, questions, and answer choices to students if necessary. Use the answer key to score the assessment, and then enter the results online.

- Use concrete objects or sketches to model and solve addition or subtraction problem-solving situations with sums or minuends up through 500.

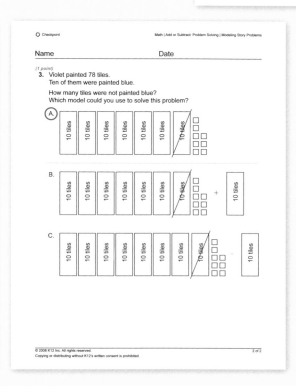

○ Checkpoint   Math | Add or Subtract: Problem Solving | Modeling Story Problems

Name _____   Date _____

Checkpoint Answer Key

Use base-10 blocks to model and solve the problem. **Models will vary.**
(2 points)
1. Dina had 147 lemon bars on her bake sale table.
She sold 134 of them.

How many lemon bars does she have left?

Dina has ___13___ lemon bars left.

Circle the answer.
(1 point)
2. Loretta ran 245 feet in the race.
Anna ran 125 feet.

Which model could you use to find how many feet they ran altogether?

A.

B.

C.

○ Checkpoint   Math | Add or Subtract: Problem Solving | Modeling Story Problems

Name _____   Date _____

(1 point)
3. Violet painted 78 tiles.
Ten of them were painted blue.

How many tiles were not painted blue?
Which model could you use to solve this problem?

A.

B.

C.

Problem Solving

▶ Lesson Objectives

Recognize and solve word problems involving sums up through 500 in which two quantities are combined.

▶ Prerequisite Skills

Use concrete objects or sketches to model and solve addition or subtraction problem-solving situations with sums or minuends up through 500.

▶ Content Background

Students know how to write an addition number sentence with a missing addend, for example, $3 + ? = 7$. Students have learned how to find the missing addend by asking themselves, "3 plus what number is the same as 7?" Subtraction is another strategy for finding the missing addend. For example, students might write, "$7 - 3 = ?$"

Students will discover that writing number sentences can make problem solving easier.

Keywords	
	count on – to add two groups by starting with the number of objects in one group and then counting up, in order, the number of objects in the other group
	inverse operations – mathematical operations that reverse or undo each other; often called opposite operations; subtraction and addition are inverse operations; division and multiplication are inverse operations

Materials to Gather

SUPPLIED

Story Problem Practice activity page

GET READY Many Ways

ONLINE 10 min

Students will see how a variety of story problems can be created using the same two numbers.

Objectives

- Use concrete objects or sketches to model and solve addition or subtraction problem-solving situations with sums or minuends up through 500.

TRY IT Solve Story Problems

ONLINE 15 min

Students will use number sentences to solve story problems.

Objectives

- Recognize and solve word problems involving sums up through 500 in which two quantities are combined.

LEARN See America

ONLINE 15 min

Students will solve problems that involve combining two quantities.

Objectives

- Recognize and solve word problems involving sums up through 500 in which two quantities are combined.

LEARN Missing Group Story Problems

ONLINE 10 min

Students will solve story problems that involve combining two groups, in which one of the groups and the total are known.

Objectives

- Recognize and solve word problems involving sums up through 500 in which two quantities are combined.

TRY IT Story Problem Practice

OFFLINE 10 min

Students will practice solving story problems by writing number sentences. Give students the Story Problem Practice activity page from their Activity Book and read the directions with them. Use the answer key to check students' answers, and then enter the results online.

Objectives

- Recognize and solve word problems involving sums up through 500 in which two quantities are combined.

Problem Solving
Story Problem Practice

Write a number sentence for each problem. Use a question mark (?) for the missing number. Then solve.

Number sentences may vary.

Example: Rob had 27 books.
He bought 12 more books.

How many books does Rob have now?

27 $+$ 12 $=$?   __39__ books

1. Mitch has 30 stickers. Rita has 58 stickers.

   How many stickers do they have altogether?

   30 $+$ 58 $=$?   __88__ stickers

   or 58 + 30 = ?

2. A jar holds 98 marbles.
   There are 45 striped marbles. The rest are solid.

   How many solid marbles are in the jar?

   98 $-$ 45 $=$?   __53__ solid marbles

   or 45 + ? = 98, ? + 45 = 98,
   98 = ? + 45, or 98 = 45 + ?

3. A toy store has 36 brown teddy bears.
   It has 41 white teddy bears.

   How many teddy bears does the store have altogether?

   36 $+$ 41 $=$?   __77__ teddy bears

   or 41 + 36 = ?

TRY IT

Write a number sentence for each problem. Use a question mark (?) for the missing number. Then solve.

Number sentences may vary.

4. Allison has 71 photos.
   There are 40 photos of her family.
   The rest are photos of flowers.

   How many photos of flowers does Allison have?

   40 $+$? $=$ 71   __31__ flower photos

   or ? + 40 = 71, 71 − 40 = ?,
   71 = 40 + ?, or 71 = ? + 40

5. One shelf has 39 books.
   Another shelf has 24 books.

   How many books are on the two shelves?

   39 $+$ 24 $=$?   __63__ books

   or 24 + 39 = ?

6. Erin has 20 shirts in her drawer.
   There are 9 shirts with long sleeves, and the rest have short sleeves.

   How many of Erin's shirts have short sleeves?

   ? $+$ 9 $=$ 20   __11__ shirts with short sleeves

   or 9 + ? = 20, 20 = 9 + ?,
   20 = ? + 9, or 20 − 9 = ?

TRY IT

Problem Solving with Combining

Lesson Overview

Skills Update	5 minutes	ONLINE
GET READY Story Problems	5 minutes	ONLINE
LEARN Combine Numbers	10 minutes	ONLINE
LEARN Greater Number Story Problems	10 minutes	ONLINE
TRY IT Solve Problems	10 minutes	ONLINE
CHECKPOINT	10 minutes	OFFLINE

▶ Lesson Objectives

Recognize and solve word problems involving sums up through 500 in which two quantities are combined.

▶ Prerequisite Skills

Use concrete objects or sketches to model and solve addition or subtraction problem-solving situations with sums or minuends up through 500.

▶ Content Background

Students will work on writing number sentences to solve story problems. They will learn that the magnitude of the numbers in the problem does not affect how students should approach the problem.

Keywords

symbol – a figure that is used to represent something else, such as + represents *plus* or *addition*, or = represents *equals*

Materials to Gather

SUPPLIED
Checkpoint (printout)

GET READY Story Problems

ONLINE
5 min

Objectives

Students will decide whether to solve story problems by adding or subtracting. Then they will choose which number sentence represents the problem. The activity should help students see that they can solve story problems with greater numbers in the same ways as those with lesser numbers.

- Use concrete objects or sketches to model and solve addition or subtraction problem-solving situations with sums or minuends up through 500.

LEARN Combine Numbers

Objectives

Students will combine numbers to solve story problems.

Students may use paper and pencil to solve the problems. If needed, review how to regroup numbers. Watch for students who try to use something other than addition for combining groups.

- Recognize and solve word problems involving sums up through 500 in which two quantities are combined.

LEARN Greater Number Story Problems

Objectives

Students will find missing numbers to solve story problems. They will learn that they can either add or subtract to find the missing number in story problems.

- Recognize and solve word problems involving sums up through 500 in which two quantities are combined.

TRY IT Solve Problems

Objectives

Students will answer questions online to demonstrate their problem-solving skills.

- Recognize and solve word problems involving sums up through 500 in which two quantities are combined.

CHECKPOINT

Objectives

Print the assessment and have students complete it on their own. Read the directions, questions, and answer choices to students if necessary. Use the answer key to score the assessment, and then enter the results online.

- Recognize and solve word problems involving sums up through 500 in which two quantities are combined.

○ Checkpoint   Math | Add or Subtract: Problem Solving | Problem Solving with Combining

Name _____ Date _____

Checkpoint Answer Key

Circle the answer.
(1 point)
1. Nina bought 205 postage stamps.
   Then she bought 153 more postage stamps.

   How many stamps did Nina buy altogether?
   A. 52   B. 253   C. 358   D. 458

(1 point)
2. Alex cooked 57 pancakes.
   Mary cooked 113 pancakes.

   How many pancakes did they cook in all?
   A. 144   B. 157   C. 160   D. 170

(1 point)
3. Dina put 55 cans of cat food on the grocery store shelf.
   Then she put 89 more cans of cat food on the shelf.

   How many cans of cat food did Dina put on the shelf altogether?
   A. 154   B. 144   C. 124   D. 34

(1 point)
4. The zoo has 36 monkeys in one area and
   115 monkeys in another area.

   How many monkeys are there in the zoo's two areas?
   A. 69   B. 79   C. 121   D. 151

Problem Solving with Change

Lesson Overview

Skills Update	5 minutes	ONLINE
GET READY How Many Are Missing?	5 minutes	ONLINE
LEARN Appear and Disappear Problems	20 minutes	ONLINE
LEARN Change Story Problems	20 minutes	ONLINE
TRY IT Solve Change Story Problems	10 minutes	OFFLINE

▶ Lesson Objectives

Recognize and solve word problems involving sums or minuends up through 500 in which one quantity changes by addition or subtraction.

▶ Prerequisite Skills

Use concrete objects or sketches to model and solve addition or subtraction problem-solving situations with sums or minuends up through 500.

▶ Content Background

Students will learn how to solve a story problem in which one quantity changes by addition.

Some story problems are called *change problems*. In these problems, a number is added to or subtracted from an original quantity. Here's a change problem: "Rosa has 5 beads. She gives 3 to Winnie. How many beads does Rosa have left?" In this problem, 5 is the original quantity. When 3 is subtracted, the original quantity changes.

Students do not need to memorize the types of problems, but instead should gain the experience and confidence necessary to read a problem, create a mental image, and figure out which quantities within the problem to add or subtract to find the solution.

Materials to Gather
SUPPLIED
Solve Change Story Problems activity page

Keywords

change problem – a problem in which one quantity changes by having an amount added or taken away

GET READY How Many Are Missing?

ONLINE
5min

Students will solve story problems in which one amount changes.

Objectives

- Use concrete objects or sketches to model and solve addition or subtraction problem-solving situations with sums or minuends up through 500.

LEARN Appear and Disappear Problems

Students will solve story problems in which one amount changes.

During the activity, watch for students who do not understand that the answer to the number sentence is the answer to the story problem. Explain that the number sentence is a number version of the story problem.

Objectives
- Recognize and solve word problems involving sums or minuends up through 500 in which one quantity changes by addition or subtraction.

LEARN Change Story Problems

Students will solve story problems in which one amount changes.

Objectives
- Recognize and solve word problems involving sums or minuends up through 500 in which one quantity changes by addition or subtraction.

TRY IT Solve Change Story Problems

Students will practice solving story problems in which one amount changes. Give students the Solve Change Story Problems activity page from their Activity Book and read the directions with them. If necessary, students may rewrite the problems vertically to solve.

Use the answer key to check students' answers, and then enter the results online.

Objectives
- Recognize and solve word problems involving sums or minuends up through 500 in which one quantity changes by addition or subtraction.

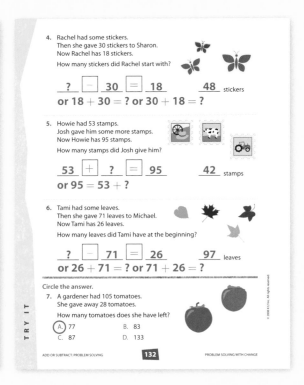

Solve Change Story Problems

Skills Update	5 minutes	ONLINE
LEARN Vegetable Story Problems	10 minutes	ONLINE
LEARN Jungle Story Problems	15 minutes	ONLINE
LEARN Story Problem Variations	10 minutes	ONLINE
TRY IT Change Problems	10 minutes	OFFLINE
CHECKPOINT	10 minutes	OFFLINE

▶ Lesson Objectives

Recognize and solve story problems involving sums or minuends up through 500 in which one quantity changes by addition or subtraction.

▶ Prerequisite Skills

- Use concrete objects or sketches to model and solve addition or subtraction problem-solving situations with sums or minuends up through 500.
- Recognize and solve story problems involving sums or minuends up through 100 in which one quantity changes by addition or subtraction.

▶ Common Errors and Misconceptions

- Students might add rather than subtract when solving story problems with an unknown difference. Using models might help students choose the correct operation.
- Students might confuse combine problems and change problems.

▶ Content Background

Students will solve story problems with sums and minuends through 500 in which one quantity changes.

Some story problems are called *change problems*. In these problems, a number is added to or subtracted from an original quantity. Here's a change problem: "Rosa has 5 beads. She gives 3 to Winnie. How many beads does Rosa have left?" In this problem, 5 is the original quantity. When 3 is subtracted, the original quantity changes.

Students do not need to memorize the types of problems but will instead gain the experience and confidence necessary to read a problem, create a mental image, and figure out which quantities within the problem to add or subtract to find the solution.

Materials to Gather

SUPPLIED
Change Problems activity page
Checkpoint (printout)

LEARN Vegetable Story Problems

ONLINE 10 min

Students will solve story problems in which the initial quantity changes by addition with sums through 500.

Objectives

- Recognize and solve word problems involving sums or minuends up through 500 in which one quantity changes by addition or subtraction.

LEARN Jungle Story Problems

ONLINE 15 min

Students will solve story problems that use the same numbers, but in different relationships.

Objectives

- Recognize and solve word problems involving sums or minuends up through 500 in which one quantity changes by addition or subtraction.

LEARN Story Problem Variations

ONLINE 10 min

Students will solve change problems. Using the numbers from those problems in different relationships, students will write new problems.

Objectives

- Recognize and solve word problems involving sums or minuends up through 500 in which one quantity changes by addition or subtraction.

TRY IT Change Problems

OFFLINE 10 min

Students will practice solving story problems involving change. Give students the Change Problems activity page from their Activity Book and read the directions with them. Use the answer key to check students' answers, and then enter the results online.

Objectives

- Recognize and solve word problems involving sums or minuends up through 500 in which one quantity changes by addition or subtraction.

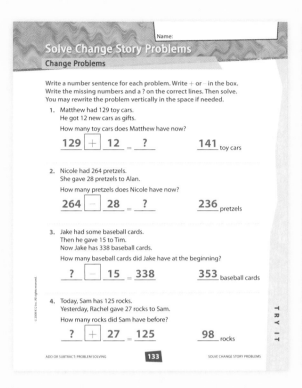

Solve Change Story Problems
Change Problems

Write a number sentence for each problem. Write + or − in the box.
Write the missing numbers and a ? on the correct lines. Then solve.
You may rewrite the problem vertically in the space if needed.

1. Matthew had 129 toy cars.
   He got 12 new cars as gifts.

   How many toy cars does Matthew have now?

   __129__ $\boxed{+}$ __12__ = __?__   __141__ toy cars

2. Nicole had 264 pretzels.
   She gave 28 pretzels to Alan.

   How many pretzels does Nicole have now?

   __264__ $\boxed{-}$ __28__ = __?__   __236__ pretzels

3. Jake had some baseball cards.
   Then he gave 15 to Tim.
   Now Jake has 338 baseball cards.

   How many baseball cards did Jake have at the beginning?

   __?__ $\boxed{}$ __15__ = __338__   __353__ baseball cards

4. Today, Sam has 125 rocks.
   Yesterday, Rachel gave 27 rocks to Sam.

   How many rocks did Sam have before?

   __?__ $\boxed{+}$ __27__ = __125__   __98__ rocks

ADD OR SUBTRACT: PROBLEM SOLVING   **133**   SOLVE CHANGE STORY PROBLEMS

TRY IT

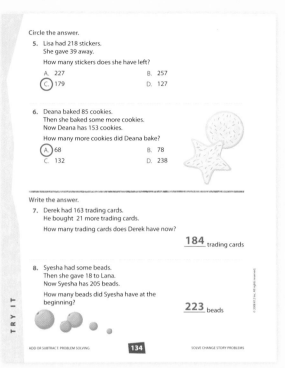

Circle the answer.

5. Lisa had 218 stickers.
   She gave 39 away.

   How many stickers does she have left?

   A. 227   B. 257
   C. 179   D. 127

6. Deana baked 85 cookies.
   Then she baked some more cookies.
   Now Deana has 153 cookies.

   How many more cookies did Deana bake?

   A. 68   B. 78
   C. 132   D. 238

Write the answer.

7. Derek had 163 trading cards.
   He bought 21 more trading cards.

   How many trading cards does Derek have now?

   __184__ trading cards

8. Syesha had some beads.
   Then she gave 18 to Lana.
   Now Syesha has 205 beads.

   How many beads did Syesha have at the beginning?

   __223__ beads

ADD OR SUBTRACT: PROBLEM SOLVING   **134**   SOLVE CHANGE STORY PROBLEMS

TRY IT

CHECKPOINT

OFFLINE
10 min

Print the assessment and have students complete it on their own. Read the directions, questions, and answer choices to students if necessary. Use the answer key to score the assessment, and then enter the results online.

Objectives

- Recognize and solve word problems involving sums or minuends up through 500 in which one quantity changes by addition or subtraction.

◇ Checkpoint   Math | Add or Subtract: Problem Solving | Solve Change Story Problems

Name _____   Date _____

Checkpoint Answer Key

Choose or write the answer.
(1 point)
1. There were 112 fish in a fish store.
   The store sold 65 fish in one day.

   How many fish did the store have then?

   A. 53   B. 47   C. 153   D. 177

(1 point)
2. Paul and his mother made 52 cookies for a party.
   He and his friends ate 38 cookies.

   How many cookies were left?

   A. 14   B. 16   C. 24   D. 26

(1 point)
3. Kobe had 109 stickers.
   He gave away 35 stickers.

   How many stickers does Kobe have now?   __74__ stickers

(1 point)
4. Michelle has 235 beads.
   She gave Dan 123 beads.

   How many beads does Michelle have now?

   A. 112   B. 212   C. 358   D. 258

(1 point)
5. Cindy picked 55 berries from her garden.
   If she eats 12 berries, how many berries will Cindy have left?

   __43__ berries

(1 point)
6. Tom baked 83 cookies.
   If he bakes 12 more cookies, how many cookies will
   Tom have baked altogether?

   A. 71   B. 95   C. 91   D. 75

Compare to Solve Story Problems

Lesson Overview

Skills Update	5 minutes	**ONLINE**
GET READY Compare Lengths and Heights	5 minutes	**ONLINE**
LEARN Compare Collections	20 minutes	**ONLINE**
LEARN Compare Quantities	20 minutes	**ONLINE**
TRY IT Compare to Solve	10 minutes	OFFLINE

▶ Lesson Objectives

Recognize and solve word problems involving numbers up to 500 in which two quantities are compared by the use of addition or subtraction.

▶ Prerequisite Skills

- Use concrete objects or sketches to model and solve addition or subtraction problem-solving situations with sums or minuends up through 500.
- Recognize and solve story problems involving numbers up through 100 in which two quantities are compared, using addition or subtraction.

▶ Common Errors and Misconceptions

Students might add rather than subtract when solving story problems with an unknown difference. Using models might help students choose the correct operation.

▶ Content Background

Students will solve story problems in which two quantities are compared. They will learn how to write number sentences so they can solve the story problems.

In *compare problems*, students must compare two groups to find how many more or fewer are in one group. Here's a compare problem: "Ron has 3 books. Alex has 5. How many more books does Alex have than Ron? Students may compare the groups in this problem by matching the objects in each group using one-to-one correspondence and then counting the objects that do not have a match to find the difference. As students move to greater numbers where counting isn't practical, they should recognize that they can subtract to find the difference.

Materials to Gather
SUPPLIED
Compare to Solve activity page

Keywords	**compare problem** – a problem in which two quantities are compared by finding the difference

GET READY Compare Lengths and Heights

ONLINE
5min

Students will solve story problems in which two lengths or two heights are compared.

Objectives

- Use concrete objects or sketches to model and solve addition or subtraction problem-solving situations with sums or minuends up through 500.
- Recognize and solve word problems involving numbers up to 100 in which two quantities are compared by the use of addition or subtraction.

LEARN Compare Collections

ONLINE
20min

Students will solve story problems in which two quantities are compared. They will be asked how to solve problems that ask how many more and how many fewer.

Objectives

- Recognize and solve word problems involving numbers up to 500 in which two quantities are compared by the use of addition or subtraction.

LEARN Compare Quantities

ONLINE
20min

Students will learn to write number sentences to solve story problems in which two quantities are compared.

Objectives

- Recognize and solve word problems involving numbers up to 500 in which two quantities are compared by the use of addition or subtraction.

TRY IT Compare to Solve

OFFLINE
10min

Students will practice writing and solving number sentences for story problems. Give students the Compare to Solve activity page from their Activity Book and read the directions with them. If necessary, students may rewrite the problems vertically to solve. Use the answer key to check students' answers, and then enter the results online.

Objectives

- Recognize and solve word problems involving numbers up to 500 in which two quantities are compared by the use of addition or subtraction.

Compare to Solve Story Problems
Compare to Solve

Write a number sentence for each problem. Write a ? for the missing number. Then solve.

1. Emma has 7 hats.
   Shannon has 16 more hats than Emma.

   How many hats does Shannon have?

   $\boxed{7}$ $\boxed{+}$ $\boxed{16}$ = ? $\underline{23}$ hats
   or 16 + 7 = ?

2. Liam collected 15 rocks.
   Evan collected 24 rocks.

   How many more rocks did Evan collect than Liam?

   $\boxed{24}$ $\boxed{-}$ $\boxed{15}$ = ? $\underline{9}$ rocks

3. Jenny has 36 buttons.
   She has 16 buttons fewer than Deana.

   How many buttons does Deana have?

   $\boxed{?}$ $\boxed{-}$ $\boxed{16}$ = $\boxed{36}$ $\underline{52}$ buttons
   or 36 + 16 = ?

4. Jason has 48 marbles.
   Cody has 83 marbles.

   How many fewer marbles does Jason have than Cody?

   $\boxed{83}$ $\boxed{-}$ $\boxed{48}$ = ? $\underline{35}$ marbles

TRY IT

Write the answer.

5. Tom has 12 crayons.
   Jerry has 2 more crayons than Tom.

   How many crayons does Jerry have? $\underline{14}$ crayons

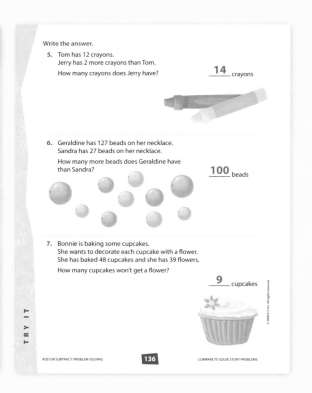

6. Geraldine has 127 beads on her necklace.
   Sandra has 27 beads on her necklace.

   How many more beads does Geraldine have than Sandra? $\underline{100}$ beads

7. Bonnie is baking some cupcakes.
   She wants to decorate each cupcake with a flower.
   She has baked 48 cupcakes and she has 39 flowers.

   How many cupcakes won't get a flower? $\underline{9}$ cupcakes

TRY IT

Compare Amounts to Solve Problems

Lesson Overview		
Skills Update	5 minutes	ONLINE
GET READY Compare Items	5 minutes	ONLINE
LEARN How Many More or Fewer?	10 minutes	ONLINE
LEARN Comparison Story Problems	15 minutes	ONLINE
LEARN Variations of a Problem	15 minutes	ONLINE
TRY IT From Words to Number Sentences	10 minutes	OFFLINE

▶ Lesson Objectives

Recognize and solve word problems involving numbers up to 500 in which two quantities are compared, using addition or subtraction.

▶ Prerequisite Skills

- Use concrete objects or sketches to model and solve addition or subtraction problem-solving situations with sums or minuends up through 500.
- Recognize and solve story problems involving numbers up through 100 in which two quantities are compared, using addition or subtraction.

▶ Common Errors and Misconceptions

Students might add rather than subtract when solving story problems with an unknown difference. Using models might help students choose the correct operation.

▶ Content Background

Students will learn to solve story problems in which two quantities are compared. Students will determine where to place numbers in a number sentence and whether to add or subtract.

In *compare problems*, students must compare two groups to find how many more or fewer are in one group. Here's a compare problem: "Ron has 3 books. Alex has 5. How many more books does Alex have than Ron?" Students may compare the groups in this problem by matching the objects in each group using one-to-one correspondence and then counting the objects that do not have a match to find the difference. As students move to greater numbers where counting isn't practical, they should recognize that they can subtract to find the difference.

Materials to Gather
SUPPLIED
From Words to Number Sentences activity page

GET READY Compare Items

Students will solve story problems in which two quantities are compared.

- Use concrete objects or sketches to model and solve addition or subtraction problem-solving situations with sums or minuends up through 500.
- Recognize and solve story problems involving numbers up through 100 in which two quantities are compared by the use of addition or subtraction.

LEARN How Many More or Fewer?

Students will solve story problems in which two quantities are compared. They will be asked how many more items or how many fewer items one group has compared to another.

Objectives

- Recognize and solve word problems involving numbers up to 500 in which two quantities are compared by the use of addition or subtraction.

LEARN Comparison Story Problems

Students will solve story problems in which two quantities are compared. They will solve a series of problems that use the same numbers but show different relationships.

Objectives

- Recognize and solve word problems involving numbers up to 500 in which two quantities are compared by the use of addition or subtraction.

LEARN Variations of a Problem

Students will solve a story problem in which two quantities are compared. Then students will solve variations of the problem, choosing and solving the correct number sentence to model each variation.

Objectives

- Recognize and solve word problems involving numbers up to 500 in which two quantities are compared by the use of addition or subtraction.

OFFLINE
10 min

TRY IT From Words to Number Sentences

Objectives

Students will practice solving story problems in which two quantities are compared. Give students the From Words to Number Sentences activity page from their Activity Book and read the directions with them. If necessary, students may rewrite the problems vertically to solve. Use the answer key to check students' answers, and then enter the results online.

- Recognize and solve story problems involving numbers up to 500 in which two quantities are compared by the use of addition or subtraction.

Name: _____

Compare Amounts to Solve Problems
From Words to Number Sentences

Write a number sentence for each problem. Write a ? for the missing number. Then solve.

1. Erin made 36 pottery bowls.
   Paul made 27 pottery bowls.
   How many fewer bowls did Paul make than Erin?

   __36__ [−] __27__ = __?__   __9__ bowls

2. Kevin took 248 photos.
   Hailey took 329 photos.
   How many more photos did Hailey take than Kevin?

   __329__ [−] __248__ = __?__   __81__ photos

3. Paige has 157 drawings.
   Abby has 16 more drawings than Paige.
   How many drawings does Abby have?

   __157__ [+] __16__ = __?__   __173__ drawings

4. There were 135 masks in the art gallery.
   The art gallery sold 28 masks.
   How many masks are in the art gallery now?

   __135__ [−] __28__ = __?__   __107__ masks

ADD OR SUBTRACT: PROBLEM SOLVING **137**   COMPARE AMOUNTS TO SOLVE PROBLEMS

T R Y   I T

Circle the answer.

5. Lana has 234 trading cards.
   May has 105 trading cards.
   How many more trading cards does Lana have than May?

   A. 339   B. 131   (C) 129   D. 239

Write the answer.

6. Shana and Leo are making houses out of building blocks.
   Shana has 53 building blocks.
   She has 23 more building blocks than Leo.
   How many building blocks does Leo have?   __30__ building blocks

7. Nick made 28 greeting cards.
   Raul made 19 greeting cards.
   How many fewer greeting cards did Raul make than Nick?

   __9__ greeting cards

8. Dina has 138 photos.
   Tom has 14 more photos than Dina.
   How many photos does Tom have?   __152__ photos

ADD OR SUBTRACT: PROBLEM SOLVING **138**   COMPARE AMOUNTS TO SOLVE PROBLEMS

T R Y   I T

Make Equal Amounts to Solve Problems

Lesson Overview		
Skills Update	5 minutes	ONLINE
GET READY In the Garden	5 minutes	ONLINE
LEARN Wild West Math	20 minutes	ONLINE
LEARN Growing Season	20 minutes	ONLINE
TRY IT Make Equal Groups	10 minutes	OFFLINE

▶ Lesson Objectives

Recognize and solve word problems involving numbers up to 500 in which one quantity must be changed to equal another quantity.

▶ Prerequisite Skills

- Recognize and solve story problems involving sums or minuends up through 500 in which one quantity changes, using addition or subtraction.
- Recognize and solve story problems involving numbers up to 100 in which one quantity must be changed to equal another quantity.

▶ Common Errors and Misconceptions

Students might add rather than subtract when solving problems with an unknown difference. Using models might help students choose the correct operation.

▶ Content Background

Some story problems are categorized as *equalize problems* because they describe situations in which a quantity is changed to equal another quantity. In this lesson, students will solve story problems of this type. Equalize problems can involve addition or subtraction.

Students do not need to memorize the types of problems but will instead gain the experience and confidence necessary to read a problem, create a mental image, and figure out which quantities within the problem to add or subtract to find the solution.

Materials to Gather

SUPPLIED

Make Equal Groups activity page

Keywords

equalize problem – a problem in which one quantity is changed to equal another quantity

GET READY In the Garden

Students will solve story problems in which one amount is changed in order to equal another amount.

- Recognize and solve story problems involving sums or minuends up through 500 in which one quantity changes, using addition or subtraction.
- Recognize and solve story problems involving numbers up to 100 in which one quantity must be changed to equal another quantity.

LEARN Wild West Math

Students will solve story problems in which one amount is changed in order to equal another amount.

- Recognize and solve word problems involving numbers up to 500 in which one quantity must be changed to equal another quantity.

LEARN Growing Season

Students will create number sentences to solve story problems in which one amount is changed in order to equal another amount.

- Recognize and solve word problems involving numbers up to 500 in which one quantity must be changed to equal another quantity.

TRY IT Make Equal Groups

Students will practice solving story problems in which one amount is changed in order to equal another amount. Give students the Make Equal Groups activity page from their Activity Book and read the directions with them.

If necessary, students may write each problem vertically to solve. Use the answer key to check students' answers, and then enter the results online.

- Recognize and solve word problems involving numbers up to 500 in which one quantity must be changed to equal another quantity.

Make Equal Amounts to Solve Problems
Make Equal Groups

Write a number sentence for each problem. Write + or − in the box and ?
for the missing number in the number sentence. Then solve.

1. Shannon has 37 beads.
   If she buys 28 more beads, then she will have the same
   number of beads as Brianna.

   How many beads does Brianna have?

   __37__ $\boxed{+}$ __28__ = _?_   __65__ beads

2. Joe has 51 jelly beans.
   If he eats 19 jelly beans, then he will have as many jelly beans as Ricky.

   How many jelly beans does Ricky have?

   __51__ $\boxed{-}$ __19__ = _?_   __32__ jelly beans

3. Tyree has 82 paper clips. Jason has 66 paper clips.

   How many paper clips does Tyree have to give away to have as many
   paper clips as Jason?

   __82__ $\boxed{-}$ __66__ = _?_   __16__ paper clips
   or 66 + ? = 82

4. Jessica needs 92 tiles to decorate a tray.
   She has 64 tiles.

   How many more tiles does she need?

   __92__ $\boxed{-}$ _?_ = __64__   __28__ tiles
   or 64 + ? = 92

T R Y   I T

Write a number sentence for each problem. Write + or − in the box and ?
for the missing number in the number sentence. Then solve.

5. Ted rode his bike 54 miles.
   Jonah rode his bike 88 miles.

   How many miles must Ted ride to have ridden the same
   number as Jonah?

   __88__ $\boxed{-}$ __54__ = _?_   __34__ miles

6. Charlotte has 361 marbles.
   If she sold 43 marbles, she would have the same number as Violet.

   How many marbles does Violet have?

   __361__ $\boxed{-}$ __43__ = _?_   __318__ marbles

7. Wallace rode his bike 54 miles.
   If he had ridden 40 more miles, he would have ridden the same number
   of miles as Brady.

   How many miles has Brady ridden?

   __54__ $\boxed{+}$ __40__ = _?_   __94__ miles

T R Y   I T

Equalize Story Problems

Lesson Overview

Skills Update	5 minutes	ONLINE
GET READY Firehouse Problems	5 minutes	ONLINE
LEARN Equal Distances	10 minutes	ONLINE
LEARN Equal Lengths	15 minutes	ONLINE
LEARN Create Story Problems	15 minutes	OFFLINE
TRY IT Outdoor Problems	10 minutes	OFFLINE
CHECKPOINT	10 minutes	OFFLINE

▶ Lesson Objectives

Recognize and solve word problems involving numbers up to 500 in which one quantity must be changed to equal another quantity.

▶ Prerequisite Skills

- Recognize and solve word problems involving sums or minuends up through 500 in which one quantity changes, using addition or subtraction.
- Recognize and solve story problems involving numbers up through 100 in which one quantity must be changed to equal another quantity.

▶ Advance Preparation

Print two copies of My Story Problems. Write the following story problem on one of the My Story Problems printouts:

- Tim has 171 cherries. If he eats 28 cherries, then he will have as many cherries as Shelby. How many cherries does Shelby have?

▶ Content Background

Some story problems are categorized as *equalize problems* because they describe situations in which one amount is changed in order to equal another amount. In this lesson, students will solve story problems of this type. Equalize problems can involve addition or subtraction.

Students do not need to memorize the types of problems, but will instead gain the experience and confidence necessary to read a problem, create a mental image, and figure out which quantities within the problem to add or subtract to find the solution.

Keywords	**quantity** – a number or amount

Materials to Gather

SUPPLIED
My Story Problems (printout) – 2
Outdoor Problems activity page
Checkpoint (printout)

GET READY Firehouse Problems

Students will solve story problems in which one amount must be changed in order to equal another amount.

Objectives

- Recognize and solve word problems involving sums or minuends up through 500 in which one quantity changes, using addition or subtraction.
- Recognize and solve story problems involving numbers up through 100 in which one quantity must be changed to equal another quantity.

LEARN Equal Distances

Objectives

Students will solve story problems in which one amount must be changed in order to to equal another amount. These problems will use greater numbers than those used in previous activities.

Objectives

- Recognize and solve word problems involving numbers up to 500 in which one quantity must be changed to equal another quantity.

LEARN Equal Lengths

Objectives

Students will solve story problems in which one amount is changed in order to equal another amount.

Objectives

- Recognize and solve word problems involving numbers up to 500 in which one quantity must be changed to equal another quantity.

LEARN Create Story Problems

Objectives

Students will solve a story problem in which one amount is changed in order to equal another amount. This type of problem is often called an *equalize problem*. Gather the My Story Problems printouts.

Objectives

- Recognize and solve word problems involving numbers up to 500 in which one quantity must be changed to equal another quantity.

1. Read the story problem to students that you wrote on the My Story Problems printout:

   Tim has 171 cherries. If he eats 28 cherries, then he will have as many cherries as Shelby. How many cherries does Shelby have?

2. **Ask:** Will you add or subtract to solve this problem?
   ANSWER: subtract

3. **Say:** Write a number sentence to solve this problem.

   Students should write $171 - 28 = ?$, and then solve to find the answer.
   (143 cherries)

4. **Say:** Now let's make another story problem using the same numbers.

Guide students to use the same numbers and characters to make new story problems. Then students should write a number sentence and solve each problem. Students should make up 3 of their own problems.

Example problems:

- Tim has 28 cherries. Shelby has 171 cherries. How many more cherries does Shelby have than Tim?
- Tim has 143 cherries. Shelby has 28 cherries. How many cherries do they have altogether?

TRY IT Outdoor Problems

Student will practice solving equalize problems. Give students the Outdoor Problems activity page from their Activity Book and read the directions with them. Use the answer key to check students' answers, and then enter the results online.

Objectives

- Recognize and solve word problems involving numbers up to 500 in which one quantity must be changed to equal another quantity.

Name:

Equalize Story Problems
Outdoor Problems

Write a number sentence for each problem. Write + or − in the box and ? for the missing number in the number sentence. Then solve.

1. Bell Park has 317 trees.
   If the city plants 129 more trees, then it will have planted the same number of trees as Redwood Park.

   How many trees does Redwood Park have?

   $317 \boxed{+} 129 = ?$ 446 trees

2. Drew and Ivana are collecting pinecones.
   Drew has 241 pinecones.
   If he drops 28 pinecones, then he will have as many pinecones as Ivana.

   How many pinecones does Ivana have?

   $241 \boxed{-} 28 = ?$ 213 pinecones

3. Meghan and Peter are selling plant seeds.
   Meghan has 412 seeds.
   Peter has 256 seeds.

   How many seeds does Meghan need to sell to have as many seeds as Peter?

   $412 \boxed{-} 256 = ?$ 156 seeds
   or $412 - ? = 256$

Write a number sentence for each problem. Write + or − in the box and ? for the missing number in the number sentence. Then solve.

4. Ralph has 227 seeds to plant.
   Wayne has 120 seeds.

   How many seeds does Wayne need to get so he has the same number as Ralph?

   $227 \boxed{-} 120 = ?$ 107 seeds

5. Hannah has 58 flowers.
   Thomas has 40 flowers.

   How many flowers does Hannah need to sell to have as many flowers as Thomas?

   $58 \boxed{-} 40 = ?$ 18 flowers

Write the answer.

6. Workers at a new park planted 128 rosebushes.
   If the workers were to plant 129 more rosebushes, then they would have planted the same number of rosebushes as the number of rosebushes in Central Park.

   How many rosebushes does Central Park have?

   257 rosebushes

CHECKPOINT

Objectives

- Recognize and solve word problems involving numbers up to 500 in which one quantity must be changed to equal another quantity.

Print the assessment and have students complete it on their own. Read the directions, questions, and answer choices to students if necessary. Use the answer key to score the assessment, and then enter the results online.

If necessary, students may rewrite Problems 3–5 vertically to solve.

Name _____ Date _____

Checkpoint Answer Key

Circle the answer.

(1 point)
1. Pam and Sam wrote about their families.
   Pam wrote 150 words and Sam wrote 212 words.

   What would Pam have to do to have the same number of words as Sam?

   (A.) Write 62 more words.   B. Write 112 more words.
   C. Erase 112 of her words.   D. Write 142 more words.

(1 point)
2. Tami needs 500 beads to make a necklace.
   She has 345 beads.

   How many more beads does she need?

   A. 144   (B.) 155
   C. 165   D. 245

Write a number sentence for each problem. Write + or – in the box and ? for the missing number. Then solve.

(1 point)
3. Mindy picked 143 apples.
   If she had picked 14 more apples, she would have picked the same number as Lisa.

   How many apples did Lisa pick?

   143 $\boxed{+}$ 14 = ?

   157 apples

Name _____ Date _____

(1 point)
4. Dean swam 35 laps.
   If he had swum 11 more laps, he would have swum the same number of laps as Ariel.

   How many laps did Ariel swim?

   35 $\boxed{+}$ 11 = ?

   46 laps

(1 point)
5. Frank has 79 stickers in his album.
   Jeff has 200 stickers.

   How many stickers will Frank have to get so he has the same number as Jeff?

   200 $\boxed{-}$ 79 = ?

   121 stickers

Unit Review

▶ Unit Objectives

This lesson reviews the following objectives:

- Use concrete objects or sketches to model and solve addition or subtraction problem-solving situations with sums or minuends up through 500.
- Recognize and solve word problems involving sums up through 500 in which two quantities are combined.
- Recognize and solve word problems involving sums or minuends up through 500 in which one quantity changes by addition or subtraction.
- Recognize and solve word problems involving numbers up to 500 in which two quantities are compared by the use of addition or subtraction.
- Recognize and solve word problems involving numbers up to 500 in which one quantity must be changed to equal another quantity.

▶ Advance Preparation

In this lesson, students will have an opportunity to review previous activities in the Add or Subtract: Problem Solving unit. Look at the suggested activities in Unit Review: Prepare for the Checkpoint online and gather any needed materials.

Materials to Gather

SUPPLIED

base-10 blocks

place-value mat

Checkpoint Practice activity page

Keywords

addend	minuend
addition	model (noun)
change problem	model (verb)
combine problem	number sentence
compare problem	operation
count on	quantity
difference	regroup; regrouping
equalize problem	sum
inverse operations	symbol

UNIT REVIEW Look Back

Objectives

• Review unit objectives.

In this unit, students have learned to solve addition and subtraction story problems with sums or minuends up through 500. Students have used concrete objects and sketches to model and solve problems with and without regrouping. Students have also learned to recognize and solve story problems in which two quantities are combined or compared. Students have used addition and subtraction to solve story problems in which one quantity changes, as well as story problems in which one quantity must be changed in order to to equal another quantity. In this lesson, students will review these concepts to prepare for the Unit Checkpoint.

UNIT REVIEW Checkpoint Practice

Objectives

• Review unit objectives.

Students will complete a Checkpoint Practice activity page to prepare for the Unit Checkpoint. If necessary, read the directions, questions, and answer choices to students. Have students answer the problems on their own. Carefully review the answers with students.

Gather the base-10 blocks and place-value mat. Students will use these materials for Problems 1 and 2.

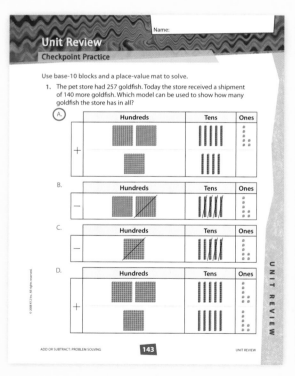

Unit Review
Checkpoint Practice

Use base-10 blocks and a place-value mat to solve.

1. The pet store had 257 goldfish. Today the store received a shipment of 140 more goldfish. Which model can be used to show how many goldfish the store has in all?

A.

	Hundreds	Tens	Ones
+			

B.

	Hundreds	Tens	Ones
−			

C.

	Hundreds	Tens	Ones
−			

D.

	Hundreds	Tens	Ones
+			

ADD OR SUBTRACT: PROBLEM SOLVING **143** UNIT REVIEW

Use base-10 blocks and a place-value mat to solve.

2. Chad has 115 blocks in his collection. Ethan has 227 blocks in his collection. How many more blocks does Ethan have than Chad?

112 more blocks

Read each problem and solve. You may wish to rewrite the problems in vertical format to solve.

3. Anna has 102 crayons in her box. Will has 25 crayons in his box. How many crayons are there in the two boxes?

102 + **25** = **127** crayons

4. Curt has 28 bottle caps and Keith has 116 bottle caps. How many do they have in all?

A. 88   B. 144
C. 154   D. 128

5. The farmer had 75 apples in a basket. He sold 36 apples. How many apples did the farmer have left?

39 apples

ADD OR SUBTRACT: PROBLEM SOLVING **144** UNIT REVIEW

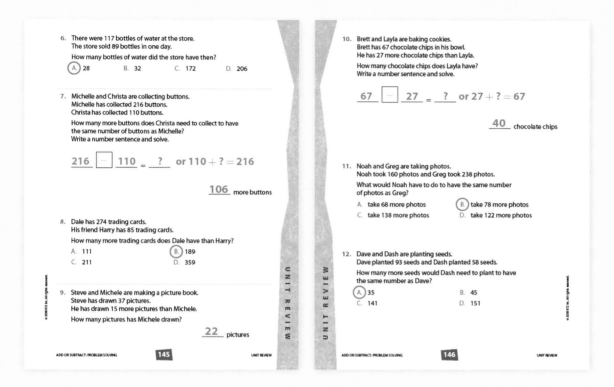

6. There were 117 bottles of water at the store.
   The store sold 89 bottles in one day.

   How many bottles of water did the store have then?

   (A.) 28　　　B. 32　　　C. 172　　　D. 206

7. Michelle and Christa are collecting buttons.
   Michelle has collected 216 buttons.
   Christa has collected 110 buttons.

   How many more buttons does Christa need to collect to have
   the same number of buttons as Michelle?
   Write a number sentence and solve.

   216 $\boxed{-}$ 110 = __?__　or 110 + ? = 216

   __106__ more buttons

8. Dale has 274 trading cards.
   His friend Harry has 85 trading cards.

   How many more trading cards does Dale have than Harry?

   A. 111　　　　　　　(B.) 189
   C. 211　　　　　　　D. 359

9. Steve and Michele are making a picture book.
   Steve has drawn 37 pictures.
   He has drawn 15 more pictures than Michele.

   How many pictures has Michele drawn?

   __22__ pictures

10. Brett and Layla are baking cookies.
    Brett has 67 chocolate chips in his bowl.
    He has 27 more chocolate chips than Layla.

    How many chocolate chips does Layla have?
    Write a number sentence and solve.

    __67__ $\boxed{-}$ __27__ = __?__　or 27 + ? = 67

    __40__ chocolate chips

11. Noah and Greg are taking photos.
    Noah took 160 photos and Greg took 238 photos.

    What would Noah have to do to have the same number
    of photos as Greg?

    A. take 68 more photos　　　(B.) take 78 more photos
    C. take 138 more photos　　　D. take 122 more photos

12. Dave and Dash are planting seeds.
    Dave planted 93 seeds and Dash planted 58 seeds.

    How many more seeds would Dash need to plant to have
    the same number as Dave?

    (A.) 35　　　　　　　B. 45
    C. 141　　　　　　　D. 151

→ UNIT REVIEW Prepare for the Checkpoint

What you do next depends on how students performed in the previous activity,
Unit Review: Checkpoint Practice. If students had difficulty with any of the
problems, complete the appropriate review activity listed in the table online.

Unit Checkpoint

| **UNIT CHECKPOINT** Online | 30 minutes | **ONLINE** |
| **UNIT CHECKPOINT** Offline | 30 minutes | **OFFLINE** |

▶ Unit Objectives

This lesson assesses the following objectives:

- Use concrete objects or sketches to model and solve addition or subtraction problem-solving situations with sums or minuends up through 500.
- Recognize and solve word problems involving sums up through 500 in which two quantities are combined.
- Recognize and solve word problems involving sums or minuends up through 500 in which one quantity changes by addition or subtraction.
- Recognize and solve word problems involving numbers up to 500 in which two quantities are compared by the use of addition or subtraction.
- Recognize and solve word problems involving numbers up to 500 in which one quantity must be changed to equal another quantity.

Materials to Gather

SUPPLIED
Unit Checkpoint (printout)
base-10 blocks
place-value mat

ONLINE
30min

UNIT CHECKPOINT Online

Objectives

- Assess unit objectives.

Students will complete this part of the Unit Checkpoint online. Read the directions, problems, and answer choices to students. If necessary, help students with keyboard or mouse operations.

OFFLINE
30min

UNIT CHECKPOINT Offline

Objectives

- Assess unit objectives.

Students will complete this part of the Unit Checkpoint offline. Print the Checkpoint and have students complete it on their own. Read the directions, problems, and answer choices to students, if necessary. Use the answer key to score the Checkpoint, and then enter the results online.

Gather the base-10 blocks and place-value mat. Students will use these materials for Problems 1–6.

Name   Date

Unit Checkpoint Answer Key

For Problems 1–6, use base-10 blocks and a place-value mat to solve.

(1 point)
1. Keith has 212 rocks in his collection.
Matt has 436 rocks in his collection.

How many more rocks does Matt have than Keith?   **224** more rocks

(1 point)
2. The Fancy Farm had 257 visitors in June.
The Fancy Farm had 183 visitors in July.

How many visitors did the Fancy Farm have in June and July?   **440** visitors

(1 point)
3. Elise has 314 bears in her collection.
Dean has 425 bears in his collection.

How many more bears does Dean have than Elise?   **111** more bears

(1 point)
4. The zoo had 159 visitors in April.
The zoo had 167 visitors in May.

How many visitors did the zoo have in April and May?   **326** visitors

(1 point)
5. Marla had some stickers.
Her sister gave her 61 more.
Now she has 273 stickers.

How many stickers did Marla start with?   **212** stickers

(1 point)
6. Shane had some trading cards.
His friend gave him 21 more.
Now Shane has 153 trading cards.

How many trading cards did Shane start with?   **132** trading cards

Name   Date

For Problems 7–8, circle the answer.
(1 point)
7. The Finicky Fish Store had 288 goldfish.
Today the store received a shipment of 120 goldfish.

Which model can be used to show how many goldfish the store has in all?

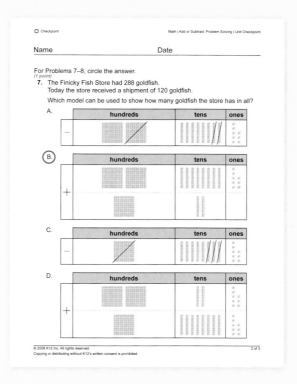

Name   Date

(1 point)
8. Thea and her Mom made 145 cupcakes for the bake sale.
Then they made 121 more.

Which model can be used to show how many cupcakes they made in all?

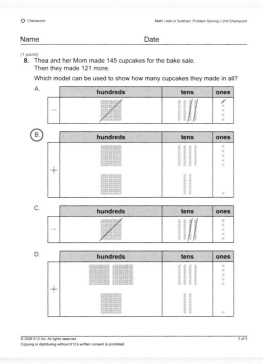

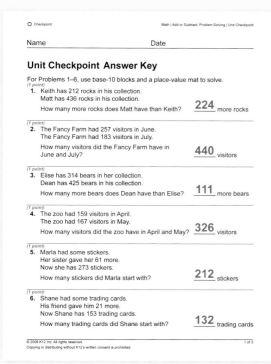

Problem Solving: Reason and Connect

Should I add or subtract to solve this story problem?

The Children's Playhouse sold 465 tickets Friday night and 184 tickets Saturday night. How many fewer tickets did the Children's Playhouse sell on Saturday than on Friday?

▶ Unit Objectives

- Write and solve addition or subtraction number sentences to represent problem-solving situations with sums and minuends up through 500.

- Check the accuracy of calculations from the context of addition or subtraction problem-solving situations with sums and minuends up through 500 with regrouping.

- Justify the procedures selected for addition or subtraction problem-solving situations with sums or minuends up through 500.

- Demonstrate an understanding of connections between similar addition or subtraction problems from problem-solving situations, involving sums and minuends up through 500.

- Give examples of problem situations that can be described by addition or subtraction number sentences, and write the sentences.

▶ Big Ideas

- The use of letters, numbers, and mathematical symbols makes it possible to translate complex situations or long word statements into concise mathematical sentences or expressions.

- An inverse operation undoes another operation. Addition and subtraction are inverse operations.

▶ Unit Introduction

In this unit, students will learn about solving story problems. They will write number sentences and use them to solve story problems that involve addition or subtraction. They will analyze a problem to check for errors and determine if the answer is correct. Students will explain solutions to story problems and learn that there can be more than one way to find the answer. They will compare story problems and will learn to recognize problems that are solved the same way. Students will also write and solve their own story problems.

Story Problems

▶ Lesson Objectives

Write and solve addition or subtraction number sentences to represent problem-solving situations with sums and minuends up through 500.

▶ Prerequisite Skills

Recognize and solve story problems involving sums or minuends up through 500 in which one quantity changes by addition or subtraction.

▶ Content Background

In this lesson, students will solve story problems involving addition and subtraction.

Keywords	**number sentence** – two expressions related by an equals symbol ($=$), a not-equal-to symbol ($\neq$), or an inequality symbol; for example, $7 - 2 = 4 + 1$; $5 \neq 4 + 4$; $6 + 2 > 1 + 4$ **story problem** – a word problem that represents a problem-solving situation

Materials to Gather

SUPPLIED

Mixed Story Problems activity page

base-10 blocks

GET READY Choose Number Sentences

ONLINE **10**min

Students will practice selecting a number sentence that represents a story problem.

Objectives

- Recognize and solve word problems involving sums or minuends up through 500 in which one quantity changes by addition or subtraction.

LEARN Write Number Sentences

ONLINE **10**min

Students will learn that they can make different problems using the same story. Students will create number sentences to represent each problem.

Objectives

- Write and solve addition or subtraction number sentences to represent problem-solving situations with sums and minuends up through 500.

LEARN Number Sentences

Students will practice writing number sentences to solve story problems using addition and subtraction.

Objectives

- Write and solve addition or subtraction number sentences to represent problem-solving situations with sums and minuends up through 500.

LEARN Mixed Story Problems

Students will describe in their own words what is happening in a story problem. They will write a number sentence and find the answer by using addition or subtraction.
Gather the base-10 blocks and the Mixed Story Problems activity page.

1. Read the story problems to students. To help students describe what is happening in the problem, ask them questions such as the following:

   - Are two amounts being put together or compared?
   - Is an amount being added or taken away?
   - Do you have to find how many there are altogether, how many more, how many less, or how many are left?

2. Guide students as they write an addition or subtraction number sentence to represent the story and solve the problem.

Objectives

- Write and solve addition or subtraction number sentences to represent problem-solving situations with sums and minuends up through 500.

Tips

Students may use base-10 blocks to model the problem and help them explain what is happening.

Name: _____

Story Problems
Mixed Story Problems

Write what is happening in each story. You may draw a sketch. Then write a number sentence to find the answer.

1. There are 76 birds in a park. You can see 32 birds on the ground.

   The rest of the birds are hiding in a tree.
   How many birds are hiding in the tree?

   Check students' summaries.

   _____

   $76 \boxed{-} 32 \boxed{=} 44$

   $\underline{44}$ birds

2. The ice cream shop opened this weekend. The shop sold 285 vanilla ice cream cones and 119 chocolate ice cream cones.

   How many cones did the shop sell in all?

   Check students' summaries.

   _____

   $285 \boxed{+} 119 \boxed{=} 404$

   $\underline{404}$ cones

3. Jill and Nathan like to collect books. Nathan has 28 fewer books than Jill. Nathan has 63 books.

   How many books does Jill have?

   Check students' summaries.

   _____

   $63 \boxed{+} 28 \boxed{=} 91$

   $\underline{91}$ books

4. Peter and Lindsey put stickers on their notebooks. Peter used 37 stickers. Lindsey used 54 stickers.

   How many more stickers did Lindsey use than Peter?

   Check students' summaries.

   _____

   $54 \boxed{-} 37 \boxed{=} 17$

   $\underline{17}$ stickers

TRY IT Solve Mixed Problems

Students will use number sentences to demonstrate what they know about solving story problems.

Objectives

- Write and solve addition or subtraction number sentences to represent problem-solving situations with sums and minuends up through 500.

More Story Problems

Skills Update	5 minutes	ONLINE
GET READY Write the Number Sentence	10 minutes	ONLINE
LEARN Problems with Larger Numbers	10 minutes	ONLINE
LEARN Which Number Sentence?	10 minutes	ONLINE
TRY IT Solve Story Problems	15 minutes	OFFLINE
CHECKPOINT	10 minutes	OFFLINE

▶ Lesson Objectives

Write and solve addition or subtraction number sentences to represent problem-solving situations with sums and minuends up through 500.

▶ Prerequisite Skills

Recognize and solve word problems involving sums or minuends up through 500 in which one quantity changes by addition or subtraction.

▶ Content Background

Students will learn to solve story problems involving 2-digit and 3-digit numbers.
  Writing a number sentence is a way for students to think about and show the process that they will use to solve a story problem. Some students think of a number sentence as the code that leads to the answer.

Keywords

addition sentence – a number sentence that involves addition only
subtraction sentence – a number sentence that involves subtraction only

Materials to Gather

SUPPLIED
blocks – B (all colors, optional)
Solve Story Problems activity page
Checkpoint (printout)

GET READY Write the Number Sentence

ONLINE
10 min

Students will practice writing a number sentence to represent a given story problem.
  Have students ask themselves questions such as the following:

- Do I have to put together two amounts to solve the problem?
- Do I have to compare the numbers to find the answer?
- Do I have to add or take away an amount to find the answer?
- Do I have to find how many altogether, how many more, how many less, or how many left?

Objectives

- Recognize and solve word problems involving sums or minuends up through 500 in which one quantity changes by addition or subtraction.

Tips

Allow students to use counting chips or draw sketches to model each problem.

LEARN Problems with Larger Numbers

Students will learn that they can use strategies they ready know to solve problems with larger numbers.

Objectives

- Write and solve addition or subtraction number sentences to represent problem-solving situations with sums and minuends up through 500.

LEARN Which Number Sentence?

Students will practice choosing number sentences to solve story problems.

Objectives

- Write and solve addition or subtraction number sentences to represent problem-solving situations with sums and minuends up through 500.

TRY IT Solve Story Problems

Students will practice writing number sentences and using them to solve addition and subtraction story problems. Give students the Solve Story Problems activity page from their Activity Book and read the directions with them. Use the answer key to check students' answers, and then enter the results online.

Objectives

- Write and solve addition or subtraction number sentences to represent problem-solving situations with sums and minuends up through 500.

Name: _____

More Story Problems

Solve Story Problems

Write and solve a number sentence for each story problem.

1. Carter has 234 stamps.
   Lee has 176 stamps.

   How many more stamps does Lee need to have the same number of stamps as Carter?

   $234 - 176 = ?$ **58** stamps

2. Billy and Val go to the library together.
   Billy reads 96 pages of his book.
   Val reads 120 pages of her book.

   How many more pages did Val read than Billy?

   $120 - 96 = ?$ **24** pages

3. Toby had 114 baseball cards.
   His grandfather gave him some boxes of baseball cards.
   There were 65 cards in the boxes.

   How many cards does Toby have now?

   $114 + 65 = ?$ **179** cards

   or $65 + 114 = ?$

Write and solve a number sentence for each story problem.

4. There are 247 dolls on the shelf.
   There are 198 dolls in a bin.
   How many dolls are there altogether?

   $247 + 198 = ?$ **445** dolls

   or $198 + 247 = ?$

5. Roscoe's Bookstore had 482 books for sale.
   Customers bought 299 of the books.

   How many books were left in the store?

   $482 - 299 = ?$ **183** books left

6. There are 243 fans cheering for the Wranglers.
   There are 222 fans cheering for the Legends.

   How many fans are there altogether?

   $243 + 222 = ?$ **465** fans

   or $222 + 243 = ?$

7. There are 368 seats in the gym.
   If there are 412 people in the gym, how many will not get a seat?

   $412 - 368 = ?$ **44** people

CHECKPOINT

Objectives

Print the assessment and have students complete it on their own. Read the directions, questions, and answer choices to students if necessary. Use the answer key to score the assessment, and then enter the results online.

- Write and solve addition or subtraction number sentences to represent problem-solving situations with sums and minuends up through 500.

Name _____ Date _____

Checkpoint Answer Key

Write a number sentence and then solve the problem.
(2 points)
1. Diana had 233 pennies in her piggy bank.
   She found 165 more pennies.

   How many pennies does Diana have now?

   $$233 + 165 = ?$$

   Diana has ___398___ pennies.

(2 points)
2. There are 234 fans cheering for the Tigers.
   There are 233 fans cheering for the Lions.

   How many fans are there altogether?

   $$234 + 233 = ?$$

   There are ___467___ fans altogether.

(2 points)
3. Margaret had 66 stickers and Michael had 123 stickers.

   How many more stickers did Michael have than Margaret?

   $$123 - 66 = ?$$

   Michael had ___57___ more stickers than Margaret.

Name _____ Date _____

Which number sentence could you use to solve the problem?
(1 point)
4. The bookshop had 56 car magazines.
   One weekend, it sold 22 of them.

   How many car magazines did the bookshop have left?

   A. 22 + 30 = ?   B. 56 + 34 = ?
   C. 56 + 22 = ?   (D.) 56 − 22 = ?

(1 point)
5. Natasha has 27 beads on her necklace.
   Her friend Tina has 60 beads on her necklace.

   How many more beads must Natasha get to have the same number of beads as Tina?

   (A.) 60 − 27 = ?   B. 27 + 20 = ?
   C. 60 + 27 = ?   D. 60 + 33 = ?

Problem Solving: Answer Check

Lesson Overview

Skills Update	5 minutes	ONLINE
GET READY Solve the Problem	5 minutes	ONLINE
LEARN Answer Check	15 minutes	ONLINE
LEARN Solve and Check	15 minutes	OFFLINE
TRY IT Is the Answer Correct?	10 minutes	OFFLINE
CHECKPOINT	10 minutes	OFFLINE

▶ **Lesson Objectives**

Check the accuracy of calculations from the context of addition or subtraction problem-solving situations with sums and minuends up through 500 with regrouping.

▶ **Prerequisite Skills**

Write and solve addition or subtraction number sentences to represent problem-solving situations with sums and minuends up through 500.

▶ **Content Background**

Students will learn how to check whether a given answer to a story problem is correct. Students will analyze the answer, and, if it is incorrect, they will determine why and provide the correct answer.

The ability to recognize common types of errors and correct them is a key to students' success in math.

Keywords	**check** – to examine for accuracy **combine problem** – an addition problem in which two quantities are put together to find a sum **compare problem** – a problem in which two quantities are compared by finding the difference

Materials to Gather

SUPPLIED

Solve and Check activity page

Is the Answer Correct? activity page

Checkpoint (printout)

GET READY Solve the Problem

ONLINE
5 min

Students will create addition or subtraction number sentences to solve story problems.

Objectives

- Write and solve addition or subtraction number sentences to represent problem-solving situations with sums and minuends up through 500.

LEARN Answer Check

Objectives

- Check the accuracy of calculations from the context of addition or subtraction problem-solving situations with sums and minuends up through 500 with regrouping.

Students will learn how to analyze the solution to a story problem. They will check the computation, determine if the given answer is correct, and describe any errors.

Students might need to review basic addition and subtraction facts or how to regroup. Point out answers where the correct operation was chosen but the calculation was done incorrectly. This is often the case when regrouping is involved.

LEARN Solve and Check

Objectives

- Check the accuracy of calculations from the context of addition or subtraction problem-solving situations with sums and minuends up through 500 with regrouping.

Students will solve story problems to check Bror's answers. If a given answer is incorrect, students will explain the error and provide the correct answer.

Gather the Solve and Check activity page.

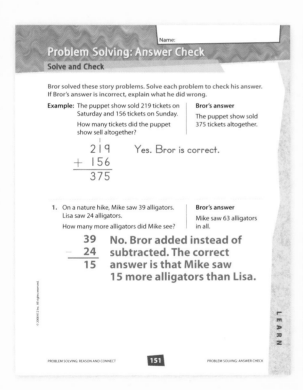

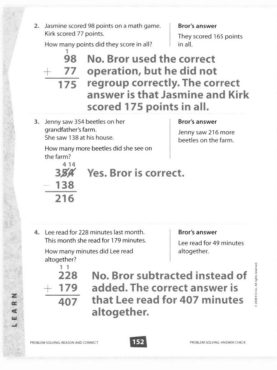

TRY IT Is the Answer Correct?

Students will practice checking answers to story problems. Give students the Is the Answer Correct? activity page from their Activity Book and read the directions with them.

Objectives

- Check the accuracy of calculations from the context of addition or subtraction problem-solving situations with sums and minuends up through 500 with regrouping.

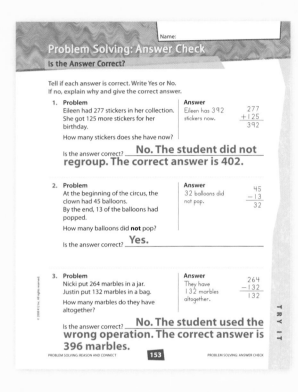

Name:

Problem Solving: Answer Check

Is the Answer Correct?

Tell if each answer is correct. Write Yes or No.
If no, explain why and give the correct answer.

1. Problem
Eileen had 277 stickers in her collection. She got 125 more stickers for her birthday.

How many stickers does she have now?

Answer
Eileen has 392 stickers now.

277
+125
392

Is the answer correct? **No. The student did not regroup. The correct answer is 402.**

2. Problem
At the beginning of the circus, the clown had 45 balloons.
By the end, 13 of the balloons had popped.

How many balloons did **not** pop?

Answer
32 balloons did not pop.

45
−13
32

Is the answer correct? **Yes.**

3. Problem
Nicki put 264 marbles in a jar.
Justin put 132 marbles in a bag.

How many marbles do they have altogether?

Answer
They have 132 marbles altogether.

264
−132
132

Is the answer correct? **No. The student used the wrong operation. The correct answer is 396 marbles.**

PROBLEM SOLVING: REASON AND CONNECT **153**   PROBLEM SOLVING: ANSWER CHECK

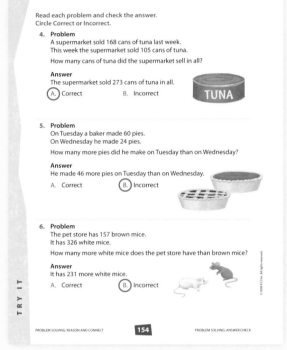

Read each problem and check the answer.
Circle Correct or Incorrect.

4. Problem
A supermarket sold 168 cans of tuna last week.
This week the supermarket sold 105 cans of tuna.

How many cans of tuna did the supermarket sell in all?

Answer
The supermarket sold 273 cans of tuna in all.

A. Correct   B. Incorrect

5. Problem
On Tuesday a baker made 60 pies.
On Wednesday he made 24 pies.

How many more pies did he make on Tuesday than on Wednesday?

Answer
He made 46 more pies on Tuesday than on Wednesday.

A. Correct   **B.** Incorrect

6. Problem
The pet store has 157 brown mice.
It has 326 white mice.

How many more white mice does the pet store have than brown mice?

Answer
It has 231 more white mice.

A. Correct   **B.** Incorrect

PROBLEM SOLVING: REASON AND CONNECT **154**   PROBLEM SOLVING: ANSWER CHECK

CHECKPOINT

Objectives

Print the assessment and have students complete it on their own. Read the directions, questions, and answer choices to students if necessary. Use the answer key to score the assessment, and then enter the results online.

- Check the accuracy of calculations from the context of addition or subtraction problem-solving situations with sums and minuends up through 500 with regrouping.

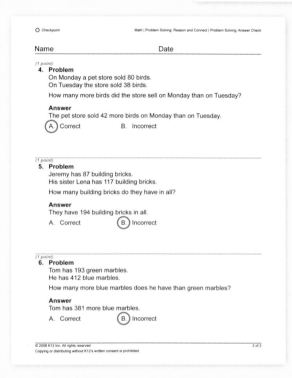

Explain Problem Solutions

Lesson Overview

Skills Update	5 minutes	ONLINE
LEARN Explain Answers	15 minutes	ONLINE
LEARN Identify Kinds of Problems	15 minutes	ONLINE
LEARN Use Sketches and Diagrams	15 minutes	OFFLINE
TRY IT Explain Solutions	10 minutes	OFFLINE

▶ Lesson Objectives

Justify the procedures selected for addition or subtraction problem-solving situations with sums or minuends up through 500.

▶ Prerequisite Skills

Check the accuracy of calculations from the context of addition or subtraction problem-solving situations with sums and minuends up through 500 with regrouping.

▶ Content Background

One of the most important skills that students need to learn is how to justify their actions, both in math and in everyday life. Math is one way to help students verbalize and write their reasons for making the choices they have made. Mathematical justification is at the heart of proof.

In this lesson, students will solve story problems and justify the solutions.

Materials to Gather

SUPPLIED
Explain Solutions activity page

ALSO NEEDED
drawing paper

LEARN Explain Answers

ONLINE **15**min

Students will learn to explain why a story problem was solved using addition or subtraction.

Objectives

- Justify the procedures selected for addition or subtraction problem-solving situations with sums or minuends up through 500.

LEARN Identify Kinds of Problems

ONLINE **15**min

Students will identify whether they would use addition or subtraction to solve a story problem, and explain that choice.

Objectives

- Justify the procedures selected for addition or subtraction problem-solving situations with sums or minuends up through 500.

LEARN Use Sketches and Diagrams

Students will solve story problems by using sketches and diagrams. Using visuals will help students decide how to solve a problem and can also help them justify why they solved the problem the way they did.

Gather drawing paper. Read each problem to students. Give suggestions for sketches or diagrams that may be used to solve the problem if necessary. Have students find each answer and explain their solution. Accept any reasonable explanation.

- Justify the procedures selected for addition or subtraction problem-solving situations with sums or minuends up through 500.

1. There were 102 flags in the park. The veterans placed 93 more flags. How many flags are in the park now?

Possible sketch: 102 base-10 blocks (1 large square, 2 small squares) plus 93 base-10 blocks (9 lines and 3 small squares).

ANSWER: 195 flags

2. The jar had 83 peanuts and 46 almonds. How many more peanuts were in the jar than almonds?

Possible sketch: Comparison chart showing the larger amount (83 peanuts), the smaller amount (46 almonds), and the difference. (Students will subtract to find the difference.)

ANSWER: 37 more peanuts

3. Mr. Mead's class has read 179 mystery books. Ms. Little's class read 156 mystery books. How many more books does Ms. Little's class need to read to have read as many books as Mr. Mead's class?

Possible sketch: Comparison chart showing the larger amount (Mr. Mead's class – 179) and the smaller amount (Ms. Little's class – 46), and the difference. (Students will subtract to find the difference.)

ANSWER: 23 books

4. Marci read a book with 214 pages and another book with 235 pages. How many pages did Marci read altogether?

Possible sketch: Part-part-total chart with 214 as one part and 235 as the second part. (Students will find the total by adding.)

ANSWER: 449 pages

TRY IT Explain Solutions

Students will practice solving story problems and explaining their solutions. Give students the Explain Solutions activity page from their Activity Book and read the directions with them. Use the answer key to check students' answers, and then enter the results online.

Objectives

- Justify the procedures selected for addition or subtraction problem-solving situations with sums or minuends up through 500.

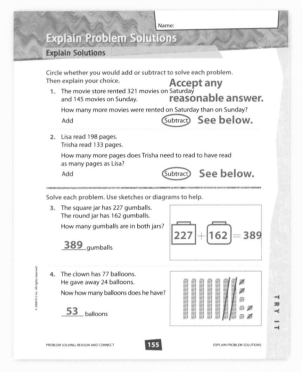

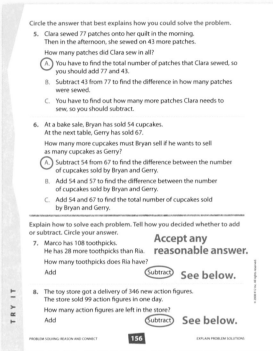

Additional Answers:

1. Students should explain that they would use subtraction to solve this problem because the problem asks them to compare two amounts. When comparing two amounts, you subtract to find the difference.

2. Students should explain that they would use subtraction to solve this problem because the problem asks how many more are needed to make the amounts the same. You should subtract to find the difference.

7. Students might say that 108 toothpicks equals 28 more toothpicks than Ria has. To find how many more than, you should subtract.

8. Students might say that they would subtract 99 from 346 because there were 346 figures to begin with and 99 were sold or taken away. To find out how many are left, you should subtract.

Justify Procedures Selected

Lesson Overview

Skills Update	5 minutes	**ONLINE**
GET READY Choose Number Sentences	5 minutes	**ONLINE**
LEARN Justify Solutions	15 minutes	**ONLINE**
LEARN Different Justifications	20 minutes	**ONLINE**
TRY IT Solve and Justify	15 minutes	**OFFLINE**

▶ Lesson Objectives

Justify the procedures selected for addition or subtraction problem-solving situations with sums or minuends up through 500.

▶ Prerequisite Skills

Check the accuracy of calculations from the context of addition or subtraction problem-solving situations with sums and minuends up through 500 with regrouping.

▶ Content Background

One of the most important skills that students need to learn is how to justify their actions, both in math and in everyday life. Math is one way to help students verbalize and write their reasons for making the choices they have made. Mathematical justification is at the heart of proof.

Students will learn to solve addition and subtraction story problems and to justify their solutions.

Keywords

justify – to explain why something is true; for example, to justify a procedure or answer to a math problem

Materials to Gather

SUPPLIED

Solve and Justify activity page

ONLINE

5min

GET READY Choose Number Sentences

Students will identify number sentences that match given story problems.

Objectives

- Recognize and solve word problems involving sums up through 500 in which two quantities are combined.

LEARN Justify Solutions

ONLINE 15min

Objectives

Students will practice justifying how to solve a story problem. Then they will solve each problem.

- Justify the procedures selected for addition or subtraction problem-solving situations with sums or minuends up through 500.

LEARN Different Justifications

ONLINE 20min

Objectives

Students will learn that some story problems can be solved in more than one way.

- Justify the procedures selected for addition or subtraction problem-solving situations with sums or minuends up through 500.

TRY IT Solve and Justify

OFFLINE 15min

Objectives

Students will practice writing number sentences, finding solutions, and justifying why the solution makes sense. Give students the Solve and Justify activity page from their Activity Book and read the directions with them. Use the answer key to check students' answers, and then enter the results online.

- Justify the procedures selected for addition or subtraction problem-solving situations with sums or minuends up through 500.

Justify Procedures Selected
Solve and Justify

Name:

Write the number sentence that solves each story problem. Then tell why you solved the problem as you did, and explain why your solution makes sense.

Answers may vary.

1. Amy's book has 265 pages.
   Amy has read 189 pages so far.
   How many more pages does she need to read to finish the book?

   $265 - 189 = 76$
   See next page.

2. There are 74 butterflies and 92 caterpillars.
   How many more caterpillars are there than butterflies?

   $92 - 74 = 18$
   See next page.

3. There were 63 pretzels on the shelf.
   The baker put 48 more pretzels on the shelf.
   How many pretzels are on the shelf now?

   $63 + 48 = 111$
   See next page.

4. Hector planted 141 red flowers and 85 white flowers.
   How many flowers did Hector plant in all?

   $141 + 85 = 226$
   See next page.

TRY IT

PROBLEM SOLVING: REASON AND CONNECT   **157**   JUSTIFY PROCEDURES SELECTED

Tell how you would solve each problem and explain why your solution makes sense.

5. There were 25 pencils in a box.
   Then 10 pencils fell out of the box.
   How many pencils were left in the box?

   See next page.

6. The Salty Sea Shop sold 87 shells in June.
   The shop sold 32 shells in July.
   How many more shells did the shop sell in June than in July?

   See next page.

7. Sandro has washed 26 cars.
   His friend Tomas has washed 44 cars.
   How many more cars does Sandro need to wash if he wants to wash as many cars as Tomas did?

   See next page.

8. Harry wrote the number sentence $145 + 43 = 188$ to solve the following problem.
   Marla has 145 leaves in her collection.
   Barb has 43 leaves in her collection.
   How many leaves do they have altogether?
   Is Harry's number sentence correct for solving this problem? Explain your answer.

   See next page.

TRY IT

PROBLEM SOLVING: REASON AND CONNECT   **158**   JUSTIFY PROCEDURES SELECTED

Additional Answers

1. Students should say that they subtracted to find how many more pages.

2. Students should say that they subtracted to compare the amounts.

3. Students should say that they added the two amounts to find the new total.

4. Students should say that they added the two amounts to find how many in all.

5. Students should say that since 10 pencils fell out, they would subtract 10 from 25 to find how many are left in the box.

6. Students should say that the problem asks how many more shells were sold in June than in July. To find out how many more, they would subtract 32 from 87.

7. Students should say that they would subtract 26 from 44 to tell how many more cars Sandro would need to wash to reach a total of 44 cars.

8. Yes, the number sentence is correct. Students should say they need to find out how many leaves there are altogether, so they would add Marla's number of leaves to Barb's number of leaves.

Justify Solutions

Lesson Overview		
Skills Update	5 minutes	ONLINE
LEARN Evaluate Solutions	15 minutes	ONLINE
LEARN Problem Variations	15 minutes	ONLINE
TRY IT Justify and Solve Problems	10 minutes	OFFLINE
CHECKPOINT	10 minutes	OFFLINE

▶ **Lesson Objectives**

Justify the procedures selected for addition or subtraction problem-solving situations with sums or minuends up through 500.

▶ **Prerequisite Skills**

Check the accuracy of calculations from the context of addition or subtraction problem-solving situations with sums and minuends up through 500 with regrouping.

▶ **Content Background**

One of the most important skills that students need to learn is how to justify their actions, both in math and in everyday life. Math is one way to help students verbalize and write their reasons for making the choices they have made. Mathematical justification is at the heart of proof.

In this lesson, students will solve story problems and justify the solutions.

Materials to Gather

SUPPLIED

Justify and Solve Problems activity page

Checkpoint (printout)

Tips

Help students understand that no one solution is best, but some solutions may be more efficient or easier to complete than others.

LEARN Evaluate Solutions

ONLINE 15 min

Students will compare two different ways of solving the same story problem. They will explain which solution they think is better and why.

Objectives

- Justify the procedures selected for addition or subtraction problem-solving situations with sums or minuends up through 500.

LEARN Problem Variations

ONLINE 15 min

Students will see how a slight change in a problem can change the solution.

Objectives

- Justify the procedures selected for addition or subtraction problem-solving situations with sums or minuends up through 500.

TRY IT Justify and Solve Problems

Objectives

- Justify the procedures selected for addition or subtraction problem-solving situations with sums or minuends up through 500.

Students will practice choosing a solution for a problem and justifying their choice. Give students the Justify and Solve Problems activity page from their Activity Book and read the directions with them.

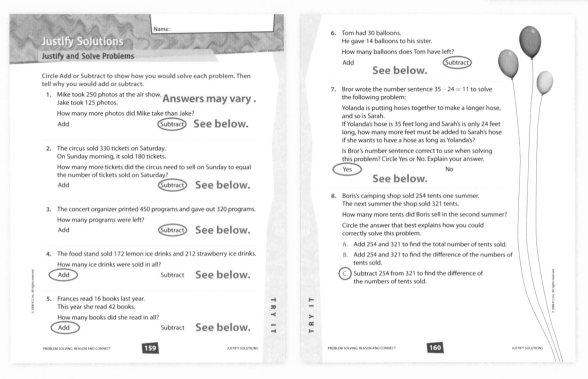

Additional Answers

1. Students should say that they would subtract to solve a problem that asks how many more than.

2. Students should say that they would subtract to find the amount that will make the number of tickets sold Sunday equal the number sold Saturday.

3. Students should say that the organizer gave out 320 programs, so they would subtract 320 from 450 to find how many are left.

4. Students should say that they would add to find how many in all.

5. Students should say that they would add to solve a problem that asks how many in all.

6. Students should say they would subtract to find the difference between how many balloons Tom started with and how many were left.

7. Students should say that the number sentence is correct because they need to find the difference between the lengths of the two hoses.

CHECKPOINT

OFFLINE 10 min

Objectives

- Justify the procedures selected for addition or subtraction problem-solving situations with sums or minuends up through 500.

Print the assessment and have students complete it on their own. Read the directions, questions, and answer choices to students if necessary. Use the answer key to score the assessment, and then enter the results online.

Name _____ Date _____

Checkpoint Answer Key

Circle the answer.

1. Nikki has 26 peaches.
   If she gives away 11, she will have the same number as Nathan has.
   How many peaches does Nathan have?
   Which of the following best explains how you could correctly solve this problem?
   (1 point)
   A. Add 26 and 11 to find the total number of peaches Nathan has.
   B. Subtract 11 from 26 to find how many peaches Nathan has.
   C. Add 26 and 26 to find the difference between the two sets of peaches.
   D. Compare 26 and 13 to see who has more peaches.

2. Trevor counted 34 blue cars and 22 red cars going by his house one morning.
   How many fewer red cars did Trevor see than blue cars?
   Which of the following best explains how you could correctly solve this problem?
   (1 point)
   A. Add 34 and 22 to find how many cars Trevor saw in all.
   B. Subtract 22 from 34 to find the difference in the number of blue and red cars.
   C. Add 22 and 34 to find the difference in the number of blue and red cars.

Answers may vary.

Circle Add or Subtract to show how you would solve each problem.
Then tell why you would add or subtract.

3. Tyler read 223 pages of his book one week and another 128 pages the following week. **Students should say they would add to find how many in all.**
   (2 points)
   How many pages did he read in all?
   (Add)   Subtract

Name _____ Date _____

4. Tim put 12 apples and 6 oranges in a bowl.
   How many oranges does Tim need to add to the bowl to have the same number of apples and oranges?
   (2 points)
   Add   **(Subtract)**

Students should say they would subtract to find the amount that will make the number of oranges in the bowl equal to the number of apples.

Write a number sentence that solves each story problem.
Tell why you chose to solve each problem as you did.

5. Six turtles were sitting on a log. Two of the turtles slid off the log into the pond.
   (2 points)
   How many turtles were left on the log?

$$6 - 2 = 4$$

Students should say they would subtract to find the how many turtles were left after two went away.

6. Liam got a new bag of marbles to add to his collection.
   The new bag had 110 marbles. He already had 50 marbles.
   (2 points)
   How many marbles does Liam have now?

$$110 + 50 = 160, \text{ or } 50 + 110 = 160$$

Students should say they would add to find how many marbles Liam has altogether.

Name _____ Date _____

7. Ben wrote the number sentence $183 + 97 = 280$ to solve the following problem:
   Mindy has 183 songs saved on her computer.
   Her friend Nita has 97 songs on her computer.
   How many more songs does Mindy have than Nita?
   Is Ben's number sentence correct to use when solving this problem?
   Circle Yes or No. Then explain your answer.
   (2 points)
   Yes   **(No)**

Students should say that the number sentence is not correct. You need to find the difference between 183 and 97, not add them together.

8. James wrote the number sentence $350 - 117 = 233$ to solve the following problem:
   A bookstore worker put 117 books onto shelves.
   Then she put 350 more books onto the shelves.
   How many books did she put onto the shelves altogether?
   Is James's number sentence correct to use when solving this problem?
   Circle Yes or No. Then explain your answer.
   (2 points)
   Yes   **(No)**

Students should say that the number sentence is not correct. You need to add 350 and 117 to find how many books altogether were put on the shelves.

Create Story Problems

▶ Lesson Objectives

Give examples of problem situations that can be described by addition or subtraction number sentences, and write the sentences.

▶ Prerequisite Skills

Write and solve addition or subtraction number sentences to represent problem-solving situations with sums and minuends up through 500.

▶ Advance Preparation

Print 2–4 copies of My Story Problems.

▶ Content Background

Students usually solve problems written by others. When writing problems of their own, students must think about all the parts needed to write a good problem.

Materials to Gather

SUPPLIED

My Story Problems (printout) –
  2–4 copies

Make Up Problems activity page

LEARN Construction Site Stories

ONLINE 20 min

Students will use online information to create story problems. They will write number sentences to solve the problems.
  Gather the My Story Problems printout.

1. Have students watch Alex make a subtraction story problem.
2. Have students make their own subtraction problems using the information on the screen. Write each problem on the My Story Problems printout. Then have students write a number sentence and solve the problem.
3. Have students watch Serena make an addition story problem.
4. Have students make their own addition problems. Write each problem on the My Story Problems printout. Then have students write a number sentence and solve the problem.

Objectives

- Give examples of problem situations that can be described by addition or subtraction number sentences, and write the sentences.

Tips

If students have trouble choosing which information to use, have them pick two items from the screen. Guide them in creating a story problem.

LEARN Carnival Stories

Students will use online information to create story problems. They will write number sentences to solve the problems.

Gather the My Story Problems printout.

1. Have students watch Alex make a subtraction story problem.
2. Have students make their own subtraction problems using the information on the screen. Write each problem on the My Story Problems printout. Then have students write a number sentence and solve the problem.
3. Have students watch Serena make an addition story problem.
4. Have students make their own addition problems. Write each problem on the My Story Problems printout. Then have students write a number sentence and solve the problem.

Objectives

- Give examples of problem situations that can be described by addition or subtraction number sentences, and write the sentences.

Tips

If students have trouble choosing which information to use, have them pick two items from the screen. Guide them in creating a story problem.

TRY IT Make Up Problems

Students will practice making story problems and writing matching number sentences. Give students the Make Up Problems activity page from their Activity Book and read the directions with them. Use the answer key to check students' answers, and then enter the results online.

Objectives

- Give examples of problem situations that can be described by addition or subtraction number sentences, and write the sentences.

Name: _____

Create Story Problems
Make Up Problems

1. Make up one addition story problem using the numbers 385 and 497. Use a ? for the missing number.

   Ryan scored 385 points in Level 1 of his game. Then he scored another 497 points.

   How many points did he score in all?

   Stories will vary. Sample answers shown.

   497 $+$ 385 $=$?

2. Make up one subtraction story problem using the numbers 385 and 497. Use a ? for the missing number.

   Gina had 497 pennies in a jar.

   She spilled 385 pennies.

   How many are still in the jar?

   497 $-$ 385 $=$?

PROBLEM SOLVING: REASON AND CONNECT　**161**　CREATE STORY PROBLEMS

TRY IT

---

3. Make up one addition story problem using the numbers 286 and 207. Use a ? for the missing number.

   Jennifer had 286 stickers in her collection.

   She got 207 more.

   How many stickers does she have now?

   286 $+$ 207 $=$?

4. Make up one subtraction story problem using the numbers 286 and 207. Use a ? for the missing number.

   Brian has 286 baseball cards.

   Steven has 207 fewer cards than Brian.

   How many cards does Steven have?

   286 $-$ 207 $=$?

PROBLEM SOLVING: REASON AND CONNECT　**162**　CREATE STORY PROBLEMS

TRY IT

Make Your Own Story Problems

Lesson Overview

Skills Update	5 minutes	**ONLINE**
LEARN Story Problems in Your Life	15 minutes	**ONLINE**
TRY IT Create Story Problems	30 minutes	**OFFLINE**
CHECKPOINT	10 minutes	**OFFLINE**

▶ Lesson Objectives

Give examples of problem situations that can be described by addition or subtraction number sentences, and write the sentences.

▶ Prerequisite Skills

Write and solve addition or subtraction number sentences to represent problem-solving situations with sums and minuends up through 500.

▶ Advance Preparation

Print My Story Problems.

▶ Content Background

Students usually solve problems written by others. When writing problems of their own, students must think about all the parts needed to write a good problem.

Materials to Gather

SUPPLIED

My Story Problems (printout)

Create Story Problems activity page

Checkpoint (printout)

LEARN Story Problems in Your Life

ONLINE 15 min

Students will use the online information to create story problems and write number sentences.

Gather the My Story Problems printout.

Objectives

- Write and solve addition or subtraction number sentences to represent problem-solving situations with sums and minuends up through 500.

TRY IT Create Story Problems

OFFLINE 30 min

Students will practice making story problems and writing number sentences. Give students the Create Story Problems activity page from their Activity Book and read the directions with them. For Problems 1–2, write the stories as students tell them. For Problems 3–5, students should write the stories on their own.

Use the answer key to check students' answers, and then enter the results online.

Objectives

- Give examples of problem situations that can be described by addition or subtraction number sentences, and write the sentences.

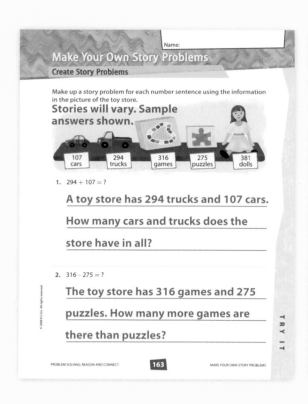

Make Your Own Story Problems
Create Story Problems

Name: _____

Make up a story problem for each number sentence using the information in the picture of the toy store.

Stories will vary. Sample answers shown.

107 cars   294 trucks   316 games   275 puzzles   381 dolls

1. 294 + 107 = ?

   A toy store has 294 trucks and 107 cars. How many cars and trucks does the store have in all?

2. 316 − 275 = ?

   The toy store has 316 games and 275 puzzles. How many more games are there than puzzles?

PROBLEM SOLVING: REASON AND CONNECT   **163**   MAKE YOUR OWN STORY PROBLEMS

T R Y   I T

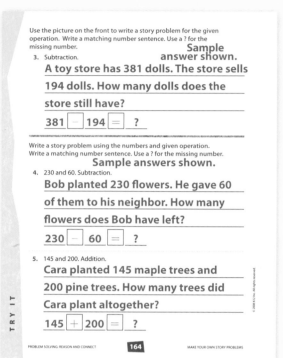

Use the picture on the front to write a story problem for the given operation. Write a matching number sentence. Use a ? for the missing number.

3. Subtraction.   **Sample answer shown.**

   A toy store has 381 dolls. The store sells 194 dolls. How many dolls does the store still have?

   381 [−] 194 [=] ?

Write a story problem using the numbers and given operation. Write a matching number sentence. Use a ? for the missing number.

Sample answers shown.

4. 230 and 60. Subtraction.

   Bob planted 230 flowers. He gave 60 of them to his neighbor. How many flowers does Bob have left?

   230 [−] 60 [=] ?

5. 145 and 200. Addition.

   Cara planted 145 maple trees and 200 pine trees. How many trees did Cara plant altogether?

   145 [+] 200 [=] ?

T R Y   I T

PROBLEM SOLVING: REASON AND CONNECT   **164**   MAKE YOUR OWN STORY PROBLEMS

CHECKPOINT

OFFLINE **10 min**

Print the assessment and have students complete it on their own. Read the directions, questions, and answer choices to students if necessary. Use the answer key to score the assessment, and then enter the results online.

Objectives

- Give examples of problem situations that can be described by addition or subtraction number sentences, and write the sentences.

○ Checkpoint   Math | Problem Solving: Reason and Connect | Make Your Own Story Problems

Name _____   Date _____

Checkpoint Answer Key

Read each problem and follow the directions.

Stories will vary possible answers shown.

1. Write an addition story problem using the numbers 22 and 16. Then write a number sentence to help solve the problem.
   (1 point)
   Janice had 22 cookies and she baked 16 more. How many cookies does she have? 22 + 16

2. Write a subtraction story problem using the numbers 21 and 14. Then write a number sentence to help solve the problem.
   (1 point)
   Kevin ran 21 laps around the track. Patrick ran 14 laps. How many more laps did Kevin run than Patrick? 21 − 14

3. Write a subtraction story problem using the numbers 120 and 15. Then write a number sentence to help solve the problem.
   (1 point)
   The bakery had 120 rolls. The bakery sold 15 rolls in the morning. How many rolls were left? 120 − 15

Similar Story Problems

▶ Lesson Objectives

Demonstrate an understanding of connections between similar addition or subtraction problems from problem-solving situations, involving sums and minuends up through 500.

▶ Prerequisite Skills

- Demonstrate an understanding of connections between similar addition or subtraction computation problems, involving sums and minuends up through 500.
- Give examples of problem situations that can be described by addition or subtraction number sentences, and write the sentences.

▶ Content Background

Problem solving is a key to success not only in math, but also in every area of life. To become good problem solvers, students need to recognize when a new problem is similar to a problem they have already solved. In this way, students build on their prior experience and develop strategies that work for many similar problems. Students build confidence by recognizing a type of problem they have seen before and have solved successfully.

Materials to Gather

SUPPLIED

Classify Problems activity page

GET READY Make a Problem

ONLINE 5 min

Students will choose two numbers to create an addition story problem. They will say the problem aloud. Then they will write a number sentence for the problem. Students will repeat the process for a subtraction problem.

Gather a pencil and paper.

Objectives

- Give examples of problem situations that can be described by addition or subtraction number sentences, and write the sentences.

LEARN The Crayon Problem

ONLINE 15min

Students will compare story problems and identify the ones that are like a given addition problem about crayons. Then students will write number sentences for problems that are alike.

Objectives

- Demonstrate an understanding of connections between similar addition or subtraction problems from problem-solving situations, involving sums and minuends up through 500.

LEARN The Jacket Problem

ONLINE 20min

Students will compare story problems and identify the ones that are like a given subtraction problem about jackets. Then students will write number sentences for problems that are alike.

Objectives

- Demonstrate an understanding of connections between similar addition or subtraction problems from problem-solving situations, involving sums and minuends up through 500.

TRY IT Classify Problems

OFFLINE 15min

Students will practice identifying similar story problems and writing number sentences. Give students the Classify Problems activity page from their Activity Book and read the directions with them. Use the answer key to check students' answers, and then enter the results online.

Objectives

- Demonstrate an understanding of connections between similar addition or subtraction problems from problem-solving situations, involving sums and minuends up through 500.

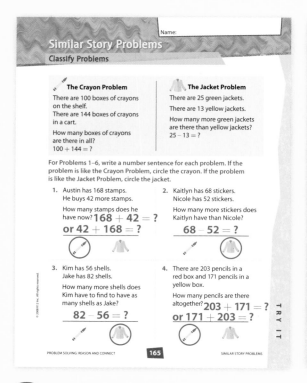

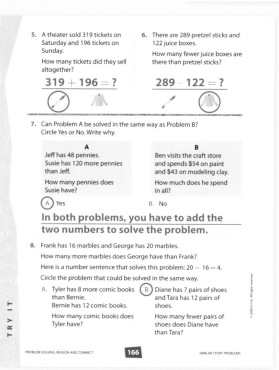

Classify Story Problems

Lesson Overview

Skills Update	5 minutes	ONLINE
GET READY Create Similar Problems	5 minutes	ONLINE
LEARN The Ribbon Problem	20 minutes	ONLINE
LEARN The Stair Problem	15 minutes	ONLINE
TRY IT Identify Similar Problems	15 minutes	OFFLINE

▶ Lesson Objectives

Demonstrate an understanding of connections between similar addition or subtraction problems from problem-solving situations, involving sums and minuends up through 500.

▶ Prerequisite Skills

Demonstrate an understanding of connections between similar addition or subtraction computation problems, involving sums and minuends up through 500.

▶ Common Errors and Misconceptions

Students might confuse combine problems with change problems. In combine problems, two numbers are put together to find a sum. The quantities do not change—for instance, two people will have the same number of objects at the end of a problem as they had at the beginning. Change problems, on the other hand, have an implied action. In change problems, one quantity changes by having an amount added or taken away.

▶ Advance Preparation

Print My Story Problems.

▶ Content Background

In this lesson, students will compare two story problems with missing-addends to see how the problems are alike.

Problem solving is a key to success not only in math but also in every area of life. To become good problem solvers, students need to recognize when a new problem is similar to a problem they have already solved. In this way, students build on their prior experience and develop strategies that work for many similar problems. Students build confidence by recognizing a type of problem they have seen before and have solved successfully.

Materials to Gather

SUPPLIED

My Story Problems (printout)

Identify Similar Problems activity page

missing addend – an unknown addend in an addition number sentence; for example, in $3 + ? = 8$, the ? represents the missing addend

missing addend problem – an addition problem in which one of the two numbers to be added is missing; for example, $3 + ? = 8$ or $? + 5 = 8$

GET READY Create Similar Problems

ONLINE **5** min

Students will create an addition story problem that is like a given problem. They will say the problem aloud. Then they will write a number sentence for the problem. Make sure that the problem combines two amounts and has an unknown total.

Students will repeat the process for a subtraction problem. Make sure that the problem compares two amounts and has an unknown total.

Gather the My Story Problems printout.

Objectives

- Demonstrate an understanding of connections between similar addition or subtraction computation problems, involving sums and minuends up through 500.

Tips

Encourage students to use *friendly numbers* that they can calculate in their heads.

LEARN The Ribbon Problem

ONLINE **20** min

Students will compare story problems and identify the ones that are like a given addition problem about ribbon. The problem gives a total and part of the total. It has a missing addend.

Students will write number sentences for the problems that are like the Ribbon Problem. They should recognize that this type of problem has a number sentence with this form: $3 + ? = 7$. The challenge is to find the missing addend.

Objectives

- Demonstrate an understanding of connections between similar addition or subtraction problems from problem-solving situations, involving sums and minuends up through 500.

LEARN The Stair Problem

ONLINE **15** min

Students will compare story problems and identify the ones that are like a given addition problem about stairs. The problem gives a total and part of the total. It has a missing addend. Students will write number sentences for the problems that are like the Stair Problem.

Objectives

- Demonstrate an understanding of connections between similar addition or subtraction problems from problem-solving situations, involving sums and minuends up through 500.

TRY IT Identify Similar Problems

Students will practice identifying story problems that can be solved the same way. They will practice writing number sentences for problems with missing addends. Give students the Identify Similar Problems activity page from their Activity Book and read the directions with them.

- Demonstrate an understanding of connections between similar addition or subtraction problems from problem-solving situations, involving sums and minuends up through 500.

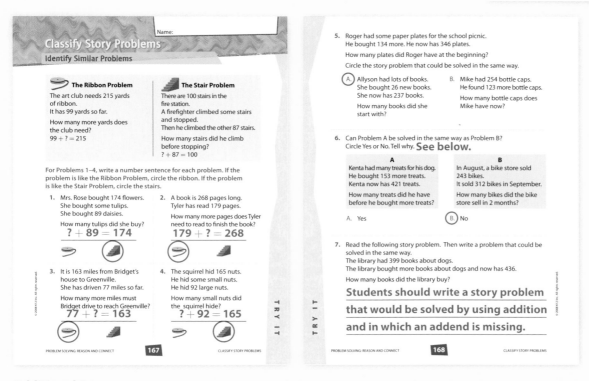

Additional Answer

6. Problem A would be solved using subtraction. Problem B would be solved using addition.

Different Kinds of Problems

Skills Update	5 minutes	ONLINE
CHECKPOINT	15 minutes	OFFLINE

▶ Lesson Objectives

Demonstrate an understanding of connections between similar addition or subtraction problems from problem-solving situations, involving sums and minuends up through 500.

▶ Prerequisite Skills

Demonstrate an understanding of connections between similar addition or subtraction computation problems, involving sums and minuends up through 500.

▶ Content Background

In this lesson, students will have a chance to show what they've learned about solving story problems. They may use any extra time today to review, using materials in Lesson Resources, before they complete the Checkpoint. They may choose instead to complete the Checkpoint and then begin the next lesson.

Materials to Gather

SUPPLIED
Checkpoint (printout)

CHECKPOINT

OFFLINE
15 min

Print the assessment and have students complete it on their own. Read the directions to students if necessary. Use the answer key to score the assessment, and then enter the results online.

Objectives

- Demonstrate an understanding of connections between similar addition or subtraction problems from problem-solving situations, involving sums and minuends up through 500.

Name _____ Date _____

Checkpoint Answer Key

Follow the directions to complete each problem.

(1 point)
1. Read the following story problem. Then find the problem that you could solve the same way. Circle A or B.

    Craig had 234 pencils.
    He bought 154 more pencils.

    How many pencils does Craig have now?

    A. Jeff had 423 seashells.
    He gave away 54 seashells.

    How many seashells does Jeff have now?

    (B.) Sara had 423 rocks.
    She got 54 more rocks.

    How many rocks does Sara have now?

(1 point)
2. Read the following story problem. Then find the problem that you could solve the same way. Circle A or B.

    The grocery store had some apples.
    It got a shipment of 176 more apples.
    The store now has 345 apples.

    How many apples did the store have before the shipment?

    A. Darren had 123 rocks.
    He found 324 more rocks.

    How many rocks does Darren have now?

    (B.) Meredith had a stamp collection.
    She got 123 more stamps.
    She now has 324 stamps.

    How many stamps did she have at the beginning?

Name _____ Date _____

(1 point)
3. Read the following story problem. Then find the problem that you could solve the same way. Circle A or B.

    Vaughn had 165 colored pencils.
    He got some more pencils just before school started.
    Vaughn now has 178 pencils.

    How many pencils did Vaughn get just before school started?

    A. Danica had 143 golf balls.
    She bought 156 more golf balls.

    How many golf balls does Danica have now?

    (B.) Laura had 143 teddy bears.
    She got more bears for her birthday.
    She now has 156 teddy bears.

    How many bears did Laura get for her birthday?

(1 point)
4. Read the following story problem. Then write a story problem that could be solved in the same way.

    Rafael had 457 baseball cards.
    He gave 168 cards to Roger.

    How many cards does Rafael have now?

    Students should write a story problem in which one quantity needs to be subtracted from another quantity.

Unit Review

Lesson Overview

UNIT REVIEW Look Back	20 minutes	ONLINE
UNIT REVIEW Checkpoint Practice	20 minutes	OFFLINE
⏩ **UNIT REVIEW** Prepare for the Checkpoint		

▶ Unit Objectives

This lesson reviews the following objectives:

- Write and solve addition or subtraction number sentences to represent problem-solving situations with sums and minuends up through 500.
- Check the accuracy of calculations from the context of addition or subtraction problem-solving situations with sums and minuends up through 500 with regrouping.
- Justify the procedures selected for addition or subtraction problem-solving situations with sums or minuends up through 500.
- Demonstrate an understanding of connections between similar addition or subtraction problems from problem-solving situations, involving sums and minuends up through 500.
- Give examples of problem situations that can be described by addition or subtraction number sentences, and write the sentences.

Materials to Gather

SUPPLIED

Checkpoint Practice activity page

▶ Advance Preparation

In this lesson, students will have an opportunity to review previous activities in the Problem Solving: Reason and Connect unit. Look at the suggested activities in Unit Review: Prepare for the Checkpoint online and gather any needed materials.

Keywords

addition sentence	missing addend
check	missing addend problem
combine problem	number sentence
compare problem	story problem
justify	subtraction sentence

UNIT REVIEW Look Back

ONLINE
20min

Objectives

- Review unit objectives.

During this unit, students have learned about solving story problems. They wrote and solved number sentences to answer story problems that involved addition or subtraction. They analyzed a problem to check for errors and determined if the answer was correct. They explained and justified solutions to story problems and learned that there can be more than one way to find the answer. They compared story problems and learned to recognize story problems that are solved the same way. They also wrote and solved their own story problems. Students will review these concepts to prepare for the Unit Checkpoint.

UNIT REVIEW Checkpoint Practice

Objectives

- Review unit objectives.

Students will complete a Checkpoint Practice activity page to prepare for the Unit Checkpoint. If necessary, read the directions, questions, and answer choices to students. Have students answer the problems on their own.

Name: _____

Unit Review
Checkpoint Practice

Answers may vary.
Write the number sentence that solves each story problem. Then tell why you solved the problem as you did. **Possible answers shown.**

1. Corkey the Clown sells balloons at the circus. He sold 76 red balloons and 91 blue balloons.

   How many more blue balloons did Corkey sell than red balloons?

   $91 - 76 = 15$

   Students should say that they subtracted to compare amounts and find how many more blue balloons Corkey sold.

2. There are 311 beads in a box. There are 125 beads in a bag.

   How many beads are there altogether?

   $311 + 125 = 436$

   Students should say that they added the two amounts to find how many altogether.

Tell if each answer is correct. If an answer is **not** correct, explain why and give the correct answer.

3. **Problem**
   Josie had 425 beads. She used 137 beads to make necklaces for her friends.

   How many beads does Josie have left?

   Student's answer
   Josie has 312 beads left.

   Is this answer correct?

   No. The student did not regroup correctly. The correct answer is 288 beads.

4. **Problem**
   Erwin has 178 stamps in his collection. His grandfather gave him 54 more stamps.

   How many stamps does Erwin have now?

   Student's answer
   Erwin has 124 stamps now.

   Is this answer correct?

   No. The student used the wrong operation. The correct answer is 232.

Follow the instructions for each problem. **Answers may vary.**

5. Write one addition story problem and one subtraction story problem with the numbers 218 and 350. Write a number sentence for each story, and use a ? for the missing number.

   Addition Story Problem **Possible answers shown**

   Roger scored 218 points in Level 1 of his computer game. Then he scored another 350 points in Level 2.

   How many points did Roger score in all?

   $218 + 350 = ?$

   Subtraction Story Problem

   Brad had 350 pennies in a jar.

   He spilled 218 pennies.

   How many pennies are still in the jar?

   $350 - 218 = ?$

---

6. Read the two story problems. Write the number sentence that you can use to solve each problem. **Answers may vary.**

   Chris is playing a computer game. He needs 500 points to move to the next level. So far he has scored 372 points. **Possible answers shown.**

   How many more points does Chris need to score to move to the next level? $372 + ? = 500$

   There are 315 seats in the cafeteria. At lunch there were 197 people. $197 + ? = 315$

   How many cafeteria seats were empty?

   Are the two problems similar? Yes

   Tell why or why not.

   Both number sentences use addition, but they have different numbers. Students might also write number sentences that use subtraction:

   $500 - 372 = ?$ and $315 - 197 = ?$

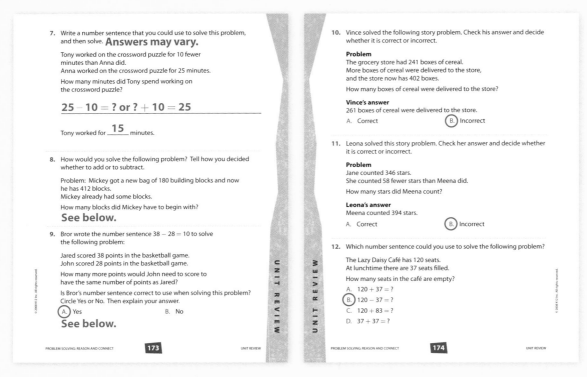

7. Write a number sentence that you could use to solve this problem, and then solve. **Answers may vary.**

Tony worked on the crossword puzzle for 10 fewer minutes than Anna did.
Anna worked on the crossword puzzle for 25 minutes.

How many minutes did Tony spend working on the crossword puzzle?

$25 - 10 = ?$ or $? + 10 = 25$

Tony worked for ___15___ minutes.

8. How would you solve the following problem? Tell how you decided whether to add or to subtract.

Problem: Mickey got a new bag of 180 building blocks and now he has 412 blocks.
Mickey already had some blocks.

How many blocks did Mickey have to begin with?
See below.

9. Bror wrote the number sentence $38 - 28 = 10$ to solve the following problem:

Jared scored 38 points in the basketball game.
John scored 28 points in the basketball game.

How many more points would John need to score to have the same number of points as Jared?

Is Bror's number sentence correct to use when solving this problem? Circle Yes or No. Then explain your answer.

(A.) Yes   B. No
See below.

10. Vince solved the following story problem. Check his answer and decide whether it is correct or incorrect.

Problem
The grocery store had 241 boxes of cereal.
More boxes of cereal were delivered to the store, and the store now has 402 boxes.

How many boxes of cereal were delivered to the store?

Vince's answer
261 boxes of cereal were delivered to the store.

A. Correct   (B.) Incorrect

11. Leona solved this story problem. Check her answer and decide whether it is correct or incorrect.

Problem
Jane counted 346 stars.
She counted 58 fewer stars than Meena did.

How many stars did Meena count?

Leona's answer
Meena counted 394 stars.

A. Correct   (B.) Incorrect

12. Which number sentence could you use to solve the following problem?

The Lazy Daisy Café has 120 seats.
At lunchtime there are 37 seats filled.

How many seats in the café are empty?

A. $120 + 37 = ?$
(B.) $120 - 37 = ?$
C. $120 + 83 = ?$
D. $37 + 37 = ?$

Additional Answers

8. Sample answer: I would subtract 180 from 412 because I need to find the difference between how many blocks Mickey has now and how many new blocks he got. This will tell me how many blocks he had to start with.

9. Sample explanation: Bror's number sentence is correct. To find out how many more points John needs to score I need to find the difference between the number of points Jared scored and the number of points John scored.

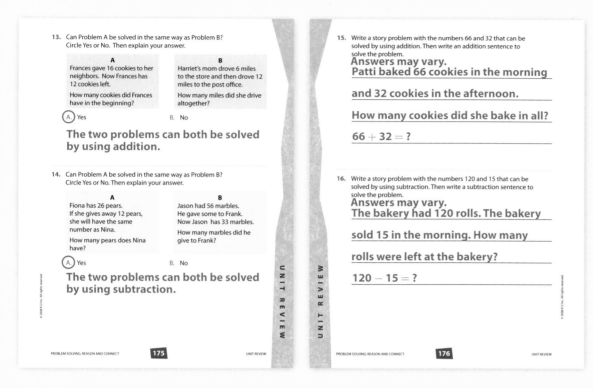

13. Can Problem A be solved in the same way as Problem B? Circle Yes or No. Then explain your answer.

A	**B**
Frances gave 16 cookies to her neighbors. Now Frances has 12 cookies left. How many cookies did Frances have in the beginning?	Harriet's mom drove 6 miles to the store and then drove 12 miles to the post office. How many miles did she drive altogether?

(A.) Yes   B. No

The two problems can both be solved by using addition.

14. Can Problem A be solved in the same way as Problem B? Circle Yes or No. Then explain your answer.

A	**B**
Fiona has 26 pears. If she gives away 12 pears, she will have the same number as Nina. How many pears does Nina have?	Jason had 56 marbles. He gave some to Frank. Now Jason has 33 marbles. How many marbles did he give to Frank?

(A.) Yes   B. No

The two problems can both be solved by using subtraction.

15. Write a story problem with the numbers 66 and 32 that can be solved by using addition. Then write an addition sentence to solve the problem.

Answers may vary.
Patti baked 66 cookies in the morning

and 32 cookies in the afternoon.

How many cookies did she bake in all?

66 + 32 = ?

16. Write a story problem with the numbers 120 and 15 that can be solved by using subtraction. Then write a subtraction sentence to solve the problem.

Answers may vary.
The bakery had 120 rolls. The bakery

sold 15 in the morning. How many

rolls were left at the bakery?

120 − 15 = ?

UNIT REVIEW

UNIT REVIEW

➔ **UNIT REVIEW** Prepare for the Checkpoint

What you do next depends on how students performed in the previous activity, Unit Review: Checkpoint Practice. If students had difficulty with any of the problems, complete the appropriate review activity listed in the table online.

Unit Checkpoint

UNIT CHECKPOINT Online	20 minutes	ONLINE
UNIT CHECKPOINT Offline	40 minutes	OFFLINE

▶ Unit Objectives

This lesson assesses the following objectives:

- Write and solve addition or subtraction number sentences to represent problem-solving situations with sums and minuends up through 500.
- Check the accuracy of calculations from the context of addition or subtraction problem-solving situations with sums and minuends up through 500 with regrouping.
- Justify the procedures selected for addition or subtraction problem-solving situations with sums or minuends up through 500.
- Demonstrate an understanding of connections between similar addition or subtraction problems from problem-solving situations, involving sums and minuends up through 500.
- Give examples of problem situations that can be described by addition or subtraction number sentences, and write the sentences.

Materials to Gather

SUPPLIED

Checkpoint (printout)

UNIT CHECKPOINT Online

ONLINE 20 min

Students will complete this part of the Unit Checkpoint online. Read the directions, problems, and answer choices to students. If necessary, help students with keyboard or mouse operations.

Objectives

- Assess unit objectives.

UNIT CHECKPOINT Offline

OFFLINE 40 min

Students will complete this part of the Unit Checkpoint offline. Print the Unit Checkpoint and have students complete it on their own. Read the directions, problems, and answer choices to students, if necessary. Use the answer key to score the Checkpoint, and then enter the results online.

Objectives

- Assess unit objectives.

Name _____   Date _____

Unit Checkpoint Answer Key

For Problem 1, write a number sentence that could be used to solve this problem. Then solve the problem.
(2 point)
1. Jack scored 6 goals in the soccer game. Percy scored 10 goals. How many more goals did Percy score than Jack? **$10 - 6 = ?$ [4]**

Answer may vary.

For Problems 2–4, how would you solve this problem? Explain why.
(2 point)
2. Ann got 5 new shirts for her birthday and now she has 12 shirts. Ann already had some shirts. How many shirts did she have to begin with?
I would subtract 5 from 12. I need to find the difference between how many shirts Ann has now, and how many she got to know how many shirts she had to begin with.

(2 point)
3. Timmy built a model by using 115 bricks. His friend Billy built a model by using 198 bricks. How many more bricks did Billy use than Timmy did?
I would subtract 115 from 198. The problem asks how many more than, so I would use subtraction.

(2 point)
4. Write a story problem with the numbers 99 and 12 that can be solved by using subtraction. Then write a number sentence to solve the problem.
The bookstore had 99 books. It sold 12 books. How many books does the bookstore have left? $99 - 12 = [87]$

Name _____   Date _____

For Problems 5–6, can Problem A be solved in the same way as Problem B? Explain your answer. **Answer may vary.**
(2 point)
5. **Problem A**. There were 38 bananas at the fruit stand. Gina bought 15 of them. How many bananas are left at the fruit stand?

Problem B. Kate read 6 fewer pages of her book than Daryl did. Daryl read 40 pages of his book. How many pages did Kate read?
The first problem asks how many are left. The second problem asks you to compare two amounts. This means that you can solve both problems using subtraction.

(2 point)
6. **Problem A**: Aidan had 56 toy airplanes. He gave 30 to his brother. How many toy airplanes does Aidan have now?

Problem B: Julia has 7 pears. If she eats 3 pears, she will have the same number as Jane. How many pears does Jane have?
The first problem asks how many are left. The second problem asks you to find the difference. You can solve both problems using subtraction.

Semester Review

SEMESTER REVIEW Look Back	30 minutes	**ONLINE**
SEMESTER REVIEW Checkpoint Practice	30 minutes	**OFFLINE**
⏩ **SEMESTER REVIEW** Prepare for the Checkpoint		

▶ Semester Objectives

This lesson reviews the following objectives:

- Identify the place value for each digit in whole numbers through 500.
- Use models to represent regrouping in addition or subtraction problems.
- Compare whole numbers through 500 by using the symbols $<, =, >$.
- Order three or more whole numbers through 500 by using the symbols $<, =, >$.
- Identify relationships between units of time, such as minutes in an hour, days in a month, weeks in a year.
- Use concrete objects or sketches to model and solve addition or subtraction computation problems with sums or minuends up through 500 with and without regrouping.
- Use dollar and cent symbols for money.
- Find the sum of two whole numbers with sums up through 500.
- Use regrouping to find the difference of two whole numbers with the minuend up through 500.
- Demonstrate that a number can be composed of other numbers in various ways.
- Decompose numbers to solve subtraction problems, such as $213 - 12 = 200 + 13 - 12$.
- Use the inverse relationship between addition and subtraction to solve problems.
- Use mental math to find the sum or difference of two 2-digit numbers.
- Identify inches on a ruler and measure the length of an object to the nearest inch.
- Identify centimeters on a ruler and measure the length of an object to the nearest centimeter.
- Use concrete objects or sketches to model and solve addition or subtraction problem-solving situations with sums or minuends up through 500.
- Recognize and solve word problems involving sums up through 500 in which two quantities are combined.
- Recognize and solve word problems involving sums or minuends up through 500 in which one quantity changes by addition or subtraction.
- Recognize and solve word problems involving numbers up through 500 in which two quantities are compared by the use of addition or subtraction.
- Recognize and solve word problems involving numbers up through 500 in which one quantity must be changed to equal another quantity.
- Write and solve addition or subtraction number sentences to represent problem-solving situations with sums and minuends up through 500.
- Justify the procedures selected for addition or subtraction problem-solving situations with sums or minuends up through 500.

Materials to Gather

SUPPLIED

base-10 blocks
place-value mat
Checkpoint Practice activity page

ALSO NEEDED

ruler – inches
spoon

- Give examples of problem situations that can be described by addition or subtraction number sentences, and write the sentences.
- Determine elapsed time in hours, such as 11:00 a.m. to 4:00 p.m.

▶ Advance Preparation

In this lesson, students will have an opportunity to review previous activities from the semester. Look at the suggested activities in Semester Review: Prepare for the Checkpoint online and be prepared to gather any needed materials.

ONLINE
30 min

SEMESTER REVIEW Look Back

Objectives

- Review semester objectives.

In this semester, students learned about numbers through 500. Students also worked with place value, and addition and subtraction with sums and minuends through 500. Students learned about time, money, and measurement. They applied their knowledge to solve story problems. Students will review key concepts from the semester to prepare for the Semester Checkpoint.

To review, students will play a game. If students answer a problem incorrectly, the correct answer will display. Be sure to help students understand why the answer is correct before students move on to the next problem. If they miss several problems, have students play the game again.

OFFLINE
30 min

SEMESTER REVIEW Checkpoint Practice

Objectives

- Review semester objectives.

Students will complete a Checkpoint Practice activity page to prepare for the Semester Checkpoint. If necessary, read the directions, questions, and answer choices to students. Have students answer the problems on their own. Carefully review the answers with students.

Gather the ruler, spoon, base-10 blocks, and place-value mat. Have students use these materials when directed on the activity page.

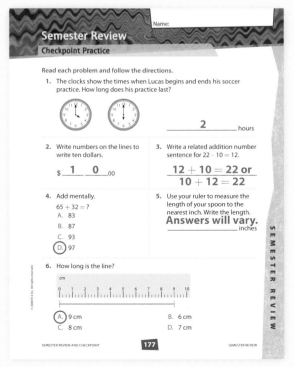

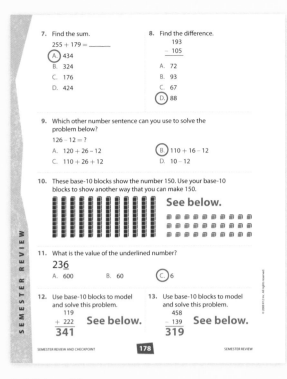

7. Find the sum.

255 + 179 = _____

(A.) 434
B. 324
C. 176
D. 424

8. Find the difference.

193
− 105

A. 72
B. 93
C. 67
(D.) 88

9. Which other number sentence can you use to solve the problem below?

126 − 12 = ?

A. 120 + 26 − 12
C. 110 + 26 + 12
(B.) 110 + 16 − 12
D. 10 − 12

10. These base-10 blocks show the number 150. Use your base-10 blocks to show another way that you can make 150.

See below.

11. What is the value of the underlined number?

23<u>6</u>

A. 600
B. 60
(C.) 6

12. Use base-10 blocks to model and solve this problem.

119
+ 222
See below.
341

13. Use base-10 blocks to model and solve this problem.

458
− 139
See below.
319

SEMESTER REVIEW AND CHECKPOINT **178** SEMESTER REVIEW

SEMESTER REVIEW

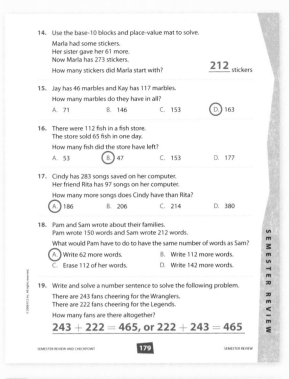

14. Use the base-10 blocks and place-value mat to solve.

Marla had some stickers.
Her sister gave her 61 more.
Now Marla has 273 stickers.
How many stickers did Marla start with?

212 stickers

15. Jay has 46 marbles and Kay has 117 marbles.
How many marbles do they have in all?

A. 71   B. 146   C. 153   (D.) 163

16. There were 112 fish in a fish store.
The store sold 65 fish in one day.
How many fish did the store have left?

A. 53   (B.) 47   C. 153   D. 177

17. Cindy has 283 songs saved on her computer.
Her friend Rita has 97 songs on her computer.
How many more songs does Cindy have than Rita?

(A.) 186   B. 206   C. 214   D. 380

18. Pam and Sam wrote about their families.
Pam wrote 150 words and Sam wrote 212 words.
What would Pam have to do to have the same number of words as Sam?

(A.) Write 62 more words.   B. Write 112 more words.
C. Erase 112 of her words.   D. Write 142 more words.

19. Write and solve a number sentence to solve the following problem.

There are 243 fans cheering for the Wranglers.
There are 222 fans cheering for the Legends.
How many fans are there altogether?

243 + 222 = 465, or 222 + 243 = 465

SEMESTER REVIEW AND CHECKPOINT **179** SEMESTER REVIEW

SEMESTER REVIEW

Additional Answers

10. Sample models include 15 tens rods, or 11 tens rods and 40 ones cubes.

12. Model should include 1 hundreds flat, 1 tens rod, and 9 ones cubes for 119. Model should include 2 hundreds flats, 2 tens rods, and 2 ones cubes for 222. Make sure students regroup the blocks correctly.

13. Model should include 4 hundreds flats, 5 tens rods, and 8 ones cubes for 458. Model should include 1 hundreds flat, 3 tens rods, and 9 ones cubes for 139. Make sure students regroup the blocks correctly.

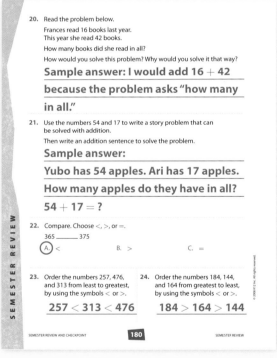

20. Read the problem below.

Frances read 16 books last year.
This year she read 42 books.
How many books did she read in all?
How would you solve this problem? Why would you solve it that way?

Sample answer: I would add 16 + 42 because the problem asks "how many in all."

21. Use the numbers 54 and 17 to write a story problem that can be solved with addition.
Then write an addition sentence to solve the problem.

Sample answer:

Yubo has 54 apples. Ari has 17 apples. How many apples do they have in all?

54 + 17 = ?

22. Compare. Choose <, >, or =.

365 _____ 375

(A.) <   B. >   C. =

23. Order the numbers 257, 476, and 313 from least to greatest, by using the symbols < or >.

257 < 313 < 476

24. Order the numbers 184, 144, and 164 from greatest to least, by using the symbols < or >.

184 > 164 > 144

SEMESTER REVIEW AND CHECKPOINT **180** SEMESTER REVIEW

SEMESTER REVIEW

➡ SEMESTER REVIEW Prepare for the Checkpoint

What you do next depends on how students performed in the previous activity, Semester Review: Checkpoint Practice. If students had difficulty with any of the problems, complete the appropriate review activity listed in the Unit Review tables online.

Because there are many concepts to review, consider using the Your Choice day to continue preparing for the Semester Checkpoint.

Semester Checkpoint

SEMESTER CHECKPOINT Offline · 60 minutes · OFFLINE

▶ Semester Objectives

This lesson assesses the following objectives:

- Decompose numbers to solve subtraction problems, such as $213 - 12 = 200 + 13 - 12$.
- Demonstrate that a number can be composed of other numbers in various ways.
- Identify the place value for each digit in whole numbers through 500.
- Use models to represent regrouping in addition or subtraction problems.
- Use concrete objects or sketches to model and solve addition or subtraction problem-solving situations with sums or minuends up through 500.
- Recognize and solve word problems involving sums up through 500 in which two quantities are combined.
- Recognize and solve word problems involving sums or minuends up through 500 in which one quantity changes by addition or subtraction.
- Recognize and solve word problems involving numbers up through 500 in which two quantities are compared by the use of addition or subtraction.
- Recognize and solve word problems involving numbers up through 500 in which one quantity must be changed to equal another quantity.
- Write and solve addition or subtraction number sentences to represent problem-solving situations with sums and minuends up through 500.
- Justify the procedures selected for addition or subtraction problem-solving situations with sums or minuends up through 500.
- Give examples of problem situations that can be described by addition or subtraction number sentences, and write the sentences.
- Compare whole numbers through 500 by using the symbols $<, =, >$.
- Order three or more whole numbers through 500 by using the symbols $<, =, >$.
- Find the sum of two whole numbers with sums up through 500.
- Use regrouping to find the difference of two whole numbers with the minuend up through 500.
- Use concrete objects or sketches to model and solve addition or subtraction computation problems with sums or minuends up through 500 with and without regrouping.

Materials to Gather

SUPPLIED

base-10 blocks

place-value mat

Semester Checkpoint (printout)

OFFLINE
60 min

SEMESTER CHECKPOINT Offline

Objectives

- Review semester objectives.

Students will complete the Semester Checkpoint offline. In Part 1, students will take a performance-based assessment. In Part 2, students will complete the problems on their own. Print the Semester Checkpoint. Read the directions, problems, and answer choices to students if necessary. Use the answer key to score the Checkpoint, and then enter the results online.

Gather the base-10 blocks and place-value mat.

Name _____   Date _____

Semester Checkpoint Answer Key

Part 1

Follow the instructions. Choose the response that best describes how the student performs on the task. When you have finished, enter the results online.

1. Show 8 tens rods and 22 ones cubes.
   Say, "These base-10 blocks show the number 102. Use your base-10 blocks to show another way you can make 102."
   (1 point)
   Sample models: 10 tens rods and 2 ones cubes; 9 tens rods and 12 ones cubes.

   Did the student show another way to make 102?

   A. Yes   B. No

Give students Part 2 of the assessment.

Name _____   Date _____

Part 2

Read each problem and follow the directions.

(1 point)
2. Find the sum.
   $$\begin{array}{r} 100 \\ +\ 201 \\ \hline \end{array}$$
   301

(1 point)
3. Find the difference.
   $$\begin{array}{r} 362 \\ -\ 77 \\ \hline \end{array}$$
   285

(1 point)
4. Which has the same value as 570 − 565?

   A. 500 − 65   B. 500 − 70   Ⓒ 70 − 65   D. 500 − 5

(1 point)
5. What is the value of the underlined number?

   41**7**

   A. 1   Ⓑ 10   C. 100

(1 point)
6. Use base-10 blocks and the place-value mat to model and solve this problem.
   $$\begin{array}{r} 254 \\ +\ 156 \\ \hline \end{array}$$
   410 See below.

(1 point)
7. Use base-10 blocks and the place-value mat to model and solve this problem.
   $$\begin{array}{r} 255 \\ -\ 179 \\ \hline \end{array}$$
   76 See below.

(1 point)
8. Use base-10 blocks and the place-value mat to solve this problem.

   Keith has 212 rocks in his collection.
   Matt has 436 rocks in his collection.
   How many more rocks does Matt have than Keith?   **224** rocks

(1 point)
9. Use base-10 blocks and the place-value mat to solve this problem.

   The Fancy Farm had 257 visitors in June.
   It had 183 visitors in July.
   How many visitors did the Fancy Farm have in June and July?   **440** visitors

Additional Answers

6. Model should include 2 hundreds flats, 5 tens rods, and 4 ones cubes for 254. Model should include 1 hundreds flat, 5 tens rods, and 6 ones cubes for 156. Make sure students regroup correctly.

7. Model should include 2 hundreds flats, 5 tens rods, and 5 ones cubes for 255. Model should include 1 hundreds flat, 7 tens rods, and 9 ones cubes for 179. Make sure students regroup correctly.

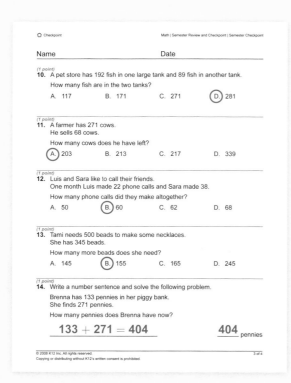

Name _____   Date _____

(1 point)
10. A pet store has 192 fish in one large tank and 89 fish in another tank.
    How many fish are in the two tanks?

    A. 117   B. 171   C. 271   Ⓓ 281

(1 point)
11. A farmer has 271 cows.
    He sells 68 cows.
    How many cows does he have left?

    Ⓐ 203   B. 213   C. 217   D. 339

(1 point)
12. Luis and Sara like to call their friends.
    One month Luis made 22 phone calls and Sara made 38.
    How many phone calls did they make altogether?

    A. 50   Ⓑ 60   C. 62   D. 68

(1 point)
13. Tami needs 500 beads to make some necklaces.
    She has 345 beads.
    How many more beads does she need?

    A. 145   Ⓑ 155   C. 165   D. 245

(1 point)
14. Write a number sentence and solve the following problem.

    Brenna has 133 pennies in her piggy bank.
    She finds 271 pennies.
    How many pennies does Brenna have now?

    133 + 271 = 404   **404** pennies

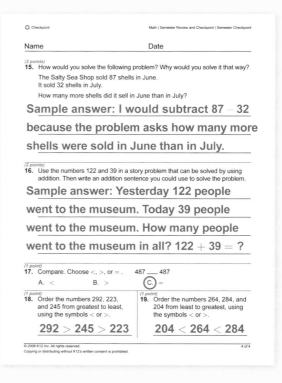

Name _____   Date _____

(2 points)
15. How would you solve the following problem? Why would you solve it that way?

    The Salty Sea Shop sold 87 shells in June.
    It sold 32 shells in July.

    How many more shells did it sell in June than in July?

    Sample answer: I would subtract 87 − 32 because the problem asks how many more shells were sold in June than in July.

(2 points)
16. Use the numbers 122 and 39 in a story problem that can be solved by using addition. Then write an addition sentence you could use to solve the problem.

    Sample answer: Yesterday 122 people went to the museum. Today 39 people went to the museum. How many people went to the museum in all? 122 + 39 = ?

(1 point)
17. Compare. Choose <, >, or =.   487 ___ 487

    A. <   B. >   Ⓒ =

(1 point)
18. Order the numbers 292, 223, and 245 from greatest to least, using the symbols < or >.

    292 > 245 > 223

(1 point)
19. Order the numbers 264, 284, and 204 from least to greatest, using the symbols < or >.

    204 < 264 < 284

Numbers Through 1,000

=

one thousand 1,000

824 >

931
nine hundred thirty-one

854 > 458

371 <

488   999 < 1,000   1,000

367 = 367   =   six hundred twelve 612

▶ Unit Objectives

- Count aloud whole numbers through 1,000.
- Read whole numbers through 1,000.
- Write number words through 1,000.
- Use models to represent numbers through 1,000.
- Demonstrate that multidigit numbers represent groups of 100s, 10s, and ones.
- Identify the place value for each digit in whole numbers through 1,000.

- Use expanded forms to represent numbers through 1,000, such as 754 = 7 hundreds + 5 tens + 4 ones.
- Order three or more whole numbers through 1,000 by using the symbols $<, =, >$.
- Compare whole numbers up through 1,000 by using the symbols $<, =, >$.

▶ Big Ideas

Place-value notation makes it easier to write and operate on large numbers.

▶ Unit Introduction

This unit focuses on counting, representing, comparing, and ordering numbers from 500 through 1,000. Although students can count aloud and write numbers, they will now extend their understanding by modeling greater numbers with base-10 blocks and learning to read and write number words. They will learn to see the connections between the number 325, the number words *three hundred twenty-five*, and the representation of the number in expanded form (325 = 3 hundreds + 2 tens + 5 ones or 325 = 300 + 20 + 5).

As students work with these representations, they will develop a deeper understanding of how the base-10 number system works. Fully understanding the number system will build confidence and skills that will help them solve problems involving greater numbers. The understanding of multiple representations of numbers and place value also will lead students to create strategies for comparing numbers through 1,000 and for properly using the greater-than ($>$), less-than ($<$), and equals ($=$) symbols.

During this unit, watch for mistakes as students count. Have students count forward and backward, starting with numbers from 500 through 1,000. Make sure they count at least 10 numbers and cross over multiples of 10 or 100 (for example, from 525 to 537, or 893 to 903). Practice skip counting by 10s from 800 through 1,000. As students develop fluency with greater numbers, they will become more confident about their mathematical skills.

Count Aloud Through 1,000

Lesson Overview

Skills Update	5 minutes	ONLINE
GET READY Count Through 500	5 minutes	ONLINE
LEARN Start Counting	15 minutes	ONLINE
LEARN Find Missing Numbers	15 minutes	ONLINE
TRY IT Practice Counting	10 minutes	OFFLINE
CHECKPOINT	10 minutes	OFFLINE

▶ Lesson Objectives

Count aloud whole numbers through 1,000.

▶ Prerequisite Skills

Count aloud whole numbers through 500.

▶ Common Errors and Misconceptions

Students might use the word *and* when reading numbers greater than 100. Explain that numbers should be read without using that word. For example, 203 should be read as *two hundred three* (not *two hundred **and** three*).

▶ Advance Preparation

On a sheet of paper, number and write the following number sequences:

1. 432, ___, 434, 435, 436
2. 648, 649, ___, 651, 652
3. 737, 738, 739, ___, 741
4. 564, 563, 562, 561, ___
5. 807, 808, ___, 810, 811
6. 996, 997, 998, 999, ___
7. 706, 705, 704, 703, 702, 701, ___

▶ Content Background

Students have learned to count through 500. In this lesson, they will extend their counting to 1,000.

Materials to Gather

SUPPLIED
Checkpoint (printout)

Keywords	**whole numbers** – zero and the counting numbers (0, 1, 2, 3, 4, 5, 6, …)

GET READY Count Through 500

ONLINE 5min

Objectives

- Count aloud whole numbers through 500.

Students will count aloud, starting from one given number to another number. During the activity, check that students count correctly.

If students incorrectly identify the next tens number during counting (e.g., 278, 279, **290**), or the next hundreds number (e.g., 398, 399, **300**), have them count by tens or hundreds until they have memorized the sequence of numbers.

LEARN Start Counting

ONLINE 15min

Objectives

- Count aloud whole numbers through 1,000.

Students will count aloud from one given number to another number. They will learn that the number 1,000 comes after 999.

The last screen instructs students to count with a partner. Act as the partner if only one student is present.

LEARN Find Missing Numbers

ONLINE 15min

Objectives

- Count aloud whole numbers through 1,000.

Students will count back from a given number. Then they will find the missing number or numbers in a sequence.

TRY IT Practice Counting

OFFLINE 10min

Objectives

- Count aloud whole numbers through 1,000.

Students will practice counting on and back from numbers through 1,000. They will count aloud and in writing.

Gather the number sequences.

1. Have students count aloud from the first given number to the second number. Use the following numbers:
   - 495 to 525
   - 595 to 611
   - 720 to 735
   - 992 to 1,000
2. Show students the number sequences. Have them count aloud and fill in the missing number as they count. Make sure students realize that for some problems they will count forward and for others they will count back.

OFFLINE
10 min

Objectives

- Count aloud whole numbers through 1,000.

Print the Checkpoint. Students will take a performance-based assessment. Read the directions and problems to students. Use the answer key to score the Checkpoint, and then enter the results online.

☼ Checkpoint   Math | Numbers Through 1,000 | Count Aloud Through 1,000

Name _____ Date _____

Checkpoint Answer Key

Follow the instructions for each item. Choose the response that best describes how the student performed on the task.

1. Write the following on a sheet of paper: 566 to 576.
   Say, "Count aloud from the first number to the second number."
   (1 point)
   Did the student count from 566 to 576?

   A. Yes   B. No

2. Write the following on a sheet of paper: 668 to 678.
   Say, "Count aloud from the first number to the second number."
   (1 point)
   Did the student count from 668 to 678?

   A. Yes   B. No

3. Write the following on a sheet of paper: 990 to 1,000.
   Say, "Count aloud from the first number to the second number."
   (1 point)
   Did the student count from 990 to 1,000?

   A. Yes   B. No

4. Write the following on a sheet of paper: 947, 948, _____, 950, 951.
   Ask, "What number is missing?"
   (1 point)
   Did the student say 949?

   A. Yes   B. No

1 of 2

☼ Checkpoint   Math | Numbers Through 1,000 | Count Aloud Through 1,000

Name _____ Date _____

5. Write the following on a sheet of paper: 991, 992, _____, 994, 995.
   Ask, "What number is missing?"
   (1 point)
   Did the student say 993?

   A. Yes   B. No

6. Write the following on a sheet of paper: 887, 888, _____, _____, 891, 892.
   Ask, "What numbers are missing?"
   (1 point)
   Did the student say 889, 890?

   A. Yes   B. No

2 of 2

Read Numbers Through 1,000

Lesson Overview

Skills Update	5 minutes	ONLINE
GET READY Read Page Numbers	5 minutes	ONLINE
LEARN Read Numbers at the Game	15 minutes	ONLINE
LEARN Read Number Words	15 minutes	ONLINE
TRY IT Practice Reading Numbers	10 minutes	OFFLINE
CHECKPOINT	10 minutes	OFFLINE

▶ Lesson Objectives

Read whole numbers through 1,000.

▶ Prerequisite Skills

Read whole numbers through 500.

▶ Common Errors and Misconceptions

Students might have difficulty writing multidigit numbers because numerals do not correspond exactly to English number words. For example, students might write twenty-five as 205 (20 and 5) instead of 25.

▶ Advance Preparation

Label each index card with one numeral or number or number word as follows:

- 541; 173; 896; 325; 747; 1,000
- six hundred eighty-seven, one thousand, four hundred fifty-five, nine hundred ninety-nine, seven hundred four
- three hundred sixty-two, six hundred eight, two hundred thirty-nine, nine hundred forty, five hundred eleven

▶ Content Background

Students will read numerals and number words through 1,000.

Keywords　　**number word** – a word that corresponds to a numerical symbol; for example, one, two, three…, twenty

Materials to Gather

SUPPLIED
Checkpoint (printout)

ALSO NEEDED
index cards – labeled with numerals and number words

GET READY Read Page Numbers

ONLINE 5 min

Students will read page numbers to practice reading numbers through 500.
Listen carefully as students read the numbers aloud.

Objectives

- Read whole numbers through 500.

LEARN Read Numbers at the Game

ONLINE 15 min

Students will read given numbers through 1,000.

If students need additional practice reading numbers through 1,000, use index cards with the digits 0 through 9 on them to create random numbers. Have students read each number by looking at each place value and reading from left to right.

Objectives

- Read whole numbers through 1,000.

Tips

Listen for students using the word *and* in hundred numbers. Explain that numbers should be read without using that word. For example, 309 should be read as *three hundred nine* (not *three hundred **and** nine*).

LEARN Read Number Words

ONLINE 15 min

Students will read number words through 1,000. Next they will type the number that corresponds to a number word. Then they will match numbers to their number words.

Objectives

- Read whole numbers through 1,000.

TRY IT Practice Reading Numbers

OFFLINE 10 min

Students will practice reading numbers and number words through 1,000.
Gather the number and number word cards.

Objectives

- Read whole numbers through 1,000.

1. Display the following number cards and have students say each number:

   541; 173; 896; 325; 747; 1,000

2. Display the following number word cards and have students say each number:

   - six hundred eighty-seven
   - four hundred fifty-five
   - seven hundred four
   - one thousand
   - nine hundred ninety-nine

3. Display the following number word cards and have students write each corresponding numeral:

   - three hundred sixty-two
   - two hundred thirty-nine
   - five hundred eleven
   - six hundred eight
   - nine hundred forty
   - one thousand

OFFLINE
10 min

Objectives

- Read whole numbers through 1,000.

Print the Checkpoint. In Part 1, students will take a performance-based assessment. In Part 2, students will complete the problems on their own. Read the directions, problems, and answer choices to students, if necessary. Use the answer key to score the Checkpoint, and then enter the results online.

⟳ Checkpoint   Math | Numbers Through 1,000 | Read Numbers Through 1,000

Name _____ Date _____

Checkpoint Answer Key

Part 1
Follow the instructions for each item. Choose the response that best describes how the student performs on the task.

1. Write the following on a sheet of paper: 936.
   Say, "Say the number aloud."
   (1 point)
   Did the student say nine hundred thirty-six?

   A. Yes   B. No

2. Write the following on a sheet of paper: 421.
   Say, "Say the number aloud."
   (1 point)
   Did the student say four hundred twenty-one?

   A. Yes   B. No

3. Write the following on a sheet of paper: six hundred thirty-two.
   Say, "Read the number aloud."
   (1 point)
   Did the student say six hundred thirty-two?

   A. Yes   B. No

1 of 3

⟳ Checkpoint   Math | Numbers Through 1,000 | Read Numbers Through 1,000

Name _____ Date _____

4. Write the following on a sheet of paper: seven hundred four.
   Say, "Read the number aloud."
   (1 point)
   Did the student say seven hundred four?

   A. Yes   B. No

5. Write the following on a sheet of paper: six hundred forty-eight.
   Say, "Read the number aloud."
   (1 point)
   Did the student say six hundred forty-eight?

   A. Yes   B. No

6. Write the following on a sheet of paper: one thousand.
   Say, "Read the number aloud."
   (1 point)
   Did the student say one thousand?

   A. Yes   B. No

Give students Part 2 of the assessment.

2 of 3

⟳ Checkpoint   Math | Numbers Through 1,000 | Read Numbers Through 1,000

Name _____ Date _____

Part 2
Circle the number that matches each number word.
(1 point)
7. six hundred forty-five

    A. 6045   (B.) 645   C. 6405   D. 60045

(1 point)
8. two hundred thirty-five

    A. 20035   B. 2035   (C.) 235   D. 2305

(1 point)
9. two hundred eighty-seven

    A. 20087   B. 20807   C. 2087   (D.) 287

(1 point)
10. three hundred sixteen

    A. 3060   B. 3016   (C.) 316   D. 360

3 of 3

Write Number Words Through 1,000

Lesson Overview

Skills Update	5 minutes	ONLINE
GET READY Read Number Words	5 minutes	ONLINE
LEARN Write Number Words	15 minutes	OFFLINE
LEARN Write More Number Words	15 minutes	OFFLINE
TRY IT Practice Writing Number Words	10 minutes	OFFLINE
CHECKPOINT	10 minutes	OFFLINE

▶ **Lesson Objectives**

Write number words through 1,000.

▶ **Prerequisite Skills**

Read number words through 500.

▶ **Common Errors and Misconceptions**

Students might have difficulty writing multidigit numbers because numerals do not correspond exactly to English number words. For example, students might write twenty-five as 205 (20 and 5) instead of 25.

▶ **Advance Preparation**

Label index cards with 0 through 9, tens through 90, and hundreds through 1,000. Write the numeral on one side of the card and the number word on the other side. Also prepare an index card with a hyphen (-). Save cards for use in future lessons.

▶ **Content Background**

In mathematics, the word *number* represents the quantity, and the word *numeral* represents the written symbol. So numerals, such as 0, 1, 2, and 3, symbolically represent numbers, or quantities. In everyday language, people say *number* to describe both the symbol and the quantity. As you speak with students, you may use *number* only.

In this lesson, the term *number word* indicates the English word for the numeral, such as "two" for the numeral 2. Students will learn how to write number words through 1,000.

Materials to Gather

SUPPLIED

Practice Writing Number Words activity page

Checkpoint (printout)

ALSO NEEDED

index cards – labeled with numerals and number words, hyphen: -

Keywords	
	digit – any one of the 10 numerals, 0–9, used to write a number
	numeral – a symbol that stands for a number

GET READY Read Number Words

Students will play a memory card game to practice matching numbers through 500 with their corresponding number words.

LEARN Write Number Words

Students will write number words through 1,000.
  Gather the labeled index cards.

1. Write the number 832 on paper. Display the number words on the 800 card, 30 card, and 2 card. Place the hyphen card between *thirty* and *two* so that students can read, "eight hundred thirty-two."

2. Explain that to write number words, students should write each word they say when they read a number aloud. Point to the number word cards as you say the following.

    Say: To read 832, we say the words *eight*, *hundred*, *thirty*, and *two*. So to write 832 in words, we would write each of those words. Look at the mark between the words *thirty* and *two*. This symbol is called a hyphen. We write a hyphen between the number words that represent the tens place value (thirty) and the ones place value (two).

3. Write the number 407.

    Say: This number is four hundred seven.

4. Display the number words on the 400 card and 7 card. Read them aloud.

    Say: To read 407, we say the words *four*, *hundred*, and *seven*. There is no hyphen because there are zero tens.

5. Shuffle the ones cards, tens cards, and hundreds cards into three separate decks, numeral side facing up. Have students choose one card from each pile to create a three-digit number. Then have them write the number word. They can flip over the cards to check their work.

LEARN Write More Number Words

Students will make and write numbers through 1,000.
  Gather the labeled index cards. Separate the ones, tens, and hundreds cards into three decks. Separate the 1,000 card from the deck.

1. Hold up the 1,000 card.

    Ask: What number is this?
    ANSWER: 1,000

2. Show students and read aloud the words *one thousand* on the card.

    Say: Write the number words for 1,000.
    Check students' work.

3. Fan out each deck of cards, numeral side up.

4. Select a card from the hundreds pile, the tens pile, and the ones pile.

    Say: I will put the three cards together to make a number.

Objectives

-   Read number words through 500.

Objectives

-   Write number words through 1,000.

Tips

Watch for students having difficulty with zero. For example, students may write *four hundred twenty* for 402. Have students read the number aloud before writing it.

  Watch for students writing the word *and* in hundred numbers. Explain that numbers should be read and written without using *and*. For example, 234 should be read and written as *two hundred thirty-four* (not *two hundred **and** thirty-four*).

  If students pick the 10 card and have difficulty, remind them that these numbers do not follow the usual rules for number words. For example, 417 is written as *four hundred seventeen*, not *four hundred ten-seven*.

Objectives

-   Write number words through 1,000.

Tips

If students have trouble deciding which words to write, remind them to first say the number then write each number they said.

5. Slide the tens card over the zeros on the hundreds card. Slide the ones card over the zero on the tens card. Now the overlapping cards should show a three-digit number.

6. Say the name of the number, and write the number word on the sheet of paper.

7. Turn over the cards.

    Say: The number I wrote matches the number words on the cards.

8. Have students repeat Steps 4–7 as time allows.

TRY IT Practice Writing Number Words

OFFLINE
10 min

Objectives

- Write number words through 1,000.

Students will practice writing number words for numerals through 1,000. Give students the Practice Writing Number Words activity page from their Activity Book and read the directions with them.

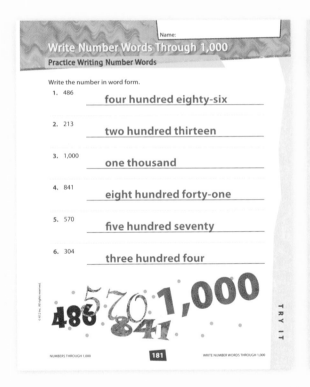

Name:

Write Number Words Through 1,000
Practice Writing Number Words

Write the number in word form.

1. 486   four hundred eighty-six

2. 213   two hundred thirteen

3. 1,000   one thousand

4. 841   eight hundred forty-one

5. 570   five hundred seventy

6. 304   three hundred four

NUMBERS THROUGH 1,000   **181**   WRITE NUMBER WORDS THROUGH 1,000

TRY IT

7. 719   seven hundred nineteen

8. 647   six hundred forty-seven

9. 612   six hundred twelve

10. 985   nine hundred eighty-five

11. 215   two hundred fifteen

12. 861   eight hundred sixty-one

NUMBERS THROUGH 1,000   **182**   WRITE NUMBER WORDS THROUGH 1,000

TRY IT

CHECKPOINT

Print the Checkpoint and have students complete it on their own. Read the directions, problems, and answer choices to students, if necessary. Use the answer key to score the Checkpoint, and then enter the results online.

Objectives

- Write number words through 1,000.

Name _____ Date _____

Checkpoint Answer Key

Write each number in word form.

(1 point)
1. 803   eight hundred three

(1 point)
2. 1,000   one thousand

(1 point)
3. 511   five hundred eleven

(1 point)
4. 722   seven hundred twenty-two

(1 point)
5. 130   one hundred thirty

(1 point)
6. 999   nine hundred ninety-nine

(1 point)
7. 675   six hundred seventy-five

(1 point)
8. 201   two hundred one

1 of 1

Represent Numbers Through 1,000

Lesson Overview

Skills Update	5 minutes	**ONLINE**
GET READY Show Numbers Different Ways	5 minutes	**OFFLINE**
LEARN Show Numbers Through 1,000	20 minutes	**OFFLINE**
LEARN Make Numbers Through 1,000	15 minutes	**ONLINE**
TRY IT Practice Showing Numbers	15 minutes	**OFFLINE**

▶ Lesson Objectives
Use models to represent numbers through 1,000.

▶ Prerequisite Skills
Represent equivalent forms of the same number through the use of physical models such as tens rods and ones cubes through 20.

▶ Common Errors and Misconceptions
- Students might not think of numbers as groups of tens, hundreds, and so forth. For example, students might think of 24 only as 24 single units, not 2 tens and 4 ones.
- Students might not realize that a digit's place-value position determines its value. For example, students might think the digits in 14 have values of 1 and 4, not 10 and 4.
- Students might have difficulty modeling multidigit numbers with counting objects. For example, when asked to model 23, students might use two objects to represent the 2 rather than using twenty objects.
- Students might have difficulty writing multidigit numbers because numerals do not correspond exactly to English number words. For example, students might write twenty-five as 205 (20 and 5) instead of 25.

▶ Advance Preparation
Print the Place-Value Mat – Thousands Column. Align the right side of the thousands column with the left side of the hundreds column on the place-value mat. Tape it to the mat so the mat has four columns.

▶ Content Background
Students will learn how to represent numbers through 1,000.

Materials to Gather

SUPPLIED
base-10 blocks
place-value mat
Place-Value Mat – Thousands Column (printout)
Practice Showing Numbers activity page

ALSO NEEDED
tape, clear

thousands cube – a block in the base-10 block set, showing 10 hundreds flat blocks and representing the thousands place; equivalent to the combination of 1,000 ones cubes or 100 tens rods

GET READY Show Numbers Different Ways

OFFLINE
5min

Objectives

- Represent equivalent forms of the same number through the use of physical models such as tens rods and ones cubes through 20.

Students will use base-10 blocks to show the same number two different ways. Gather the base-10 blocks.

1. Display the number 13 with the blocks in two different ways. First show 1 tens rod and 3 ones cubes. Then show 13 ones cubes.

   Say: Each group of blocks shows the number 13. The two groups use different blocks to show the same number.

2. Have students show the following numbers two different ways using the base-10 blocks:

   - 15 (1 tens rod and 5 ones cubes; 15 ones cubes)
   - 20 (2 tens rods; 1 tens rod and 10 ones cubes; 20 ones cubes)

LEARN Show Numbers Through 1,000

OFFLINE
20min

Objectives

- Use models to represent numbers through 1,000.

Students will identify numbers represented by base-10 blocks. They also will use base-10 blocks to model numbers through 1,000. Gather the base-10 blocks, dry-erase marker, dry-erase eraser, and place-value mat with the thousands column attached.

1. Display a ones cube, a tens rod, and a hundreds flat, and ask students to identify each.

2. Have students line up ones cubes to match a tens rod. Then have them line up tens rods to match a hundreds flat.

3. Display the thousands cube.

   Say: This is a thousands cube. It represents 1,000. One thousands cube equals 10 hundreds flats. Stack 10 hundreds flats and compare them to the thousands cube.

   Students should stack 10 hundreds flats to compare to the thousands cube.

4. Display 6 hundreds flats, 3 tens rods, and 1 ones cubes. Have students identify the number of hundreds, tens, and ones and write each value on the place-value mat. Then have them write the number that the blocks represent.

5. Repeat Step 4 with the following numbers: 507, 74, and 1,000.

6. Now have students use the base-10 blocks to show the following numbers: 728, 570, 405, and 1,000. Then have them write each number.

LEARN Make Numbers Through 1,000

ONLINE 15 min

Objectives

- Use models to represent numbers through 1,000.

Students will use the Place Value Learning Tool to model numbers through 1,000 with base-10 blocks.

DIRECTIONS FOR USING THE PLACE VALUE LEARNING TOOL

1. Click Begin Setup and choose the following:
   - Work with NUMBERS up to: 999
   - Use regrouping: YES
   - Computer Makes Questions
2. Have students complete the problems given. Continue as time allows.

   Go to the next screen to continue with the Learn activity.

Tips

Allow students to use base-10 blocks to model the problems.

TRY IT Practice Showing Numbers

OFFLINE 15 min

Objectives

- Use models to represent numbers through 1,000.

This Try It activity has two parts.

PART 1

Students will practice modeling numbers through 1,000 using base-10 blocks. Gather the base-10 blocks and place-value mat with the thousands column attached.

Have students use base-10 blocks to model the following numbers on their place-value mat: 376, 701, 920, 853, 546, 652, 904, and 1,000.

PART 2

Students will practice choosing the model that represents a number through 1,000. Give students the Practice Showing Numbers activity page from their Activity Book and read the directions with them.

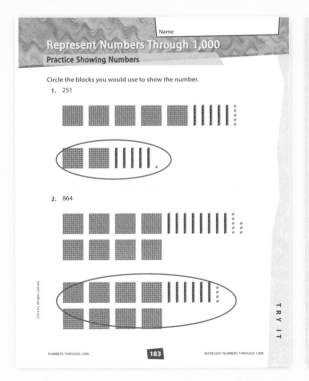

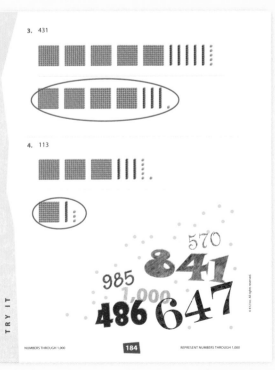

Work with Numbers Through 1,000

Skills Update	5 minutes	ONLINE
GET READY Base-10 Blocks	5 minutes	OFFLINE
LEARN Place Value Through 1,000	5 minutes	ONLINE
LEARN Make Groups	20 minutes	ONLINE
LEARN Model Greater Numbers	15 minutes	ONLINE
TRY IT Represent Numbers Through 1,000	10 minutes	OFFLINE

▶ Lesson Objectives

Demonstrate that multidigit numbers represent groups of 100s, 10s, and ones.

▶ Prerequisite Skills

Demonstrate understanding of place value by recording the number represented by groupings of tens and ones (for example, given 5 tens rods and 2 ones cubes or hearing "5 tens and 2 ones," record 52).

▶ Common Errors and Misconceptions

- Students might not think of numbers as groups of tens, hundreds, and so forth. For example, students might think of 24 only as 24 single units, not 2 tens and 4 ones.

- Students might not realize that a digit's place-value position determines its value. For example, students might think the digits in 14 have values of 1 and 4, not 10 and 4.

- Students might have difficulty modeling multidigit numbers with counting objects. For example, when asked to model 23, students might use two objects to represent the 2 rather than using twenty objects.

- Students might have difficulty writing multidigit numbers because numerals do not correspond exactly to English number words. For example, students might write twenty-five as 205 (20 and 5) instead of 25.

▶ Content Background

Students often struggle with understanding what each digit in a number represents. In this lesson, they will represent numbers through 1,000 using models, groups, and numerals. They will learn to identify numbers shown in each of these ways.

Materials to Gather

SUPPLIED

base-10 blocks

Represent Numbers Through 1,000 activity page

GET READY Base-10 Blocks

Objectives

- Demonstrate understanding of place value by recording the number represented by groupings of tens and ones (for example, given 5 tens rods and 2 ones cubes or hearing "5 tens and 2 ones," record 52).

Students will identify the number of hundreds, tens, and ones in a number and then write that number.

Gather the base-10 blocks.

1. Tell students to show 235 with the base-10 blocks. Make sure that students show 2 hundreds flats, 3 tens rods, and 5 ones cubes.

2. **Ask:** How many hundreds, tens, and ones are in the number 235?
ANSWER: 2 hundreds, 3 tens, and 5 ones

3. **Say:** Now write the number shown by the base-10 blocks.
ANSWER: 235

LEARN Place Value Through 1,000

Objectives

- Demonstrate that multidigit numbers represent groups of 100s, 10s, and ones.

Students will identify numbers through 1,000 shown with base-10 blocks, place-value groups, words, and numerals. They will develop a stronger ability to move between these representations, deepening their understanding of the base-10 number system.

LEARN Make Groups

Objectives

- Demonstrate that multidigit numbers represent groups of 100s, 10s, and ones.

Students will learn to use the fewest number of base-10 blocks to model numbers. They will also identify the value of a single digit in a multidigit number.

For the second activity, students will use the Place Value Learning Tool.

DIRECTIONS FOR USING THE PLACE VALUE LEARNING TOOL

1. Click Begin Setup and choose the following:
   - Work with NUMBERS up to: 999
   - Use regrouping: YES
   - Teacher or Parent Makes Questions

2. Enter the number 163, and click Submit.

3. **Say:** One way to show 163 would be with 15 tens rods and 13 ones cubes, but let's show 163 using the fewest number of blocks we can.

4. Have students use 1 hundreds flat, 6 tens rods, and 3 ones cubes. Then click Check.

5. Click Next Problem to enter a new number. Have students show the following numbers using the fewest blocks: 485 and 216.

ONLINE
15min

Objectives

- Demonstrate that multidigit numbers represent groups of 100s, 10s, and ones.

Students will see base-10 blocks modeling greater numbers. They will type the number that the blocks represent.

OFFLINE
10min

TRY IT **Represent Numbers Through 1,000**

Objectives

- Demonstrate that multidigit numbers represent groups of 100s, 10s, and ones.

Students will practice representing and identifying numbers through 1,000. Give students the Represent Numbers Through 1,000 activity page from their Activity Book and read the directions with them.

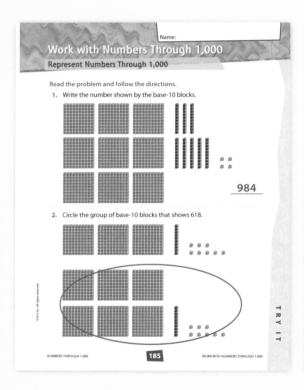

Name:

Work with Numbers Through 1,000

Represent Numbers Through 1,000

Read the problem and follow the directions.

1. Write the number shown by the base-10 blocks.

984

2. Circle the group of base-10 blocks that shows 618.

TRY IT

NUMBERS THROUGH 1,000   **185**   WORK WITH NUMBERS THROUGH 1,000

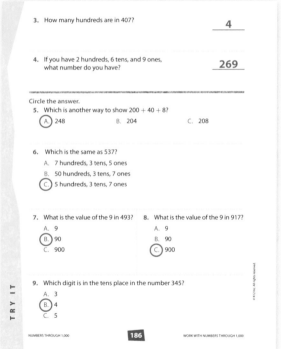

3. How many hundreds are in 407?   **4**

4. If you have 2 hundreds, 6 tens, and 9 ones, what number do you have?   **269**

Circle the answer.

5. Which is another way to show 200 + 40 + 8?

   A. 248   B. 204   C. 208

6. Which is the same as 537?

   A. 7 hundreds, 3 tens, 5 ones

   B. 50 hundreds, 3 tens, 7 ones

   C. 5 hundreds, 3 tens, 7 ones

7. What is the value of the 9 in 493?   8. What is the value of the 9 in 917?

   A. 9   A. 9

   B. 90   B. 90

   C. 900   C. 900

9. Which digit is in the tens place in the number 345?

   A. 3

   B. 4

   C. 5

TRY IT

NUMBERS THROUGH 1,000   **186**   WORK WITH NUMBERS THROUGH 1,000

Model Numbers Through 1,000

Skills Update	5 minutes	ONLINE
LEARN Write Expanded Form	10 minutes	ONLINE
LEARN Hundreds, Tens, and Ones	15 minutes	ONLINE
LEARN Numbers with Zero	10 minutes	ONLINE
TRY IT Models and Groups	10 minutes	OFFLINE
CHECKPOINT	10 minutes	OFFLINE

▶ Lesson Objectives

- Demonstrate that multidigit numbers represent groups of 100s, 10s, and ones.
- Use models to represent numbers through 1,000.

▶ Prerequisite Skills

Demonstrate understanding of place value by recording the number represented by groupings of tens and ones (for example, given 5 tens rods and 2 ones cubes or hearing "5 tens and 2 ones," record 52).

▶ Common Errors and Misconceptions

- Students might not think of numbers as groups of tens, hundreds, and so forth. For example, students might think of 24 only as 24 single units, not 2 tens and 4 ones.
- Students might not realize that a digit's place-value position determines its value. For example, students might think the digits in 14 have values of 1 and 4, not 10 and 4.
- Students might have difficulty thinking of numbers as groups of tens, hundreds, and so forth because some English number words do not emphasize place value. For example, the number word *twelve* does not suggest 1 ten and 2 ones.
- Students might have difficulty writing multidigit numbers because numerals do not correspond exactly to English number words. For example, students might write twenty-five as 205 (20 and 5) instead of 25.

▶ Content Background

Students often struggle with understanding what each digit in a number represents. To understand place value, they must first understand that the numbers 0 through 9 are called *digits*. The digits 0 through 9 can be used to write any number in the base-10 system. The place where a digit is located is its value. For example, in the number 254, the 2 is in the hundreds place, so its value is 200. Each digit's value in a number is called *place value*.

Students will learn to represent numbers through 1,000 using models, groups, and numerals. They will also learn to identify numbers shown in these various forms.

Materials to Gather

SUPPLIED

base-10 blocks

Models and Groups activity page

Checkpoint (printout)

LEARN Write Expanded Form

ONLINE 10min

Students are familiar with place value and representing numbers. In this activity, they will write a number in expanded form after being given a number in standard form. They will write expanded form using words and numbers (for example, 2 hundreds + 5 tens + 3 ones) and numbers only (for example, 200 + 50 + 3).

Objectives

- Demonstrate that multidigit numbers represent groups of 100s, 10s, and ones.

LEARN Hundreds, Tens, and Ones

ONLINE 15min

Students will identify numbers shown by models and groups. They will also create models to represent numbers. When students reach the Place Value Learning Tool, follow the directions below.

DIRECTIONS FOR USING THE PLACE VALUE LEARNING TOOL

1. Click Begin Setup and choose the following:
   - Work with NUMBERS up to: 999
   - Use regrouping: YES
   - Teacher or Parent Makes Questions
2. Use the following numbers: 216, 624, and 123.

   Go to the next screen to continue with the Learn activity.

Objectives

- Demonstrate that multidigit numbers represent groups of 100s, 10s, and ones.
- Use models to represent numbers through 1,000.

LEARN Numbers with Zero

ONLINE 10min

Students have used models, words, and numerals to represent numbers. In this activity, they will focus on representing numbers that have internal zeros, and will then use the Place Value Learning Tool to represent numbers with virtual base-10 blocks. When students reach the Place Value Learning Tool follow the directions below.

DIRECTIONS FOR USING THE PLACE VALUE LEARNING TOOL

1. Click Begin Setup and choose the following:
   - Work with NUMBERS up to: 999
   - Use regrouping: YES
   - Teacher or Parent Makes Questions
2. Use the following numbers: 270, 830, and 405.

   Go to the next screen to continue with the Learn activity.

Objectives

- Demonstrate that multidigit numbers represent groups of 100s, 10s, and ones.

TRY IT Models and Groups

Students will practice identifying equivalent representations of numbers (as models, groups, and numerals). Give students the Models and Groups activity page from their Activity Book and read the directions with them. Use the answer key to check students' answers, and then enter the results online.

Objectives

- Demonstrate that multidigit numbers represent groups of 100s, 10s, and ones.
- Use models to represent numbers through 1,000.

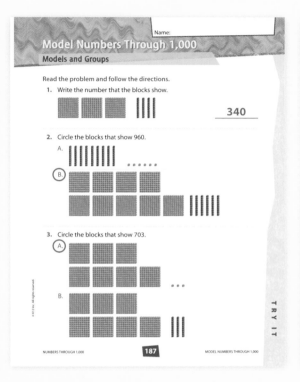

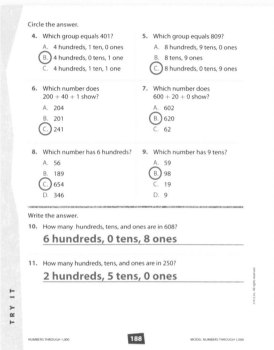

CHECKPOINT

Objectives

- Demonstrate that multidigit numbers represent groups of 100s, 10s, and ones.
- Use models to represent numbers through 1,000.

Print the Checkpoint. In Part 1, students will take a performance-based assessment. In Part 2, students will complete the problems on their own. Read the directions, problems, and answer choices to students, if necessary. Use the answer key to score the Checkpoint, and then enter the results online.

Gather the base-10 blocks, and give them to students for Problems 1 and 2.

Checkpoint   Math | Numbers Through 1,000 | Model Numbers Through 1,000

Name _____ Date _____

Checkpoint Answer Key

Part 1

Follow the instructions for each problem. Choose the response that best describes how the student performed on the task.

1. Say, "Use the base-10 blocks to model the number 853."
   Sample answer: 8 hundreds flats, 5 tens rods, 3 ones cubes
   (1 point)
   Did the student model 853?

   A. Yes   B. No

2. Say, "Use the base-10 blocks to model the number 208."
   Sample answer: 2 hundreds flats, 8 ones cubes
   (1 point)
   Did the student model 208?

   A. Yes   B. No

Give students Part 2 of the assessment.

Checkpoint   Math | Numbers Through 1,000 | Model Numbers Through 1,000

Name _____ Date _____

Part 2

Write the answer.

(1 point)
3. How many hundreds are in 154?   **1**

(1 point)
4. How many hundreds are in 456?   **4**

(1 point)
5. How many tens are in 36?   **3**

(1 point)
6. How many tens are in 428?   **2 or 42**

(1 point)
7. How many hundreds, tens, and ones are in 541?

   5 hundreds, 4 tens, 1 one

Circle the answer.

(1 point)
8. Which number has 8 tens?

   A. 8   B. 28   C. 18   (D.) 87

(1 point)
9. Which number is modeled below?

   A. 446   B. 644   (C.) 464   D. 466

(1 point)
10. Circle the blocks that you would use to show the number 142.

Place Value Through 1,000

Skills Update	5 minutes	ONLINE
GET READY Place Value Through 500	15 minutes	ONLINE
LEARN Place Value with Blocks	20 minutes	ONLINE
TRY IT Practice Place Value	20 minutes	OFFLINE

▶ Lesson Objectives

Identify the place value for each digit in whole numbers through 1,000.

▶ Prerequisite Skills

Identify the place value for each digit in whole numbers through 500.

▶ Common Errors and Misconceptions

- Students might not think of numbers as groups of tens, hundreds, and so forth. For example, students might think of 24 only as 24 single units, not 2 tens and 4 ones.

- Students might not realize that a digit's place-value position determines its value. For example, students might think the digits in 14 have values of 1 and 4, not 10 and 4.

- Students might have difficulty modeling multidigit numbers with counting objects. For example, when asked to model 23, students might use two objects to represent the 2 rather than using twenty objects.

- Students might have difficulty writing multidigit numbers because numerals do not correspond exactly to English number words. For example, students might write twenty-five as 205 (20 and 5) instead of 25.

▶ Content Background

Students often struggle with understanding what each digit in a number represents. To understand place value, they must first understand that the numbers 0 through 9 are called *digits*. The digits 0 through 9 can be used to write any number in the base-10 system. The place where a digit is located is its value. For example, in the number 254, the 2 is in the hundreds place, so its value is 200. Each digit's value in a number is called its *place value*.

Students will identify the place value for each digit in numbers through 1,000. They will learn about the thousands place and that the 1 in 1,000 is in the thousands place.

Materials to Gather

SUPPLIED

Practice Place Value activity page

place value – the value of a digit, given its position in a number; for example, 23 means 2 tens and 3 ones

value – an assigned or calculated quantity; often used with place value or monetary value; for example, the 2 in 23 has a value of 20; $2.50 has a value of 2 dollars and 50 cents

GET READY Place Value Through 500

ONLINE **15**min

Students will identify whether an underlined digit in a number is in the ones, tens, or hundreds place.

First have students try the game in Practice mode. Then have them click Play to compete against a timer.

Objectives

- Identify the place value for each digit in whole numbers through 500.

LEARN Place Value with Blocks

ONLINE **20**min

Students will identify whether an underlined digit is in the ones, tens, or hundreds place. Then they will identify the digit's value, connecting these ideas to the place-value chart and base-10 blocks.

Students should begin to memorize the place-value positions. Encourage them to first state the digit's place-value position without using the place-value chart as reference.

Objectives

- Identify the place value for each digit in whole numbers through 1,000.

TRY IT Practice Place Value

OFFLINE **20**min

Students will practice identifying a digit's place-value position and value. Give students the Practice Place Value activity page from their Activity Book and read the directions with them.

Objectives

- Identify the place value for each digit in whole numbers through 1,000.

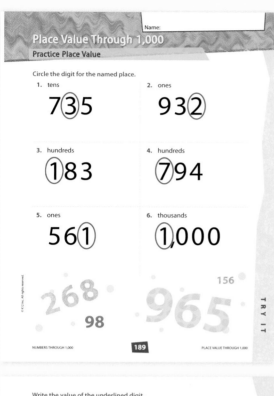

Name: _____

Place Value Through 1,000
Practice Place Value

Circle the digit for the named place.

1. tens
7(3)5

2. ones
93(2)

3. hundreds
(1)83

4. hundreds
(7)94

5. ones
56(1)

6. thousands
(1),000

268

156

965

98

TRY IT

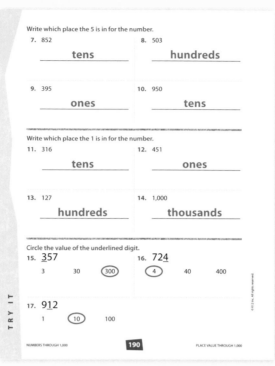

Write which place the 5 is in for the number.

7. 852
_____ tens

8. 503
_____ hundreds

9. 395
_____ ones

10. 950
_____ tens

Write which place the 1 is in for the number.

11. 316
_____ tens

12. 451
_____ ones

13. 127
_____ hundreds

14. 1,000
_____ thousands

Circle the value of the underlined digit.

15. <u>3</u>57
3   30   (300)

16. 7<u>2</u>4
(4)   40   400

17. 9<u>1</u>2
1   (10)   100

TRY IT

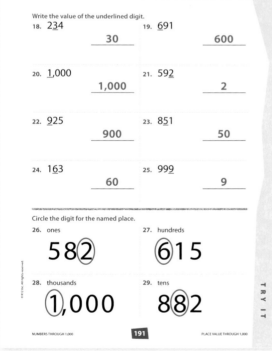

Write the value of the underlined digit.

18. 2<u>3</u>4
_____ 30

19. <u>6</u>91
_____ 600

20. <u>1</u>,000
_____ 1,000

21. 59<u>2</u>
_____ 2

22. <u>9</u>25
_____ 900

23. 8<u>5</u>1
_____ 50

24. 1<u>6</u>3
_____ 60

25. 99<u>9</u>
_____ 9

Circle the digit for the named place.

26. ones
58(2)

27. hundreds
(6)15

28. thousands
(1),000

29. tens
8(8)2

TRY IT

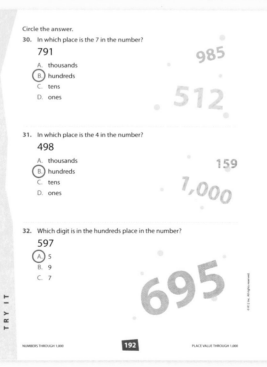

Circle the answer.

30. In which place is the 7 in the number?
791
A. thousands
(B.) hundreds
C. tens
D. ones

985

512

31. In which place is the 4 in the number?
498
A. thousands
(B.) hundreds
C. tens
D. ones

159

1,000

32. Which digit is in the hundreds place in the number?
597
(A.) 5
B. 9
C. 7

695

TRY IT

Standard to Expanded Form

Lesson Overview

Skills Update	5 minutes	ONLINE
GET READY Match Expanded Form	5 minutes	ONLINE
LEARN Expanded Form Through 1,000	20 minutes	ONLINE
LEARN More Expanded Form	20 minutes	OFFLINE
TRY IT Practice Expanded Form	10 minutes	OFFLINE

▶ Lesson Objectives

Use expanded forms to represent numbers through 1,000, such as
754 = 7 hundreds + 5 tens + 4 ones.

▶ Prerequisite Skills

Use expanded forms to represent numbers through 500, such as
345 = 3 hundreds + 4 tens + 5 ones = 300 + 40 + 5.

▶ Common Errors and Misconceptions

- Students might not think of numbers as groups of tens, hundreds, and so forth. For example, students might think of 24 only as 24 single units, not 2 tens and 4 ones.
- Students might not realize that a digit's place-value position determines its value. For example, students might think the digits in 14 have values of 1 and 4, not 10 and 4.
- Students might have difficulty modeling multidigit numbers with counting objects. For example, when asked to model 23, students might use two objects to represent the 2 rather than using twenty objects.
- Students might have difficulty writing multidigit numbers because numerals do not correspond exactly to English number words. For example, students might write twenty-five as 205 (20 and 5) instead of 25.

▶ Advance Preparation

Label index cards with numerals 0 through 9 (two sets), tens through 90, and hundreds through 1,000. Or gather the cards you prepared previously. Also label two index cards with the plus symbol (+) and three index cards with the words **hundreds**, **tens**, and **ones**. Save cards for use in future lessons.

▶ Content Background

Expanded form is a way to write numbers to show the place value for each digit. The number 365 can be written in expanded form as 300 + 60 + 5 or 3 hundreds + 6 tens + 5 ones. When numbers are written in the conventional way, such as 365, they are said to be written in *standard form*. Students will write the expanded form when given the standard form of a number.

Materials to Gather

SUPPLIED

base-10 blocks

place-value mat

Practice Expanded Form activity page

ALSO NEEDED

index cards – labeled with numerals, symbol: + (2), **hundreds**, **tens**, **ones**

GET READY Match Expanded Form

Students will play a memory card game to practice matching numbers through 500 in standard form with their equivalents in expanded form.

- Use expanded forms to represent numbers through 500, such as 345 = 3 hundreds + 4 tens + 5 ones = 300 + 40 + 5.

LEARN Expanded Form Through 1,000

Students will write numbers in expanded form given the standard form and a base-10 block model. They will write the expanded form using words and numbers (for example, 5 hundreds + 2 tens + 7 ones) and numbers only (for example, 500 + 20 + 7).

Have students use the blocks online to help them determine the answers. They should count the flats by 100s, rods by 10s, and cubes by ones to understand the value of each digit in the number.

Students might have difficulty writing the expanded form of a number that has zero as a digit.

Explain that because zero means none, there are no tens (or ones) in that place. For example, in the number 803, there are no tens, so the expanded form would be 8 hundreds + 0 tens + 3 ones (or 800 + 0 + 3).

Objectives

- Use expanded forms to represent numbers through 1,000, such as 754 = 7 hundreds + 5 tens + 4 ones.

LEARN More Expanded Form

Students will use base-10 blocks and number, word, and symbol cards to write expanded form for numbers through 1,000. Then they will write the expanded form for numbers in standard form without using base-10 blocks.

Gather the base-10 blocks, place-value mat, and labeled index cards.

1. Show the number 739 with base-10 blocks.

   Ask: What number do the blocks show?
   ANSWER: 739

2. Place the hundreds, tens, and ones cards in a row with plus symbols between them. Leave room for students to place a number card in front of each word.

3. **Ask:** How many hundreds are in 739?
   ANSWER: 7

   Have students place the 7 card in front of hundreds.

4. Repeat Step 3 with the tens and ones places. (The cards should show 7 hundreds + 3 tens + 9 ones.)

5. **Say:** Now show the expanded form using numbers.

   Ask: What is the value of the digit in the hundreds place?
   ANSWER: 700

   Have students place the 700 card below 7 hundreds.

6. Repeat Step 5 with the tens and ones places to show the 30 card below 3 tens and 9 card below 9 ones.

Objectives

- Use expanded forms to represent numbers through 1,000, such as 754 = 7 hundreds + 5 tens + 4 ones.

Tips

If students have difficulty naming the value of each digit, have them count the base-10 blocks, counting by 100s, 10s, or ones as appropriate.

7. **Say:** The expanded form of 739 is $700 + 30 + 9$. We can use the cards to check the answer.

   Slide the 30 card over the 700 card to cover the zeros in 700 and show 730. Place the 9 card on top to show 739.

8. Repeat Steps 1–7 with the number 972.

9. Show students the thousands cube, and ask them to tell you its value. (1,000)

10. Write the number 1,000 on a sheet of paper. Below the number, write ___ thousands + ___ hundreds + ___ tens + ___ ones. Guide students in filling in the blanks. (1; 0; 0; 0)

11. Guide students in writing 1,000 in expanded form with numbers. $(1,000 + 0 + 0 + 0)$

12. Repeat Steps 9–11 with the following numbers: 508, 999, 710, and 603. Begin with the written number; do not show the number with blocks. Repeat with additional three-digit numbers greater than 500 as time allows.

TRY IT Practice Expanded Form

OFFLINE

10 min

Objectives

Students will practice writing numbers in expanded form. Give students the Practice Expanded Form activity page from their Activity Book and read the directions with them.

- Use expanded forms to represent numbers through 1,000, such as $754 = 7$ hundreds + 5 tens + 4 ones.

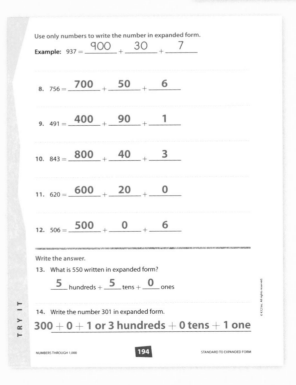

Standard to Expanded Form
Practice Expanded Form

Name: _____

Use numbers and words to write the number in expanded form.

Example: $267 = \underline{2}$ hundreds + $\underline{6}$ tens + $\underline{7}$ ones

1. $842 = \underline{8}$ hundreds + $\underline{4}$ tens + $\underline{2}$ ones

2. $604 = \underline{6}$ hundreds + $\underline{0}$ tens + $\underline{4}$ ones

3. $519 = \underline{5}$ hundreds + $\underline{1}$ tens + $\underline{9}$ ones

4. $370 = \underline{3}$ hundreds + $\underline{7}$ tens + $\underline{0}$ ones

5. $1,000 = \underline{1}$ thousands + $\underline{0}$ hundreds + $\underline{0}$ tens + $\underline{0}$ ones

Circle the expanded form of the number.

6. 975
   A. $900 + 70 + 5$ *(circled)*
   B. $900 + 700 + 5$
   C. $9 + 7 + 5$
   D. $90 + 75$

7. 718
   A. $7 + 1 + 8$
   B. $700 + 10 + 8$ *(circled)*
   C. $700 + 18 + 8$
   D. $7 + 18$

Use only numbers to write the number in expanded form.

Example: $937 = \underline{900} + \underline{30} + \underline{7}$

8. $756 = \underline{700} + \underline{50} + \underline{6}$

9. $491 = \underline{400} + \underline{90} + \underline{1}$

10. $843 = \underline{800} + \underline{40} + \underline{3}$

11. $620 = \underline{600} + \underline{20} + \underline{0}$

12. $506 = \underline{500} + \underline{0} + \underline{6}$

Write the answer.

13. What is 550 written in expanded form?
    $\underline{5}$ hundreds + $\underline{5}$ tens + $\underline{0}$ ones

14. Write the number 301 in expanded form.
    $300 + 0 + 1$ or 3 hundreds + 0 tens + 1 one

Expanded to Standard Form

Lesson Overview		
Skills Update	5 minutes	ONLINE
GET READY Expanded and Standard Form	5 minutes	ONLINE
LEARN Find the Standard Form	20 minutes	ONLINE
LEARN Write the Standard Form	15 minutes	OFFLINE
TRY IT Expanded Form to Standard Form	10 minutes	OFFLINE
CHECKPOINT	5 minutes	OFFLINE

▶ Lesson Objectives

Use expanded forms to represent numbers through 1,000, such as 754 = 7 hundreds + 5 tens + 4 ones.

▶ Prerequisite Skills

Use expanded forms to represent numbers through 500, such as 345 = 3 hundreds + 4 tens + 5 ones = 300 + 40 + 5.

▶ Common Errors and Misconceptions

- Students might not think of numbers as groups of tens, hundreds, and so forth. For example, students might think of 24 only as 24 single units, not 2 tens and 4 ones.

- Students might not realize that a digit's place-value position determines its value. For example, students might think the digits in 14 have values of 1 and 4, not 10 and 4.

- Students might have difficulty modeling multidigit numbers with counting objects. For example, when asked to model 23, students might use two objects to represent the 2 rather than using twenty objects.

- Students might have difficulty writing multidigit numbers because numerals do not correspond exactly to English number words. For example, students might write twenty-five as 205 (20 and 5) instead of 25.

▶ Advance Preparation

Label index cards with numerals 0 through 9, tens through 90, and hundreds through 900. Also label two other index cards with the plus symbol (+). Or gather the cards you prepared previously.

▶ Content Background

Expanded form is a way to write numbers to show the place value for each digit. The number 365 can be written in expanded form as 300 + 60 + 5 or 3 hundreds + 6 tens + 5 ones. When numbers are written in the conventional way, such as 365, they are said to be written in *standard form*. Students will write the standard form when given the expanded form of a number.

Materials to Gather

SUPPLIED

Expanded Form to Standard Form activity page

Checkpoint (printout)

ALSO NEEDED

index cards – labeled with numerals, symbol: + (2)

GET READY Expanded and Standard Form

Students will play a memory card game to practice matching numbers through 500 in standard form with their equivalents in expanded form. Expanded form may be shown in two different ways. For example, 216 can be written as

- $200 + 10 + 6$
- 2 hundreds + 1 ten + 6 ones

As students play the game, ask questions such as the following:

- If the expanded form starts with 200, what digit will be in the hundreds place?
- If the expanded form contains the number 10, what digit will be in the tens place?
- If the expanded form contains the number 6, what digit will be in the ones place?

- Use expanded forms to represent numbers through 500, such as $345 = 3$ hundreds + 4 tens + 5 ones $= 300 + 40 + 5$.

LEARN Find the Standard Form

Students will learn how to write the standard form of a number given the expanded form. First they will use place-value models to write the expanded form of a number two ways. Then they will use the expanded form to write the standard form.

Encourage students to count by 100s, 10s, and ones when counting the blocks on the place-value mat in order to write the expanded form. When students are writing the standard form, ask questions such as the following:

- If the expanded form starts with 400, what digit will be in the hundreds place?
- If the expanded form has 70, what digit will be in the tens place?
- If the expanded form has 5, what digit will be in the ones place?

- Use expanded forms to represent numbers through 1,000, such as $754 = 7$ hundreds + 5 tens + 4 ones.

LEARN Write the Standard Form

Students will use the number and symbol index cards to show numbers in expanded form. Then they'll write these numbers in standard form.

Gather the labeled index cards.

1. Divide the cards into three stacks.
   - Hundreds (100–900)
   - Tens (10–90)
   - Ones (1–9)

   Be sure to shuffle each stack.
2. Have students choose a card from each stack. Have them place the hundreds, tens, and ones cards in a row with plus symbols between them—for example, $400 + 20 + 6$.

- Use expanded forms to represent numbers through 1,000, such as $754 = 7$ hundreds + 5 tens + 4 ones.

3. Have students say the number represented by the cards. Then have them write the number in standard form on a sheet of paper.

4. Have students check their work by first sliding the tens card over the hundreds card to cover the zeros on the hundreds card and then sliding the ones card over the tens card to cover the zero on the tens card.

5. Repeat Steps 2–4 at least five times.

OFFLINE
10 min

TRY IT Expanded Form to Standard Form

Students will practice writing the standard form of a number given the expanded form. Give students the Expanded Form to Standard Form activity page from their Activity Book and read the directions with them.

Objectives

- Use expanded forms to represent numbers through 1,000, such as 754 = 7 hundreds + 5 tens + 4 ones.

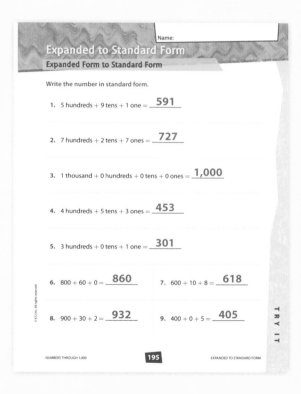

Name:

Expanded to Standard Form
Expanded Form to Standard Form

Write the number in standard form.

1. 5 hundreds + 9 tens + 1 one = **591**

2. 7 hundreds + 2 tens + 7 ones = **727**

3. 1 thousand + 0 hundreds + 0 tens + 0 ones = **1,000**

4. 4 hundreds + 5 tens + 3 ones = **453**

5. 3 hundreds + 0 tens + 1 one = **301**

6. 800 + 60 + 0 = **860**   7. 600 + 10 + 8 = **618**

8. 900 + 30 + 2 = **932**   9. 400 + 0 + 5 = **405**

NUMBERS THROUGH 1,000   **195**   EXPANDED TO STANDARD FORM

TRY IT

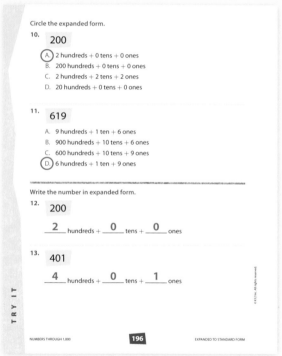

Circle the expanded form.

10. 200
   A. 2 hundreds + 0 tens + 0 ones
   B. 200 hundreds + 0 tens + 0 ones
   C. 2 hundreds + 2 tens + 2 ones
   D. 20 hundreds + 0 tens + 0 ones

11. 619
   A. 9 hundreds + 1 ten + 6 ones
   B. 900 hundreds + 10 tens + 6 ones
   C. 600 hundreds + 10 tens + 9 ones
   D. 6 hundreds + 1 ten + 9 ones

Write the number in expanded form.

12. 200
   2 hundreds + **0** tens + **0** ones

13. 401
   4 hundreds + **0** tens + **1** ones

NUMBERS THROUGH 1,000   **196**   EXPANDED TO STANDARD FORM

TRY IT

CHECKPOINT

OFFLINE
5min

Objectives

Print the Checkpoint and have students complete it on their own. Read the directions, problems, and answer choices to students, if necessary. Use the answer key to score the Checkpoint, and then enter the results online.

- Use expanded forms to represent numbers through 1,000, such as 754 = 7 hundreds + 5 tens + 4 ones.

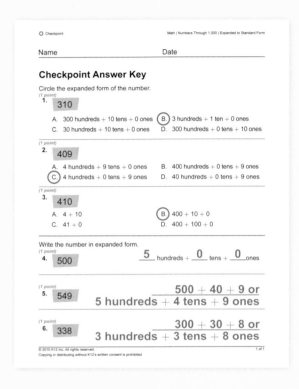

Compare and Order Numbers

Lesson Overview

Skills Update	5 minutes	ONLINE
GET READY Label the Number Line	5 minutes	ONLINE
LEARN Use Place Value to Compare	15 minutes	ONLINE
LEARN Compare and Order with Cards	15 minutes	OFFLINE
TRY IT Comparing and Ordering	10 minutes	OFFLINE
CHECKPOINT	10 minutes	OFFLINE

▶ ## Lesson Objectives

- Order three or more whole numbers through 1,000 by using the symbols $<, =, >$.
- Compare whole numbers up through 1,000 by using the symbols $<, =, >$.

▶ ## Prerequisite Skills

- Order three or more whole numbers through 500 by using the symbols $<, =, >$.
- Compare whole numbers up through 500 by using the symbols $<, =, >$.

▶ ## Common Errors and Misconceptions

- Students might not think of numbers as groups of tens, hundreds, and so forth. For example, students might think of 24 only as 24 single units, not 2 tens and 4 ones.
- Students might not realize that a digit's place-value position determines its value. For example, students might think the digits in 14 have values of 1 and 4, not 10 and 4.
- Students might have difficulty modeling multidigit numbers with counting objects. For example, when asked to model 23, students might use two objects to represent the 2 rather than using twenty objects.
- Students might have difficulty writing multidigit numbers because numerals do not correspond exactly to English number words. For example, students might write twenty-five as 205 (20 and 5) instead of 25.

▶ ## Advance Preparation

Label three sets of index cards with numerals 0 through 9. Also label three index cards with the greater-than symbol ($>$), three index cards with the less-than symbol ($<$), and one index card with the equals symbol ($=$). Save cards for use in future lessons.

Materials to Gather

SUPPLIED

Practice Comparing and Ordering activity page

Checkpoint (printout)

ALSO NEEDED

index cards – labeled with numerals (3 sets); symbols: $>$ (3), $<$ (3), $=$

▶ Content Background

In this lesson, students will compare and order numbers through 1,000. They will learn to compare the digits in each place-value position to judge which number is greater. So when comparing two numbers, students should first compare the digits in the hundreds place. If the hundreds are the same, they should compare the digits in the tens place. If the tens are the same, they should compare the digits in the ones place. For example, when comparing 745 and 729, students should see that both numbers have a 7 in the hundreds place, but 745 has 4 tens and 729 has only 2 tens. So 745 is greater than 729.

The greater-than symbol (>) points to the right, and the less-than symbol (<) points to the left. However, it may be more helpful for students to know that the comparison symbol points to the lesser number and opens to the greater number.

Although the phrases *greater-than sign* and *less-than sign* are often used in everyday language, *greater-than symbol* and *less-than symbol* are more accurate mathematical terms. In math, *sign* refers specifically to positive signs and negative signs.

Keywords

compare numbers – to find the difference in value between numbers; to identify that a number is greater than, less than, or equal to another number

equals symbol (=) – a symbol that shows the relationship between two equal values

greater-than symbol (>) – a symbol indicating that an amount or number is greater than another amount or number

greatest – the largest in value of three or more numbers or amounts

least – the smallest in value of three or more numbers or amounts

less-than symbol (<) – a symbol indicating that an amount or number is less than another amount or number

order numbers – to place numbers in a sequence from least to greatest or greatest to least

ONLINE
5 min

GET READY Label the Number Line

Drawing upon their knowledge of the order of numbers and the number line, students will place numbers on a partially completed number line. This activity will prepare them to order greater numbers.

Objectives

- Order three or more whole numbers through 500 by using the symbols $<, =, >$.
- Compare whole numbers through 500 by using the symbols $<, =, >$.

LEARN Use Place Value to Compare

Students will compare and order numbers through 1,000 using the greater-than, less-than, and equals symbols. They will use place-value charts to compare the value of the digits before comparing or ordering the numbers.

Review the greater-than and less-than symbols with students. Explain that the symbols point to the lesser number and open to the greater number.

- Order three or more whole numbers through 1,000 by using the symbols $<, =, >$.
- Compare whole numbers up through 1,000 by using the symbols $<, =, >$.

LEARN Compare and Order with Cards

Students will use number and symbol cards to compare and order numbers. They will order numbers from least to greatest and from greatest to least.

Gather the number and symbol cards.

- Order three or more whole numbers through 1,000 by using the symbols $<, =, >$.
- Compare whole numbers up through 1,000 by using the symbols $<, =, >$.

1. Hold up each symbol card and review its name and meaning.

2. Make the numbers 1,000 and 974 using the index cards. Display the two numbers with 1,000 on the left.

   Ask: Which number is greater?
   ANSWER: 1,000

   Ask: How do you know?
   ANSWER: It has 1 in the thousands place, and 974 doesn't have anything in the thousands place.

   If students can't say which number is greater, show them that the base-10 thousands cube is made up of 10 hundreds flats, which is more than the 9 hundreds flats in 974.

3. **Say:** Thousands are greater than hundreds, so 1,000 is greater than 974. Put the correct symbol between the two numbers.

   Students should place the $>$ card between the numbers.

4. Make the number 971 and display it below 1,000 $>$ 974.

   Say: Place 971 to the right of 974 to order the numbers from greatest to least. Place the correct symbol card between the numbers.

   Check that the number sentence shows 1,000 $>$ 974 $>$ 971.

5. Have students order several sets of three numbers greater than 500. Have them practice ordering both from greatest to least and from least to greatest.

6. Have students order at least two sets of four numbers greater than 500.

TRY IT Practice Comparing and Ordering

Students will practice comparing and ordering numbers greater than 500. Give students the Practice Comparing and Ordering activity page from their Activity Book and read the directions with them.

- Order three or more whole numbers through 1,000 by using the symbols $<, =, >$.
- Compare whole numbers up through 1,000 by using the symbols $<, =, >$.

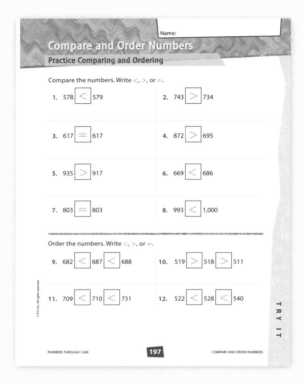

Name: _____

Compare and Order Numbers

Practice Comparing and Ordering

Compare the numbers. Write $<$, $>$, or $=$.

1. 578 $<$ 579   2. 743 $>$ 734

3. 617 $=$ 617   4. 872 $>$ 695

5. 935 $>$ 917   6. 669 $<$ 686

7. 803 $=$ 803   8. 993 $<$ 1,000

Order the numbers. Write $<$, $>$, or $=$.

9. 682 $<$ 687 $<$ 688   10. 519 $>$ 518 $>$ 511

11. 709 $<$ 710 $<$ 731   12. 522 $<$ 528 $<$ 540

T R Y   I T

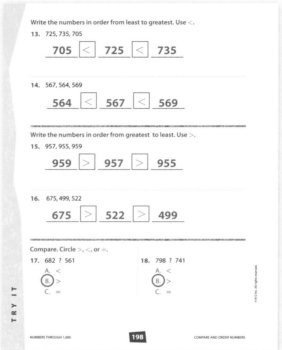

T R Y   I T

Write the numbers in order from least to greatest. Use $<$.

13. 725, 735, 705

705 $<$ 725 $<$ 735

14. 567, 564, 569

564 $<$ 567 $<$ 569

Write the numbers in order from greatest to least. Use $>$.

15. 957, 955, 959

959 $>$ 957 $>$ 955

16. 675, 499, 522

675 $>$ 522 $>$ 499

Compare. Circle $>$, $<$, or $=$.

17. 682 ? 561
A. $<$
B. $>$
C. $=$

18. 798 ? 741
A. $<$
B. $>$
C. $=$

CHECKPOINT

Objectives

- Order three or more whole numbers through 1,000 by using the symbols $<, =, >$.

- Compare whole numbers up through 1,000 by using the symbols $<, =, >$.

Print the Checkpoint and have students complete it on their own. Read the directions, problems, and answer choices to students if necessary. Use the answer key to score the Checkpoint, and then enter the results online.

◯ Checkpoint   Math | Numbers Through 1,000 | Compare and Order Numbers

Name _____   Date _____

Checkpoint Answer Key

Compare the numbers. Write $<$, $>$, or $=$.

(1 point)
1. 659 ____$<$____ 743

(1 point)
2. 934 ____$>$____ 920

Order the numbers. Write $<$ or $>$.

(1 point)
3. 903 __$<$__ 906 __$<$__ 910

(1 point)
4. 736 __$>$__ 732 __$>$__ 730

Write the numbers in order from greatest to least. Use $>$.
(1 point)
5. 864, 849, 828

864 $>$ 849 $>$ 828

Write the numbers in order from least to greatest. Use $<$.
(1 point)
6. 658, 549, 724

549 $<$ 658 $<$ 724

---

1 of 1

Unit Review

Lesson Overview

UNIT REVIEW Look Back	20 minutes	**ONLINE**
UNIT REVIEW Checkpoint Practice	20 minutes	**OFFLINE**
⏵ **UNIT REVIEW** Prepare for the Checkpoint		

▶ Unit Objectives

This lesson reviews the following objectives:

- Count aloud whole numbers through 1,000.
- Read whole numbers through 1,000.
- Write number words through 1,000.
- Use models to represent numbers through 1,000.
- Demonstrate that multidigit numbers represent groups of 100s, 10s, and ones.
- Identify the place value for each digit in whole numbers through 1,000.
- Use expanded forms to represent numbers through 1,000, such as
  $754 = 7$ hundreds $+ 5$ tens $+ 4$ ones.
- Order three or more whole numbers through 1,000 by using the symbols
  $<, =, >$.
- Compare whole numbers up through 1,000 by using the symbols
  $<, =, >$.

Materials to Gather

SUPPLIED

Checkpoint Practice activity page

▶ Advance Preparation

In this lesson, students will have an opportunity to review previous activities in the Numbers Through 1,000 unit. Look at the suggested activities in Unit Review: Prepare for the Checkpoint online and gather any needed materials.

Keywords

compare numbers	number word
digit	numeral
equals symbol ($=$)	order numbers
greater-than symbol ($>$)	place value
greatest	thousands cube
least	value
less-than symbol ($<$)	whole numbers

UNIT REVIEW Look Back

In this unit, students have learned how to count, write number words for, and read numbers through 1,000. They've also learned how to represent these numbers using place-value models, including base-10 blocks, groups, and expanded form. They used these models to help them learn how to identify the place value of each digit in a given number, and finally to compare and order numbers. Students will review these concepts to prepare for the Unit Checkpoint.

UNIT REVIEW Checkpoint Practice

Students will complete a Checkpoint Practice activity page to prepare for the Unit Checkpoint. If necessary, read the directions, problems, and answer choices to students. Have students answer the problems on their own. Carefully review the answers with students.

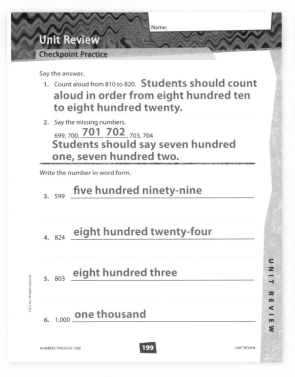

Unit Review

Checkpoint Practice

Name:

Say the answer.

1. Count aloud from 810 to 820. **Students should count aloud in order from eight hundred ten to eight hundred twenty.**

2. Say the missing numbers.
699, 700, **701**, **702**, 703, 704
Students should say seven hundred one, seven hundred two.

Write the number in word form.

3. 599   five hundred ninety-nine

4. 824   eight hundred twenty-four

5. 803   eight hundred three

6. 1,000   one thousand

UNIT REVIEW

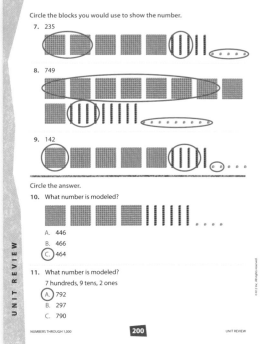

Circle the blocks you would use to show the number.

7. 235

8. 749

9. 142

Circle the answer.

10. What number is modeled?
A. 446
B. 466
C. 464

11. What number is modeled?
7 hundreds, 9 tens, 2 ones
A. 792
B. 297
C. 790

UNIT REVIEW

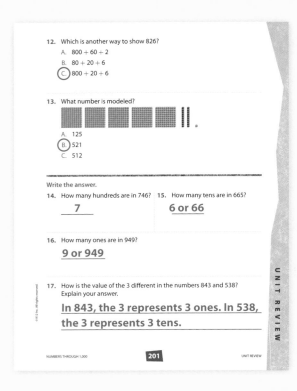

12. Which is another way to show 826?
    A. 800 + 60 + 2
    B. 80 + 20 + 6
    C. 800 + 20 + 6 ✓

13. What number is modeled?

    A. 125
    B. 521 ✓
    C. 512

Write the answer.

14. How many hundreds are in 746?

    7

15. How many tens are in 665?

    6 or 66

16. How many ones are in 949?

    9 or 949

17. How is the value of the 3 different in the numbers 843 and 538? Explain your answer.

    In 843, the 3 represents 3 ones. In 538, the 3 represents 3 tens.

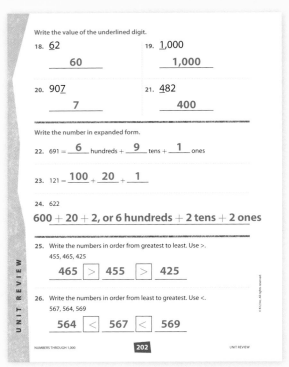

Write the value of the underlined digit.

18. 6̲2

    60

19. 1̲,000

    1,000

20. 90̲7

    7

21. 4̲82

    400

Write the number in expanded form.

22. 691 = __6__ hundreds + __9__ tens + __1__ ones

23. 121 = __100__ + __20__ + __1__

24. 622

    600 + 20 + 2, or 6 hundreds + 2 tens + 2 ones

25. Write the numbers in order from greatest to least. Use >.
    455, 465, 425

    465 > 455 > 425

26. Write the numbers in order from least to greatest. Use <.
    567, 564, 569

    564 < 567 < 569

⮕ UNIT REVIEW Prepare for the Checkpoint

What you do next depends on how students performed in the previous activity, Unit Review: Checkpoint Practice. If students had difficulty with any of the problems, complete the appropriate review activity listed in the table online.

Unit Checkpoint

UNIT CHECKPOINT Offline · 60 minutes · **OFFLINE**

▶ Unit Objectives

This lesson assesses the following objectives:

- Count aloud whole numbers through 1,000.
- Read whole numbers through 1,000.
- Write number words through 1,000.
- Use models to represent numbers through 1,000.
- Demonstrate that multidigit numbers represent groups of 100s, 10s, and ones.
- Identify the place value for each digit in whole numbers through 1,000.
- Use expanded forms to represent numbers through 1,000, such as $754 = 7$ hundreds $+ 5$ tens $+ 4$ ones.
- Order three or more whole numbers through 1,000 by using the symbols $<, =, >$.
- Compare whole numbers up through 1,000 by using the symbols $<, =, >$.

Materials to Gather

SUPPLIED

place-value mat

base-10 blocks

Unit Checkpoint (printout)

UNIT CHECKPOINT Offline

OFFLINE 60 min

Objectives

- Assess unit objectives.

Students will complete the Unit Checkpoint offline. In Part 1, students will take a performance-based assessment. In Part 2, students will complete the problems on their own. Print the Unit Checkpoint. Read the directions, problems, and answer choices to students, if necessary. Use the answer key to score the Checkpoint, and then enter the results online.

Gather the base-10 blocks and place-value mat.

☼ Checkpoint   Math | Numbers Through 1,000 | Unit Checkpoint

Name _____   Date _____

Unit Checkpoint Answer Key

Part 1
Follow the instructions for each item. Choose the response that best describes how the student performs on the task.

1. Write the following on a sheet of paper: 234 to 244.
   Say, "Count aloud from the first number to the second number."
   (1 point)
   Did the student count from 234 to 244?

   A. Yes   B. No

2. Write the following on a sheet of paper: 899, 900, ____, ____, 903, 904.
   Ask, "What numbers are missing?"
   (1 point)
   Did the student say 901 and 902?

   A. Yes   B. No

3. Write the number 612 on a sheet of paper.
   Ask, "What number is this?"
   (1 point)
   Did the student say six hundred twelve?

   A. Yes   B. No

4. Say, "Use the base-10 blocks to model the number 208."
   Sample answer: 2 hundreds flats, 8 ones cubes
   (1 point)
   Did the student model 208?

   A. Yes   B. No

Give students Part 2 of the assessment.

Name _____ Date _____

Part 2
Follow the directions below.
(1 point)
5. Jose read a book that was two hundred two pages long. Circle the number of pages Jose read.

   (A.) 202   B. 2002   C. 222   D. 2204

Write the number in word form.

(1 point)
6. 511   **five hundred eleven**

(1 point)
7. 722   **seven hundred twenty-two**

Write the answer.

(1 point)
8. How many hundreds are in 356?   **3**

(1 point)
9. How many hundreds are in 487?   **4**

(1 point)
10. How many tens are in 76?   **7**

(1 point)
11. How many tens are in 120? **2 or 12**

Name _____ Date _____

(1 point)
12. How many ones are in 9?   **9**

(1 point)
13. How many ones are in 385? **5 or 385**

(1 point)
14. How is the value of the 7 different in the two numbers below? Explain your answer.

    78   27

In 78, the 7 represents 7 tens, and in 27, the 7 represents 7 ones.

(1 point)
15. How is the value of the 5 different in the two numbers below? Explain your answer.

    53   542

In 53, the 5 represents 5 tens, and in 542, the 5 represents 5 hundreds.

(1 point)
16. How many hundreds, tens, and ones are in 510?

    5 hundreds, 1 ten, 0 ones

Name _____ Date _____

Circle the answer.
(1 point)
17. Which digit is in the hundreds place in the number below?

    765

   (A.) 7   B. 6   C. 5

(1 point)
18. What is the value of the 1 in the number below?

    193

    A. 1   B. 10   (C.) 100   D. 1,000

(1 point)
19. Choose the expanded form of the number below.

    717

    A. $700 + 100 + 700$ B. $700 + 0 + 7$
    C. $700 + 10 + 70$ (D.) $700 + 10 + 7$

Follow the directions below.

(1 point)
20. Write 809 in expanded form. **8** hundreds + **0** tens + **9** ones

(1 point)
21. Choose the correct symbol to order the numbers from least to greatest.

    941 ☐ 955 ☐ 956

    A. >   (B.) <   C. =

Name _____ Date _____

22. Choose the correct symbol to order the numbers from greatest to least.
(1 point)

    711 ☐ 710 ☐ 705

   (A.) >   B. <   C. =

(1 point)
23. Order the numbers below from greatest to least, using the symbol >.

    675, 499, 522   **675 > 522 > 499**

(1 point)
24. Order the numbers below from least to greatest, using the symbol <.

    611, 602, 755   **602 < 611 < 755**

(1 point)
25. Compare. Choose <, >, or =.

    798 ☐ 741

    A. <   (B.) >   C. =

(1 point)
26. Look at the numbers below. Write the symbol that belongs in the box.

    899 **>** 788

Plane and Solid Figures

▶ Unit Objectives

- Identify and describe plane figures according to the number of sides and vertices, such as triangle, square, rectangle, circle, oval.

- Classify plane figures according to similarities and differences, such as triangle, square, rectangle, circle, oval.

- Describe solid figures according to the number and shape of faces, such as sphere, pyramid, cube, rectangular prism.

- Classify solid figures according to the number and shape of faces and the number of edges, such as sphere, pyramid, cube, rectangular prism.

- Put geometric figures together to form other geometric figures.

- Take geometric figures apart to form other geometric figures.

▶ Big Ideas

- Geometric figures can be described and classified by the shapes of their faces and by how many faces, sides, edges, or vertices they have.

- Shapes can be constructed from other shapes.

▶ Unit Introduction

In this unit, students will learn how to describe plane figures by their number of sides and vertices. They will also learn how to describe solid figures by their number and shape of faces and their number of edges. They will sort figures based on these characteristics. Lastly students will learn how to combine and divide shapes to form other shapes.

Plane Figures

Skills Update	5 minutes	ONLINE
GET READY Name That Shape	5 minutes	ONLINE
LEARN Describe the Figure	10 minutes	ONLINE
LEARN Sort the Figures	10 minutes	ONLINE
LEARN Guess My Shape	10 minutes	OFFLINE
TRY IT Plane Figure Assortment	10 minutes	OFFLINE
CHECKPOINT	10 minutes	OFFLINE

▶ Lesson Objectives

- Identify and describe plane figures according to the number of sides and vertices, such as triangle, square, rectangle, circle, oval.
- Classify plane figures according to similarities and differences, such as triangle, square, rectangle, circle, oval.

▶ Prerequisite Skills

Identify, describe, and compare plane figures such as rectangle, square, triangle, circle, oval, including those on the faces of solid figures.

▶ Common Errors and Misconceptions

- Students might have heard some geometric vocabulary words, but their definitions of these words might be incorrect.
- Students might not recognize that a shape might be positioned different ways. For example, students might not recognize that the second shape is a square:

    ■ ◆

- Students might inappropriately use *converse reasoning* when classifying shapes. For example, they might say, "All squares have 4 sides. This shape has 4 sides, so it must be a square."

▶ Content Background

Students will learn how to identify and describe plane figures by their number of sides and vertices. The number of sides refers to the number of straight sides. Therefore a curved figure, such as a circle or oval, is said to have no sides.

A vertex is a corner. *Vertices* is the plural form of the word *vertex*. A vertex is formed when two lines come together. A vertex, or corner, can be either square or not square. Square corners are corners with right angles and can be found in squares, rectangles, and right triangles.

Materials to Gather

SUPPLIED

Plane Figure Assortment activity page

Checkpoint (printout)

circle – a plane figure with no straight sides or corners; the edge of a circle is a curve with all points the same distance from the center

corner – the point where two segments, lines, surfaces, or edges meet

curved figure – a 2-dimensional geometric figure with a rounded side, such as a circle

hexagon – a 6-sided polygon

oval – a plane figure resembling the outline of an egg, but often more symmetrical

plane figure – a 2-dimensional geometric figure

rectangle – a plane figure with 4 sides and 4 square corners with opposite sides of equal length

rhombus – a parallelogram with equal sides; often slanted, but a square is also a rhombus

side – a segment that forms the edge of a shape

square – a plane figure with 4 sides of equal length and 4 square corners

square corner – a vertex where two sides of a figure meet to form a right angle

square pyramid – a geometric solid with a square base and triangular faces that come to a point, or vertex

trapezoid – a quadrilateral that has only one pair of parallel sides

triangle – a plane figure with 3 sides and 3 corners

vertex – the point at which two sides of a plane figure meet and the point at which three or more edges of a solid figure meet; the point of a cone is also called a vertex

GET READY Name That Shape

ONLINE **5 min**

Objectives

- Identify, describe, and compare plane figures such as rectangle, square, triangle, circle, oval, including those on the faces of solid figures.

Students will identify shapes. As they identify each shape, have them describe it. Then students will sort shapes using the Attribute Blocks Learning Tool.

DIRECTIONS FOR USING THE ATTRIBUTE BLOCKS LEARNING TOOL

1. Click Single Attribute Mode and choose the following:
   - Sort by: Shape
   - Shapes: 10
   - Containers: 4
   - Options: Visual Cues and Rotate Shapes
2. Click Start Sorting.
3. Have students sort the shapes. If students sort a square as a rectangle, explain that sometimes a shape fits into more than one category. Squares are also rectangles. But the best name for this shape is a square. This name tells most about the shape.

LEARN Describe the Figure

Objectives

Students will count the sides and vertices of various plane figures, including circles, in order to describe shapes based on these characteristics.

- Identify and describe plane figures according to the number of sides and vertices, such as triangle, square, rectangle, circle, oval.

LEARN Sort the Figures

Objectives

Students will sort plane figures according to shape, number of sides, and number and type of vertices.

- Identify and describe plane figures according to the number of sides and vertices, such as triangle, square, rectangle, circle, oval.

LEARN Guess My Shape

Objectives

By playing a question game, students will practice identifying plane figures based on their characteristics. You will think of a shape, and students will ask Yes or No questions to guess the shape you chose.

There are no materials to gather for this activity.

- Identify and describe plane figures according to the number of sides and vertices, such as triangle, square, rectangle, circle, oval.

1. Choose one of the following shapes: square, circle, triangle, rectangle, or oval.

   Say: I'm thinking of a shape. Can you guess it?

2. Instruct students to ask Yes or No questions about the shape's sides, vertices, and type of corners. Sample questions include the following:

   - Does it have 3 sides? (Yes)
     Is it a triangle? (Yes)

   - Does it have 4 sides? (Yes)
     Are they all the same length? (No)
     Is it a rectangle? (Yes)

   Continue the activity as time allows.

TRY IT Plane Figure Assortment

Students will practice identifying the number of sides and vertices of plane figures and then answer questions about these characteristics. Give students the Plane Figure Assortment activity page from their Activity Book and read the directions with them.

Objectives

- Identify and describe plane figures according to the number of sides and vertices, such as triangle, square, rectangle, circle, oval.
- Classify plane figures according to similarities and differences, such as triangle, square, rectangle, circle, oval.

Name: _____

Plane Figures
Plane Figure Assortment

Write how many sides and vertices the plane figure has.

1. __4__ sides __4__ vertices

2. __3__ sides __3__ vertices

3. __0__ sides __0__ vertices

4. __4__ sides __4__ vertices

5. __6__ sides __6__ vertices

6. __4__ sides __4__ vertices

PLANE AND SOLID FIGURES **203** PLANE FIGURES

Write the answer.

7. How many sides does an oval have? __0__

8. How many vertices does a square have? __4__

9. Name a shape with 3 vertices. __triangle__

Circle the answer.

10. Which shape has more sides, a triangle or a rhombus?
A. triangle (B.) rhombus

11. Which shape has more vertices, a hexagon or a square?
(A.) hexagon B. square

12. Which shape has 4 vertices?
A. circle B. oval
C. triangle (D.) rectangle

13. Which shape has 4 sides?
(A.) square B. circle
C. triangle D. oval

14. Which shape has no vertices?
A. square (B.) oval
C. triangle D. rectangle

PLANE AND SOLID FIGURES **204** PLANE FIGURES

CHECKPOINT

Print the Checkpoint and have students complete it on their own. Read the directions, problems, and answer choices to students, if necessary. Use the answer key to score the Checkpoint, and then enter the results online.

Objectives

- Identify and describe plane figures according to the number of sides and vertices, such as triangle, square, rectangle, circle, oval.

- Classify plane figures according to similarities and differences, such as triangle, square, rectangle, circle, oval.

○ Checkpoint   Math | Plane and Solid Figures | Plane Figures

Name _____ Date _____

Checkpoint Answer Key

Read each problem and follow the directions.
(1 point)
1. Tell what is different about these two shapes.

Sample answer: The triangle has 3 sides and the square has 4 sides.

(1 point)
2. Tell what is the same about these two shapes.

Sample answer: Both shapes are curved, so neither shape has sides or vertices.

(1 point)
3. How many vertices does a circle have?

(A.) 0   B. 3   C. 4   D. 5

4. Draw a line under the shapes with 3 sides.

○ Checkpoint   Math | Plane and Solid Figures | Plane Figures

Name _____ Date _____

Circle the answer.
(1 point)
5. Which shape has 3 sides?

A. square   (B.) triangle   C. oval   D. rectangle

(1 point)
6. Which shape has 4 sides?

(A.) square   B. triangle   C. oval   D. circle

(1 point)
7. How many vertices does an oval have?

(A.) 0   B. 3   C. 4   D. 5

(1 point)
8. Which shape has 0 straight sides?

A. triangle   B. rhombus   C. hexagon   (D.) circle

(1 point)
9. Circle all the shapes with 4 sides and 4 vertices.

Write the answer.
(1 point)
10. Name the shape that has 6 sides and 6 vertices.

hexagon

(1 point)
11. How many sides does a rectangle have?

_____4_____ sides

Solid Figures

▶ Lesson Objectives

- Describe solid figures according to the number and shape of faces, such as sphere, pyramid, cube, rectangular prism.
- Classify solid figures according to the number and shape of faces and the number of edges, such as sphere, pyramid, cube, rectangular prism.

▶ Prerequisite Skills

Identify, describe, and compare plane figures such as rectangle, square, triangle, circle, oval, including those on the faces of solid figures.

▶ Common Errors and Misconceptions

- Students might have heard some geometric vocabulary words, but their definitions of these words might be incorrect.
- Students might not recognize that a shape might be positioned different ways. For example, students might not recognize that the second shape is a square:

- Students might inappropriately use *converse reasoning* when classifying shapes. For example, they might say, "All square have 4 sides. This shape has 4 sides, so it must be a square."

▶ Safety

Supervise students when they are working with the geometric solid blocks. These blocks have sharp corners.

▶ Content Background

Students will learn to describe solid figures by the number and shape of faces. They will then use this information, along with the number of edges, to sort solid figures.

Solid figures are three-dimensional shapes, such as cubes and pyramids. Everyday examples of solid figures include a baseball (sphere) and soup can (cylinder). *Face* refers to the flat, traceable part of a solid. Therefore a curved solid, such as a sphere, is said to have no faces.

Materials to Gather

SUPPLIED
blocks – P, Q, R, T, U, V
Faces of a Solid activity page
Faces and Edges of a Solid activity page
Solids activity page
Checkpoint (printout)

cone – a geometric solid with a circular base and a curved surface that comes to a point, or vertex

cube – a geometric solid with 6 equal-sized square faces

curved solid – a geometric solid with a rounded surface, such as a cone or cylinder

cylinder – a geometric solid with a curved surface and parallel circular bases

edge – a line formed at the intersection of two faces on a solid figure

face of a solid figure – a flat surface on a solid figure, such as a square face on a cube

geometric solids – a group of 3-dimensional figures, such as a cone, a cylinder, and a cube

pyramid – a geometric solid with a polygon for a base and triangular faces that come to a point, or vertex; for example, the Egyptian pyramids have a square base

rectangular prism – a geometric solid with 3 pairs of parallel rectangular faces, where each pair of faces is identical; a box is an example

rectangular pyramid – a geometric solid with a rectangular base and triangular faces that come to a point, or vertex

solid figure – a 3-dimensional geometric figure, such as a cube, cylinder, pyramid, or prism

sphere – a perfectly round geometric solid, such as a ball

triangular prism – a geometric solid with a pair of identical parallel triangular bases joined by rectangular faces

GET READY Shape Finder

ONLINE
5min

Objectives

Students will identify different shapes based on sets of clues.

Review the names of the basic shapes and their characteristics. For example, "A square has 4 sides that are all the same length."

- Identify, describe, and compare plane figures such as rectangle, square, triangle, circle, oval, including those on the faces of solid figures.

LEARN Faces of a Solid

OFFLINE
15min

Objectives

Students will explore solid figures and describe each solid figure by the number and shape of its faces.

Gather the geometric solid blocks, sheet of paper, and Faces of a Solid activity page from the Activity Book. Students will complete only the front of this activity page in this activity.

- Describe solid figures according to the number and shape of faces, such as sphere, pyramid, cube, rectangular prism.

The rectangular prism in the block set (block Q) has all rectangular faces. However, a rectangular prism may have 1 pair of opposite faces that are squares. The answers to the questions in the activity refer to the rectangular prism in the block set.

1. Give students the geometric solid blocks.
2. For each solid, have students say its name. Have students give a general description of the solid.
3. Give students the activity page and a sheet of paper.
4. **Say:** The flat side of a solid figure is called a face. Place the cube on the paper and trace one of the faces.

   Ask: What shape did you make?
   ANSWER: a square

   Ask: Are all the faces on a cube the same shape?
   ANSWER: Yes

   Ask: How many faces does a cube have?
   ANSWER: 6
5. Have students complete the first row of the activity page.
6. Repeat Steps 4 and 5 for each solid on the activity page.
7. After students have completed the activity page, ask questions about the information in the chart. Possible questions include the following:
   - Which shapes have square faces? (cube, square pyramid)
   - Which shape has 6 faces? (cube, rectangular prism)
   - Which shapes have circular faces? (cylinder, cone)

Name: _____

Solid Figures
Faces of a Solid

Complete the chart. You may use the blocks.

Solid	Number of Faces of the Shape				Total Number of Faces
	Square	Rectangle	Circle	Triangle	
cube	6				6
rectangular prism		6			6
square pyramid	1			4	5
cylinder			2		2
cone			1		1
sphere					0

PLANE AND SOLID FIGURES 205 SOLID FIGURES

OFFLINE
15 min

LEARN Faces and Edges of a Solid

Students will learn about edges, and they will count the edges of common solid figures. Then they will sort and compare solid figures according to the number and shape of their faces and the number of their edges.

Gather the geometric solid blocks and Faces and Edges of a Solid activity page, which is the back of the Faces of a Solid activity page.

COUNT EDGES

1. Using the blocks, review the number and shape of each solid's faces. Have students complete the first two columns of the chart.
2. **Say:** You can also count a solid's edges. An edge is where two faces, or a face and a curved surface, meet.

3. Have students hold the cube. Point to one of the cube's edges.

   Say: This is an edge. Count the edges on the cube.

   Ask: How many edges does a cube have?
   ANSWER: 12

4. Have students write 12 in the Number of Edges column for the cube on the activity page.

5. Repeat Steps 3 and 4 for each solid on the activity page. Point out that in pictures of cones and cylinders, the curved surface may look like an edge where it curves around to the back side of the figure. Have students feel all surfaces of the cone and cylinder blocks to be certain they can identify the curved surface, the faces, and the edges where a curved surface and face meet.

SORT SOLIDS

6. Line up the solids. Have students sort the solids using different criteria, such as the following:

   - square faces
   - triangular faces
   - 12 edges
   - no faces or edges

7. Have students select two solids and tell you what is alike and what is different about them. Repeat with another pair of solids.

8. Briefly discuss with students that some solid figures with two or more faces can stack, and that solids with a curved surface can roll. Ask questions such as the following:

   - Which solids can stack? (cube, rectangular prism, cylinder)
   - Which solids can roll? (cylinder, cone, sphere)
   - Can any solids do both? (cylinder)

Faces and Edges of a Solid

Complete the chart. You may use the blocks.

Solid	Shapes of the Faces	Number of Faces	Number of Edges
cube	square	6	12
rectangular prism	rectangle	6	12
square pyramid	square and triangle	5	8
cylinder	circle	2	2
cone	circle	1	1
sphere	none	0	0

PLANE AND SOLID FIGURES   206   SOLID FIGURES

TRY IT Solids

OFFLINE
10 min

Students will practice answering questions about solid figures. Give students the geometric solid blocks and Solids activity page from their Activity Book. Read the directions with them.

Objectives

- Describe solid figures according to the number and shape of faces, such as sphere, pyramid, cube, rectangular prism.

- Classify solid figures according to the number and shape of faces and the number of edges, such as sphere, pyramid, cube, rectangular prism.

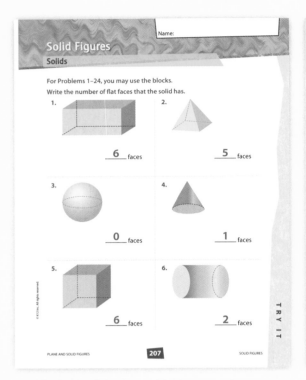

Solid Figures

Solids

Name:

For Problems 1–24, you may use the blocks.

Write the number of flat faces that the solid has.

1. **6** faces

2. **5** faces

3. **0** faces

4. **1** faces

5. **6** faces

6. **2** faces

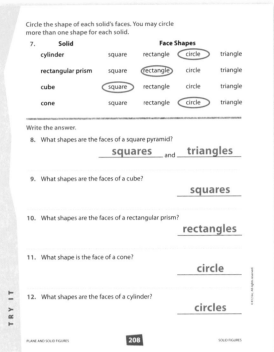

Circle the shape of each solid's faces. You may circle more than one shape for each solid.

7.
Solid		Face Shapes		
cylinder	square	rectangle	(circle)	triangle
rectangular prism	square	(rectangle)	circle	triangle
cube	(square)	rectangle	circle	triangle
cone	square	rectangle	(circle)	triangle

Write the answer.

8. What shapes are the faces of a square pyramid?

    squares and **triangles**

9. What shapes are the faces of a cube?

    squares

10. What shapes are the faces of a rectangular prism?

    rectangles

11. What shape is the face of a cone?

    circle

12. What shapes are the faces of a cylinder?

    circles

TRY IT

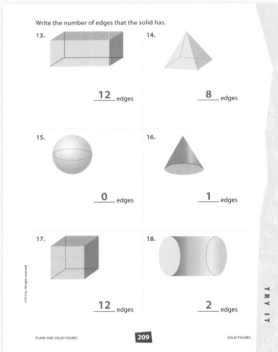

Write the number of edges that the solid has.

13. **12** edges

14. **8** edges

15. **0** edges

16. **1** edges

17. **12** edges

18. **2** edges

TRY IT

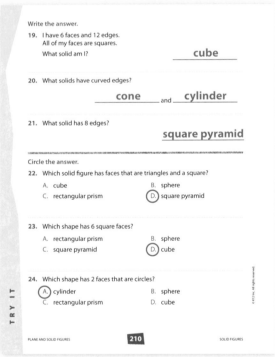

Write the answer.

19. I have 6 faces and 12 edges. All of my faces are squares. What solid am I?

    cube

20. What solids have curved edges?

    cone and **cylinder**

21. What solid has 8 edges?

    square pyramid

Circle the answer.

22. Which solid figure has faces that are triangles and a square?
    A. cube
    B. sphere
    C. rectangular prism
    (D.) square pyramid

23. Which shape has 6 square faces?
    A. rectangular prism
    B. sphere
    C. square pyramid
    (D.) cube

24. Which shape has 2 faces that are circles?
    (A.) cylinder
    B. sphere
    C. rectangular prism
    D. cube

TRY IT

CHECKPOINT

Objectives

Print the Checkpoint and have students complete it on their own. Read the directions, problems, and answer choices to students, if necessary. Use the answer key to score the Checkpoint, and then enter the results online.

Gather the geometric solid blocks and allow students to use the blocks as needed.

- Describe solid figures according to the number and shape of faces, such as sphere, pyramid, cube, rectangular prism.

- Classify solid figures according to the number and shape of faces and the number of edges, such as sphere, pyramid, cube, rectangular prism.

⟳ Checkpoint   Math | Plane and Solid Figures | Solid Figures

Name _____ Date _____

Checkpoint Answer Key

Write the answer. You may use the blocks to help you answer the problems.

(1 point)
1. What solid has 1 face that is a square and 4 faces that are triangles?

square pyramid

(1 point)
2. How many faces are on a rectangular prism? **6** faces

(1 point)
3. How many flat faces does a cylinder have? **2** faces

(1 point)
4. What shape is the flat face of a cone? **circle**

(1 point)
5. What solid has no flat faces? **sphere**

(1 point)
6. What solid has 1 flat face and 1 edge? **cone**

(1 point)
7. What solid has 2 flat faces and 2 edges? **cylinder**

   1 of 2

⟳ Checkpoint   Math | Plane and Solid Figures | Solid Figures

Name _____ Date _____

Circle the answer.
(1 point)
8. How many edges does a sphere have?

  (A) 0   B. 2   C. 4   D. 6

(1 point)
9. Which solid has 8 edges?

  A. cube   B. sphere
  (C) square pyramid   D. rectangular prism

(1 point)
10. Which solid has 12 edges?

  (A) cube   B. sphere
  C. square pyramid   D. cone

(1 point)
11. Which solid has 6 faces and 12 edges?

  A. cone   (B) rectangular prism
  C. square pyramid   D. cylinder

   2 of 2

Build and Take Apart Shapes

Lesson Overview

Skills Update	5 minutes	ONLINE
GET READY Make a Shape	5 minutes	ONLINE
LEARN Make and Break Shapes	20 minutes	OFFLINE
LEARN Hexagon Craze	10 minutes	OFFLINE
TRY IT Construction Zone	10 minutes	OFFLINE
CHECKPOINT	10 minutes	OFFLINE

▶ Lesson Objectives
- Put geometric figures together to form other geometric figures.
- Take geometric figures apart to form other geometric figures.

▶ Prerequisite Skills
Use concrete objects to show how two or more shapes can be put together or taken apart to create a different shape.

▶ Common Errors and Misconceptions
- Students might have heard some geometric vocabulary words, but their definitions of these words might be incorrect.
- Students might not recognize that a shape might be positioned different ways. For example, students might not recognize that the second shape is a square:

  ■ ◆

- Students might inappropriately use *converse reasoning* when classifying shapes. For example, they might say, "All squares have 4 sides. This shape has 4 sides, so it must be a square."

▶ Content Background
Students will learn how to combine and divide shapes to form other geometric shapes. They will use these blocks both online and offline.

triangle   square   rhombus   trapezoid   hexagon

Materials to Gather

SUPPLIED

blocks – E (3 yellow), K (6), L (3), M (2), N (1)

Make and Break Shapes activity page

Hexagon Craze activity page

Construction Zone activity page

Checkpoint (printout)

Keywords   **semicircle** – half of a full circle

GET READY Make a Shape

Students will put together two given shapes to make a new shape.

DIRECTIONS FOR USING THE PATTERN BLOCKS LEARNING TOOL

1. Click Free Play. Then read the instructions, and click Start.

2. Drag two green triangles to the canvas. Show students how to rotate the triangles using the Rotate arrows.

3. **Say:** Put the triangles together to make another shape.

   Ask: What shape did you make?
   ANSWER: rhombus

4. Click the broom to clear the triangles.

5. Repeat Steps 3 and 4 with the following shapes:

   - two squares (to make a rectangle)

   - two rhombuses (to make a parallelogram)

   - two trapezoids (to make a hexagon)

Objectives

- Use concrete objects to show how two or more shapes can be put together or taken apart to create a different shape.

LEARN Make and Break Shapes

Students will explore putting together and taking apart shapes to make other shapes.

Give students the blocks and Make and Break Shapes activity page from their Activity Book. Read the directions with them.

1. Point to the first shape in the table on the activity page, the blue rhombus. Ask students to name the shape.

2. Ask students what shapes they think they could use to make a rhombus. Allow them to explore options with the blocks. Students should figure out that they can put together two green triangles to make a rhombus.

3. Have students cover the rhombus on the activity page with two green triangles.

4. Instruct students to draw a line on the rhombus in the Break column to show how to break, or cut, the rhombus into two triangles.

5. Repeat Steps 1–4 with each shape in the table.

6. Have students complete Problems 2–7. The shapes they make do not have to match block shapes.

7. After students complete the activity page, allow time for them to explore building and breaking apart shapes with the blocks.

Objectives

- Put geometric figures together to form other geometric figures.
- Take geometric figures apart to form other geometric figures.

Tips

Have students use a straightedge or a ruler to draw the lines to break apart the shapes.

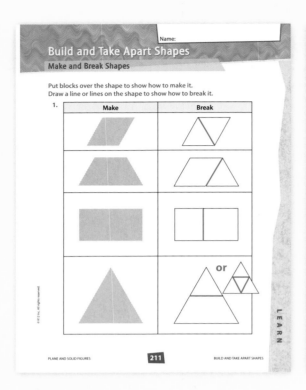

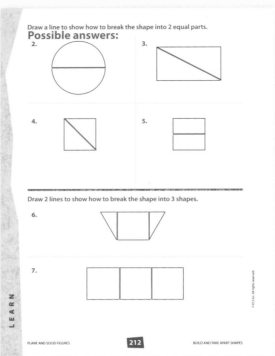

LEARN Hexagon Craze

OFFLINE
10min

Objectives

- Put geometric figures together to form other geometric figures.
- Take geometric figures apart to form other geometric figures.

Students will explore putting together and taking apart shapes to make new shapes. In this activity, they will explore different ways to make a hexagon. Give students the blocks and Hexagon Craze activity page from their Activity Book. Read the directions with them.

Guide students through the activity page as needed. As they work through the problems, have them tell you the names of the shapes they are using.

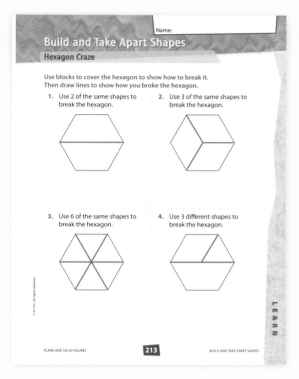

Build and Take Apart Shapes
Hexagon Craze

Use blocks to cover the hexagon to show how to break it.
Then draw lines to show how you broke the hexagon.

1. Use 2 of the same shapes to break the hexagon.

2. Use 3 of the same shapes to break the hexagon.

3. Use 6 of the same shapes to break the hexagon.

4. Use 3 different shapes to break the hexagon.

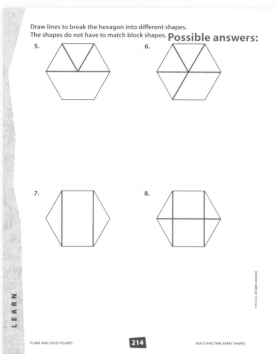

Draw lines to break the hexagon into different shapes.
The shapes do not have to match block shapes. **Possible answers:**

5.

6.

7.

8.

TRY IT Construction Zone

OFFLINE 10 min

Students will practice putting together and taking apart shapes to make other shapes. Give students the blocks and Construction Zone activity page from their Activity Book. Read the directions with them.

Encourage students to use blocks to model the problems.

Objectives

- Put geometric figures together to form other geometric figures.
- Take geometric figures apart to form other geometric figures.

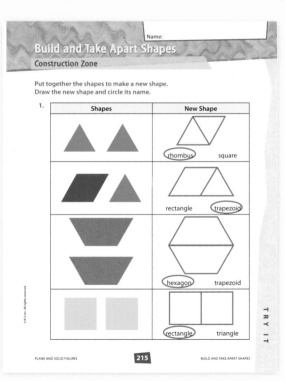

Build and Take Apart Shapes
Construction Zone

Put together the shapes to make a new shape.
Draw the new shape and circle its name.

1.

Shapes	New Shape
	(rhombus)　square
	rectangle　(trapezoid)
	(hexagon)　trapezoid
	(rectangle)　triangle

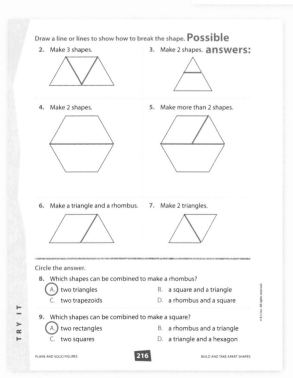

Draw a line or lines to show how to break the shape. **Possible**

2. Make 3 shapes.

3. Make 2 shapes. **answers:**

4. Make 2 shapes.

5. Make more than 2 shapes.

6. Make a triangle and a rhombus.

7. Make 2 triangles.

Circle the answer.

8. Which shapes can be combined to make a rhombus?
   - (A.) two triangles
   - B. a square and a triangle
   - C. two trapezoids
   - D. a rhombus and a square

9. Which shapes can be combined to make a square?
   - (A.) two rectangles
   - B. a rhombus and a triangle
   - C. two squares
   - D. a triangle and a hexagon

CHECKPOINT

OFFLINE 10 min

Print the Checkpoint and have students complete it on their own. Read the directions, problems, and answer choices to students, if necessary. Use the answer key to score the Checkpoint, and then enter the results online.

Gather the blocks, and give them to students for Problems 6 and 7.

Objectives

- Put geometric figures together to form other geometric figures.
- Take geometric figures apart to form other geometric figures.

Checkpoint — Math | Plane and Solid Figures | Build and Take Apart Shapes

Name Date

Checkpoint Answer Key

Read each problem and follow the directions.

(1 point)
1. Draw the shape that you could form if you put these two shapes together.

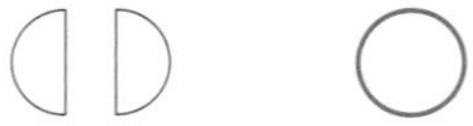

(1 point)
2. Draw the shape that you could form if you put these two shapes together.

(1 point)
3. Draw a line on the rectangle to form two triangles.

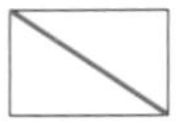

(1 point)
4. Draw a line on the triangle to form two more triangles.

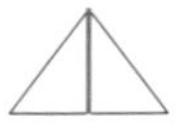

(1 point)
5. Draw a line on the rectangle to form two squares.

 1 of 2

Checkpoint — Math | Plane and Solid Figures | Build and Take Apart Shapes

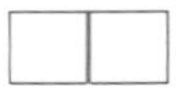

Name Date

Circle the answer.

(1 point)
6. Use the blocks. Which shapes can be combined to completely cover the yellow hexagon?
   A. two green triangles
   B. a blue rhombus and a green triangle
   (C.) two red trapezoids
   D. a blue rhombus and a yellow square

(1 point)
7. Use the blocks. Which shapes can be combined to completely cover the red trapezoid?
   A. two green triangles
   (B.) a blue rhombus and a green triangle
   C. two blue rhombuses
   D. a blue rhombus and a yellow square

 2 of 2

Unit Review

UNIT REVIEW Look Back	20 minutes	**ONLINE**
UNIT REVIEW Checkpoint Practice	20 minutes	**OFFLINE**
⏩ **UNIT REVIEW** Prepare for the Checkpoint		

▶ Unit Objectives

This lesson reviews the following objectives:

- Identify and describe plane figures according to the number of sides and vertices, such as triangle, square, rectangle, circle, oval.
- Classify plane figures according to similarities and differences, such as triangle, square, rectangle, circle, oval.
- Describe solid figures according to the number and shape of faces, such as sphere, pyramid, cube, rectangular prism.
- Classify solid figures according to the number and shape of faces and the number of edges, such as sphere, pyramid, cube, rectangular prism.
- Put geometric figures together to form other geometric figures.
- Take geometric figures apart to form other geometric figures.

▶ Advance Preparation

In this lesson, students will have an opportunity to review previous activities in the Plane and Solid Figures unit. Look at the suggested activities in Unit Review: Prepare for the Checkpoint online and gather any needed materials.

▶ Safety

Supervise students when they are working with the geometric solid blocks. These blocks have sharp corners.

Materials to Gather

SUPPLIED

blocks – E, K, L, M, N (2 of each)
blocks – P, Q, R, T, U, V
Checkpoint Practice activity page

Keywords

circle	rectangular prism
cone	rectangular pyramid
corner	rhombus
cube	semicircle
curved figure	side
curved solid	solid figure
cylinder	sphere
edge	square
face of a solid figure	square corner
geometric solids	square pyramid
hexagon	trapezoid
oval	triangle
plane figure	triangular prism
pyramid	vertex
rectangle	

UNIT REVIEW Look Back

In this unit, students have learned to describe plane figures by their number of sides and vertices. They also learned to describe solid figures by their number and shape of faces and their number of edges. They sorted figures based on these characteristics. Students also learned to combine and divide shapes to form other shapes. Students will review these concepts to prepare for the Unit Checkpoint.

OFFLINE
20min

Objectives

UNIT REVIEW Checkpoint Practice

Students will complete a Checkpoint Practice activity page to prepare for the Unit Checkpoint. If necessary, read the directions, problems, and answer choices to students. Have students answer the problems on their own. Carefully review the answers with students.

Gather the E, K, L, M, and N blocks and geometric solid blocks, and allow students to use the blocks as needed.

Unit Review
Checkpoint Practice

Name:

For Problems 1–20, you may use the blocks.
Write the answer.

1. Name a shape that has 3 sides. **triangle**

2. How many vertices does a square have? **4** vertices

3. How many vertices does a triangle have? **3** vertices

4. How many sides does a rectangle have? **4** sides

5. How are these two shapes different?

Sample answer: The trapezoid has 4 sides and 4 corners. The circle has no sides or corners.

PLANE AND SOLID FIGURES **217** UNIT REVIEW

6. What is the same about these two shapes?

Sample answer: Both shapes are curved.

Look at the solid. Write the shapes of its faces. Then write the number of faces it has.

7. square, triangle shapes **5** faces

8. circle shapes **1** faces

9. square, rectangle shapes **6** faces

10. square shapes **6** faces

PLANE AND SOLID FIGURES **218** UNIT REVIEW

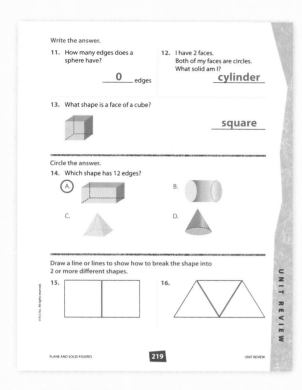

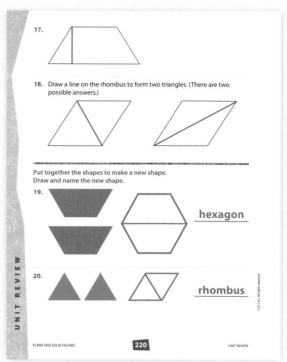

UNIT REVIEW Prepare for the Checkpoint

What you do next depends on how students performed in the previous activity, Unit Review: Checkpoint Practice. If students had difficulty with any of the problems, complete the appropriate review activity listed in the table online.

Unit Checkpoint

UNIT CHECKPOINT Online	30 minutes	**ONLINE**
UNIT CHECKPOINT Offline	30 minutes	**OFFLINE**

▶ Unit Objectives

This lesson assesses the following objectives:

- Identify and describe plane figures according to the number of sides and vertices, such as triangle, square, rectangle, circle, oval.
- Classify plane figures according to similarities and differences, such as triangle, square, rectangle, circle, oval.
- Describe solid figures according to the number and shape of faces, such as sphere, pyramid, cube, rectangular prism.
- Classify solid figures according to the number and shape of faces and the number of edges, such as sphere, pyramid, cube, rectangular prism.
- Put geometric figures together to form other geometric figures.
- Take geometric figures apart to form other geometric figures.

Materials to Gather

SUPPLIED

blocks – E, K, L, M, N (3 of each)

blocks – P, Q, R, S, T, U, V

Checkpoint (printout)

▶ Safety

Supervise students when they are working with the geometric solid blocks. These blocks have sharp corners.

UNIT CHECKPOINT Online

ONLINE 30min

Students will complete this part of the Unit Checkpoint online. Read the directions, problems, and answer choices to students. If necessary, help students with keyboard or mouse operations.

Objectives

- Assess unit objectives.

UNIT CHECKPOINT Offline

OFFLINE 30min

Students will complete this part of the Unit Checkpoint offline. Print the Checkpoint and have students complete it on their own. Read the directions, problems, and answer choices to students, if necessary. Use the answer key to score the Checkpoint, and then enter the results online.

Gather the E, K, L, M, and N blocks and geometric solid blocks and allow students to use the blocks as needed.

Objectives

- Assess unit objectives.

Name _____ Date _____

Unit Checkpoint Answer Key

Circle the answer. You may use your blocks to check your answer.
(1 point)

1. Which solid has 6 faces and 12 edges?

   A.   B.

   C.   (D.)

(1 point)

2. Which shape could you make if you put these two shapes together?

   (A.) circle   B. oval
   C. triangle   D. square

(1 point)

3. Which solid has 2 flat faces and 2 edges?

   A. cone   B. square pyramid
   (C.) cylinder   D. cube

Name _____ Date _____

Draw a line or lines to show how to break the shape. You may use your blocks to check your answer.
(1 point)

4. Make 2 squares.

(1 point)

5. Make 2 triangles.

(1 point)

6. Make 3 triangles.

Add or Subtract Numbers Through 1,000

**The Children's Theater has 1,000 seats.
527 children bought tickets for Saturday's play.
How many more children will be able to attend the play?**

$$\begin{array}{r} 1{,}000 \\ -\ \ 527 \\ \hline ? \end{array}$$

$$\begin{array}{r} 527 \\ +\ \ ? \\ \hline 1{,}000 \end{array}$$

- Find the sum or difference of two whole numbers with sums and minuends up through 1,000.

- Recognize and solve word problems involving sums up through 1,000 in which two quantities are combined.

- Recognize and solve word problems involving sums or minuends up through 1,000 in which one quantity changes by addition or subtraction.

- Recognize and solve word problems involving numbers up to 1,000 in which two quantities are compared by the use of addition or subtraction.

- Recognize and solve word problems involving numbers up to 1,000 in which one quantity must be changed to equal another quantity.

- Write and solve addition or subtraction number sentences to represent problem-solving situations with sums and minuends up through 1,000.

- Demonstrate an understanding of connections between similar addition or subtraction problem-solving situations, involving sums and minuends up through 1,000.

- Check the accuracy of calculations from the context of addition or subtraction problem-solving situations with sums and minuends up through 1,000 with regrouping.

- Justify the procedures selected for addition or subtraction problem-solving situations with sums or minuends up through 1,000.

- Recognize examples of problems that could be solved by addition or subtraction with regrouping.

▶ Big Ideas

- The use of letters, numbers, and mathematical symbols makes possible the translation of complex situations or long word statements into concise mathematical sentences or expressions.

- An inverse operation undoes another operation. Addition and subtraction are inverse operations.

▶ Unit Introduction

Students will extend their knowledge of adding and subtracting with sums and minuends up through 1,000. They will explore the connections between addition and subtraction computation problems. Building upon this exploration, they will learn how to solve the following types of addition and subtraction story problems: change problems, combine problems, equalize problems, and compare problems. Finally, they will learn how to check these problems for accuracy.

Sums and Differences

Skills Update	5 minutes	**ONLINE**
GET READY Add or Subtract	5 minutes	**ONLINE**
LEARN Work with Greater Numbers	20 minutes	**ONLINE**
LEARN Find the Sum or Difference	15 minutes	OFFLINE
TRY IT Practice Adding and Subtracting	10 minutes	OFFLINE
CHECKPOINT	5 minutes	OFFLINE

▶ Lesson Objectives

Find the sum or difference of two whole numbers with sums and minuends up through 1,000.

▶ Prerequisite Skills

- Find the sum of two whole numbers with sums up through 500.
- Use regrouping to find the difference of two whole numbers with the minuend up through 500.

▶ Advance Preparation

- Print the Place-Value Chart (Thousands).
- Print the Place-Value Mat – Thousands Column. Align the right side of the thousands column with the left side of the hundreds column on the place-value mat. Tape it to the mat so the mat has four columns.

▶ Content Background

Students know how to add and subtract with sums and minuends through 500. They will now extend this skill to include sums and minuends through 1,000.

The *sum* is the answer to an addition problem, and the *minuend* is the number students subtract from in a subtraction problem. The answer to a subtraction problem is called the *difference*. When speaking to students, you should use the terms *sum* and *difference*. (It's not necessary to use the term *minuend* with students.)

An *algorithm* is a repeated, step-by-step process. The traditional recording of regrouping (formerly called *carrying* in addition and *borrowing* in subtraction) is the recording of the algorithm. Although students have already encountered the algorithm while recording what they are doing with their base-10 blocks, the purpose of this lesson and previous lessons is to move students toward using the algorithm on its own—without models.

Materials to Gather

SUPPLIED

base-10 blocks

place-value mat

Place-Value Mat – Thousands Column (printout)

Place-Value Chart (Thousands) (printout)

Find the Sum or Difference activity page

Practice Adding and Subtracting activity page

Checkpoint (printout)

ALSO NEEDED

tape, clear

addend – one of the two or more numbers that are added to determine a sum

algorithm – a repeated step-by-step mathematical procedure

difference – the solution to a subtraction problem

minuend – in subtraction, the quantity or number from which another number is subtracted; 8 is the minuend in the problem $8 - 7 = ?$

regroup – to use place-value concepts to rename numbers, such as 1 ten and 3 ones = 13 ones; often used in addition and subtraction

sum – the answer to an addition problem

GET READY Add or Subtract

ONLINE
5 min

Objectives

- Find the sum of two whole numbers with sums up through 500.
- Use regrouping to find the difference of two whole numbers with the minuend up through 500.

Students will practice solving addition and subtraction problems with sums or minuends through 500. They should first solve the problems on paper before checking their answers online. They may use base-10 blocks and a place-value mat to model the problems if needed.

LEARN Work with Greater Numbers

ONLINE
20 min

Objectives

- Find the sum or difference of two whole numbers with sums and minuends up through 1,000.

Students have used base-10 blocks to add and subtract numbers through 500. Now they will use base-10 blocks to add and subtract numbers through 1,000.

Gather the Place-Value Chart (Thousands) printout. In the first part of the activity, students will use online base-10 blocks to learn how to find a sum of 1,000. Then they'll use the online base-10 blocks to learn how to subtract a number from 1,000. As students work through the screens, have them record the problems on the printout.

In the second part of the activity, students will use the Place Value Addition and Place Value Subtraction Learning Tools to practice adding and subtracting greater numbers.

DIRECTIONS FOR USING THE PLACE VALUE ADDITION LEARNING TOOL

1. Click Begin Setup and choose the following:
   - QUESTIONS set by: Computer
   - Present addition problems with SUMS up to: 999
   - Allow REGROUPING in problems: YES
2. Have students complete one addition problem.

DIRECTIONS FOR USING THE PLACE VALUE SUBTRACTION LEARNING TOOL

1. Click Begin Setup and choose the following:
   - QUESTIONS set by: Computer
   - Present subtraction problems with MINUENDS up to: 999
   - Allow REGROUPING in problems: YES
2. Have students complete two subtraction problems.

LEARN Find the Sum or Difference

Objectives

- Find the sum or difference of two whole numbers with sums and minuends up through 1,000.

Students will make the transition from using base-10 blocks and place-value charts to using an algorithm to add and subtract numbers through 1,000.

Give students the place-value mat with the thousands column attached, base-10 blocks, and Find the Sum or Difference activity page from their Activity Book. Read the directions with them.

1. Have students model Problems 1–3 using the base-10 blocks and place-value mat.

2. Have students solve Problems 4–6 using the algorithm only. Students should add or subtract beginning with the ones column, regrouping as necessary. If students have difficulty distinguishing the columns, have them copy the problems onto grid paper or the Place-Value Chart (Thousands) printout.

Name:

Sums and Differences

Find the Sum or Difference

Read the problem and follow the directions.

1. Find the difference. Use base-10 blocks to show the starting number. Then take away blocks to find the difference.

H Hundreds	T Tens	O Ones
8	0	4
— 1	9	9
6	**0**	**5**

2. Find the sum. Use base-10 blocks to show the addends.

Th Thousands	,	H Hundreds	T Tens	O Ones
		4	8	6
+		5	1	4
1	**,**	**0**	**0**	**0**

3. Find the difference. Use base-10 blocks to show the starting number. Then take away blocks to find the difference.

Th Thousands	,	H Hundreds	T Tens	O Ones
1	,	0	0	0
—		3	2	9
		6	**7**	**1**

4. Find the sum without using base-10 blocks.

$$\begin{array}{r} 517 \\ + 158 \\ \hline 675 \end{array}$$

5. Find the difference without using base-10 blocks.

$$\begin{array}{r} 1{,}000 \\ - 297 \\ \hline 703 \end{array}$$

6. Find the difference without using base-10 blocks.

$$\begin{array}{r} 894 \\ - 407 \\ \hline 487 \end{array}$$

LEARN

TRY IT Practice Adding and Subtracting

Students will practice adding and subtracting greater numbers. Give students the Practice Adding and Subtracting activity page from their Activity Book and read the directions with them.

Sums and Differences
Practice Adding and Subtracting

Name:

Add or subtract. Write the answer.

1. $\begin{array}{r} 58 \\ +\ 71 \\ \hline 129 \end{array}$

2. $\begin{array}{r} 217 \\ +\ 452 \\ \hline 669 \end{array}$

3. $\begin{array}{r} 486 \\ +\ 91 \\ \hline 577 \end{array}$

4. $\begin{array}{r} 118 \\ +\ 640 \\ \hline 758 \end{array}$

5. $\begin{array}{r} 306 \\ +\ 306 \\ \hline 612 \end{array}$

6. $\begin{array}{r} 715 \\ +\ 285 \\ \hline 1{,}000 \end{array}$

7. $\begin{array}{r} 476 \\ -\ 145 \\ \hline 331 \end{array}$

8. $\begin{array}{r} 519 \\ -\ 57 \\ \hline 462 \end{array}$

9. $\begin{array}{r} 711 \\ -\ 408 \\ \hline 303 \end{array}$

10. $\begin{array}{r} 860 \\ -\ 214 \\ \hline 646 \end{array}$

11. $\begin{array}{r} 1{,}000 \\ -\ 562 \\ \hline 438 \end{array}$

12. $\begin{array}{r} 908 \\ -\ 374 \\ \hline 534 \end{array}$

TRY IT

Add or subtract. Write the answer.

13. $\begin{array}{r} 53 \\ +\ 11 \\ \hline 64 \end{array}$

14. $\begin{array}{r} 459 \\ -\ 278 \\ \hline 181 \end{array}$

Add or subtract. Circle the answer.

15. $\begin{array}{r} 821 \\ +\ 76 \end{array}$

   A. 897   B. 855
   C. 745   D. 845

16. $\begin{array}{r} 634 \\ -\ 460 \end{array}$

   A. 234   B. 240
   C. 184   D. 174

TRY IT

CHECKPOINT

Print the Checkpoint and have students complete it on their own. Read the directions, problems, and answer choices to students, if necessary. Use the answer key to score the Checkpoint, and then enter the results online.

Objectives

- Find the sum or difference of two whole numbers with sums and minuends up through 1,000.

○ Checkpoint   Math | Add or Subtract Numbers Through 1,000 | Sums and Differences

Name _____   Date _____

Checkpoint Answer Key

Solve. Circle the answer.
(1 point)
1. 111
   + 234

   (A.) 345   B. 245
   C. 134   D. 234

(1 point)
2. 650
   + 77

   A. 707   (B.) 727
   C. 573   D. 773

(1 point)
3. 567
   − 184

   A. 623   (B.) 383
   C. 423   D. 380

Solve. Write the answer.
(1 point)   *(1 point)*
4. 753   5. 541
   + 77   − 303
   830   **238**

© 2010 K12 Inc. All rights reserved.   1 of 1
Copying or distributing without K12's written consent is prohibited.

Story Problems Through 1,000

Lesson Overview

Skills Update	5 minutes	**ONLINE**
Get Ready Story Problems Through 500	5 minutes	**ONLINE**
LEARN Combine Story Problems	15 minutes	**ONLINE**
LEARN Change Story Problems	15 minutes	**ONLINE**
TRY IT Practice Story Problems	10 minutes	OFFLINE
CHECKPOINT	10 minutes	OFFLINE

▶ Lesson Objectives

- Recognize and solve word problems involving sums up through 1,000 in which two quantities are combined.
- Recognize and solve word problems involving sums or minuends up through 1,000 in which one quantity changes by addition or subtraction.

▶ Prerequisite Skills

- Recognize and solve word problems involving sums up through 500 in which two quantities are combined.
- Recognize and solve word problems involving sums or minuends up through 500 in which one quantity changes by addition or subtraction.

▶ Common Errors and Misconceptions

- Students might add rather than subtract numbers in a compare problem. For example, when asked how many greater 5 is than 4, students might write the number sentence $5 + 4 = 9$ rather than $5 - 4 = 1$.
- Students might confuse combine problems and change problems.

▶ Content Background

Students will solve addition and subtraction story problems with sums and differences through 1,000.

When students encounter story problems in which one quantity in the problem changes through addition or subtraction, they may find that using a start-change-result model will help them understand how to write the number sentence that represents the problem. The start-change-result model is very similar to the part-part-total model, which students may have used before. While these models can be used interchangeably in story problems involving a change of an amount, the start-change-result model suggests the action of a change problem more clearly. Therefore, this model helps students more easily recognize a problem involving change versus one where two parts are simply combined.

Materials to Gather

SUPPLIED

Practice Story Problems activity page

Checkpoint (printout)

GET READY Story Problems Through 500

ONLINE 5 min

Students will solve addition and subtraction story problems with sums and differences through 500. They may use any methods they wish to solve the problems.

Objectives

- Recognize and solve word problems involving sums up through 500 in which two quantities are combined.
- Recognize and solve word problems involving sums or minuends up through 500 in which one quantity changes by addition or subtraction.

LEARN Combine Story Problems

ONLINE 15 min

Students will solve story problems that involve combining two groups. In some problems, they will be given both addends and will need to find the sum: $30 + 45 = ?$. In other problems, they will need to find a missing addend: $30 + ? = 75$.

Problems with a missing addend can be solved in two ways: counting on and subtracting. To solve $30 + ? = 75$ by counting on, students would start at 30 and count by tens: 40, 50, 60, 70. Then they would use reasoning to solve the problems: "I've counted 4 tens. I need to count on 5 more ones to get to 75. 4 tens and 5 ones is 45." Students can raise a finger for each ten they count to keep track.

To solve $30 + ? = 75$ by subtracting, students would rewrite the number sentence as subtraction, and solve: $75 - 30 = 45$.

In this activity, students will see both methods. Encourage them to use whichever method they find easier. As they work with greater and greater numbers, they will most likely find it easier to subtract.

Objectives

- Recognize and solve word problems involving sums up through 1,000 in which two quantities are combined.

Tips

Review regrouping if needed.

LEARN Change Story Problems

Students will solve story problems that involve an amount that changes. They will solve four types of problems:

- *Add a given amount to another given amount.* Example: Al had 20 cards. Pam gave him 10 more. How many cards does Al have now?

- *Take away a given amount from another given amount.* Example: Peter had 25 marbles. He gave 10 to his brother. How many marbles does Peter have now?

- *Add an unknown amount to a given amount.* Example: Amy had 2 pretzels. Mary gave her some more pretzels. Now Amy has 5 pretzels. How many pretzels did Mary give her?

- *Take away a given amount from an unknown amount.* Example: Sarah had some stickers. Then she gave 2 stickers to Beth. Now Sarah has 3 stickers. How many stickers did Sarah have at the beginning?

Objectives

- Recognize and solve word problems involving sums or minuends up through 1,000 in which one quantity changes by addition or subtraction.

TRY IT Practice Story Problems

Students will practice solving combine and change story problems with sums and differences through 1,000. Give students the Practice Story Problems activity page from their Activity Book and read the directions with them.

Objectives

- Recognize and solve word problems involving sums up through 1,000 in which two quantities are combined.

- Recognize and solve word problems involving sums or minuends up through 1,000 in which one quantity changes by addition or subtraction.

Name:

Story Problems Through 1,000
Practice Story Problems

Circle Add or Subtract. Then write the correct symbol in the problem on the right and solve.

1. The girls in the nature club collected 347 cans for recycling. The boys in the club collected 534 cans for recycling.

   How many cans did both the girls and the boys collect?

   $+$ 347 / 534

   881

   (Add)   Subtract

   881 cans

2. A toy store had 673 toy cars. They sold 425 toy cars.

   How many toy cars did the toy store have left?

   $-$ 673 / 425

   248

   Add   (Subtract)

   248 toy cars

3. Tanya has 675 clear marbles. She has some colored marbles. Tanya has 939 marbles in all.

   How many colored marbles does Tanya have?

   $-$ 939 / 675

   264

   Add   (Subtract)

   264 marbles

4. Brian has 393 baseball cards in a shoebox. He has 528 cards in his album.

   How many baseball cards does Brian have?

   $+$ 393 / 528

   921

   (Add)   Subtract

   921 baseball cards

Write the answer.

5. Melia drove to the Grand Canyon. She drove a total of 988 miles in two days. On the first day, Melia drove 455 miles.

   How far did Melia drive the second day?   **533** miles

Circle the answer.

6. Mia and Jed are saving up their reward points for a new soccer ball. Mia has saved 332 reward points. Jed has saved 288 reward points.

   How many reward points do they have together?

   A. 44   B. 156
   C. 510   (D.) 620

7. This year the fundraising committee raised $178. They had already raised $765.

   How much money does the committee have now?

   A. $587   B. $611
   C. $833   (D.) $943

8. Jose drove a total of 420 miles on Saturday and Sunday. He drove 177 miles on Sunday. How many miles did Jose drive on Saturday?

   (A.) 243 miles   B. 353 miles
   C. 357 miles   D. 597 miles

CHECKPOINT

Print the Checkpoint and have students complete it on their own. Read the directions, problems, and answer choices to students, if necessary. Use the answer key to score the Checkpoint, and then enter the results online.

- Recognize and solve word problems involving sums up through 1,000 in which two quantities are combined.

- Recognize and solve word problems involving sums or minuends up through 1,000 in which one quantity changes by addition or subtraction.

○ Checkpoint   Math | Add or Subtract Numbers Through 1,000 | Story Problems Through 1,000

Name _____   Date _____

Checkpoint Answer Key

Write the answer.
(1 point each)

1. Mykola is saving his pennies in two containers. One container has 387 pennies. The second container has 582 pennies. What is the total number of pennies that Mykola has saved?

   969 pennies

2. Jen has 500 pennies in two jars. The first jar has 291 pennies. How many pennies are in the second jar?

   209 pennies

3. Kanu is planning a vacation. She has a total of $900 to spend. She spent $235 on airfare. How much money does Kanu have left?

   $ **665**

4. Zoe is collecting magazines. Last month she collected 218 magazines. This month she collected 182 magazines. How many magazines has Zoe collected in the last two months?

   400 magazines

Circle the answer.
(1 point each)

5. There are 613 restaurants in the city. 356 of them are fast food restaurants and the rest are sit-down restaurants. How many sit-down restaurants are in the city?

   (A.) 257
   B. 365
   C. 961
   D. 971

6. Steve began the week with 800 minutes on his calling card. By the end of the week, he had 231 minutes left. How many minutes had Steve used on his calling card?

   A. 531 minutes
   (B.) 569 minutes
   C. 679 minutes
   D. 1031 minutes

Compare and Equalize Problems

Skills Update	5 minutes	ONLINE
GET READY Solve Story Problems	5 minutes	ONLINE
LEARN Equalize Story Problems	15 minutes	ONLINE
LEARN Compare Story Problems	15 minutes	OFFLINE
TRY IT More Story Problems	10 minutes	OFFLINE
CHECKPOINT	10 minutes	ONLINE

▶ ## Lesson Objectives

- Recognize and solve word problems involving numbers up to 1,000 in which two quantities are compared by the use of addition or subtraction.
- Recognize and solve word problems involving numbers up to 1,000 in which one quantity must be changed to equal another quantity.

▶ ## Prerequisite Skills

- Recognize and solve word problems involving numbers up to 500 in which two quantities are compared by the use of addition or subtraction.
- Recognize and solve word problems involving numbers up to 500 in which one quantity must be changed to equal another quantity.

▶ ## Common Errors and Misconceptions

- Students might add rather than subtract numbers in a compare problem. For example, when asked how many greater 5 is than 4, students might write the number sentence $5 + 4 = 9$ rather than $5 - 4 = 1$.
- Students might confuse combine problems and change problems.

▶ ## Content Background

Students will solve story problems that require them to compare groups or make two groups equal.

Throughout the activity, students should come to realize that *how many more one group has than the other* is the same as *how many fewer the other group has than that group*. Once they understand this concept, they will be ready to learn how to *equalize* groups, or determine how many more should be added to one group to make it equal to the other group. Students should make the connection that the difference they find when comparing two groups is the same as the number needed to make the groups equal.

Materials to Gather

SUPPLIED

blocks – B
Compare Story Problems activity page
More Story Problems activity page

GET READY Solve Story Problems

Students will solve a guided comparison problem about the number of paperback and hardcover books on Alexander's bookshelf. They will learn that the difference between the number of hardcover books and paperbacks is equal to each of the following:

- How many more hardcover books there are than paperbacks
- How many fewer paperbacks there are than hardcover books
- How many more paperbacks are needed to equal the number of hardcover books

Emphasize these connections as students work through the activity.

If students have difficulty, practice comparing groups. For example, give students 11 yellow cubes and 8 red cubes. Have them make pairs to find how many fewer red cubes there are. Then ask them related questions:

- How many more yellow cubes are there?
- How many more red cubes do you need to equal the number of yellow cubes?
- What is 11 minus 8?

Objectives

- Recognize and solve word problems involving numbers up to 500 in which two quantities are compared by the use of addition or subtraction.
- Recognize and solve word problems involving numbers up to 500 in which one quantity must be changed to equal another quantity.

LEARN Equalize Story Problems

Students will equalize quantities by identifying how many of one group is needed to equal the quantity of the other group. Students will first see a simpler problem solved and will see that they can subtract to find the solution.

As students work on the problems online, guide them to use paper and pencil to subtract if necessary.

Objectives

- Recognize and solve word problems involving numbers up to 1,000 in which one quantity must be changed to equal another quantity.

LEARN Compare Story Problems

Objectives

- Recognize and solve word problems involving numbers up to 1,000 in which two quantities are compared by the use of addition or subtraction.

Students will compare quantities to identify how many more or fewer one group has than the other. They will learn that when working with greater numbers, they should subtract to compare.

Gather the circle blocks and the Compare Story Problems activity page. Read the directions and Problem 1 aloud. If students are unsure how to proceed, follow the following these steps:

1. Guide students to make a row of circles to represent the birds, and beneath it, a row of circles to represent the puppies. Line up the two rows so that the circles match one-to-one. Have students count the extra circles that do not have a match to find out how many more birds there are than puppies.

2. Guide students to subtract to compare the birds and puppies. Point out that both methods give the same answer. Explain that the answer represents how many *more* birds than puppies there are, as well as how many *fewer* puppies than birds there are.

3. Read Problem 2 aloud. Ask students which method they would use to solve this problem. Explain that both methods would give the same answer, but it would be difficult and time consuming to model with circles and make pairs to solve this problem. Guide students to subtract to solve Problem 2.

Have students subtract to solve the remaining problems. Assist them as needed.

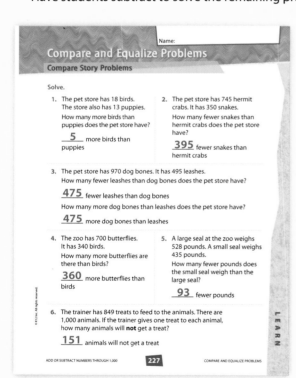

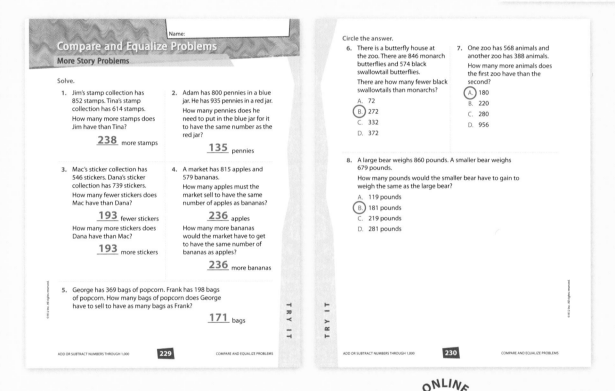

TRY IT More Story Problems

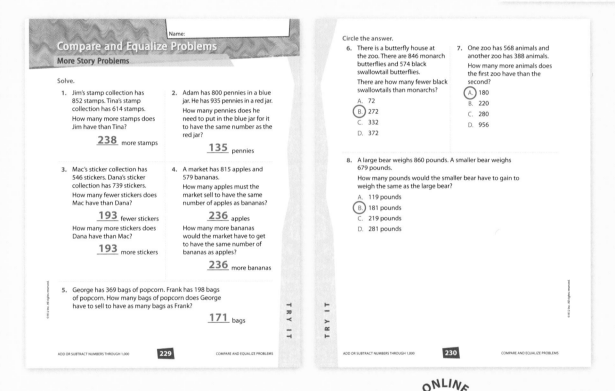

OFFLINE 10 min

Students will practice solving compare and equalize story problems with numbers through 1,000. Give students the More Story Problems activity page from their Activity Book and read the directions with them.

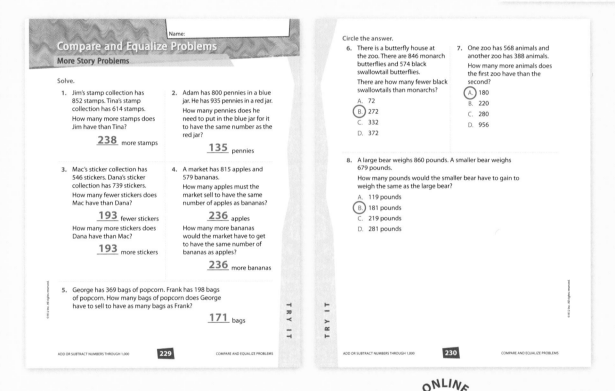

Objectives

- Recognize and solve word problems involving numbers up to 1,000 in which two quantities are compared by the use of addition or subtraction.

- Recognize and solve word problems involving numbers up to 1,000 in which one quantity must be changed to equal another quantity.

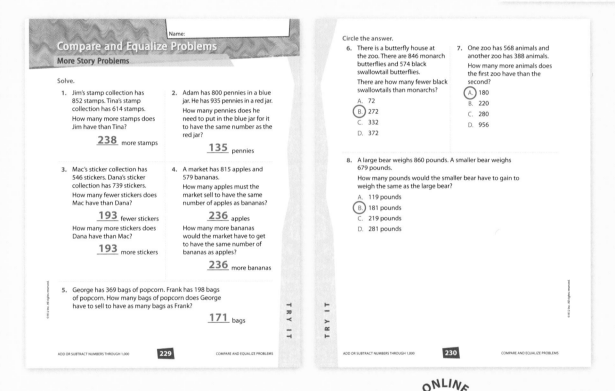

Name: _____

Compare and Equalize Problems
More Story Problems

Solve.

1. Jim's stamp collection has 852 stamps. Tina's stamp collection has 614 stamps.
   How many more stamps does Jim have than Tina?

   238 more stamps

2. Adam has 800 pennies in a blue jar. He has 935 pennies in a red jar.
   How many pennies does he need to put in the blue jar for it to have the same number as the red jar?

   135 pennies

3. Mac's sticker collection has 546 stickers. Dana's sticker collection has 739 stickers.
   How many fewer stickers does Mac have than Dana?

   193 fewer stickers

   How many more stickers does Dana have than Mac?

   193 more stickers

4. A market has 815 apples and 579 bananas.
   How many apples must the market sell to have the same number of apples as bananas?

   236 apples

   How many more bananas would the market have to get to have the same number of bananas as apples?

   236 more bananas

5. George has 369 bags of popcorn. Frank has 198 bags of popcorn. How many bags of popcorn does George have to sell to have as many bags as Frank?

   171 bags

 TRY IT

 ADD OR SUBTRACT NUMBERS THROUGH 1,000 **229** COMPARE AND EQUALIZE PROBLEMS

Circle the answer.

6. There is a butterfly house at the zoo. There are 846 monarch butterflies and 574 black swallowtail butterflies.
   There are how many fewer black swallowtails than monarchs?
   A. 72
   B. 272
   C. 332
   D. 372

7. One zoo has 568 animals and another zoo has 388 animals.
   How many more animals does the first zoo have than the second?
   A. 180
   B. 220
   C. 280
   D. 956

8. A large bear weighs 860 pounds. A smaller bear weighs 679 pounds.
   How many pounds would the smaller bear have to gain to weigh the same as the large bear?
   A. 119 pounds
   B. 181 pounds
   C. 219 pounds
   D. 281 pounds

TRY IT

ADD OR SUBTRACT NUMBERS THROUGH 1,000 **230** COMPARE AND EQUALIZE PROBLEMS

CHECKPOINT

ONLINE 10 min

Students will complete an online Checkpoint. Read the directions, problems, and answer choices to students. If necessary, help students with keyboard or mouse operations.

Objectives

- Recognize and solve word problems involving numbers up to 1,000 in which two quantities are compared by the use of addition or subtraction.

- Recognize and solve word problems involving numbers up to 1,000 in which one quantity must be changed to equal another quantity.

Write Sentences for Story Problems

Lesson Overview

Skills Update	5 minutes	**ONLINE**
GET READY Represent Story Problems	5 minutes	**ONLINE**
LEARN Write Sentences for Problems	15 minutes	**ONLINE**
LEARN Set Up Story Problems	15 minutes	**ONLINE**
TRY IT Practice Setting Up Problems	10 minutes	**OFFLINE**
CHECKPOINT	10 minutes	**OFFLINE**

▶ Lesson Objectives

Write and solve addition or subtraction number sentences to represent problem-solving situations with sums and minuends up through 1,000.

▶ Prerequisite Skills

Write and solve addition or subtraction number sentences to represent problem-solving situations with sums and minuends up through 500.

▶ Common Errors and Misconceptions

- Students might add rather than subtract numbers in a compare problem. For example, when asked how many greater 5 is than 4, students might write the number sentence $5 + 4 = 9$ rather than $5 - 4 = 1$.
- Students might confuse combine problems and change problems.

▶ Content Background

Students will learn how to write addition and subtraction number sentences to solve combine, compare, change, and equalize problems. By writing a number sentence, students show the process they will use to solve the story problem. They will first write the number sentence, and then find the missing number in the number sentence to solve the problem. Some students think of the number sentence as the code that leads to the answer.

Students do not need to memorize the types of story problems. Instead, they should gain the experience and confidence necessary to read a problem, create a mental image, and form a plan for solving the problem.

- In *change problems*, students must add to or take away from a group—the number of objects in the group *changes*.
- In *combine problems*, students must put together two or more groups to find the total. In some combine problems, however, students will be given the sum and will need to find one of the parts.
- In *compare problems*, students must compare two groups to determine how many more or fewer objects are in one group.
- In *equalize problems*, students must determine how many to add to or subtract from a group to make it equal to another group.

Materials to Gather

SUPPLIED

Practice Setting Up Problems activity page

Checkpoint (printout)

GET READY Represent Story Problems

ONLINE 5 min

Objectives

Students will write and solve a number sentence to solve a combine story problem. They will be guided to write a particular number sentence to solve the problem; however, there is more than one correct number sentence for most problems. In some cases, students will be able to either add or subtract.

- Write and solve addition or subtraction number sentences to represent problem-solving situations with sums and minuends up through 500.

LEARN Write Sentences for Problems

ONLINE 15 min

Objectives

Students will write and solve number sentences for story problems that either combine or compare numbers. They can enter correct number sentences in different ways. If time permits, discuss different number sentences they could use to solve the story problems.

The last screen asks students to make up a story problem. They may say the problem and number sentence, or they may write it. If time permits, students may make up multiple problems.

- Write and solve addition or subtraction number sentences to represent problem-solving situations with sums and minuends up through 1,000.

LEARN Set Up Story Problems

ONLINE 15 min

Objectives

Students will write and solve number sentences for story problems that either equalize or change numbers. They can enter correct number sentences in different ways. If time permits, discuss different number sentences they could use to solve the story problems.

The last screen asks students to make up a story problem. They may say the problem and number sentence, or they may write it. If time permits, students may make up multiple problems.

- Write and solve addition or subtraction number sentences to represent problem-solving situations with sums and minuends up through 1,000.

TRY IT Practice Setting Up Problems

OFFLINE 10 min

Objectives

Students will practice writing and solving number sentences in order to solve story problems. Give students the Practice Setting Up Problems activity page from their Activity Book and read the directions with them.

- Write and solve addition or subtraction number sentences to represent problem-solving situations with sums and minuends up through 1,000.

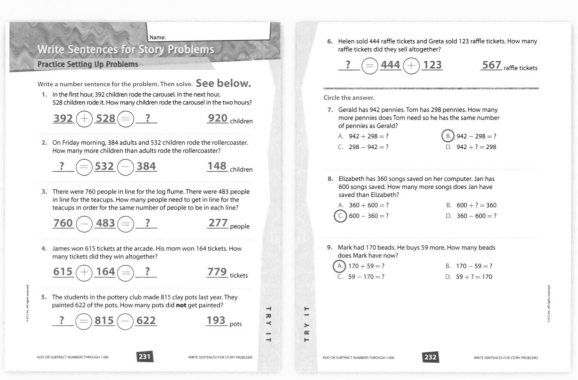

Write Sentences for Story Problems

Practice Setting Up Problems

Write a number sentence for the problem. Then solve. **See below.**

1. In the first hour, 392 children rode the carousel. In the next hour, 528 children rode it. How many children rode the carousel in the two hours?

   $392 \ (+) \ 528 \ (=) \ ?$ 920 children

2. On Friday morning, 384 adults and 532 children rode the rollercoaster. How many more children than adults rode the rollercoaster?

   $? \ (=) \ 532 \ (-) \ 384$ 148 children

3. There were 760 people in line for the log flume. There were 483 people in line for the teacups. How many people need to get in line for the teacups in order for the same number of people to be in each line?

   $760 \ (-) \ 483 \ (=) \ ?$ 277 people

4. James won 615 tickets at the arcade. His mom won 164 tickets. How many tickets did they win altogether?

   $615 \ (+) \ 164 \ (=) \ ?$ 779 tickets

5. The students in the pottery club made 815 clay pots last year. They painted 622 of the pots. How many pots did they **not** get painted?

   $? \ (=) \ 815 \ (-) \ 622$ 193 pots

TRY IT

ADD OR SUBTRACT NUMBERS THROUGH 1,000 | **231** | WRITE SENTENCES FOR STORY PROBLEMS

---

6. Helen sold 444 raffle tickets and Greta sold 123 raffle tickets. How many raffle tickets did they sell altogether?

   $? \ (=) \ 444 \ (+) \ 123$ 567 raffle tickets

Circle the answer.

7. Gerald has 942 pennies. Tom has 298 pennies. How many more pennies does Tom need so he has the same number of pennies as Gerald?

   A. $942 + 298 = ?$ B. $942 - 298 = ?$ ⟵ circled
   C. $298 - 942 = ?$ D. $942 + ? = 298$

8. Elizabeth has 360 songs saved on her computer. Jan has 600 songs saved. How many more songs does Jan have saved than Elizabeth?

   A. $360 + 600 = ?$ B. $600 + ? = 360$
   C. $600 - 360 = ?$ ⟵ circled   D. $360 - 600 = ?$

9. Mark had 170 beads. He buys 59 more. How many beads does Mark have now?

   A. $170 + 59 = ?$ ⟵ circled   B. $170 - 59 = ?$
   C. $59 - 170 = ?$ D. $59 + ? = 170$

TRY IT

ADD OR SUBTRACT NUMBERS THROUGH 1,000 | **232** | WRITE SENTENCES FOR STORY PROBLEMS

Additional Answers

1-6. Sample answers shown. Check students' work. Other correct number sentences are acceptable.

OFFLINE
10 min

CHECKPOINT

Print the Checkpoint and have students complete it on their own. Read the directions, problems, and answer choices to students, if necessary. Use the answer key to score the Checkpoint, and then enter the results online.

Objectives

- Write and solve addition or subtraction number sentences to represent problem-solving situations with sums and minuends up through 1,000.

⟳ Checkpoint   Math | Add or Subtract Numbers Through 1,000 | Write Sentences for Story Problems

Name _____   Date _____

Checkpoint Answer Key

Which number sentence could be used to correctly solve these problems? Circle the answer.
(1 point each)

1. Jamie got a new bag of blocks. The new bag has 700 blocks in it. Jamie already had 121 blocks. How many blocks does Jaime have now?

   A. $700 + 121 = ?$ ⟵ circled
   B. $700 + ? = 121$
   C. $700 - 121 = ?$
   D. $121 - 700 = ?$

2. Connie is baking some cupcakes. She wants to decorate each of the cupcakes with a flag. She has baked 48 cupcakes and she has 39 flags. How many cupcakes won't get a flag?

   A. $48 + 39 = ?$
   B. $48 + ? = 39$
   C. $48 - 39 = ?$ ⟵ circled
   D. $39 - 48 = ?$

Write a number sentence which could be used to solve these problems, and then solve them.

3. Amy has 543 cookies. Sara has 269 cookies. How many cookies does Amy have to sell to have as many cookies as Sara?

   $? \ (=) \ 543 \ (-) \ 269$ 274 cookies
   (1 point)   *(1 point)*

4. There were 345 more fans at the baseball game than at the football game. There were 300 fans at the football game. How many fans were at the baseball game?

   $300 \ (+) \ 345 \ (=) \ ?$ 645 fans
   (1 point)   *(1 point)*

5. Jillian had 99 marbles. Una gave her some more. Now Jillian has 107 marbles. How many marbles did Una give Jillian?

   $107 \ (-) \ 99 \ (=) \ ?$ 8 marbles
   (1 point)   *(1 point)*

Find Similarities and Differences

▶ **Lesson Objectives**

Demonstrate an understanding of connections between similar addition or subtraction problem-solving situations, involving sums and minuends up through 1,000.

▶ **Prerequisite Skills**

Demonstrate an understanding of connections between similar addition or subtraction problems from problem-solving situations, involving sums and minuends up through 500.

▶ **Content Background**

Students will learn to look for similarities in story problems. Then they will solve similar problems using the same approach.

Problem solving is not only a key to success in math, but also in every area of life. To become good problem solvers, students need to recognize when a new problem is similar to another problem they have already solved. In this way, they build on their prior experiences with problems and develop strategies that work for many similar problems. Instead of treating every problem they encounter as a new experience, they build confidence in knowing that they have not only seen a type of problem before, but they have had success with that type of problem.

Materials to Gather

SUPPLIED

Are They Alike? activity page

Solve the Same Way? activity page

Checkpoint (printout)

GET READY How Are Problems the Same?

ONLINE
5 min

Objectives

Students will determine if two problems can be solved in the same way. They will read two problems and tell how they would solve each. Then they will compare their proposed solutions and decide if the solutions use the same method.

- Demonstrate an understanding of connections between similar addition or subtraction problems from problem-solving situations, involving sums and minuends up through 500.

LEARN Similarities in Story Problems

Objectives

Students will determine if pairs of problems with sums and minuends through 1,000 can be solved in the same way. With guidance, they will devise a plan for solving each problem. Then they will compare their proposed solutions and decide if the solutions use the same method.

Encourage students to read an entire story problem carefully before determining how they will solve it. Skimming for key words, such as *more*, may lead them to choose the wrong operation.

- Demonstrate an understanding of connections between similar addition or subtraction problem-solving situations, involving sums and minuends up through 1,000.

LEARN Are They Alike?

Objectives

Students will analyze pairs of story problems to determine whether both problems can be solved the same way (both with addition or both with subtraction).

Give students the How Are They Alike? activity page from their Activity Book and read the directions with them. Guide students through the problems. Ask questions such as the following:

- What do you know?
- What do you need to find out?
- Do you need to add or subtract to find the answer?
- What is the number sentence for each problem?
- Can both story problems be solved the same way?

- Demonstrate an understanding of connections between similar addition or subtraction problem-solving situations, involving sums and minuends up through 1,000.

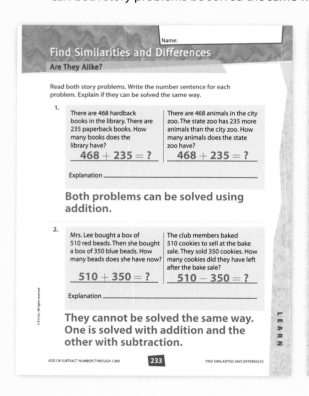

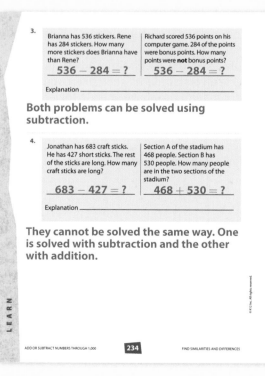

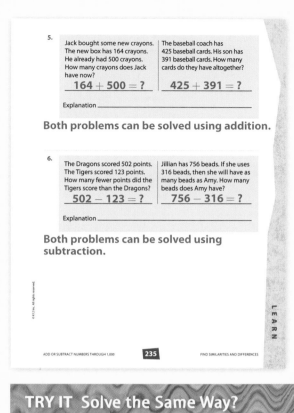

5.

Jack bought some new crayons. The new box has 164 crayons. He already had 500 crayons. How many crayons does Jack have now?	The baseball coach has 425 baseball cards. His son has 391 baseball cards. How many cards do they have altogether?
$164 + 500 = ?$	$425 + 391 = ?$

Explanation _____

Both problems can be solved using addition.

6.

The Dragons scored 502 points. The Tigers scored 123 points. How many fewer points did the Tigers score than the Dragons?	Jillian has 756 beads. If she uses 316 beads, then she will have as many beads as Amy. How many beads does Amy have?
$502 - 123 = ?$	$756 - 316 = ?$

Explanation _____

Both problems can be solved using subtraction.

L E A R N

OFFLINE

10 min

TRY IT Solve the Same Way?

Students will practice determining how to solve similar story problems. Then they will practice identifying a story problem that is similar to another story problem. Give students the Solve the Same Way? activity page from their Activity Book and read the directions with them. Use the answer key to check students' answers, and then enter the results online.

Objectives

- Demonstrate an understanding of connections between similar addition or subtraction problem-solving situations, involving sums and minuends up through 1,000.

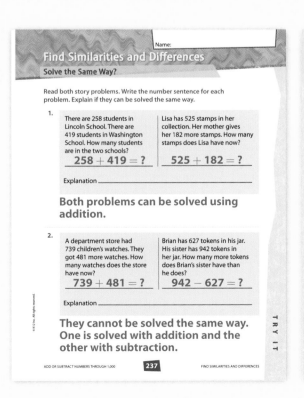

Name: _____

Find Similarities and Differences

Solve the Same Way?

Read both story problems. Write the number sentence for each problem. Explain if they can be solved the same way.

1.

There are 258 students in Lincoln School. There are 419 students in Washington School. How many students are in the two schools?	Lisa has 525 stamps in her collection. Her mother gives her 182 more stamps. How many stamps does Lisa have now?
$258 + 419 = ?$	$525 + 182 = ?$

Explanation _____

Both problems can be solved using addition.

2.

A department store had 739 children's watches. They got 481 more watches. How many watches does the store have now?	Brian has 627 tokens in his jar. His sister has 942 tokens in her jar. How many more tokens does Brian's sister have than he does?
$739 + 481 = ?$	$942 - 627 = ?$

Explanation _____

They cannot be solved the same way. One is solved with addition and the other with subtraction.

T R Y   I T

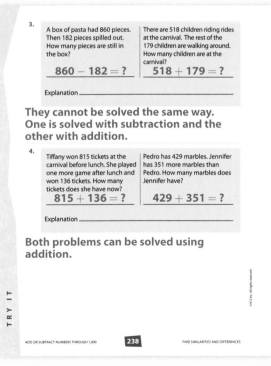

3.

A box of pasta had 860 pieces. Then 182 pieces spilled out. How many pieces are still in the box?	There are 518 children riding rides at the carnival. The rest of the 179 children are walking around. How many children are at the carnival?
$860 - 182 = ?$	$518 + 179 = ?$

Explanation _____

They cannot be solved the same way. One is solved with subtraction and the other with addition.

4.

Tiffany won 815 tickets at the carnival before lunch. She played one more game after lunch and won 136 tickets. How many tickets does she have now?	Pedro has 429 marbles. Jennifer has 351 more marbles than Pedro. How many marbles does Jennifer have?
$815 + 136 = ?$	$429 + 351 = ?$

Explanation _____

Both problems can be solved using addition.

T R Y   I T

Circle the answer.

5. Read the complete problem before answering.

Dario walked for 30 minutes in the morning and for 45 minutes in the afternoon. What is the total number of minutes that Dario walked?

A student solved this problem by adding the two numbers. $30 + 45 = ?$

Which of the following problems could be solved the same way?

A. Jason has 26 red balloons. 13 of them popped. How many balloons does Jason have left?

B. Charles baked 53 muffins. He ate 4 of them. How many muffins are left?

C. Emily painted 36 tiles red and 49 tiles orange. How many tiles did Emily paint altogether?

6. Which is the same about these problems?

$700 + 200$

$500 + 300$

A. Both have zeros in the hundreds place.

B. Both have zeros in the tens place only.

C. Both have zeros in the tens and the ones places.

D. Both have a sum of 900.

7. Read the complete problem before answering.

There are 8 carrots on the grass. There are 19 rabbits who want a carrot. If each rabbit tries to get one carrot, how many rabbits will **not** get a carrot?

A student solved this problem by subtracting the two numbers. $19 - 8 = ?$

Which of the following problems could be solved the same way?

A. Tony baked 17 vanilla cupcakes and 15 chocolate cupcakes. How many cupcakes did Tony bake altogether?

B. Hilda is baking pies. She has 8 pie crusts but only has 6 pie dishes. She can only put one pie crust in each dish. How many pie crusts will Hilda have left over?

C. Harry planted some flowers in his yard. He planted 17 roses and 19 tulips. How many flowers did he plant altogether?

8. Read the complete problem before answering.

Joe's Café has 236 seats. Jill's Café has 310 seats. How many fewer seats does Joe's Café have than Jill's?

A student solved this problem by subtracting the two numbers. $310 - 236 = ?$

Which of the following problems could be solved the same way?

A. Lisa rode her bike for 35 minutes. Brooke rode her bike for 45 minutes. How many more minutes did Brooke ride than Lisa?

B. Isabelle has 18 red plums and 15 yellow plums. How many plums does Isabelle have altogether?

C. David had some oranges. He gave 13 oranges away and he has 19 left. How many oranges did David have in the beginning?

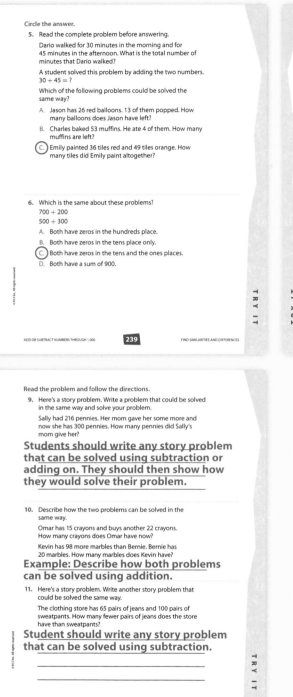

Read the problem and follow the directions.

9. Here's a story problem. Write a problem that could be solved in the same way and solve your problem.

Sally had 216 pennies. Her mom gave her some more and now she has 300 pennies. How many pennies did Sally's mom give her?

Students should write any story problem that can be solved using subtraction or adding on. They should then show how they would solve their problem.

10. Describe how the two problems can be solved in the same way.

Omar has 15 crayons and buys another 22 crayons. How many crayons does Omar have now?

Kevin has 98 more marbles than Bernie. Bernie has 20 marbles. How many marbles does Kevin have?

Example: Describe how both problems can be solved using addition.

11. Here's a story problem. Write another story problem that could be solved the same way.

The clothing store has 65 pairs of jeans and 100 pairs of sweatpants. How many fewer pairs of jeans does the store have than sweatpants?

Student should write any story problem that can be solved using subtraction.

CHECKPOINT

Objectives

Print the Checkpoint and have students complete it on their own. Read the directions, problems, and answer choices to students, if necessary. Use the answer key to score the Checkpoint, and then enter the results online.

- Demonstrate an understanding of connections between similar addition or subtraction problem-solving situations, involving sums and minuends up through 1,000.

Checkpoint   Math | Add or Subtract Numbers Through 1,000 | Find Similarities and Differences

Name _____ Date _____

Checkpoint Answer Key

Read each problem and follow the directions.

(2 points)
1. Here's a story problem. Write a problem that could be solved in the same way and solve your problem.

   Liza has 124 songs saved on her computer. Janet has 72 songs saved. How many fewer songs does Janet have saved than Liza?

   Students should write a word problem that can be solved using subtraction. (1 point)

   Students should then show how they would solve their problem. (1 point)

(2 points)
2. Can problem 1 be solved in the same way as problem 2? Explain your answer

Problem 1	Problem 2
Jessica baked 48 cupcakes. She baked 12 vanilla cupcakes and the rest were chocolate. How many cupcakes were chocolate?	Paula washed 38 large plates and 16 small plates. How many plates did Paula wash altogether?

   Students should answer no, the problems would not be solved in the same way. (1 point)

   A valid explanation should be given. Example explanation: Problem 1 would be solved using subtraction. For example, 48 − 12 = ? or 48 − 12 = 36. Problem 2 would be solved using addition. For example, 38 + 16 = ? or 38 + 16 = 54. (1 point)

1 of 3

Checkpoint   Math | Add or Subtract Numbers Through 1,000 | Find Similarities and Differences

Name _____ Date _____

(1 point)
3. Describe how the two problems below could be solved in the same way.

Problem 1	Problem 2
There were 38 bananas and 54 plums. There were how many more plums than bananas?	Katie read 16 fewer pages of her book than Daryl. Daryl read 40 pages. How many pages did Katie read?

   Describe how both problems could be solved using subtraction.

   _____

   _____

(1 point)
4. Read the complete problem before answering.

   Franz has 160 marbles and Jordan has 205 marbles. How many more marbles does Jordan have than Franz?

   A student solved this problem by subtracting the two numbers.
   205 − 160 = ?

   Which of the following problems could be solved the same way? Circle the answer.

   A. Tyler has 8 more comics than Bernie. Bernie has 12 comics. How many comics does Tyler have?

   B. Diane has 7 pairs of shoes and Tara has 12 pairs of shoes. How many fewer pairs of shoes does Diane have than Tara?

   C. Keith played volleyball for 3 hours on Monday and 5 hours on Tuesday. What is the total number of hours that Keith played volleyball?

2 of 3

Checkpoint   Math | Add or Subtract Numbers Through 1,000 | Find Similarities and Differences

Name _____ Date _____

(1 point)
5. Read the complete problem before answering.

   Jesse has to take 120 pictures for a class project. So far he has taken 65 pictures. How many more pictures does Jesse need to take?

   A student solved this problem by subtracting the two numbers.
   120 − 65 = ?

   Which of the following problems could be solved the same way? Circle the answer.

   A. Kylie painted 16 red tiles and 19 blue tiles. How many tiles did she paint altogether?

   B. Fawn ran 8 laps around the track in the morning and then another 10 laps in the afternoon. How many laps did Fawn run that day?

   C. Jackie has to read 22 pages in her science book. She has already read 15 pages. How many more pages must Jackie read?

3 of 3

Check Story Problem Solutions

Skills Update	5 minutes	ONLINE
GET READY Check Solutions Through 500	5 minutes	ONLINE
LEARN Check Solutions Through 1,000	15 minutes	ONLINE
LEARN Check Answers	15 minutes	OFFLINE
TRY IT Practice Checking Answers	10 minutes	OFFLINE
CHECKPOINT	10 minutes	OFFLINE

▶ Lesson Objectives

Check the accuracy of calculations from the context of addition or subtraction problem-solving situations with sums and minuends up through 1,000 with regrouping.

▶ Prerequisite Skills

Check the accuracy of calculations from the context of addition or subtraction problem-solving situations with sums and minuends up through 500 with regrouping.

▶ Content Background

In this lesson, students will check if a given answer to a story problem is correct or incorrect.

When students solve story problems, much of their thinking goes into visualizing the problem and deciding what operation to use. A key last step in problem solving is checking whether the final answer makes sense by reading the original problem again and then asking and answering these questions: "Did I use the correct operation? Did I do the calculation accurately?" This step is often not the most popular with students, but it is definitely one of the most important.

Materials to Gather

SUPPLIED

Check Answers activity page

Practice Checking Answers activity page

Checkpoint (printout)

GET READY Check Solutions Through 500

ONLINE 5 min

Students will determine if Rosa's approach to a story problem is correct. Then they will solve the problem.

Objectives

- Check the accuracy of calculations from the context of addition or subtraction problem-solving situations with sums and minuends up through 500 with regrouping.

LEARN Check Solutions Through 1,000

Students will learn different strategies to use to check answers to story problems. When checking an answer, they should always check whether the correct operation was used. They can do this by checking if the answer makes sense. Once they are sure of the correct operation, they should check the computation.

As students progress through the activity, have them ask themselves questions similar to the following:

- Am I putting amounts together? Am I adding to one amount? If so, I need to add.

- Am I taking away one amount from another? Am I comparing two sets of objects to see which has more or which has fewer? If so, I need to subtract.

- Did I add or subtract correctly? Do I need to regroup? Can I use inverse operations to help me check?

Objectives

- Check the accuracy of calculations from the context of addition or subtraction problem-solving situations with sums and minuends up through 1,000 with regrouping.

Tips

Point out that in some of the problems online, the student used a correct number sentence but then added or subtracted incorrectly. In these cases, remind students to regroup carefully when checking the computation.

LEARN Check Answers

Students will check answers to Rosa's story problems by working the problems themselves. If they find Rosa's answers are incorrect, students will explain Rosa's error and provide the correct answer.

Give students the Check Answers activity page from their Activity Book and read the directions with them. Check each problem as students complete it. Assist students as needed to help them find the correct answers.

Objectives

- Check the accuracy of calculations from the context of addition or subtraction problem-solving situations with sums and minuends up through 1,000 with regrouping.

Name:

Check Story Problem Solutions
Check Answers

Rosa solved these story problems. Solve each problem to check her answers. If Rosa's answer is incorrect, explain what she did wrong.

Story Problem	Rosa's Work	Solve to Check Rosa's Work	Circle Correct or Incorrect. Explain why Rosa's incorrect answers are wrong.
1. The movie theater sold 418 tickets on Saturday and 532 tickets on Sunday. How many tickets did the theater sell for the two days?	418 $+532$ $\overline{950}$ The theater sold 950 tickets.	$\overset{1}{418}$ $+532$ $\overline{950}$ 950 tickets	(Correct) Incorrect Explain if incorrect: _____
2. Carlos has 874 baseball cards. Derrick has 581 cards. How many more cards does Carlos have than Derrick?	874 -581 $\overline{313}$ Carlos has 313 more cards.	$\overset{7\ 17}{874}$ -581 $\overline{293}$ 293 more cards	Correct (Incorrect) Explain if incorrect: **See below.**
3. Lenny scored 483 points on the first level of his video game. He scored 301 points on the second level. How many points did he score altogether?	483 -301 $\overline{182}$ Lenny scored 182 points altogether.	483 $+301$ $\overline{784}$ 784 points	Correct (Incorrect) Explain if incorrect: **See below.**

Story Problem	Rosa's Work	Solve to Check Rosa's Work	Circle Correct or Incorrect. Explain why Rosa's incorrect answers are wrong.
4. Cindy has 145 swirled marbles. She has 771 solid marbles. How many marbles does she have in all?	145 $+771$ $\overline{816}$ Cindy had 816 marbles in all.	$\overset{1}{145}$ $+771$ $\overline{916}$ 916 marbles	Correct (Incorrect) Explain if incorrect: **See below.**
5. There were 963 people at the circus. Then 656 people left the circus. How many people are still at the circus?	$\overset{5\ 13}{9\cancel{6}3}$ -656 $\overline{307}$ There are 307 people still at the circus.	$\overset{5\ 13}{963}$ -656 $\overline{307}$ 307 people	(Correct) Incorrect Explain if incorrect: _____
6. Steven has 268 nickels. He has 694 pennies. How many fewer nickels does he have than pennies?	$\overset{1\ 1}{268}$ $+694$ $\overline{962}$ Steven has 962 fewer nickels.	$\overset{8\ 14}{69\cancel{4}}$ -268 $\overline{426}$ 426 fewer nickels	Correct (Incorrect) Explain if incorrect: **Rosa added instead of subtracting.**

Additional Answers

2. Rosa used the correct operation, but she did not regroup correctly.

3. Rosa subtracted instead of adding.

4. Rosa used the correct operation, but she did not regroup.

TRY IT Practice Checking Answers

OFFLINE 10 min

Students will practice checking answers to story problems and explaining why the answers are correct or incorrect. Give students the Practice Checking Answers activity page from their Activity Book and read the directions with them.

Objectives

- Check the accuracy of calculations from the context of addition or subtraction problem-solving situations with sums and minuends up through 1,000 with regrouping.

Name: _____

Check Story Problem Solutions
Practice Checking Answers

Rosa solved these story problems. Solve each problem to check her answers. If Rosa's answer is incorrect, explain what she did wrong.

Story Problem	Rosa's Work	Solve to Check Rosa's Work	Circle Correct or Incorrect. Explain why Rosa's incorrect answers are wrong.
1. There are 762 baseballs on the store shelf. There are 690 bats on display. How many more baseballs are there than bats?	762 − 690 132 There are 132 more baseballs than bats.	6 16 7̶6̶2 − 690 72 72 more baseballs	Correct (Incorrect) Explain if incorrect: **See below.**
2. Sharon has 316 puzzle pieces in the box. She puts in 154 more. How many puzzle pieces are in the box now?	316 + 154 460 There are 460 puzzle pieces in the box.	316 + 154 470 470 pieces	Correct (Incorrect) Explain if incorrect: **See below.**
3. An art class had 845 craft sticks. Then the students used 380 craft sticks. How many craft sticks are left?	7 14 845 − 380 465 There are 465 craft sticks left.	7 14 845 − 380 465 465 craft sticks	(Correct) Incorrect Explain if incorrect: _____

ADD OR SUBTRACT NUMBERS THROUGH 1,000 **245** CHECK STORY PROBLEM SOLUTIONS

TRY IT

Read the problem and follow the directions.

4. **Rosa solved this story problem.**

An art gallery has 349 paintings of landscapes. It has 501 paintings of buildings.

How many paintings does it have altogether?

Which sentence about Rosa's answer is correct? Circle the answer.

A. Rosa added and did the math correctly.

(B.) Rosa added but made a math mistake.

C. Rosa should have subtracted.

Rosa's answer:
It has 750 paintings altogether.

5. **Ron solved this story problem.**

Gina sold 234 raffle tickets. Toby sold 432 raffle tickets.

How many more raffle tickets did Toby sell than Gina?

Write an addition number sentence to check to see if Ron's answer is correct.

198 (+) 234 (=) 432

Sample number sentence shown.

Is Ron correct? __Yes__

Ron's answer:
Toby sold 198 more raffle tickets than Gina.

ADD OR SUBTRACT NUMBERS THROUGH 1,000 **246** CHECK STORY PROBLEM SOLUTIONS

TRY IT

---

6. **Winnie solved this story problem.**

Adam wrote a story that was 341 words long. He later added some more words to the story and now it has 565 words.

How many words did Adam add to his story?

Write a number sentence to check to see if Winnie's answer is correct.

565 (−) 341 (=) 224

Sample number sentence shown.

Is Winnie correct? __Yes__

Winnie's answer:
Adam added 224 words.

7. Solve this problem and then check your answer using another way to solve the problem.

The farm store sold 512 eggs the first week. The second week the store sold 88 more eggs than the first week. How many eggs did the store sell the second week?

600 eggs; methods will vary. Sample answer: Add 2 to 88 to make 90 and subtract 2 from 512 to make 510. Then add these two numbers to make 600.

ADD OR SUBTRACT NUMBERS THROUGH 1,000 **247** CHECK STORY PROBLEM SOLUTIONS

TRY IT

Additional Answers

1. Rosa used the correct operation, but she did not regroup correctly.

2. Rosa used the correct operation, but she did not regroup correctly.

CHECKPOINT

Objectives

- Check the accuracy of calculations from the context of addition or subtraction problem-solving situations with sums and minuends up through 1,000 with regrouping.

Print the Checkpoint and have students complete it on their own. Read the directions, problems, and answer choices to students, if necessary. Use the answer key to score the Checkpoint, and then enter the results online.

Name _____ Date _____

Checkpoint Answer Key

Circle the answer.
(1 point)
1. Ron solved this story problem.

Darren had 137 toy cars. He gave away some toy cars and now he has 112 cars left.

How many cars did Darren give away?

Ron's answer: 25 cars

Which sentence about Ron's answer is correct?

(**A.**) Ron subtracted and did the math correctly.

B. Ron subtracted but made a math mistake.

C. Ron should have added.

(1 point)
2. Winnie solved this story problem.

Melly bought 166 boxes of crayons for her scout troop. She gave the troop some of the boxes of crayons and she has 120 left over.

How many boxes of crayons did Melly give to the troop?

Winnie's solution: $166 - 120 = 46$

Which number sentence could be used to check Winnie's work?

A. $120 - 46 = ?$ C. $166 + 46 = ?$

(**B.**) $120 + 46 = ?$ D. $166 + 120 = ?$

Name _____ Date _____

Write the answer.

3. Rosa solved this story problem.

Kayley has 243 stickers in her album. She buys some more and now she has 410 stickers.

How many stickers did Kayley buy?

Rosa's answer: 167 stickers
(1 point)
Write an addition number sentence to see if Rosa's answer is correct.

Sample answer:
$$243 \; (+) \; 167 \; (=) \; 410$$

(1 point)
Is Rosa correct? **Yes**

---

4. Johnny solved this story problem.

Melissa walked around her neighborhood for 96 minutes. She took a rest and then walked another 65 minutes. How many minutes did Melissa walk?

Johnny's answer: 31 minutes
(1 point)
Solve this problem.

161 minutes
(1 point)
Is Johnny's answer correct? **No**

---

5. Solve this problem and then explain how you checked your answer.

There were 656 fans at the baseball game. During the 7th inning, some fans went home and there were 234 fans left.
(1 point)
How many fans went home?

422 fans
(1 point)
Explanation: **Sample answer: Add 422 to 234 to find the original number of fans, 656.**

Explain Operations to Solve

Lesson Overview		
Skills Update	5 minutes	ONLINE
LEARN How to Solve Problems	10 minutes	OFFLINE
LEARN How Would You Solve?	15 minutes	OFFLINE
TRY IT Explain Your Choice	15 minutes	OFFLINE
CHECKPOINT	15 minutes	ONLINE

▶ Lesson Objectives

Justify the procedures selected for addition or subtraction problem-solving situations with sums or minuends up through 1,000.

▶ Prerequisite Skills

Justify the procedures selected for addition or subtraction problem-solving situations with sums or minuends up through 500.

▶ Advance Preparation

Cut out each of the strips that show a problem and its explanation from the How Would You Solve? activity page. Fold each strip so that the problem is on the front and the explanation is on the back.

▶ Content Background

In this lesson, students will explain which operation to use to solve a variety of story problems. The problems will include sums or minuends to 1,000.

One of the most important mathematical skills students must learn is how to justify their decisions. Justifying actions verbally and in writing is the heart of mathematical proof. Students will also use this skill in their other academic subjects and, indeed, in everyday life.

Materials to Gather

SUPPLIED
base-10 blocks
How to Solve Problems activity page
How Would You Solve? activity page
Explain Your Choice activity page

ALSO NEEDED
paper, drawing – 1 sheet
scissors, adult

OFFLINE

10 min

LEARN How to Solve Problems

Students will solve story problems by using sketches or models. Using visuals will help students decide how to solve a problem and can also help them justify why they solved the problem the way they did.

Gather the drawing paper, base-10 blocks, and How to Solve Problems activity page. Read each problem to students. Guide them to either use base-10 blocks or make the type of sketch that is suggested for each problem in the answers. Have students find each answer and explain their solution. Accept any reasonable explanation.

Objectives

- Justify the procedures selected for addition or subtraction problem-solving situations with sums or minuends up through 1,000.

Explain Operations to Solve
How to Solve Problems

Use a model or sketch to solve the problem and explain your solution. **Example answers are shown.**

1. The toy store ordered 573 small marbles. It also ordered 322 large marbles. How many marbles did the toy store order?

   See below.

   895 marbles

2. The toy store's baby section had 338 bibs and 226 rattles. How many more bibs than rattles were in the baby section?

   See below.

   112 more bibs than rattles

L E A R N

3. Fun Town Toy Store has 429 books. Bozo's Toy Store has 516 books. How many more books does Fun Town need to order to have as many books as Bozo's?

   516
   − _ _
   +
   429   ?

   516 − 429 = 87
   87 books

4. During its big sale, Bozo's Toy Store had 664 customers. Fun Town Toy Store only had 336 customers during its sale. How many customers shopped at the two stores altogether during the sales?

Total	
?	
664	336
Part	Part

   664 + 336 = 1,000
   1,000 customers

L E A R N

Additional Answers

1. $573 + 322 = 895$

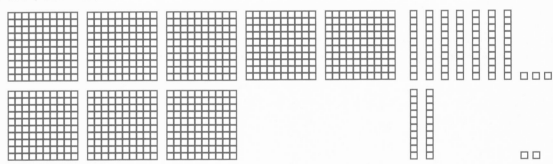

2. $338 − 226 = 112$

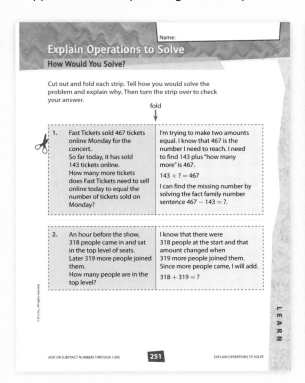

LEARN How Would You Solve?

Students will practice deciding how to solve a story problem and justifying their decision. Once you have cut out the problems with their explanations from the How Would You Solve? activity page, read each problem with students. Ask them to explain how they would solve the problem and why, including the number sentence they would use. Once they have explained their reasoning, go over the explanation on the back of the problem strip to verify their explanation or to hear a different explanation. Students do not need to explain their problem exactly as it appears on the strip, as long as their explanation is correct.

Objectives

- Justify the procedures selected for addition or subtraction problem-solving situations with sums or minuends up through 1,000.

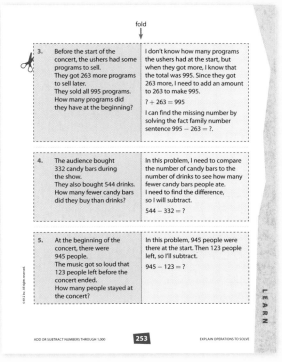

TRY IT Explain Your Choice

Students will practice justifying problem-solving procedures. Give students the base-10 blocks and Explain Your Choice activity page from their Activity Book. Read the directions with them.

Objectives

- Justify the procedures selected for addition or subtraction problem-solving situations with sums or minuends up through 1,000.

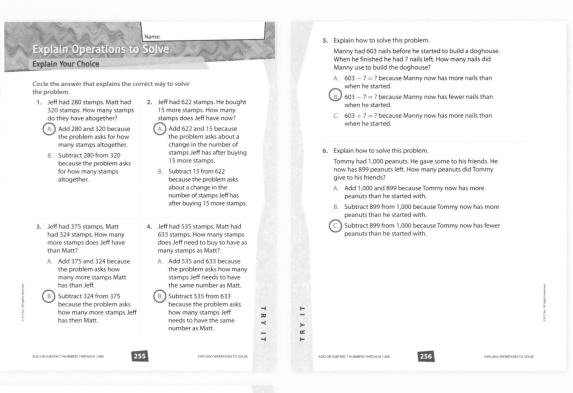

Name:

Explain Operations to Solve

Explain Your Choice

Circle the answer that explains the correct way to solve the problem.

1. Jeff had 280 stamps. Matt had 320 stamps. How many stamps do they have altogether?

   A. Add 280 and 320 because the problem asks for how many stamps altogether.

   B. Subtract 280 from 320 because the problem asks for how many stamps altogether.

2. Jeff had 622 stamps. He bought 15 more stamps. How many stamps does Jeff have now?

   A. Add 622 and 15 because the problem asks about a change in the number of stamps Jeff has after buying 15 more stamps.

   B. Subtract 15 from 622 because the problem asks about a change in the number of stamps Jeff has after buying 15 more stamps.

3. Jeff had 375 stamps. Matt had 324 stamps. How many more stamps does Jeff have than Matt?

   A. Add 375 and 324 because the problem asks how many more stamps Matt has than Jeff.

   B. Subtract 324 from 375 because the problem asks how many more stamps Jeff has then Matt.

4. Jeff had 535 stamps. Matt had 633 stamps. How many stamps does Jeff need to buy to have as many stamps as Matt?

   A. Add 535 and 633 because the problem asks how many stamps Jeff needs to have the same number as Matt.

   B. Subtract 535 from 633 because the problem asks how many stamps Jeff needs to have the same number as Matt.

5. Explain how to solve this problem.

   Manny had 603 nails before he started to build a doghouse. When he finished he had 7 nails left. How many nails did Manny use to build the doghouse?

   A. $603 - 7 = ?$ because Manny now has more nails than when he started.

   B. $603 - 7 = ?$ because Manny now has fewer nails than when he started.

   C. $603 + 7 = ?$ because Manny now has more nails than when he started.

6. Explain how to solve this problem.

   Tommy had 1,000 peanuts. He gave some to his friends. He now has 899 peanuts left. How many peanuts did Tommy give to his friends?

   A. Add 1,000 and 899 because Tommy now has more peanuts than he started with.

   B. Subtract 899 from 1,000 because Tommy now has more peanuts than he started with.

   C. Subtract 899 from 1,000 because Tommy now has fewer peanuts than he started with.

ADD OR SUBTRACT NUMBERS THROUGH 1,000 **255** EXPLAIN OPERATIONS TO SOLVE

TRY IT

ADD OR SUBTRACT NUMBERS THROUGH 1,000 **256** EXPLAIN OPERATIONS TO SOLVE

TRY IT

7. Explain how to solve this problem.

   There were 23 dogs at the dog park. Someone brought 15 balls for the dogs to play with. If each dog was given 1 ball, how many dogs did **not** get a ball to play with?

   A. $23 + 15 = ?$ because there are lots of dogs and balls.

   B. $23 - 15 = ?$ because all of the dogs won't get a ball.

   C. $15 - 23 = ?$ because all of the dogs won't get a ball.

8. Read this problem.

   There were 550 people in the park.
   120 people left the park when it started to rain.
   How many people are in the park now?

   Which number sentence could be used to solve this problem? Why?

   A. $550 + 120 = ?$
   There will be more people in the park after it starts to rain.

   B. $550 - 120 = ?$
   There will be fewer people in the park after it starts to rain.

   C. $120 - 550 = ?$
   There will be fewer people in the park after it starts to rain.

ADD OR SUBTRACT NUMBERS THROUGH 1,000 **257** EXPLAIN OPERATIONS TO SOLVE

TRY IT

CHECKPOINT

ONLINE 15min

Students will complete an online Checkpoint. Read the directions, problems, and answer choices to students. If necessary, help students with keyboard or mouse operations.

Objectives

- Justify the procedures selected for addition or subtraction problem-solving situations with sums or minuends up through 1,000.

Choose the Problem

Lesson Overview

Skills Update	5 minutes	ONLINE
GET READY Solve Story Problems	5 minutes	ONLINE
LEARN Find the Problem	15 minutes	ONLINE
LEARN Add or Subtract?	15 minutes	OFFLINE
TRY IT Choose the Operation	10 minutes	OFFLINE
CHECKPOINT	10 minutes	OFFLINE

▶ Lesson Objectives

Recognize examples of problems that could be solved by addition or subtraction with regrouping.

▶ Prerequisite Skills

Write and solve addition or subtraction number sentences to represent problem-solving situations with sums and minuends up through 1,000.

▶ Content Background

In this lesson, students will see a variety of story problems and will determine the operation they would use to solve each problem. They will solve the problems, but the focus will not be on the answers. Rather, they will focus on whether a problem can be solved with addition or subtraction. Problems will have sums and minuends to 1,000 and computation will include regrouping.

Materials to Gather

SUPPLIED

Add or Subtract? activity page
Choose the Operation activity page
Checkpoint (printout)

ONLINE
5min

GET READY Solve Story Problems

Students will be guided to write and solve number a number sentence to solve a story problem.

Objectives

- Write and solve addition or subtraction number sentences to represent problem-solving situations with sums and minuends up through 1,000.

LEARN Find the Problem

ONLINE 15 min

Students will choose the story problem that can more easily be solved with a given operation.

Review which operations can be used to solve certain types of problems. Students should subtract when finding how many more, how many fewer, when objects are being taken away, or when an addition problem has a missing addend. They should add when combining groups or adding to an existing group.

As students work through the problems, ask them questions such as, "Are some being added or taken away?" and "Do you need to find the difference?" and "Is one part missing?"

Emphasize that there is often more than one way to solve a problem. Accept students' explanations as long as their explanations are mathematically correct.

- Recognize examples of problems that could be solved by addition or subtraction with regrouping.

LEARN Add or Subtract?

OFFLINE 15 min

Objectives

Students will choose which story problem can be solved with a given operation.

Give students the Add or Subtract? activity page from their Activity Book and read the directions with them.

1. Point to Problem 1.

   Ask: When do you use addition?
   ANSWER: I add when I put groups together or when I add more things to a group.

2. **Ask:** Which problem would you solve by adding?
   ANSWER: the second problem

   If students have difficulty, have them either act out the problems or make sketches of the problems. Discuss which of the scenarios involve addition.

3. Repeat Steps 1 and 2 for Problem 2.

4. Point to Problem 3.

   Ask: When do you use subtraction?
   ANSWER: I subtract when I need to take away or find the difference between numbers or if I have an addition problem with a missing part.

   Ask: Which problem would you solve by subtracting?
   ANSWER: the first problem

5. Have students complete the activity page. Assist them as needed to help them choose the correct answers.

- Recognize examples of problems that could be solved by addition or subtraction with regrouping.

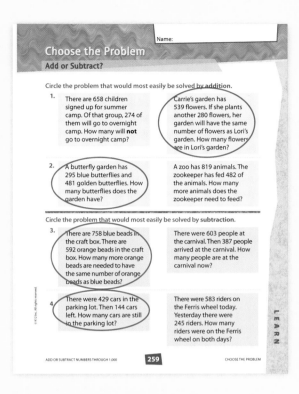

Choose the Problem

Add or Subtract?

Name: _____

Circle the problem that would most easily be solved by **addition**.

1. There are 658 children signed up for summer camp. Of that group, 274 of them will go to overnight camp. How many will **not** go to overnight camp?

   Carrie's garden has 539 flowers. If she plants another 280 flowers, her garden will have the same number of flowers as Lori's garden. How many flowers are in Lori's garden?

2. A butterfly garden has 295 blue butterflies and 481 golden butterflies. How many butterflies does the garden have?

   A zoo has 819 animals. The zookeeper has fed 482 of the animals. How many more animals does the zookeeper need to feed?

Circle the problem that would most easily be solved by **subtraction**.

3. There are 758 blue beads in the craft box. There are 592 orange beads in the craft box. How many more orange beads are needed to have the same number of orange beads as blue beads?

   There were 603 people at the carnival. Then 387 people arrived at the carnival. How many people are at the carnival now?

4. There were 429 cars in the parking lot. Then 144 cars left. How many cars are still in the parking lot?

   There were 583 riders on the Ferris wheel today. Yesterday there were 245 riders. How many riders were on the Ferris wheel on both days?

ADD OR SUBTRACT NUMBERS THROUGH 1,000   **259**   CHOOSE THE PROBLEM

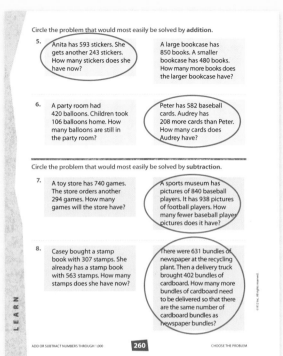

Circle the problem that would most easily be solved by **addition**.

5. Anita has 593 stickers. She gets another 243 stickers. How many stickers does she have now?

   A large bookcase has 850 books. A smaller bookcase has 480 books. How many more books does the larger bookcase have?

6. A party room had 420 balloons. Children took 106 balloons home. How many balloons are still in the party room?

   Peter has 582 baseball cards. Audrey has 208 more cards than Peter. How many cards does Audrey have?

Circle the problem that would most easily be solved by **subtraction**.

7. A toy store has 740 games. The store orders another 294 games. How many games will the store have?

   A sports museum has pictures of 840 baseball players. It has 938 pictures of football players. How many fewer baseball players pictures does it have?

8. Casey bought a stamp book with 307 stamps. She already has a stamp book with 563 stamps. How many stamps does she have now?

   There were 631 bundles of newspaper at the recycling plant. Then a delivery truck brought 402 bundles of cardboard. How many more bundles of cardboard need to be delivered so that there are the same number of cardboard bundles as newspaper bundles?

ADD OR SUBTRACT NUMBERS THROUGH 1,000   **260**   CHOOSE THE PROBLEM

OFFLINE

10 min

TRY IT Choose the Operation

Objectives

Students will choose which story problem can be solved with a given operation. Give students the Choose the Operation activity page from their Activity Book and read the directions with them.

- Recognize examples of problems that could be solved by addition or subtraction with regrouping.

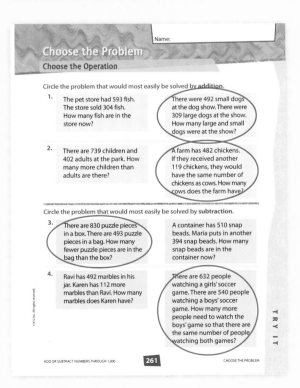

Choose the Problem

Choose the Operation

Name: _____

Circle the problem that would most easily be solved by **addition**.

1. The pet store had 593 fish. The store sold 304 fish. How many fish are in the store now?

   There were 492 small dogs at the dog show. There were 309 large dogs at the show. How many large and small dogs were at the show?

2. There are 739 children and 402 adults at the park. How many more children than adults are there?

   A farm has 482 chickens. If they received another 119 chickens, they would have the same number of chickens as cows. How many cows does the farm have?

Circle the problem that would most easily be solved by **subtraction**.

3. There are 830 puzzle pieces in a box. There are 493 puzzle pieces in a bag. How many fewer puzzle pieces are in the bag than the box?

   A container has 510 snap beads. Maria puts in another 394 snap beads. How many snap beads are in the container now?

4. Ravi has 492 marbles in his jar. Karen has 112 more marbles than Ravi. How many marbles does Karen have?

   There are 632 people watching a girls' soccer game. There are 540 people watching a boys' soccer game. How many more people need to watch the boys' game so that there are the same number of people watching both games?

ADD OR SUBTRACT NUMBERS THROUGH 1,000   **261**   CHOOSE THE PROBLEM

Circle the answer.

5. Can this problem be solved by adding the two numbers in the problem?

Joe has 527 pennies. Jen has 208 pennies. How many pennies do they have altogether?

(A.) Yes   B. No

6. Which problem could be solved by subtracting one number in the problem from the other?

A. Zen ran 750 yards. She then ran 250 more yards. How far did she run?

(B.) Anne had 540 pennies. She gave her mother 175 pennies. How many pennies does Anne have left?

C. Tom ran 350 yards on Monday and 500 yards on Tuesday. How many yards did Tom run in all?

D. Anne had 546 pennies. Her mother gave her 175 more pennies. How many pennies does Anne have now?

7. Which expression could be used to solve this problem?

A shelf in a music store will hold 600 CDs. There are 152 CDs on the shelf now. How many more CDs can be put on the shelf?

A. 600 + 152

(B.) 600 − 152

C. 152 − 600

8. Can this problem be solved by subtracting one number in the problem from the other?

There were 409 children at the carnival. 102 more children arrived. How many children are at the carnival now?

A. Yes   (B.) No

TRY IT

ADD OR SUBTRACT NUMBERS THROUGH 1,000   **262**   CHOOSE THE PROBLEM

OFFLINE

10 min

CHECKPOINT

Objectives

Print the Checkpoint and have students complete it on their own. Read the directions, problems, and answer choices to students, if necessary. Use the answer key to score the Checkpoint, and then enter the results online.

- Recognize examples of problems that could be solved by addition or subtraction with regrouping.

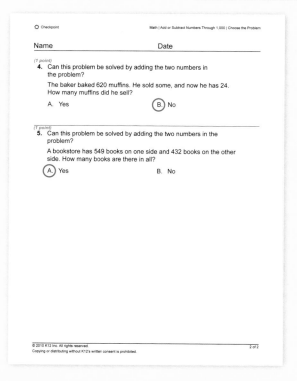

Checkpoint   Math | Add or Subtract Numbers Through 1,000 | Choose the Problem

Name _____ Date _____

Checkpoint Answer Key

Circle the answer.

(1 point)
1. Which problem could be solved by adding the two numbers in the problem?

A. Sadie baked 534 cookies. She gave some to her friend, and now she has 218. How many cookies did she give to her friend?

B. Geri baked 593 cookies. 14 of the cookies burned. How many cookies did not burn?

(C.) Daphne had 455 stamps. Her father gave her 250 more stamps. How many stamps does Daphne have now?

(1 point)
2. Which problem could be solved by subtracting one number in the problem from the other?

A. Susie ran 515 yards one day and 426 the next day. How many yards did she run in all?

B. Jimmy saved $19. He got $4 more for washing his mom's car. How much money does Jimmy have now?

(C.) Patty ran 525 yards. John ran 710 yards. How many more yards did John run than Patty?

D. Gino has 27 red toy cars and 38 blue toy cars. How many red and blue cars does he have altogether?

(1 point)
3. Can this problem be solved by subtracting one number in the problem from the other?

There were 522 people at the park. Some are in the playground and the rest are on the field. There are 145 people in the playground. How many people are on the field?

(A.) Yes   B. No

   1 of 2

Checkpoint   Math | Add or Subtract Numbers Through 1,000 | Choose the Problem

Name _____ Date _____

(1 point)
4. Can this problem be solved by adding the two numbers in the problem?

The baker baked 620 muffins. He sold some, and now he has 24. How many muffins did he sell?

A. Yes   (B.) No

(1 point)
5. Can this problem be solved by adding the two numbers in the problem?

A bookstore has 549 books on one side and 432 books on the other side. How many books are there in all?

(A.) Yes   B. No

   2 of 2

Unit Review

Lesson Overview

UNIT REVIEW Look Back	20 minutes	ONLINE
UNIT REVIEW Checkpoint Practice	20 minutes	OFFLINE
▶ **UNIT REVIEW** Prepare for the Checkpoint		

▶ Unit Objectives

This lesson reviews the following objectives:

- Find the sum or difference of two whole numbers with sums and minuends up through 1,000.
- Recognize and solve word problems involving sums up through 1,000 in which two quantities are combined.
- Recognize and solve word problems involving sums or minuends up through 1,000 in which one quantity changes by addition or subtraction.
- Recognize and solve word problems involving numbers up to 1,000 in which two quantities are compared by the use of addition or subtraction.
- Recognize and solve word problems involving numbers up to 1,000 in which one quantity must be changed to equal another quantity.
- Write and solve addition or subtraction number sentences to represent problem-solving situations with sums and minuends up through 1,000.
- Demonstrate an understanding of connections between similar addition or subtraction problem-solving situations, involving sums and minuends up through 1,000.
- Check the accuracy of calculations from the context of addition or subtraction problem-solving situations with sums and minuends up through 1,000 with regrouping.
- Justify the procedures selected for addition or subtraction problem-solving situations with sums or minuends up through 1,000.
- Recognize examples of problems that could be solved by addition or subtraction with regrouping.

▶ Advance Preparation

In this lesson, students will have an opportunity to review previous activities in the Add or Subtract Numbers Through 1,000 unit. Look at the suggested activities in Unit Review: Prepare for the Checkpoint online and gather any needed materials.

Materials to Gather

SUPPLIED
Checkpoint Practice activity page

Keywords

addend	missing addend
algorithm	regroup
difference	sum
minuend	

UNIT REVIEW Look Back

Objectives

- Review unit objectives.

In this unit, students have learned to write number sentences and solve addition and subtraction problems with numbers through 1,000. They have solved different types of story problems, and learned to check their answers and to explain their thinking. Students will review these concepts to prepare for the Unit Checkpoint.

UNIT REVIEW Checkpoint Practice

Objectives

- Review unit objectives.

Students will complete a Checkpoint Practice activity page to prepare for the Unit Checkpoint. If necessary, read the directions, problems, and answer choices to students. Have students answer the problems on their own. Carefully review the answers with students.

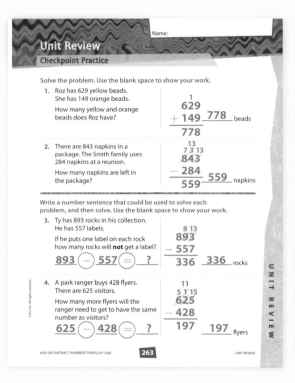

Additional Answers

5. Students should explain that both problems can be solved using addition.

6. Students should explain that both problems can be solved using subtraction.

7. Incorrect. Rosa used the correct operation, but she did not regroup correctly. There are 80 more trucks than cars.

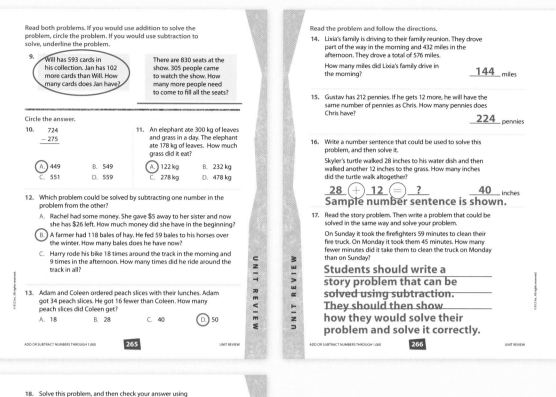

Read both problems. If you would use addition to solve the problem, circle the problem. If you would use subtraction to solve, underline the problem.

9.
(Will has 593 cards in his collection. Jan has 102 more cards than Will. How many cards does Jan have?)

There are 830 seats at the show. 305 people came to watch the show. How many more people need to come to fill all the seats?

Circle the answer.

10.
724
− 275

A. 449   B. 549
C. 551   D. 559

11. An elephant ate 300 kg of leaves and grass in a day. The elephant ate 178 kg of leaves. How much grass did it eat?

A. 122 kg   B. 232 kg
C. 278 kg   D. 478 kg

12. Which problem could be solved by subtracting one number in the problem from the other?

A. Rachel had some money. She gave $5 away to her sister and now she has $26 left. How much money did she have in the beginning?

B. A farmer had 118 bales of hay. He fed 59 bales to his horses over the winter. How many bales does he have now?

C. Harry rode his bike 18 times around the track in the morning and 9 times in the afternoon. How many times did he ride around the track in all?

13. Adam and Coleen ordered peach slices with their lunches. Adam got 34 peach slices. He got 16 fewer than Coleen. How many peach slices did Coleen get?

A. 18   B. 28   C. 40   D. 50

ADD OR SUBTRACT NUMBERS THROUGH 1,000   **265**   UNIT REVIEW

Read the problem and follow the directions.

14. Lixia's family is driving to their family reunion. They drove part of the way in the morning and 432 miles in the afternoon. They drove a total of 576 miles.

How many miles did Lixia's family drive in the morning?   __144__ miles

15. Gustav has 212 pennies. If he gets 12 more, he will have the same number of pennies as Chris. How many pennies does Chris have?   __224__ pennies

16. Write a number sentence that could be used to solve this problem, and then solve it.

Skyler's turtle walked 28 inches to his water dish and then walked another 12 inches to the grass. How many inches did the turtle walk altogether?

__28__ (+) __12__ (=) __?__   __40__ inches
Sample number sentence is shown.

17. Read the story problem. Then write a problem that could be solved in the same way and solve your problem.

On Sunday it took the firefighters 59 minutes to clean their fire truck. On Monday it took them 45 minutes. How many fewer minutes did it take them to clean the truck on Monday than on Sunday?

Students should write a story problem that can be solved using subtraction. They should then show how they would solve their problem and solve it correctly.

ADD OR SUBTRACT NUMBERS THROUGH 1,000   **266**   UNIT REVIEW

18. Solve this problem, and then check your answer using another way to solve the problem.

Alan painted 79 feet of fence on Sunday and another 21 feet of fence on Monday. How many feet of fence did Alan paint altogether?   __100__ feet

Students should check their work. Answers will vary. One way to check would be add 1 to 79 to make 80 and take away 1 from 21 to make 20 and then add 20 + 80 to get 100. They could also use the related sentence 100 − 21 = ? to see if they get 79.

19. Solve this problem, and then explain why you solved it the way you did.

Eliza had 9 oranges in one basket and 17 oranges in another basket. How many oranges did Eliza have altogether?   __26__ oranges

Students should explain why they added. Answers will vary. A sample explanation is they wanted to combine the number of oranges in each basket and the total will be more than the number of oranges in either basket.

ADD OR SUBTRACT NUMBERS THROUGH 1,000   **267**   UNIT REVIEW

➔ UNIT REVIEW Prepare for the Checkpoint

What you do next depends on how students performed in the previous activity, Unit Review: Checkpoint Practice. If students had difficulty with any of the problems, complete the appropriate review activity listed in the table online.

Unit Checkpoint

Lesson Overview

UNIT CHECKPOINT Online	30 minutes	**ONLINE**
UNIT CHECKPOINT Offline	30 minutes	**OFFLINE**

▶ Unit Objectives

This lesson assesses the following objectives:

- Find the sum or difference of two whole numbers with sums and minuends up through 1,000.
- Recognize and solve word problems involving sums up through 1,000 in which two quantities are combined.
- Recognize and solve word problems involving sums or minuends up through 1,000 in which one quantity changes by addition or subtraction.
- Recognize and solve word problems involving numbers up to 1,000 in which two quantities are compared by the use of addition or subtraction.
- Recognize and solve word problems involving numbers up to 1,000 in which one quantity must be changed to equal another quantity.
- Write and solve addition or subtraction number sentences to represent problem-solving situations with sums and minuends up through 1,000.
- Demonstrate an understanding of connections between similar addition or subtraction problem-solving situations, involving sums and minuends up through 1,000.
- Check the accuracy of calculations from the context of addition or subtraction problem-solving situations with sums and minuends up through 1,000 with regrouping.
- Justify the procedures selected for addition or subtraction problem-solving situations with sums or minuends up through 1,000.
- Recognize examples of problems that could be solved by addition or subtraction with regrouping.

Materials to Gather

SUPPLIED
Unit Checkpoint (printout)

UNIT CHECKPOINT Online

ONLINE 30 min

Students will complete this part of the Unit Checkpoint online. Read the directions, problems, and answer choices to students. If necessary, help students with keyboard or mouse operations.

Objectives

- Assess unit objectives.

UNIT CHECKPOINT Offline

OFFLINE 30 min

Students will complete this part of the Unit Checkpoint offline. Print the Checkpoint and have students complete it on their own. Read the directions, problems, and answer choices to students, if necessary. Use the answer key to score the Checkpoint, and then enter the results online.

Objectives

- Assess unit objectives.

Name _____   Date _____

Unit Checkpoint Answer Key

Solve.

(1 point)
1.   987
    − 530
      457

(1 point)
2. Jack scored 756 points on his new video game. This is 183 points less than Hannah's score. How many points did Hannah score?

   939 points

(1 point)
3. Julian's favorite baseball team scored 528 runs last year. This year they scored 413 runs. How many runs has the team scored in the last two years?

   941 runs

(1 point)
4. Jaime has 176 grapes. If Jaime eats 37 grapes he will have the same number of grapes as Sam. How many grapes does Sam have?

   139 grapes

(2 points)
5. Alex solved this story problem.

   Pam planted 67 sunflower seeds and 55 poppy seeds in her garden. How many seeds did Pam plant altogether?

   Alex's answer: 122

   Write a subtraction number sentence to check to see if Alex's answer is correct. Is Alex's answer correct?

   _____ **See below.** _____

(1 point)
6. What is one way to solve this problem?

   Alon was on page 203 in his book. He read 28 more pages. How many pages has Alon read in all?

   _____ **by adding 203 + 28** _____

Additional Answers

5. Students should write a subtraction number sentence.
   Example: $122 - 55 = 67$ *(1 point)*
   Students should say that Alex's answer is correct. *(1 point)*

Multiplication and Number Patterns

$5 \times 5 = 25$

$4 \times 10 = 40$

$2 \times 6 = 12$

$2 \times 5 = 10$

- Use concrete objects or sketches of arrays to model multiplication problems.
- Use concrete objects or sketches to model and explain multiplication as repeated addition.
- Use grouping to solve simple multiplication problems.
- Describe linear patterns, such as 3, 6, 9, using the wheels on 1 tricycle, 2 tricycles, 3 tricycles as an example.
- Determine a next term and extend a linear pattern, such as 3, 6, 9, … as the wheels on 1 tricycle, 2 tricycles, 3 tricycles, and extending it to 12 wheels on 4 tricycles as an example.
- Solve problems involving simple number patterns.
- Use models and math symbols to represent multiplication.

- Recognize that the $\times$ sign refers to multiplication.
- Correctly use the symbol $\times$ for multiplication.
- Use counting by multiples of 2 to understand multiplication facts for 2.
- Demonstrate automatic recall of multiplication facts for 2 through 10×2.
- Use counting by multiples of 10 to understand multiplication facts for 10.
- Demonstrate automatic recall of multiplication facts for 10 through 10×10.
- Use counting by multiples of 5 to understand multiplication facts for 5.
- Demonstrate automatic recall of multiplication facts for 5 through 10×5.

▶ Big Ideas

- Multiplication can be represented by showing partitioned and shaded squares (area models) or using rows and columns (array models).
- Rules can be used to generate number patterns.
- Models and mathematical symbols can represent multiplication and division.

▶ Unit Introduction

In this unit, students will students learn about multiplication. They will explore arrays as a way to model multiplication and relate multiplication to repeated addition and equal groups. They will use these models to solve multiplication computations. Students will learn about number patterns—pattern rules involving multiplication and addition— and apply the rule to extend patterns. They will use drawings, models, and symbols to represent multiplication. Lastly they will explore the 2s, 5s, and 10s facts and work on automatic recall of these basic multiplication facts.

Model Multiplication with Arrays

Lesson Overview

Skills Update	5 minutes	**ONLINE**
GET READY Addition and Subtraction Models	5 minutes	**ONLINE**
LEARN What Is an Array?	15 minutes	**ONLINE**
LEARN Model and Match Arrays	15 minutes	**OFFLINE**
TRY IT Label and Draw Arrays	10 minutes	**OFFLINE**
CHECKPOINT	10 minutes	**ONLINE**

▶ Lesson Objectives

Use concrete objects or sketches of arrays to model multiplication problems.

▶ Prerequisite Skills

- Use models and math symbols to represent addition.
- Use models and math symbols to represent subtraction.

▶ Advance Preparation

Print the Inch Grid Paper.

▶ Content Background

Students have learned how to add and subtract. They have shown these operations with models, sketches, and symbols. Now students will learn about a new operation: multiplication.

Multiplication is an operation used to solve problems involving equal groups. A multiplication number sentence is composed of two or more numbers, called *factors*, which are multiplied to produce the solution, or *product*. In this course, students will only multiply two factors.

Students will first model multiplication with arrays. An *array* is a rectangular arrangement of objects in rows and columns. The number of rows represents the first factor in a multiplication number sentence. The number of columns represents the second factor. The total number of objects in an array represents the product. Students will use hands-on materials to create an array to match a multiplication sentence, and then, given an array, they will identify the multiplication sentence that it represents.

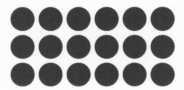

$3 \times 6 = 18$

Materials to Gather

SUPPLIED

blocks – B (all colors)

Inch Grid Paper (printout)

Label and Draw Arrays activity page

The commutative property of multiplication states that the order of the factors in a multiplication sentence can be changed without affecting the product. For example, since $3 \times 6 = 18$ and $6 \times 3 = 18$, then $3 \times 6 = 6 \times 3$. Multiplication is commutative.

Keywords

array – a pattern of objects or numbers placed in a rectangular formation of rows and columns
multiplication – an operation that is a shortcut for adding the same number over and over a certain number of times

GET READY Addition and Subtraction Models

ONLINE 5 min

Students have added in many ways, including counting, skip counting, and calculating. They will use this knowledge to figure out ways to quickly count equal groups of objects—a skill they'll need as they prepare to learn about multiplication.

Objectives

- Use models and math symbols to represent addition.

LEARN What Is an Array?

ONLINE 15 min

Students will be introduced to multiplication through arrays. As students progress through the first part of the activity, have them ask themselves questions such as the following:

- How many rows are in the array?
- How many objects are in each row?
- How many objects are there altogether?
- What are three ways I can talk about the number of rows and the number of objects in each row?

For the second part of the activity, students will use the Array Learning Tool.

Objectives

- Use concrete objects or sketches of arrays to model multiplication problems.

DIRECTIONS FOR USING THE ARRAY LEARNING TOOL

1. Have students choose an object.
2. Have students drag the sliders to show 3 rows of 6 objects.
3. **Say:** This array shows *3 rows of 6*. That's the same as *3 groups of 6*. It's also the same as the multiplication expression *3 times 6*.
4. Ask students to make an array that shows the multiplication expression *2 times 5*. (Students should drag the sliders to show 2 rows of 5 objects.) If students have difficulty, remind them that *2 times 5* can mean 2 rows of 5 objects.
5. Repeat Step 4 with *4 times 8*.
6. Have students make an array using any numbers they'd like. Then have them tell you what multiplication expression it shows.

LEARN Model and Match Arrays

Students will use circle blocks to make arrays to match a given expression. They can think of the blocks as round fruit in a display.

- Use concrete objects or sketches of arrays to model multiplication problems.

Students will also rotate an array to informally explore the commutative property of multiplication. They can turn their paper a quarter turn to see, for example, that 4 rows of 3 is the same as 3 rows of 4. Students do not need to know the name of the property; however, they should see that both arrangements have the same number of total objects, 12.

Gather the circle blocks and Inch Grid Paper.

1. Make a 4 by 3 array of circles (4 rows of 3 circles) on the grid paper. Explain that this is an array of 12 circles.

   Ask: How many rows are there?
   ANSWER: 4

   Ask: How many circles are there in each row?
   ANSWER: 3

2. On a sheet of paper, write the following:
   ___ *rows of* ___ is 12
   ___ *groups of* ___ is 12
   ___ *times* ___ is 12

   Say: This array shows 4 rows of 3 that make 12 total circles. You write this as *4 rows of 3 is 12*, *4 groups of 3 is 12*, or the short way, *4 times 3 is 12*.

3. Carefully rotate the grid paper a quarter turn so students see 3 rows of 4.

   Ask: How many rows there are now?
   ANSWER: 3

   ASK: How many circles there are in each row?
   ANSWER: 4

   Explain that when you turned the 4 by 3 array, it became a 3 by 4 array. Both arrays have 12 circles—12 as 4 rows of 3 or as 3 rows of 4.

4. Have students show an array of 2 rows of 8. Have them describe the array in three ways. (2 rows of 8 is 16, 2 groups of 8 is 16, and 2 times 8 is 16.)

   Ask: What is the total number of circles in the array?
   ANSWER: 16

5. Ask students to create an array of 8 rows of 2. Some students will turn their 2 by 8 array a quarter turn, walk around to the view the array as 8 rows of 2, rearrange the current circles, or gather new circles to make a new array. If students did not rotate the paper to create the new array, show them how to do so.

   Ask: How many total circles are in the array?
   ANSWER: 16

   Have them describe the array in three ways. (8 rows of 2 is 16, 8 groups of 2 is 16, 8 times 2 is 16)

6. Repeat Steps 4 and 5 for an array with 1 row of 6 circles and then for another array with 5 rows of 4 circles.

7. Lastly have the students create an array with 6 rows of 6 circles and notice that the array is exactly the same either way they view it.

TRY IT Label and Draw Arrays

Objectives

- Use concrete objects or sketches of arrays to model multiplication problems.

Students will practice interpreting and creating arrays. Give students the circle blocks, grid paper you printed for the previous activity, and Label and Draw Arrays activity page from their Activity Book. Read the directions with them.

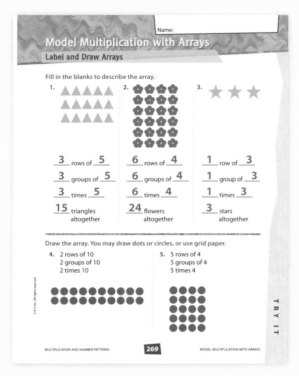

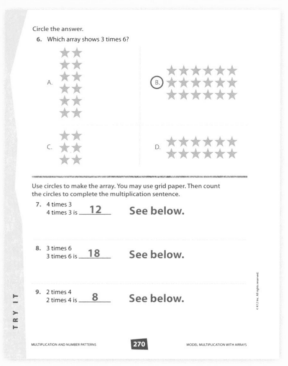

Additional Answers

7. Students' model should show 4 rows of 3 circle blocks.
   Students should solve the problem to find 4 times 3 equals 12.

8. Students' model should show 3 rows of 6 circle blocks.
   Students should solve the problem to find 3 times 6 equals 18.

9. Students' model should show 2 rows of 4 circle blocks.
   Students should solve the problem to find 2 times 4 equals 8.

CHECKPOINT

Objectives

- Use concrete objects or sketches of arrays to model multiplication problems.

Students will complete an online Checkpoint. Read the directions, problems, and answer choices to students. If necessary, help students with keyboard or mouse operations.

Repeated Addition and Grouping

Lesson Overview

Skills Update	5 minutes	**ONLINE**
GET READY Arrays	10 minutes	**ONLINE**
LEARN Repeated Addition	15 minutes	**OFFLINE**
LEARN Use Groups to Multiply	15 minutes	**OFFLINE**
TRY IT Model and Multiply	15 minutes	**OFFLINE**

▶ Lesson Objectives

- Use concrete objects or sketches to model and explain multiplication as repeated addition.
- Use grouping to solve simple multiplication problems.

▶ Prerequisite Skills

Use concrete objects or sketches of arrays to model multiplication problems.

▶ Common Errors and Misconceptions

- Students might add the second factor too many or too few times when using repeated addition. For example, for 5×4, students might add $4 + 4 + 4 + 4$.
- Students might undercount or overcount when using the count-by-n strategy.

▶ Content Background

Multiplication is an operation used to solve problems involving equal groups. A multiplication number sentence is composed of two or more numbers, called *factors*, which are multiplied to produce the solution, or *product*. In this course, students will only multiply two factors.

Students have learned that they can make arrays to show multiplication. In this lesson, they'll build on what they have learned about *groups of* in their study of arrays to solve multiplication problems using repeated addition and grouping. For example, to solve the problem 4×5, students know that they can set up an array of 4 rows of 5 objects and think of the rows as 4 groups of 5. Also, rather than arrange 4 groups of 5 in an array, they could simply create 4 groups that have 5 objects in each group, such as 4 bags of marbles with 5 marbles in each bag. To figure out how many marbles there are in all, or the answer to 4×5, they can reason that 4 groups of 5 is $5 + 5 + 5 + 5$, or 20 marbles. This process of repeated addition leads students into a greater understanding of multiplication by showing them the repetition of 5 added 4 times or *4 times 5*. Once students develop an understanding of how multiplication works, they will memorize the multiplication facts.

Materials to Gather

SUPPLIED
blocks – O (all colors)
Repeated Addition activity page
Use Groups to Multiply activity page
Model and Multiply activity page

ALSO NEEDED
paper, drawing – 1 sheet

GET READY Arrays

ONLINE
10 min

Objectives

- Use concrete objects or sketches of arrays to model multiplication problems.

Students will make arrays to model multiplication problems.

DIRECTIONS FOR USING THE ARRAY LEARNING TOOL

1. Have students choose an object.
2. Have students drag the sliders to show 7 rows of 3 objects.
3. Have students complete these statements to describe the array:

   _?_ rows of _?_

   _?_ groups of _?_

   _?_ times _?_

4. **Say:** This array shows *7 rows of 3, 7 groups of 3*, and *7 times 3.*
5. Have students count the objects in the array. (21)
6. Repeat Steps 1–5 with a 2 by 5 array (2 rows of 5 objects).

LEARN Repeated Addition

OFFLINE
15 min

Objectives

- Use concrete objects or sketches to model and explain multiplication as repeated addition.
- Use grouping to solve simple multiplication problems.

Students will use concrete objects or sketches to model and explain multiplication as repeated addition.

Give students the cubes and Repeated Addition activity page from their Activity Book. Read the directions with them.

1. Read aloud Problem 1.

   Say: You need to make an array that shows 3 times 5.

   Ask: How many rows of cubes should you make? How many cubes will be in each row?
   ANSWER: 3 rows of 5

2. Have students make 3 rows of 5 cubes in the grid on the activity page.
3. Have students count the cubes in each row and write the number of cubes on the line at the end of each row. (5)
4. Point to each 5 that students wrote.

   Say: Each row has 5 cubes. To find the total, we can add 5 plus 5 plus 5. Adding to find the answer to multiplication problems is called repeated addition.

5. Help students complete the repeated addition sentence for the problem. $(5 + 5 + 5 = 15)$

6. Have students complete Problems 2 and 3. Guide them as necessary using the process described in Steps 1–5. For each problem, emphasize how the repeated addition sentence matches the number of objects in each row of the array.

7. Read aloud Problem 4.

   Say: You can also use repeated addition to solve story problems. First sketch an array to show the problem.

8. After students sketch the array, have them count the sketches in each row and write the number of sketches at the end of each row. (10)

9. **Say:** Each row has 10 sketches. To find how many flowers Mandy planted, you can add 10 plus 10 plus 10.

10. Help students complete the repeated addition sentence and solve the problem.

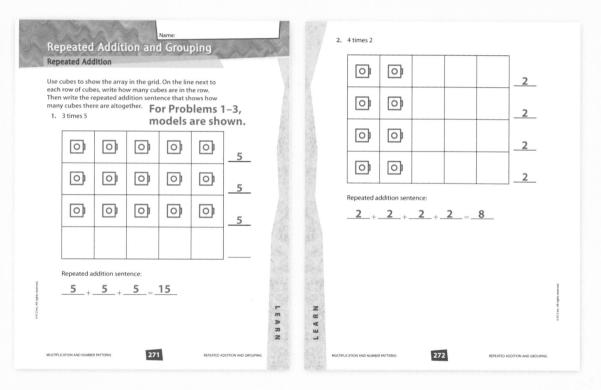

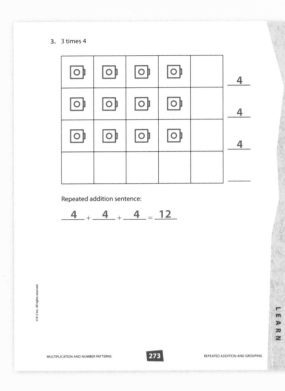

3. 3 times 4

Repeated addition sentence:

__4__ + __4__ + __4__ = __12__

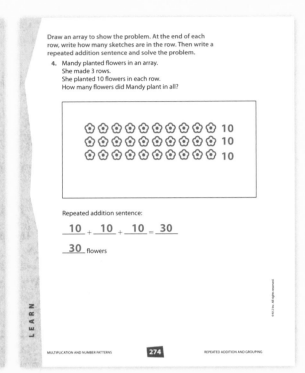

Draw an array to show the problem. At the end of each row, write how many sketches are in the row. Then write a repeated addition sentence and solve the problem.

4. Mandy planted flowers in an array.
She made 3 rows.
She planted 10 flowers in each row.
How many flowers did Mandy plant in all?

Repeated addition sentence:

__10__ + __10__ + __10__ = __30__

__30__ flowers

OFFLINE
15 min

LEARN Use Groups to Multiply

Objectives

- Use grouping to solve simple multiplication problems.

Tips

When students skip count, encourage them to point to each group as they count it so they don't count too many or too few groups.

Students will learn how skip counting can help them find the answer to a multiplication problem. They will also review the other two methods that they learned: counting and repeated addition. Then students will solve several problems, choosing which method to use before solving each problem.

Give students the Use Groups to Multiply activity page from their Activity Book and read the directions with them.

1. Read aloud Problem 1. Explain that students know how to use repeated addition to find the answer to 2 times 5. Both models in the problem show 2 times 5. One model shows an array; the other model shows groups.

2. Point to the array.

   Say: The array shows 2 times 5 as 2 rows of 5. To find the total, you can add the rows. There are 2 rows, and each row has 5 stars in it. Point to the rows and add: 5 plus 5 equals 10. There are 10 stars.

3. Point to the group model.

   Say: You can also skip count to find the total. 2 rows of 5 is the same as 2 groups of 5. The objects don't have to be in rows like an array. There are 2 groups of 5, so skip count by 5s two times. Point to the groups and count along: 5, 10. There are 10 stars.

4. Have students complete the multiplication sentence.

5. Repeat Steps 1–4 with Problem 2, explaining to students the two ways they could solve the problem.

6. For Problems 3–5, have students explain how they would solve the problem using skip counting. Then have them complete the multiplication sentence.

7. Discuss with students what they like best about each method: repeated addition and skip counting. Many students will find that skip counting is the fastest method if the problem has groups of 2, 5, or 10.

8. For Problems 6 and 7, point out to students that they can solve some story problems by using repeated addition and skip counting. Have students choose either method to solve the problem. Have them tell you why they chose that particular method. Then have them complete the multiplication sentence.

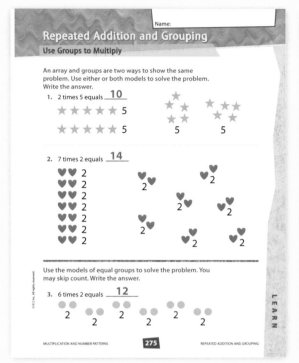
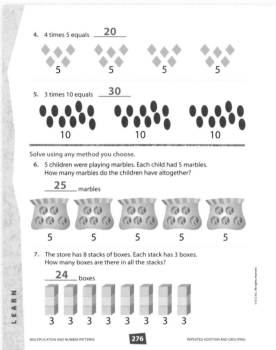

OFFLINE
15 min

TRY IT Model and Multiply

Students will practice multiplying by using repeated addition and by skip counting groups. Give students the cubes, drawing paper, and Model and Multiply activity page from their Activity Book. Read the directions with them.

Objectives

- Use concrete objects or sketches to model and explain multiplication as repeated addition.
- Use grouping to solve simple multiplication problems.

Tips

To prevent students from skip counting the same group twice, have them move aside each group of cubes as they skip count it.

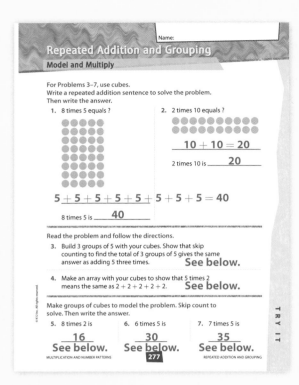

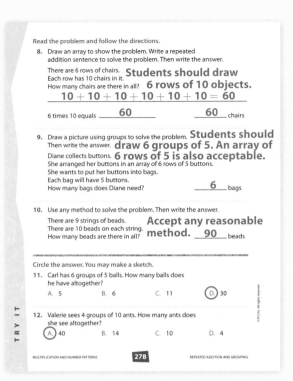

Additional Answers

3. Students should arrange the cubes into 3 groups with 5 cubes in each group. Then they should figure out that there are 15 altogether by counting by 5s. Then students should explain that this is the same as adding $5 + 5 + 5$.

4. Students should make 5 rows with 2 cubes each and say that this is 10 altogether. Then they should add $2 + 2 + 2 + 2 + 2$ and say this equals 10. Both the array and repeated addition have the same answer.

5. Students should make 8 groups of 2 cubes each. They should point to the groups as they skip count by 2s: 2, 4, 6, 8, 10, 12, 14, 16.

6. Students should make 6 groups of 5 cubes each. They should point to the groups as they skip count by 5s: 5, 10, 15, 20, 25, 30.

7. Students should make 7 groups of 5 cubes each. They should point to the groups as they skip count by 5s: 5, 10, 15, 20, 25, 30, 35.

Model and Solve Multiplication

Skills Update	5 minutes	**ONLINE**
LEARN Equivalent Arrays and Groups	20 minutes	**ONLINE**
LEARN Groups of Beads	10 minutes	**ONLINE**
TRY IT Model to Multiply	15 minutes	**OFFLINE**
CHECKPOINT	10 minutes	**OFFLINE**

▶ Lesson Objectives

- Use concrete objects or sketches to model and explain multiplication as repeated addition.
- Use grouping to solve simple multiplication problems.

▶ Prerequisite Skills

Use concrete objects or sketches of arrays to model multiplication problems.

▶ Common Errors and Misconceptions

- Students might add the second factor too many or too few times when using repeated addition. For example, for 5×4, students might add $4 + 4 + 4 + 4$.
- Students might undercount or overcount when using the count-by-n strategy.

▶ Content Background

Students will continue to model multiplication problems with arrays and group models and solve the problems with repeated addition and skip counting. They will also begin to explore the idea that the order in which two numbers are multiplied does not affect the product, or answer, to the multiplication problem.

Materials to Gather

SUPPLIED

blocks – B (all colors)
Model to Multiply activity page
Checkpoint (printout)

ALSO NEEDED

paper, drawing – 1 sheet

Keywords

expression — a number or a combination of numbers and symbols that represents a given value, such as $2 + 3$ or $10 - 4 + 1$

LEARN Equivalent Arrays and Groups

ONLINE 20min

Objectives

- Use concrete objects or sketches to model and explain multiplication as repeated addition.
- Use grouping to solve simple multiplication problems.

Students have learned how to model multiplication expressions as groups and as arrays. They will practice modeling the same expression both ways. Then they will use repeated addition to find the total.

Students will also learn that if they rotate an array, they will create an array that shows an equivalent multiplication expression. For example, if an array of 3 rows of 6 is rotated 90 degrees, it will become an array of 6 rows of 3. When the array is rotated, the total does not change—3 rows of 6 equals 18, and 6 rows of 3 equals 18. Emphasize this idea with students as they work through the activity.

3 times 6 equals 18

6 times 3 equals 18

LEARN Groups of Beads

ONLINE 10min

Objectives

- Use concrete objects or sketches to model and explain multiplication as repeated addition.
- Use grouping to solve simple multiplication problems.

Students will learn how to model multiplication story problems using group models. They will then use their models to skip count or repeatedly add to solve the problems.

Students will also use grouping to explore the idea that the order of the factors, or numbers being multiplied, does not affect the product. For example, 5 groups of 3 is equal to 15, and 3 groups of 5 is also equal to 15. Emphasize this idea with students as they work through the activity.

3 times 5 equals 15   5 times 3 equals 15

TRY IT Model to Multiply

OFFLINE

15 min

Objectives

- Use concrete objects or sketches to model and explain multiplication as repeated addition.

- Use grouping to solve simple multiplication problems.

Students will practice making arrays and group models to solve multiplication problems. Then they will choose which type of model to use to solve multiplication story problems. Give students the circle blocks and the Model to Multiply activity page from their Activity Book. Read the directions with them.

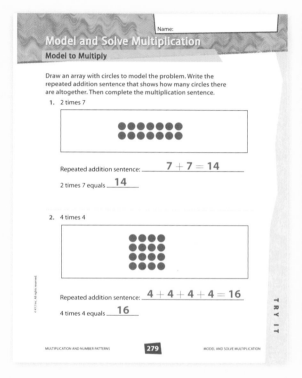

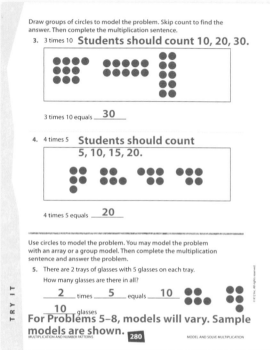

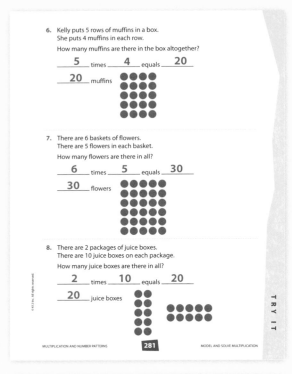

6. Kelly puts 5 rows of muffins in a box.
   She puts 4 muffins in each row.

   How many muffins are there in the box altogether?

   ___5___ times ___4___ equals ___20___

   ___20___ muffins

7. There are 6 baskets of flowers.
   There are 5 flowers in each basket.

   How many flowers are there in all?

   ___6___ times ___5___ equals ___30___

   ___30___ flowers

8. There are 2 packages of juice boxes.
   There are 10 juice boxes on each package.

   How many juice boxes are there in all?

   ___2___ times ___10___ equals ___20___

   ___20___ juice boxes

TRY IT

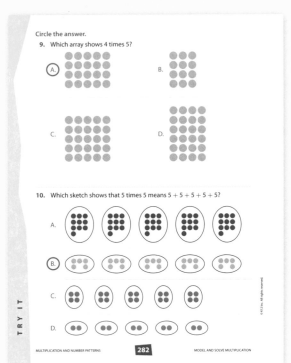

Circle the answer.

9. Which array shows 4 times 5?

   A.   B.

   C.   D.

10. Which sketch shows that 5 times 5 means $5 + 5 + 5 + 5 + 5$?

    A.

    B.

    C.

    D.

TRY IT

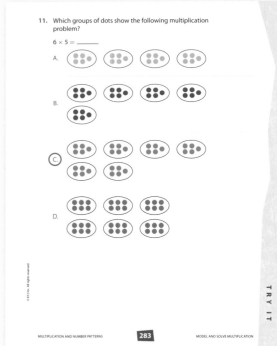

11. Which groups of dots show the following multiplication problem?

    $6 \times 5 =$ _____

    A.

    B.

    C.

    D.

TRY IT

CHECKPOINT

Print the Checkpoint. In Part 1, students will take a performance-based assessment. In Part 2, students will complete the problems on their own. Read the directions, problems, and answer choices to students, if necessary. Use the answer key to score the Checkpoint, and then enter the results online.

Gather the circle blocks and drawing paper. Give students the circle blocks for Problems 1 and 2 and drawing paper for Problem 3.

- Use concrete objects or sketches to model and explain multiplication as repeated addition.
- Use grouping to solve simple multiplication problems.

○ Checkpoint   Math | Multiplication and Number Patterns | Model and Solve Multiplication

Name _____ Date _____

Checkpoint Answer Key

Part 1

Follow the instructions for each item. Choose the response that best describes how the student performed on the task.

1. Say, "Use circle blocks to model and solve the problem '4 times 5.'"
(1 point)
Did the student model the problem using circle blocks and find the answer, 20?

A. Yes   B. No

2. Say, "Use the circle blocks to show that multiplying 7 times 5 gives the same answer as adding 5 seven times."
(1 point)
Did the student answer correctly?

Answers may vary. Example: The student could make an array with 7 groups of 5 circles each and count the circles to find that there are 35. Then the student could explain that counting the circles is the same as adding $5 + 5 + 5 + 5 + 5 + 5 + 5$.

A. Yes   B. No

3. Say, "Draw a picture to show that 2 times 10 means the same as $10 + 10$. Explain your picture."
(1 point)
Did the student answer correctly?

Answers may vary. Example: The student could draw 20 dots in 2 groups of 10. The student could explain that the drawing shows that multiplying 2 times 10 means the same as adding $10 + 10$, because the total number is 20 in each case.

A. Yes   B. No

Give students Part 2 of the assessment.

○ Checkpoint   Math | Multiplication and Number Patterns | Model and Solve Multiplication

Name _____ Date _____

Part 2
Circle the answer.
(1 point)
4. Which picture shows 7 times 2?

A.   B.   C.   (D.)

(1 point)
5. Cindy has 7 groups of 2 balloons. How many balloons does she have altogether?

A. 2   B. 7   C. 9   (D.) 14

(1 point)
6. Ben has 4 groups of 6 baseball cards. How many baseball cards does he have altogether?

A. 16   B. 18   (C.) 24   D. 46

(1 point)
7. Pete has 3 groups of 4 seashells. How many seashells does he have altogether?

A. 2   B. 7   C. 9   (D.) 12

Linear Patterns

Lesson Overview

Skills Update	5 minutes	ONLINE
GET READY Skip-Counting Patterns	5 minutes	ONLINE
LEARN Describe Patterns	15 minutes	ONLINE
LEARN Extend Patterns	15 minutes	ONLINE
TRY IT Pattern Rules and What's Next	10 minutes	OFFLINE
CHECKPOINT	10 minutes	OFFLINE

▶ Lesson Objectives

- Describe linear patterns, such as 3, 6, 9, using the wheels on 1 tricycle, 2 tricycles, 3 tricycles as an example.
- Determine a next term and extend a linear pattern, such as 3, 6, 9, … as the wheels on 1 tricycle, 2 tricycles, 3 tricycles, and extending it to 12 wheels on 4 tricycles as an example.

▶ Prerequisite Skills

- Count by 2s through 100.
- Count by 5s through 100.
- Count by 10s through 100.

▶ Content Background

Mathematics is often described as the study of patterns—patterns of all kinds. In this lesson, students will learn how to recognize number patterns. They will identify a rule that describes the pattern and use the rule to find the value of more terms in the pattern.

The study of number patterns in the early years leads to a better understanding of algebraic concepts, such as functions and graphing. In simple number patterns, the rule of the patterns describes the relationship between the number of the term and the value of that term in the pattern. In the table, the term numbers, in the Term row, are 1, 2, 3, 4, and so on, and the values of those terms are 3, 4, 5, 6, and so on.

Rule: add 2				
Term	1	2	3	4	…
Value	3	4	5	6	…

The rule is *add 2* because any of the terms numbers plus 2 will give the value of that term. Students can use the rule to find the value of any term. For example, if they know the rule for this pattern, they can find the value of the 10th term without counting up that high, because they know that the rule says that 10 plus 2 will give them the value of that term, 12.

Materials to Gather

SUPPLIED

Pattern Rules and What's Next activity page

Checkpoint (printout)

The rule for a number pattern can be very simple or very complex and use any operation. Students will encounter very simple patterns that either add, subtract, or multiply the term number by specific number. Such patterns are called *linear patterns*.

Be sure that students *use the rule* with the Term number in the chart to get the value of the term. They may be tempted to just look at the values only to get the next number in the pattern, but doing so will not help them with future work with patterns and functions. When students learn their basic facts and how to use a rule for a pattern to find the value of a term, they can find the value of any term, without counting up—even the 100th term!

Keywords	**linear pattern** – a pattern of numbers where the value of the next number goes up or down by adding or subtracting the same amount each time, such as 3, 6, 9, 12, … or 10, 8, 6, 4, …

ONLINE 5 min

GET READY Skip-Counting Patterns

Objectives

- Count by 2s through 100.
- Count by 5s through 100.
- Count by 10s through 100.

Students will identify a skip-counting pattern on the number line. By skip counting, they will be identifying the next term in a pattern. Skip counting will prepare students for learning about linear patterns and multiplication facts.

DIRECTIONS FOR USING THE NUMBER LINE LEARNING TOOL

1. Click Count and choose the following:
   - Start Number Line at: 0
   - End Number Line at: 20
   - Count by: 2s

   Click OK.

2. Students should click on each number to count by 2s through 20. As they click each number, the frog will hop to the number and the number will be said aloud.

3. Repeat the activity, having students count by 5s and then by 10s.

ONLINE 15 min

LEARN Describe Patterns

Objectives

- Describe linear patterns, such as 3, 6, 9, using the wheels on 1 tricycle, 2 tricycles, 3 tricycles as an example.

Students will explore number patterns using familiar objects such as the wheels on a bicycle or the fingers on a hand. They will also learn how to figure out the rule for a pattern, such as *add 2* or *times 3*. Notice that the rule is applied to the number in the left column in a vertical chart to get the value of the corresponding number in the right column. In a horizontal chart, the rule is applied to the number in the top row in the chart to get the value of the corresponding number in the bottom row.

LEARN Extend Patterns

Students have learned how to describe patterns with a rule, such as *add 2*. Now students will learn how to use a rule to extend, or continue, a pattern.

Be sure that students *use the rule* by using the Term number to get the value of that term. Students may be tempted to just look down the right column to get the next number in the pattern.

- Describe linear patterns, such as 3, 6, 9, using the wheels on 1 tricycle, 2 tricycles, 3 tricycles as an example.

- Determine a next term and extend a linear pattern, such as 3, 6, 9, … as the wheels on 1 tricycle, 2 tricycles, 3 tricycles, and extending it to 12 wheels on 4 tricycles as an example.

TRY IT Pattern Rules and What's Next

Students will practice determining the rules for patterns and extending patterns. Give students the Pattern Rules and What's Next activity page from their Activity Book and read the directions with them.

- Describe linear patterns, such as 3, 6, 9, using the wheels on 1 tricycle, 2 tricycles, 3 tricycles as an example.

- Determine a next term and extend a linear pattern, such as 3, 6, 9, … as the wheels on 1 tricycle, 2 tricycles, 3 tricycles, and extending it to 12 wheels on 4 tricycles as an example.

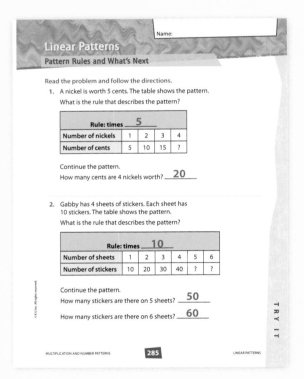

Name:

Linear Patterns
Pattern Rules and What's Next

Read the problem and follow the directions.

1. A nickel is worth 5 cents. The table shows the pattern.

   What is the rule that describes the pattern?

Rule: times 5				
Number of nickels	1	2	3	4
Number of cents	5	10	15	?

   Continue the pattern.
   How many cents are 4 nickels worth? **20**

2. Gabby has 4 sheets of stickers. Each sheet has 10 stickers. The table shows the pattern.

   What is the rule that describes the pattern?

Rule: times 10						
Number of sheets	1	2	3	4	5	6
Number of stickers	10	20	30	40	?	?

   Continue the pattern.
   How many stickers are there on 5 sheets? **50**

   How many stickers are there on 6 sheets? **60**

TRY IT

MULTIPLICATION AND NUMBER PATTERNS   285   LINEAR PATTERNS

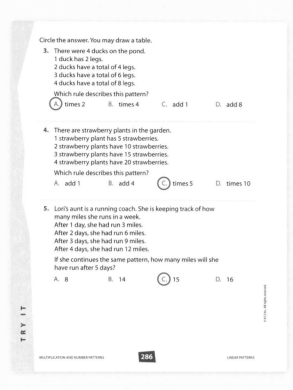

Circle the answer. You may draw a table.

3. There were 4 ducks on the pond.
1 duck has 2 legs.
2 ducks have a total of 4 legs.
3 ducks have a total of 6 legs.
4 ducks have a total of 8 legs.

Which rule describes this pattern?

(A.) times 2   B. times 4   C. add 1   D. add 8

4. There are strawberry plants in the garden.
1 strawberry plant has 5 strawberries.
2 strawberry plants have 10 strawberries.
3 strawberry plants have 15 strawberries.
4 strawberry plants have 20 strawberries.

Which rule describes this pattern?

A. add 1   B. add 4   (C.) times 5   D. times 10

5. Lori's aunt is a running coach. She is keeping track of how many miles she runs in a week.
After 1 day, she had run 3 miles.
After 2 days, she had run 6 miles.
After 3 days, she had run 9 miles.
After 4 days, she had run 12 miles.

If she continues the same pattern, how many miles will she have run after 5 days?

A. 8   B. 14   (C.) 15   D. 16

T R Y   I T

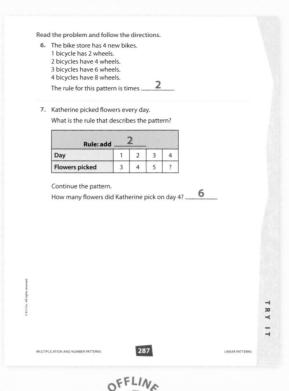

Read the problem and follow the directions.

6. The bike store has 4 new bikes.
1 bicycle has 2 wheels.
2 bicycles have 4 wheels.
3 bicycles have 6 wheels.
4 bicycles have 8 wheels.

The rule for this pattern is times ____2____

7. Katherine picked flowers every day.
What is the rule that describes the pattern?

Rule: add ___2___			
Day	1	2	3	4
Flowers picked	3	4	5	?

Continue the pattern.
How many flowers did Katherine pick on day 4? ____6____

T R Y   I T

CHECKPOINT

OFFLINE
10 min

Print the Checkpoint and have students complete it on their own. Read the directions, problems, and answer choices to students, if necessary. Use the answer key to score the Checkpoint, and then enter the results online.

Objectives

- Describe linear patterns, such as 3, 6, 9, using the wheels on 1 tricycle, 2 tricycles, 3 tricycles as an example.

- Determine a next term and extend a linear pattern, such as 3, 6, 9, … as the wheels on 1 tricycle, 2 tricycles, 3 tricycles, and extending it to 12 wheels on 4 tricycles as an example.

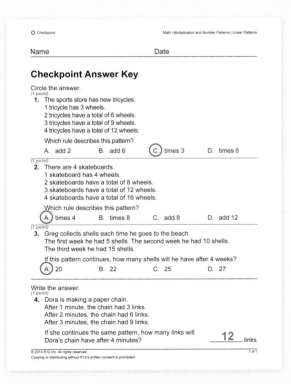

⚙ Checkpoint   Math | Multiplication and Number Patterns | Linear Patterns

Name _____   Date _____

Checkpoint Answer Key

Circle the answer.
(1 point)
1. The sports store has new tricycles.
1 tricycle has 3 wheels.
2 tricycles have a total of 6 wheels.
3 tricycles have a total of 9 wheels.
4 tricycles have a total of 12 wheels.

Which rule describes this pattern?
A. add 2   B. add 6   (C.) times 3   D. times 6

(1 point)
2. There are 4 skateboards.
1 skateboard has 4 wheels.
2 skateboards have a total of 8 wheels.
3 skateboards have a total of 12 wheels.
4 skateboards have a total of 16 wheels.

Which rule describes this pattern?
(A.) times 4   B. times 8   C. add 8   D. add 12

(1 point)
3. Greg collects shells each time he goes to the beach.
The first week he had 5 shells. The second week he had 10 shells.
The third week he had 15 shells.

If this pattern continues, how many shells will he have after 4 weeks?
(A.) 20   B. 22   C. 25   D. 27

Write the answer.
(1 point)
4. Dora is making a paper chain.
After 1 minute, the chain had 3 links.
After 2 minutes, the chain had 6 links.
After 3 minutes, the chain had 9 links.

If she continues the same pattern, how many links will Dora's chain have after 4 minutes? ____12____ links

                                                            1 of 1

Number Patterns

Skills Update	5 minutes	ONLINE
GET READY Skip Count on a Number Line	10 minutes	ONLINE
LEARN Number Pattern Stories	20 minutes	ONLINE
TRY IT What's Missing?	15 minutes	OFFLINE
CHECKPOINT	10 minutes	OFFLINE

▶ Lesson Objectives

Solve problems involving simple number patterns.

▶ Prerequisite Skills

Determine a next term and extend a linear pattern, such as 3, 6, 9, … as the wheels on 1 tricycle, 2 tricycles, 3 tricycles, and extending it to 12 wheels on 4 tricycles as an example.

▶ Advance Preparation

Print the Number Line 0–20.

▶ Content Background

Mathematics is often described as the study of patterns—patterns of all kinds. In this lesson, students will continue to learn how to recognize number patterns. They will identify a rule that describes the pattern and use the rule to find the value of more terms in the pattern.

The study of number patterns in the early years leads to a better understanding of algebraic concepts, such as functions and graphing. In simple number patterns, the rule of the patterns describes the relationship between the number of the term and the value of that term in the pattern. In the table, the term numbers, in the Term row, are 1, 2, 3, 4, and so on, and the values of those terms are 3, 4, 5, 6, and so on.

Rule: add 2				
Term	1	2	3	4	…
Value	3	4	5	6	…

The rule is *add 2* because any of the terms numbers plus 2 will give the value of that term. Students can use the rule to find the value of any term. For example, if they know the rule for this pattern, they can find the value of the 10th term without counting up that high, because they know that the rule says that 10 plus 2 will give them the value of that term, 12.

Materials to Gather

SUPPLIED

Number Line 0–20 (printout)
Number Line 0–100 (optional printout)
What's Missing? activity page
Checkpoint (printout)

ALSO NEEDED

crayon

The rule for a number pattern can be very simple or very complex and use any operation. Students will encounter very simple patterns that either add, subtract, or multiply the term number by specific number. Such patterns are called *linear patterns*.

Be sure that students *use the rule* with the Term number in the chart to get the value of the term. They may be tempted to just at the values only to get the next number in the pattern, but doing so will not help them with future work with patterns and functions. When students learn their basic facts and how to use a rule for a pattern to find the value of a term, they can find the value of any term, without counting up—even the 100th term!

GET READY Skip Count on a Number Line

ONLINE 10 min

Students will use a number line to see a number pattern.
    Gather the Number Line 0–20 printout.

Objectives

- Determine a next term and extend a linear pattern, such as 3, 6, 9, … as the wheels on 1 tricycle, 2 tricycles, 3 tricycles, and extending it to 12 wheels on 4 tricycles as an example.

LEARN Number Pattern Stories

ONLINE 20 min

Students will read a story problem and see a table that shows the pattern in the problem. They will determine the rule and extend the pattern. They will then solve problems on their own with the table given only as a hint.

Objectives

- Solve problems involving simple number patterns.

TRY IT What's Missing?

OFFLINE 15 min

Students will practice finding the missing number in patterns. Give students the What's Missing? activity page from their Activity Book and read the directions with them.

Objectives

- Solve problems involving simple number patterns.

Tips

Allow students to use the Number Line 0–100 printout to help them find the missing numbers.

Number Patterns

What's Missing?

Read the problem and follow the directions.

1. Corey is arranging his rock collection into groups with 5 rocks in each pile.
1 group has 5 rocks.
2 groups have a total of 10 rocks.
3 groups have a total of 15 rocks.

Corey has 6 groups of rocks. How many rocks does Corey have? Circle the answer.

A. 26   B. 27

C. 28   (D.) 30

Corey's Rocks	
Number of groups	Number of rocks
1	5
2	10
3	15
4	20
5	25
6	?

2. Carly is handing out tennis balls for the students in the tennis class.
Each student will be given 2 tennis balls.
If there is 1 student, Carly will need 2 tennis balls.
If there are 2 students, Carly will need 4 tennis balls.
If there are 3 students, Carly will need 6 tennis balls.

How many tennis balls will Carly need if there are 7 students?

_____**14**_____ tennis balls

Tennis Balls	
Number of students	Number of tennis balls
1	2
2	4
3	6
4	?
5	?
6	?
7	?

3. Lina is putting her pictures into her photo album.
She puts 5 photos on each page.
Lina noticed that if she uses 1 page, she has a total of 5 photos.
If she uses 2 pages, she has a total of 10 photos.
If she uses 3 pages, she has a total of 15 photos.

How many photos does Lina have if she uses 9 pages?

_____**45**_____ photos

Lina's Photos	
Number of pages	Number of photos
1	5
2	10
3	15
4	20
5	25
6	30
7	35
8	40
9	?

4. Mrs. Walker is making the skirts for the ballet students.
Each skirt needs 10 ribbons.
If she makes 1 skirt, she needs 10 ribbons.
If she makes 2 skirts, she needs 20 ribbons.
If she makes 3 skirts, she needs 30 ribbons.

How many ribbons will Mrs. Walker need to make 8 skirts? Circle the answer.

A. 70   (B.) 80

C. 90   D. 100

Ballet Skirts	
Number of students	Number of ribbons
1	10
2	20
3	30
4	40
5	50
6	60
7	?
8	?

T R Y I T

5. Wally is putting dimes in his empty piggy bank.
A dime is worth 10 cents.
The chart shows the number of dimes Wally puts in his bank.

How many cents are 6 dimes?

_____**60**_____ cents

Dimes	
Number of dimes	Amount of money in cents
1	10
2	20
3	30
4	40
5	?
6	?

Circle the number that comes next in the pattern.

6. 4, 6, 8, 10, 12, _____

A. 12   B. 13   (C.) 14   D. 16

7. 20, 30, 40, 50, 60, _____

A. 40   B. 60   C. 65   (D.) 70

8. 15, 20, 25, 30, 35, _____

(A.) 40   B. 45   C. 50   D. 56

Fill in the missing number in the pattern.

9. 6, 8, 10, 12, 14, __**16**__, 18

T R Y I T

CHECKPOINT

Print the Checkpoint and have students complete it on their own. Read the directions, problems, and answer choices to students, if necessary. Use the answer key to score the Checkpoint, and then enter the results online.

- Solve problems involving simple number patterns.

Checkpoint   Math | Multiplication and Number Patterns | Number Patterns

Name   Date

Checkpoint Answer Key

Circle the number that comes next in the pattern.
(1 point)
1. 10, 12, 14, 16, 18, 20, _____

    A. 17   B. 18   C. 20   **(D.)** 22

(1 point)
2. 10, 20, 30, 40, 50, _____

    A. 55   **(B.)** 60   C. 65   D. 70

Fill in the missing number in the pattern.
(1 point)
3. 5, 10, 15, 20, 25, 30, __**35**__, 40

(1 point)
4. 20, 30, 40, 50, __**60**__, 70

Find the missing number.
(1 point)
5. Mr. Chow is making bags of apples for his grocery store. He puts 10 apples into each bag.
If he makes 1 bag, he will need 10 apples.
If he makes 2 bags, he will need 20 apples.
If he makes 3 bags, he will need 30 apples.

How many apples will Mr. Chow need to make 10 bags?

__**100**__ apples

Bags of Apples	
Number of Bags	Number of Apples
1	10
2	20
3	30
4	40
5	50
6	60
7	70
8	80
9	90
10	?

Represent Multiplication

Lesson Overview

Skills Update	5 minutes	ONLINE
GET READY Model Multiplication	5 minutes	ONLINE
LEARN The Multiplication Symbol	20 minutes	ONLINE
LEARN Write Multiplication Sentences	10 minutes	ONLINE
TRY IT Multiplication Sentences	10 minutes	OFFLINE
CHECKPOINT	10 minutes	OFFLINE

▶ Lesson Objectives

- Use models and math symbols to represent multiplication.
- Recognize that the × sign refers to multiplication.
- Correctly use the symbol × for multiplication.

▶ Prerequisite Skills

- Use concrete objects or sketches of arrays to model multiplication problems.
- Use concrete objects or sketches to model and explain multiplication as repeated addition.
- Recognize that the + sign refers to addition.
- Recognize that the − sign refers to subtraction.

▶ Content Background

Students understand the meaning of multiplication and can model multiplication using arrays and sketches. They have also solved simple multiplication problems using repeated addition. In this lesson, students will learn about the multiplication symbol and how to use it to write multiplication number sentences.

Multiplication is an operation used to solve problems involving equal groups. The multiplication symbol (×) is used to say "groups of" or "rows of." For example, 3 groups of 5 objects would be shown with the expression 3 × 5. And 5 rows of 3 objects would be shown with the expression 5 × 3.

Materials to Gather

SUPPLIED

base-10 blocks – 20 ones cubes
Multiplication Sentences activity page
Checkpoint (printout)

Keywords

factor – one of two or more numbers that are multiplied
multiplication symbol (×) – a symbol indicating that factors will be multiplied, as in 4 × 3 = 12
number sentence – two expressions related by an equals symbol (=), a not-equal-to symbol (≠), or an inequality symbol; for example, $7 - 2 = 4 + 1; 5 \neq 4 + 4; 6 + 2 > 1 + 4$
product – the answer to a multiplication problem

GET READY Model Multiplication

Students will look at an array to review the meaning of multiplication as equal groups and equal rows. Then they will use repeated addition to find the total number of objects in the array. As students work through the activity, help them connect the array to the words, numbers, and symbols.

Objectives

- Use concrete objects or sketches of arrays to model multiplication problems.
- Use concrete objects or sketches to model and explain multiplication as repeated addition.

LEARN The Multiplication Symbol

Students will learn about the multiplication symbol ($\times$), which is read as "times." They will write multiplication number sentences using the multiplication symbol and equals symbol. They will also interpret multiplication sentences that use the symbols.

Objectives

- Use models and math symbols to represent multiplication.
- Recognize that the $\times$ sign refers to multiplication.
- Correctly use the symbol $\times$ for multiplication.

LEARN Write Multiplication Sentences

Students will use the multiplication symbol ($\times$) and equals symbol ($=$) to write number sentences to match a given array or picture. They will also identify the missing symbol in a number sentence.

Focus on students' understanding of the multiplication symbol and the equals symbol. Guide students to write number sentences that match the pictures, reinforcing that the number before the multiplication symbol is the number of groups or rows and the number after the multiplication symbol is the number of objects in each group or row. The number that represents the total number of objects is the called the *product*.

Objectives

- Use models and math symbols to represent multiplication.
- Recognize that the $\times$ sign refers to multiplication.
- Correctly use the symbol $\times$ for multiplication.

Tips

When students are talking about the symbol for multiplication ($\times$), encourage them to call the symbol the multiplication symbol, not the times sign.

TRY IT Multiplication Sentences

Students will practice writing and interpreting multiplication number sentences. Give students the ones cubes and Multiplication Sentences activity page from their Activity Book. Read the directions with them.

Objectives

- Use models and math symbols to represent multiplication.
- Recognize that the $\times$ sign refers to multiplication.
- Correctly use the symbol $\times$ for multiplication.

Represent Multiplication
Multiplication Sentences

Draw a picture to match the multiplication sentence.

1. $2 \times 6 = 12$

Students should draw 2 rows of 6 items or 2 groups of 6 items.

2. $3 \times 3 = 9$

Students should draw 3 rows of 3 items or 3 groups of 3 items.

3. $7 \times 3 = 21$

Students should draw 7 rows of 3 items or 7 groups of 3 items.

4. $2 \times 5 = 10$

Students should draw 2 rows of 5 items or 2 groups of 5 items.

TRY IT

Write a multiplication sentence to match the picture.

5. 　$6 \times 3 = 18$

6. 　$2 \times 6 = 12$

7. 　$7 \times 2 = 14$

8. 　$4 \times 5 = 20$

TRY IT

Write a multiplication sentence to match the words.

9. 3 groups of 4 people is 12 people.　$3 \times 4 = 12$

10. 18 is 9 rows of 2.　$18 = 9 \times 2$

Read the problem and follow the directions.

11. Use the ones cubes to model the problem.

$3 \times 5 = \underline{\hspace{2cm}}$

Students should model 3 rows of 5 ones cubes or 3 groups of 5 ones cubes.

12. Write a multiplication sentence for the model.

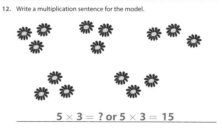

$5 \times 3 = ?$ or $5 \times 3 = 15$

TRY IT

---

13. What does this symbol mean? Say the answer.

$3 \times 4 = 12$
↑

Students should explain that the multiplication symbol means "groups of" or "rows of" or "times."

14. Which symbol goes in the box to make the number sentence true? Circle the answer.

$5 \square 2 = 5$ groups of 2

A. $+$
B. $-$
C. $\times$
D. $\div$

TRY IT

CHECKPOINT

- Use models and math symbols to represent multiplication.
- Recognize that the × sign refers to multiplication.
- Correctly use the symbol × for multiplication.

Print the Checkpoint and have students complete it on their own. Read the directions, problems, and answer choices to students, if necessary. Use the answer key to score the Checkpoint, and then enter the results online.

Gather the ones cubes and give them to students for Problem 1.

Checkpoint　　　　Math | Multiplication and Number Patterns | Represent Multiplication

Name _____ Date _____

Checkpoint Answer Key

Read each problem and follow the directions.

(1 point)
1. Use the ones cubes to model this problem:

    $2 \times 6 =$ _____

    Students should model 2 rows of 6 ones cubes or 2 groups of 6 ones cubes.

(1 point)
2. Write a multiplication sentence for the model.

    ☆☆　　☆☆　　☆☆

    ☆☆　　☆☆

    5 × 2 = ? or 5 × 2 = 10

(1 point)
3. What does the × symbol in the number sentence $2 \times 5 = 10$ mean? Circle the answer.

    A. add　　B. subtract　　Ⓒ multiply　　D. divide

(1 point)
4. Write the symbol that goes in the circle to make the number sentence true.

    3 (×) 5 = 15

Multiply by 2

Lesson Overview

Skills Update	5 minutes	**ONLINE**
GET READY Skip Count	5 minutes	**ONLINE**
LEARN Use 2s to Multiply	20 minutes	**ONLINE**
LEARN 2s Facts Games	20 minutes	**OFFLINE**
TRY IT Practice Multiplying by 2	10 minutes	**OFFLINE**

▶ Lesson Objectives

- Use counting by multiples of 2 to understand multiplication facts for 2.
- Demonstrate automatic recall of multiplication facts for 2 through 10×2.

▶ Prerequisite Skills

- Use concrete objects or sketches to model and explain multiplication as repeated addition.
- Use models and math symbols to represent multiplication.

▶ Advance Preparation

- Number index cards 1 through 10, or gather the numbered cards you created previously.
- If you do not have a number cube, use a dry-erase marker to write 1–6 on the sides of the large red cube in the block set (block P), or create small cards with 1 through 6 written on the cards and draw them out of a bag.

▶ Content Background

Students will learn that the 2s facts are basic multiplication problems where a number through 10 is multiplied by 2. At this point, they will not multiply by 0, so the multiplication facts they will learn are 1×2, 2×2, 3×2, 4×2, up through 10×2. Students will learn that they can find the product by making equal groups or skip counting on a number line. They will also learn that they can use addition doubles facts that they know to find the product of a number times 2. For example, if they know that $4 + 4 = 8$, they can use that knowledge to find $4 \times 2 = 8$. They will learn that using doubles facts is a quick way of finding the product of a 2s fact.

Materials to Gather

SUPPLIED
Number Line 0–20 (optional printout)
Practice Multiplying by 2 activity page

ALSO NEEDED
index cards – numbered 1–10
household objects – number cube

Keywords

multiplication facts – the set of multiplication problems with factors of 1 through 10; these problems should be memorized for easy computation
multiply – to use the shortcut for adding the same number over and over a certain number of times

GET READY Skip Count

Objectives

- Use concrete objects or sketches to model and explain multiplication as repeated addition.
- Use models and math symbols to represent multiplication.

Students will skip count by 2s using the Number Line Learning Tool.

DIRECTIONS FOR USING THE NUMBER LINE LEARNING TOOL

1. Click Count and choose the following:
   - Start Number Line at: 0
   - End Number Line at: 20
   - Count by: 2s
   - Click OK.

2. Students should click on each number to count by 2s. As they click each number, the frog will hop to the number and it will be said aloud. The number line will slide over automatically when necessary to display more numbers. When they reach 20, students should click Count Again and repeat.

3. Each time a student skip counts by 2, write the multiplication sentence they are solving. For example, if they skip count by 2s seven times, they are solving the multiplication fact $7 \times 2 = 14$.

   Have students count by 2s to solve these problems:
   - Count 7 times to solve $7 \times 2 = ?$.
   - Count 4 times to solve $4 \times 2 = ?$.
   - Count 8 times to solve $8 \times 2 = ?$.
   - Count 3 times to solve $3 \times 2 = ?$.
   - Count 10 times to solve $10 \times 2 = ?$.

LEARN Use 2s to Multiply

Objectives

- Use counting by multiples of 2 to understand multiplication facts for 2.
- Demonstrate automatic recall of multiplication facts for 2 through 10×2.

Students are familiar with the meaning of multiplication. Now they will learn the 2s multiplication facts. The 2s multiplication facts are multiplication problems where a number through 10 is multiplied by 2: $1 \times 2, 2 \times 2, 3 \times 2, 4 \times 2$, and so on through 10×2.

Students will review methods for solving multiplication problems: skip counting using either a number line or their fingers, making an array using their circle blocks, or using what they learned about addition doubles facts.

Students will see both horizontal and vertical facts. Explain that both formats mean the same thing.

LEARN 2s Facts Games

Objectives

- Use counting by multiples of 2 to understand multiplication facts for 2.
- Demonstrate automatic recall of multiplication facts for 2 through 10×2.

Students will play games to help them memorize the 2s facts.
Gather the index cards and number cube.

1. On a sheet of paper, have students write all the 2s facts (1×2 through 10×2) in vertical form. In each fact, 2 should be the second factor. Tell students they can skip count or use other ways that work for them.

$$\begin{array}{ccccc} 1 & 2 & 3 & 4 & 5 \\ \underline{\times\,2} & \underline{\times\,2} & \underline{\times\,2} & \underline{\times\,2} & \underline{\times\,2} \\ 2 & 4 & 6 & 8 & 10 \end{array}$$

2. Ask students about the patterns they see in the problems. Tell students that the answers to the 2s multiplication facts are the numbers they say when they skip count by 2s to 20. Also tell them that each answer is 2 more than the one before it.

3. Explain to students that learning the 2s multiplication facts will help them quickly solve harder math problems in the future. Tell students that they will play some games to help them learn these facts.

4. Lay out the index cards in a random order.

   Say: Pick a card. Multiply that number by 2. Say the answer. For example, if you pick the 5 card, you would say "5 times 2 equals 10." If you get the answer right, keep the card. If you don't know the answer right away, use one of the ways you've learned to figure out the answer. Then put the card back. Try to collect all the cards.

5. Play the game until students have collected all the cards.

6. **Say:** Now let's play a game called Double Up. We'll take turns rolling a number cube. For each roll, we earn double the points of the number shown. For example, if you roll a 3, you double it to earn 6 points. Whoever has the most points after five rolls each is the winner. You announce the points for each roll, and I will write them down. Then we'll add up the points.

OFFLINE
10 min

TRY IT Practice Multiplying by 2

Students will practice solving 2s multiplication facts. Give students the Practice Multiplying by 2 activity page from their Activity Book and read the directions with them. Allow students to use the Number Line 0–20 printout, if necessary.

Objectives

- Use counting by multiples of 2 to understand multiplication facts for 2.
- Demonstrate automatic recall of multiplication facts for 2 through 10×2.

Multiply by 2
Practice Multiplying by 2

Name: _____

Write the answer.

1. $3 \times 2 = $ __6__   2. $1 \times 2 = $ __2__

3. $4 \times 2 = $ __8__   4. $9 \times 2 = $ __18__

5. $\begin{array}{r} 10 \\ \times 2 \\ \hline 20 \end{array}$ 6. $\begin{array}{r} 7 \\ \times 2 \\ \hline 14 \end{array}$

7. $\begin{array}{r} 6 \\ \times 2 \\ \hline 12 \end{array}$ 8. $\begin{array}{r} 2 \\ \times 2 \\ \hline 4 \end{array}$

9. $\begin{array}{r} 8 \\ \times 2 \\ \hline 16 \end{array}$ 10. $\begin{array}{r} 5 \\ \times 2 \\ \hline 10 \end{array}$

11. $\begin{array}{r} 1 \\ \times 2 \\ \hline 2 \end{array}$ 12. $\begin{array}{r} 9 \\ \times 2 \\ \hline 18 \end{array}$

13. $\begin{array}{r} 4 \\ \times 2 \\ \hline 8 \end{array}$ 14. $\begin{array}{r} 3 \\ \times 2 \\ \hline 6 \end{array}$

15. $2 \times 2 = $ __4__   16. $5 \times 2 = $ __10__

17. $7 \times 2 = $ __14__

TRY IT

TRY IT

Multiplication: 2s Facts

Lesson Overview

Skills Update	5 minutes	ONLINE
LEARN Match the 2s Facts	10 minutes	ONLINE
LEARN Jumping 2s Facts	15 minutes	OFFLINE
LEARN Post the 2s Facts	10 minutes	OFFLINE
TRY IT Practice the 2s Facts	10 minutes	OFFLINE
CHECKPOINT	10 minutes	OFFLINE

▶ Lesson Objectives

Demonstrate automatic recall of multiplication facts for 2 through 10 × 2.

▶ Prerequisite Skills

Use models and math symbols to represent multiplication.

▶ Advance Preparation

- Number index cards 1 through 10, or gather the numbered cards you created previously.
- Print the Multiplication Facts Chart. Cut out the sections on each page and arrange as shown.

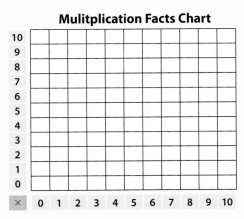

Mulitplication Facts Chart

- Optional: Tape or glue the cut-out sections of the Multiplication Facts Chart onto poster board.

▶ Content Background

Students will continue to practice the 2s facts through 10 (1 × 2, 2 × 2, up through 10 × 2). Through activities and games, they will work toward memorizing these facts.

Materials to Gather

SUPPLIED

Multiplication Facts Chart (printout)

Number Line 0–20 (optional printout)

Practice the 2s Facts activity page

Checkpoint (printout)

ALSO NEEDED

index cards – numbered 1–10

scissors, adult

poster board – 1 piece, 22 in. by 28 in. (optional)

tape, clear or glue stick (optional)

timer

LEARN Match the 2s Facts

ONLINE 10 min

Students will play a hidden picture game to help them memorize the 2s multiplication facts. Throughout the activity, encourage students to first try to recall the fact without using a model. If students have difficulty, have them solve the problems using a strategy they have learned, including the number line, circle blocks, or their fingers.

Objectives

- Demonstrate automatic recall of multiplication facts for 2 through 10 × 2.

LEARN Jumping 2s Facts

OFFLINE 15 min

Students will play games to help them memorize the 2s multiplication facts. Throughout the activity, encourage students to first try to recall the fact without using a model. If students have difficulty, have them solve the problems using a strategy they have learned, including the number line, circle blocks, or their fingers.

Gather the numbered index cards.

1. Lay out the index cards face down in a random order.
2. **Say:** Let's play a multiplication game. Turn over a card. Multiply that number by 2. Say the answer. Then do that number of jumping jacks. For example, if you pick the 4 card, you would say "4 times 2 equals 8" and do eight jumping jacks. If you can say the correct answer right away, you can keep the card.
3. Play the game until students have collected all the cards.

   Say: Now let's play a different game. I will hold up some fingers. Multiply the number of fingers I'm holding up by 2. Say the answer. For example, if I hold up six fingers, you would say "6 times 2 equals 12." After you say the answer, we'll switch—you will hold up fingers, and I'll multiply by 2. We'll get points for each fact we answer right away.
4. Be sure to purposely give a few wrong answers so that students have to correct you. Also, keep track of the facts that students have difficulty with and repeat those facts.

Objectives

- Demonstrate automatic recall of multiplication facts for 2 through 10 × 2.

Tips

If students are not able to do jumping jacks, have them do something else physical, such as clapping their hands, stomping their feet, or snapping their fingers.

Allow students to use the circle blocks and the Number Line 0–20 printout, if necessary.

LEARN Post the 2s Facts

OFFLINE 10 min

Show students the Multiplication Facts Chart you created. Students will work on 2s facts through 10. They will not yet work on 0 × 2.

The Multiplication Facts Chart will help students keep track of the multiplication facts they have memorized and the ones they still need to learn. Students write the products on the chart that they can automatically recall.

1. **Say:** The Multiplication Facts Chart will help you keep track of the multiplication facts you have memorized and the ones you still need to learn.

Objectives

- Demonstrate automatic recall of multiplication facts for 2 through 10 × 2.

Tips

Only have students write the product on the chart when they can state the fact quickly—without having to skip count or use a model. You may also want to put a small sticker in the squares of the multiplication facts they know.

2. Explain that the product of $5 \times 2 = 10$. As you say 5, move along the bottom of the chart to the 5, and as you say 2, move up the 5 column to the 2 row. Tell students that when they have shown you that they know 5×2 by saying it quickly and often, they will be able to write a 10 with a pencil in the square where the row meets the column. Point to this square.

3. Tell them that in several days, if they have memorized the facts and can recall them quickly, they can rewrite them with a marker.

4. **Say:** Now you try. What is 1×2?

   If students are able to quickly recall the product (2), have them write it in pencil in the square that is 1 over and 2 up. If not, tell them that they will need to practice 1×2 some more before placing the product on the chart.

5. Repeat Step 4 with the 2s facts through 10, but do not give the multiplication facts in order. Students should only write a fact on the chart when they have it memorized and can say it quickly. Practice facts that students have difficulty with until they can say the facts quickly.

   Note: Students will fill out the chart in stages. Keep the chart for use in future lessons. At the end of this lesson, the chart should look like the one shown, but only if students have automatic recall of these facts.

Mulitplication Facts Chart

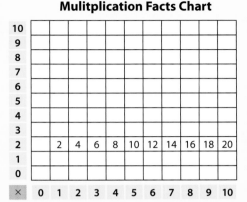

TRY IT Practice the 2s Facts

OFFLINE
10 min

Objectives

Students will practice solving 2s facts. Give students the Practice the 2s Facts activity page from their Activity Book and read the directions with them. Students should not be given any models during this Try It.

If students have attained automatic recall, they should be able to complete the Try It in 2 minutes. Time students as they complete the Try It.

- Demonstrate automatic recall of multiplication facts for 2 through 10×2.

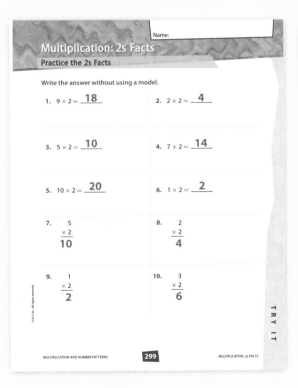

OFFLINE
10 min

Objectives

- Demonstrate automatic recall of multiplication facts for 2 through 10 × 2.

Print the Checkpoint and have students complete it on their own. Read the directions, problems, and answer choices to students, if necessary. Use the answer key to score the Checkpoint, and then enter the results online.

⚙ Checkpoint   Math | Multiplication and Number Patterns | Multiplication: 2s Facts

Name _____ Date _____

Checkpoint Answer Key _____

Write the answer.

(1 point)
1. Count by 2s to find the answer to 10 × 2.
   A. 18   (B.) 20
   C. 19   D. 16

(1 point)
2. Find the correct answer to 7 × 2 by counting by 2s.
   __14__

(1 point)
3. 2 × 2 = __4__

(1 point)
4. $\begin{array}{r} 6 \\ \times\ 2 \\ \hline 12 \end{array}$

(1 point)
5. $\begin{array}{r} 9 \\ \times\ 2 \\ \hline 18 \end{array}$

(1 point)
6. $\begin{array}{r} 7 \\ \times\ 2 \\ \hline 14 \end{array}$

(1 point)
7. $\begin{array}{r} 8 \\ \times\ 2 \\ \hline 16 \end{array}$

(1 point)
8. $\begin{array}{r} 4 \\ \times\ 2 \\ \hline 8 \end{array}$

(1 point)
9. 3 × 2 = __6__

(1 point)
10. 5 × 2 = __10__

(1 point)
11. 1 × 2 = __2__

(1 point)
12. 10 × 2 = __20__

1 of 1

Multiply by 10

▶ Lesson Objectives

- Use counting by multiples of 10 to understand multiplication facts for 10.
- Demonstrate automatic recall of multiplication facts for 10 through 10×10.

▶ Prerequisite Skills

- Use counting by multiples of 2 to understand multiplication facts for 2.
- Demonstrate automatic recall of multiplication facts for 2 through 10×2.

▶ Content Background

Students will learn that the 10s facts are multiplication problems where a number through 10 is multiplied by 10: 1×10, 2×10, 3×10, 4×10, and so on through 10×10. They will learn that they can find the product by making equal groups or skip counting on a number line. Students are familiar with the products of the 10s multiplication facts because they know how to count by 10s to 100.

Materials to Gather

SUPPLIED

Number Line 0–100 (optional printout)

Practice Multiplying by 10 activity page

ALSO NEEDED

index cards – 20 blank

marker, coloring – any color

timer

GET READY Skip Count by 10s

ONLINE 5 min

Objectives

- Use counting by multiples of 10 to understand multiplication facts for 10.

Students will skip count by 10s on a hundred chart. Later in the lesson they'll learn that the numbers that they say when they skip count by 10s are the products of the 10s facts.

DIRECTIONS FOR USING THE HUNDRED CHART LEARNING TOOL

1. Have students click the blue circle tool and count by 10s on the chart by clicking every tenth number as they count aloud. When they click, the number will be circled and will be said aloud. If an incorrect number is clicked, simply have them click it again to remove the circle. When they have counted by 10s through 100, have them click the speaker icon to hear the numbers counted aloud.

2. Have students look for patterns on the chart. Examples: the numbers appear in columns on the chart; the numbers end in 0. Then click Print to print a copy of students' hundred chart.

LEARN Use 10s to Multiply

Students are familiar with the meaning of multiplication. Now they will learn the 10s multiplication facts. The 10s facts are multiplication problems where a number through 10 is multiplied by 10: 1×10, 2×10, 3×10, 4×10, and so on through 10×10.

   Students will review methods for solving multiplication problems: skip counting using either a number line or their fingers, making an array, or using what they know about place value with the tens rods. They will see both horizontal and vertical facts. Explain that both formats mean the same thing.

Objectives

- Use counting by multiples of 10 to understand multiplication facts for 10.
- Demonstrate automatic recall of multiplication facts for 10 through 10×10.

LEARN Games for 10s

Student will play games that have students recall the multiplication facts for 10. Gather the index cards and marker.

1. Put 10 index cards in a row and have students write down these facts without answers, in vertical form, each on its own index card:

$$\begin{array}{r} 1 \\ \times\, 10 \\ \hline \end{array} \qquad \begin{array}{r} 2 \\ \times\, 10 \\ \hline \end{array} \quad \text{and so on through} \quad \begin{array}{r} 10 \\ \times\, 10 \\ \hline \end{array}$$

2. Put a blank index card under each fact. Have students fill in the answers starting with the left card and working their way through the facts.

3. As students solve each problem, discuss any patterns they may see, such as the following:

   - The answers are numbers you say when you skip count by 10.
   - The answers have a zero in the ones place.
   - In each answer, the number in the tens place increases by 1.

4. **Say:** Now we will play concentration with the cards we just made.

   Mix up the 10 cards with the problems on them and place them face down in 2 rows of 5. Then mix up the 10 cards with the answers on them and place them face down in 2 rows of 5 below the other set.

5. **Say:** We'll take turns. Turn one card over from each set of cards. If you choose a 10s fact and an answer card that match, you get to keep the pair. If they do not match, you will turn them back over and try to remember where they are. The goal is to match up all the correct pairs.

6. Allow students to use any of the ways they have learned to decide if the fact is a match to the answer card. Take turns playing concentration. Make an occasional error for students to catch by saying that you have a matching pair that doesn't actually match. Continue until all the cards have been paired.

7. **Say:** Now we will play another game. You will count by 10s as you hold up one finger for each 10 until I say stop. When I say stop, look at how many fingers you are holding up and say what that number times 10 is. For example, if you count by 10 four times and have four fingers up when I say stop, you would look at your four fingers and say $4 \times 10 = 40$.

8. Play this game with students trying to use all the facts; repeat facts that students have difficulty with.

Objectives

- Use counting by multiples of 10 to understand multiplication facts for 10.
- Demonstrate automatic recall of multiplication facts for 10 through 10×10.

Tips

Allow students to use the Number Line 0–100 printout until they have memorized the facts.

TRY IT Practice Multiplying by 10

Students will practice solving 10s facts. Give students the Practice Multiplying by 10 activity page from their Activity Book and read the directions with them.

If students have attained automatic recall, they should be able to complete the Try It in 2 minutes. Time students as they complete the Try It.

Multiply by 10
Practice Multiplying by 10

Name:

Write the answer.

1. $9 \times 10 = \underline{90}$

2. $1 \times 10 = \underline{10}$

3. $10 \times 10 = \underline{100}$

4. $4 \times 10 = \underline{40}$

5. $3 \times 10 = \underline{30}$

6. $5 \times 10 = \underline{50}$

7. $6 \times 10 = \underline{60}$

8. $2 \times 10 = \underline{20}$

9. $8 \times 10 = \underline{80}$

10. $7 \times 10 = \underline{70}$

11.
$$\begin{array}{r} 10 \\ \times\ 10 \\ \hline 100 \end{array}$$

12.
$$\begin{array}{r} 9 \\ \times\ 10 \\ \hline 90 \end{array}$$

13.
$$\begin{array}{r} 2 \\ \times\ 10 \\ \hline 20 \end{array}$$

14.
$$\begin{array}{r} 6 \\ \times\ 10 \\ \hline 60 \end{array}$$

15.
$$\begin{array}{r} 5 \\ \times\ 10 \\ \hline 50 \end{array}$$

16.
$$\begin{array}{r} 7 \\ \times\ 10 \\ \hline 70 \end{array}$$

17.
$$\begin{array}{r} 3 \\ \times\ 10 \\ \hline 30 \end{array}$$

18.
$$\begin{array}{r} 8 \\ \times\ 10 \\ \hline 80 \end{array}$$

Solve.

19. Count by 10s to find the answer to 10×10.
$\underline{100}$

MULTIPLICATION AND NUMBER PATTERNS   **301**   MULTIPLY BY 10

TRY IT

TRY IT

MULTIPLICATION AND NUMBER PATTERNS   **302**   MULTIPLY BY 10

Multiplication: 10s Facts

Lesson Overview

Skills Update	5 minutes	**ONLINE**
GET READY Jumping 10s Facts	5 minutes	**ONLINE**
LEARN 10s Fast Facts	10 minutes	**ONLINE**
LEARN Games for 10s Facts	15 minutes	**OFFLINE**
LEARN Post the 10s Facts	5 minutes	**OFFLINE**
TRY IT Practice the 10s Facts	10 minutes	**OFFLINE**
CHECKPOINT	10 minutes	**OFFLINE**

▶ Lesson Objectives

Demonstrate automatic recall of multiplication facts for 10 through 10 × 10.

▶ Prerequisite Skills

Demonstrate automatic recall of multiplication facts for 2 through 10 × 2.

▶ Advance Preparation

- Number index cards 1 through 10. Number another set of index cards with multiples of 10 through 100 (10, 20, 30, and so on through 100), or gather the numbered cards you created previously.
- Gather the Multiplication Facts Chart from the Multiplication: 2s Facts lesson. If you do not have the chart, refer to the Multiplication: 2s Facts lesson in the Lesson Guide for instructions on how to create it.

▶ Content Background

Students will continue to practice the 10s facts through 10 (1 × 10, 2 × 10, through 10 × 10). Through activities and games, they will work toward memorizing these facts.

Materials to Gather

SUPPLIED

base-10 blocks – 10 tens rods
Number Line 0–100 (optional printout)
Practice the 10s Facts activity page
Checkpoint (printout)

ALSO NEEDED

index cards – numbered 1–10 and with multiples of 10–100
Multiplication Facts Chart from the Multiplication: 2s Facts lesson
timer

GET READY Jumping 10s Facts

ONLINE 5min

Students will skip count by 10s using the Number Line Learning Tool.

DIRECTIONS FOR USING THE NUMBER LINE LEARNING TOOL

1. Click Count and choose the following:
   - Start Number Line at: 0
   - End Number Line at: 100
   - Count by: 10s

   Click OK.

2. Students should click on each number to count by 10s. As they click each number, the frog will hop to the number and it will be said aloud. The number line will slide over automatically when necessary to display more numbers. When they reach 100, students should click Count Again and repeat.

3. Each time students skip count by 10, write the multiplication sentence they are solving. For example, if they skip count by 10s seven times, they are solving the multiplication fact $7 \times 10 = 70$.

   Have students count by 10s to solve these problems:
   - Count 7 times to solve $7 \times 10 = ?$.
   - Count 4 times to solve $4 \times 10 = ?$.
   - Count 8 times to solve $8 \times 10 = ?$.
   - Count 3 times to solve $3 \times 10 = ?$.
   - Count 10 times to solve $10 \times 10 = ?$.

Objectives

- Use models and math symbols to represent multiplication.

LEARN 10s Fast Facts

ONLINE 10min

Student will play the Fast Facts game to practice quickly recalling 2s and 10s multiplication facts. Throughout the activity, encourage students to first try to recall the fact without using a model. If they have difficulty, have them solve the problems using a strategy they have learned, including the number line, circle blocks, or their fingers.

DIRECTIONS FOR USING THE FAST FACTS LEARNING TOOL

1. Have students enter their name and car number as well as choose the color of their car.

2. Choose the following options:
   - Choose the facts you want to practice: Multiplication
   - Choose multiples: 2 column (1×2, 2×2, 3×2, and so on through 10×2) and 10 column (1×10, 2×10, 3×10, and so on through 10×10).
   - Mode: Race Mode

Objectives

- Demonstrate automatic recall of multiplication facts for 10 through 10×10.

Tips

If you want students to get used to the game first, go to Test Drive Mode and enter 5 for the number of problems. Then move to Race Mode.

Allow students to use circle blocks and the Number Line 0–100 printout, if necessary.

3. As each problem appears on the screen, have students type the answer and then press Enter. After students finish, review the results on the "Fast Facts Results" screen. Note how many problems students answered incorrectly. Also record their time for future reference. You can click under the Lap tables on this screen to see exactly which problems students answered correctly (shown in white) and which ones they missed (shown in red).

4. Repeat the activity. Have students try to beat their time and improve their accuracy.

5. If time remains, customize the "Choose multiples" screen and specifically choose the facts with which students had difficulty. Then have them run another race.

OFFLINE

15 min

LEARN Games for 10s Facts

Objectives

- Demonstrate automatic recall of multiplication facts for 10 through 10×10.

Student will play games to help them memorize the 10s multiplication facts. Throughout the activity, encourage students to first try to recall the fact without using a model. If students have difficulty, have them solve the problems using a strategy they have learned, including the number line, picturing tens rods, or using their fingers.

Gather the numbered index cards and tens rods.

Tips

Allow students to use the Number Line 0–100 printout, if necessary.

1. Lay out the 1–10 cards face down in a random order. Lay out the other cards (10, 20, 30, and so on through 100) face up out of order.

2. **Say:** Let's play some games to practice the 10s facts. Turn over a card, and multiply that number by 10. Then pick up the card that shows the answer. For example, if you turned over the 6 card, you would say "6 times 10 equals 60" and pick up the 60 card. If you can say the correct answer without skip counting, you can keep the cards.

3. Play the game until students have collected all the cards.

4. **Say:** Let's play another game now. Grab some tens rods without looking. Multiply the number of tens rods you pick up by 10. For example, if you pick up three rods, you would count 10, 20, 30 and say "3 times 10 equals 30."

5. Play the game, reviewing each of the 10s facts. Keep track of the facts that students have difficulty with, and repeat these facts.

LEARN Post the 10s Facts

- Demonstrate automatic recall of multiplication facts for 10 through 10 × 10.

Students will add the 10s facts to the Multiplication Facts chart. Gather the Multiplication Facts chart from the Multiplication: 2s Facts lesson.

1. **Say:** Let's add the 10s facts to the chart. What is 3 × 10?

2. Move along the bottom of the chart to the 3, and as you say 10, move up the 3 column to the 10 row. Point to this square.

3. If students are able to quickly recall the product (30), have them write 30 with a pencil in the square where the row meets the column. If not, tell them they need to practice 3 × 10 some more before writing the product on the chart.

4. Remind them that in several days, if they have memorized the facts and can recall them quickly, they can rewrite them with a colored marker.

5. Repeat Step 1 with all the 10s facts. Be sure that you ask the facts in a random order. Also ask any 2s facts that students have not yet written on the chart. They should only write a fact on the chart when they have it memorized and can say it quickly. Practice facts that students have difficulty with until they can say the facts quickly.

Note: Students will fill out the chart in stages. Keep the chart for use in future lessons. At the end of the lesson, the chart should look like the one shown, but only if students have automatic recall of these facts.

Tips

Only have students write the product on the chart when they can state the fact quickly—without having to skip count or use a model. You may also want to put a small sticker in the squares of the multiplication facts they know.

Mulitplication Facts Chart

×	0	1	2	3	4	5	6	7	8	9	10
10		10	20	30	40	50	60	70	80	90	100
9											
8											
7											
6											
5											
4											
3											
2		2	4	6	8	10	12	14	16	18	20
1											
0											

TRY IT Practice the 10s Facts

- Demonstrate automatic recall of multiplication facts for 10 through 10 × 10.

Students will practice solving 10s facts. The goal is to complete the problems by automatically recalling the answers to these facts. Give students the Practice the 10s Facts activity page from their Activity Book and read the directions with them.

If students have attained automatic recall, they should be able to complete the Try It in 2 minutes. Time students as they complete the Try It.

Multiplication: 10s Facts
Practice the 10s Facts

Name: _____

Write the answer without using a model.

1. $9 \times 10 = \underline{90}$

2. $10 \times 10 = \underline{100}$

3. $5 \times 10 = \underline{50}$

4. $7 \times 10 = \underline{70}$

5. $2 \times 10 = \underline{20}$

6. $1 \times 10 = \underline{10}$

7. $4 \times 10 = \underline{40}$

8. $8 \times 10 = \underline{80}$

9. $3 \times 10 = \underline{30}$

10. $6 \times 10 = \underline{60}$

T R Y   I T

---

11. $\begin{array}{r} 3 \\ \times\ 10 \\ \hline 30 \end{array}$

12. $\begin{array}{r} 8 \\ \times\ 10 \\ \hline 80 \end{array}$

13. $\begin{array}{r} 6 \\ \times\ 10 \\ \hline 60 \end{array}$

14. $\begin{array}{r} 4 \\ \times\ 10 \\ \hline 40 \end{array}$

15. $\begin{array}{r} 9 \\ \times\ 10 \\ \hline 90 \end{array}$

16. $\begin{array}{r} 7 \\ \times\ 10 \\ \hline 70 \end{array}$

17. $\begin{array}{r} 5 \\ \times\ 10 \\ \hline 50 \end{array}$

18. $\begin{array}{r} 2 \\ \times\ 10 \\ \hline 20 \end{array}$

19. $\begin{array}{r} 1 \\ \times\ 10 \\ \hline 10 \end{array}$

20. $\begin{array}{r} 10 \\ \times\ 10 \\ \hline 100 \end{array}$

T R Y   I T

CHECKPOINT

OFFLINE **10 min**

Print the Checkpoint and have students complete it on their own. Read the directions, problems, and answer choices to students, if necessary. Use the answer key to score the Checkpoint, and then enter the results online.

Objectives

- Demonstrate automatic recall of multiplication facts for 10 through 10×10.

○ Checkpoint

Math | Multiplication and Number Patterns | Multiplication: 10s Facts

Name _____   Date _____

Checkpoint Answer Key

Write the answer.

(1 point)
1. $5 \times 10 = \underline{50}$

(1 point)
2. $8 \times 10 = \underline{80}$

(1 point)
3. $2 \times 10 = \underline{20}$

(1 point)
4. $3 \times 10 = \underline{30}$

(1 point)
5. $9 \times 10 = \underline{90}$

(1 point)
6. $4 \times 10 = \underline{40}$

(1 point)
7. $10 \times 10 = \underline{100}$

(1 point)
8. $7 \times 10 = \underline{70}$

1 of 1

Multiply by 5

▶ Lesson Objectives

- Use counting by multiples of 5 to understand multiplication facts for 5.
- Demonstrate automatic recall of multiplication facts for 5 through 10×5.

▶ Prerequisite Skills

Use counting by multiples of 10 to understand multiplication facts for 10.

▶ Advance Preparation

Number index cards 1 through 10 or gather the numbered cards you created previously.

▶ Content Background

Students will learn that the 5s multiplication facts are multiplication problems where a number through 10 is multiplied by 5: $1 \times 5, 2 \times 5, 3 \times 5, 4 \times 5$, and so on through 10×5. They will learn that they can find the product by making equal groups or skip counting on a number line. Students are familiar with the products of the 5s multiplication facts because they know how to count by 5s through 50.

Materials to Gather

SUPPLIED

Number Line 0–100 (optional printout)

Practice Multiplying by 5 activity page

ALSO NEEDED

index cards – numbered 1–10

index cards – 10 blank

marker, coloring – any color

Students will first skip count by 10s on a number line and then by 5s. Have them say the values as they skip count by 10s and tell them that when they skip count by 5s, they will say some of the same numbers. Later in the lesson, they'll learn that the numbers that they say when they skip count by 5s are the products of the 5s facts. Students might make this connection on their own because of their familiarity with other multiplication facts.

- Use counting by multiples of 10 to understand multiplication facts for 10.
- Use counting by multiples of 5 to understand multiplication facts for 5.

DIRECTIONS FOR USING THE NUMBER LINE LEARNING TOOL

1. Click Count and choose the following:
   - Start Number Line at: 0
   - End Number Line at: 50
   - Count by: 10s

   Click OK.

2. Students should click on each number to count by 10s. As they click each number, the frog will hop to the number and it will be said aloud. The number line will slide over automatically when necessary to display more numbers. When they reach 50, students should click Count Again and repeat.

3. Click Count and choose the following:
   - Start Number Line at: 0
   - End Number Line at: 50
   - Count by: 5s

   Click OK.

4. Students should click on each number to count by 5s. As they click each number, the frog will hop to the number and it will be said aloud. The number line will slide over automatically when necessary to display more numbers. When they reach 50, students should click Count Again and repeat.

5. Ask students if they can see patterns that are similar when counting by 5s and 10s. (For example, every two skips of 5 is the same as one skip of 10.)

Students are familiar with the meaning of multiplication. Now they will learn the 5s multiplication facts. The 5s facts are multiplication problems where a number through 10 is multiplied by 5: $1 \times 5, 2 \times 5, 3 \times 5, 4 \times 5$, and so on through 10×5.

Students will review methods for solving multiplication problems: skip counting using either a number line or their fingers or making an array. They will see both horizontal and vertical facts. Explain that both formats mean the same thing.

- Use counting by multiples of 5 to understand multiplication facts for 5.
- Demonstrate automatic recall of multiplication facts for 5 through 10×5.

Tips

Allow students to use the Number Line 0–100 printout, if necessary.

LEARN Games for 5s

Student will play games to help them recall the multiplication facts for 5. Gather the index cards and marker.

1. Put 10 index cards in a row and have students write down these facts without answers, in vertical form, each on its own index card:

   $$\begin{array}{ccc} 1 & 2 & 10 \\ \underline{\times\ 5} & \underline{\times\ 5} & \underline{\times\ 5} \end{array}$$ and so on through

2. Put a blank index card under each fact. Have students fill in the answers starting with the left card and working their way through the facts.

3. As students solve each problem, discuss any patterns they may see, such as the following:

   - Skip counting is by 5s.
   - The answers switch from having a 5 to a 0 in the ones place.
   - Each pair of answers, starting with 10 and 15, has the same number in the tens place.

4. **Say:** Now we will play a game.

   Give the students all of the cards with the answers 5, 10, 15, and so on through 50. You will have the cards with the problems in your hand. Draw one of your cards and say the problem to students. They should put down the answer to that card. Then place the problem above the card. If the students get the answer correct, they get both cards. Play the game until students have collected all the cards.

5. **Say:** Now we will play concentration with the cards we just made.

   Mix up the 10 cards with the problems on them and place them face down in 2 rows of 5. Then mix up the 10 cards with the answers on them and place them face down in 2 rows of 5 below the other set.

6. **Say:** We'll take turns. You will turn one card over from each set of cards. If you choose a 5s fact and an answer card that that match, you get to keep the pair. If they do not match, you will turn them back over and try to remember where they are. The goal is to match up all the correct pairs.

7. Allow students to use any of the ways they have learned to decide if the fact is a match to the answer card. Take turns playing concentration. Make an occasional error for students to catch by saying that you have a matching pair that doesn't actually match. Continue until all the cards have been paired.

8. **Say:** Let's play another game. I'm going to hold up a certain number of fingers. Then you will tell me the product of that number times 5. For example, if I held up four fingers, you would say "4 times 5 equals 20." If you don't know the answer, you can point to my fingers as you skip count by 5s.

9. Hold up fingers for each of the numbers through 10, showing the numbers in a random order. If students have difficulty, put up your fingers one at a time and have students count by 5s for each finger.

Objectives

- Use counting by multiples of 5 to understand multiplication facts for 5.
- Demonstrate automatic recall of multiplication facts for 5 through 10 × 5.

Tips

Allow students to use the Number Line 0–100 printout until they have memorized the facts.

TRY IT Practice Multiplying by 5

Students will practice solving 5s multiplication facts. Give students the Practice Multiplying by 5 activity page from their Activity Book and read the directions with them.

Multiply by 5
Practice Multiplying by 5

Name:

Write the answer.

1. $9 \times 5 =$ __45__   2. $1 \times 5 =$ __5__

3. $5 \times 5 =$ __25__   4. $4 \times 5 =$ __20__

5. $3 \times 5 =$ __15__   6. $2 \times 5 =$ __10__

7. $6 \times 5 =$ __30__   8. $10 \times 5 =$ __50__

9. $8 \times 5 =$ __40__   10. $7 \times 5 =$ __35__

TRY IT

MULTIPLICATION AND NUMBER PATTERNS   **305**   MULTIPLY BY 5

11. $\begin{array}{r} 5 \\ \times\ 5 \\ \hline 25 \end{array}$ 12. $\begin{array}{r} 9 \\ \times\ 5 \\ \hline 45 \end{array}$

13. $\begin{array}{r} 10 \\ \times\ 5 \\ \hline 50 \end{array}$ 14. $\begin{array}{r} 6 \\ \times\ 5 \\ \hline 30 \end{array}$

15. $\begin{array}{r} 2 \\ \times\ 5 \\ \hline 10 \end{array}$ 16. $\begin{array}{r} 7 \\ \times\ 5 \\ \hline 35 \end{array}$

17. $\begin{array}{r} 3 \\ \times\ 5 \\ \hline 15 \end{array}$ 18. $\begin{array}{r} 8 \\ \times\ 5 \\ \hline 40 \end{array}$

Solve.
19. Count by 5s to find the answer to 10×5.
   __50__

TRY IT

MULTIPLICATION AND NUMBER PATTERNS   **306**   MULTIPLY BY 5

Objectives

- Use counting by multiples of 5 to understand multiplication facts for 5.
- Demonstrate automatic recall of multiplication facts for 5 through 10×5.

Tips

Allow students to use the Number Line 0–100 printout, if necessary.

Multiplication: 5s Facts

Lesson Overview

Skills Update	5 minutes	ONLINE
GET READY Model 5s Facts	5 minutes	ONLINE
LEARN Boat Facts	10 minutes	ONLINE
LEARN Games for 5s Facts	15 minutes	OFFLINE
LEARN Post the 5s Facts	5 minutes	OFFLINE
TRY IT Practice the 5s Facts	10 minutes	OFFLINE
CHECKPOINT	10 minutes	OFFLINE

▶ Lesson Objectives
Demonstrate automatic recall of multiplication facts for 5 through 10 × 5.

▶ Prerequisite Skills
Demonstrate automatic recall of multiplication facts for 10 through 10 × 10.

▶ Advance Preparation
- Label an index card with each of the 5s multiplication facts. On the front of the card, write the multiplication expression vertically or horizontally. On the back, write the answer. You should make cards for the following facts.

Front	Back
1 × 5	5
2 × 5	10
3 × 5	15
4 × 5	20
5 × 5	25
6 × 5	30
7 × 5	35
8 × 5	40
9 × 5	45
10 × 5	50

- Follow the directions on the 10-Section Spinner printout and also write the numbers 1 through 10 in the tens sections of the 10-Section Spinner printout.
- Gather the Multiplication Facts Chart from the Multiplication: 10s Facts lesson. If you do not have the chart, refer to the Multiplication: 2s Facts lesson in the Lesson Guide for instructions on how to create it.

Materials to Gather

SUPPLIED
10-Section Spinner (printout)
Number Line 0–100 (optional printout)
Practice the 5s Facts activity page
Checkpoint (printout)

ALSO NEEDED
index cards – 10 blank
household objects – paper clip
Multiplication Facts Chart from the
    Multiplication: 2s Facts lesson
marker, coloring – any color
timer

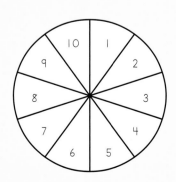

▶ Content Background

Students will continue to practice the 5s multiplication facts through 10 (1 × 5, 2 × 5, 3 × 5, 4 × 5, and so on through 10 × 5). Through activities and games, they will work toward memorizing these facts.

GET READY Model 5s Facts

ONLINE 5 min

Objectives

- Demonstrate automatic recall of multiplication facts for 5 through 10 × 5.

Students will skip count by 5s on a hundred chart.

DIRECTIONS FOR USING THE HUNDRED CHART LEARNING TOOL

1. Have students click the blue circle tool and count by 5s on the chart by clicking every fifth number as they count aloud. When they click, the number will be circled and will be said aloud. If an incorrect number is clicked, simply have them click it again to remove the circle. When they have counted by 5s through 100, have them click the speaker icon to hear the numbers counted aloud.

2. Have students look for patterns on the chart. Examples: the numbers appear in columns on the chart; the numbers end in 0 and 5. Then click Print to print a copy of students' hundred chart.

LEARN Boat Facts

ONLINE 10 min

Objectives

- Demonstrate automatic recall of multiplication facts for 5 through 10 × 5.

Student will play a game to practice quickly recalling 2s, 5s, and 10s multiplication facts. Throughout the activity, encourage students to first try to recall the fact without using a model. If they have difficulty, have them solve the problems using a strategy they have learned, including the number line, blocks, their fingers, or addition doubles for 2s.

LEARN Games for 5s Facts

OFFLINE 15 min

Objectives

- Demonstrate automatic recall of multiplication facts for 5 through 10 × 5.

Student will play games to help them memorize the 5s multiplication facts. Throughout the activity, encourage students to first try to recall the fact without using a model. If students have difficulty, have them solve using a strategy they have learned, including the number line, blocks, or their fingers.
  Gather the labeled index cards.

1. Shuffle the cards and place them in a stack. Make sure the front of each card (the facts without the answers) are face up.

   Say: You'll use multiplication flash cards to help you memorize the 5s facts. Pick up the first card, say the answer, and then flip the card over to see if you are correct. If you can say the correct answer very quickly, keep the card. If not, put the card at the bottom of the stack

2. Play the game until students have collected all the cards.

3. Gather the 10-Section Spinner and paper clip.

   Say: Let's play another game. Spin the paper clip on the spinner. Multiply the number in the section where the spinner lands by 5. For example, if the spinner lands in the 4 section, you would say "4 times 5 equals 20."

Tips

Allow students to use circle blocks and the Number Line 0–100 printout, if necessary.

4. Play until students have landed in all the sections.

5. If time permits, play this game with the 2s and 10s multiplication facts, too.

LEARN Post the 5s Facts

OFFLINE
5 min

Students will add the 5s facts to the Multiplication Facts Chart.

Gather the Multiplication Facts Chart from the Multiplication: 2s Facts lesson and the marker.

1. **Say:** Let's add the 5s facts to the chart. What is 6 × 5?

   If students are able to quickly recall the product (30), have them write a 30 with a pencil in the square where the row meets the column. If not, tell them they need to practice 6 × 5 some more before writing the product on the chart.

2. Repeat Step 1 with all the 5s facts, asking the facts in a random order. Also ask any 2s or 10s facts that students may have not yet placed on the chart. Students should only place a fact on the chart when they have it memorized and can say it quickly. Practice facts that students have difficulty with until they can say the facts quickly.

3. When reviewing the 2s and 10s, if you believe that the students have truly memorized these facts, have students write the products on the chart with a marker.

4. If students clearly know other facts within the chart, even those they haven't been formally taught, encourage them to fill in those facts, at least with pencil. However, students are only responsible for knowing the facts they have studied and do not need to learn any others at this time.

   Note: Students will fill out the chart in stages. Keep the chart for use as consistent review. At the end of the lesson, the chart should look like the one shown, but only if students have automatic recall of these facts. Some sections may be written in color marker, possibly with stickers, too.

Objectives

- Demonstrate automatic recall of multiplication facts for 5 through 10 × 5.

Tips

Only have students write the product on the chart when they can state the fact quickly—without having to skip count or use a model. You may also want to put a small sticker in the squares of the multiplication facts they know.

Mulitplication Facts Chart

	0	1	2	3	4	5	6	7	8	9	10
10		10	20	30	40	50	60	70	80	90	100
9											
8											
7											
6											
5		5	10	15	20	25	30	35	40	45	50
4											
3											
2		2	4	6	8	10	12	14	16	18	20
1											
0											
×	0	1	2	3	4	5	6	7	8	9	10

TRY IT Practice the 5s Facts

OFFLINE
10 min

Students will practice solving 5s facts. Give students the Practice the 5s Facts activity page from their Activity Book and read the directions with them.

If students have attained automatic recall, they should be able to complete the Try It in 2 minutes. Time students as they complete the Try It.

Objectives

- Demonstrate automatic recall of multiplication facts for 5 through 10 × 5.

Multiplication: 5s Facts

Practice the 5s Facts

Write the answer without using a model.

1. $9 \times 5 = \underline{45}$

2. $10 \times 5 = \underline{50}$

3. $5 \times 5 = \underline{25}$

4. $7 \times 5 = \underline{35}$

5. $2 \times 5 = \underline{10}$

6. $1 \times 5 = \underline{5}$

7. $\begin{array}{r} 3 \\ \times 5 \\ \hline 15 \end{array}$

8. $\begin{array}{r} 8 \\ \times 5 \\ \hline 40 \end{array}$

9. $\begin{array}{r} 6 \\ \times 5 \\ \hline 30 \end{array}$

10. $\begin{array}{r} 4 \\ \times 5 \\ \hline 20 \end{array}$

11. $4 \times 5 = \underline{20}$

12. $8 \times 5 = \underline{40}$

13. $6 \times 5 = \underline{30}$

14. $3 \times 5 = \underline{15}$

15. $1 \times 5 = \underline{5}$

16. $5 \times 5 = \underline{25}$

17. $\begin{array}{r} 9 \\ \times 5 \\ \hline 45 \end{array}$

18. $\begin{array}{r} 7 \\ \times 5 \\ \hline 35 \end{array}$

19. $\begin{array}{r} 10 \\ \times 5 \\ \hline 50 \end{array}$

20. $\begin{array}{r} 2 \\ \times 5 \\ \hline 10 \end{array}$

TRY IT

TRY IT

OFFLINE

10 min

CHECKPOINT

Print the Checkpoint and have students complete it on their own. Read the directions, problems, and answer choices to students, if necessary. Use the answer key to score the Checkpoint, and then enter the results online.

Objectives

- Demonstrate automatic recall of multiplication facts for 5 through 10×5.

Checkpoint   Math | Multiplication and Number Patterns | Multiplication: 5s Facts

Name _____   Date _____

Checkpoint Answer Key

Write the answer.

(1 point)
1. Count by 5s to find the answer to 10×5.
   A. 5   (B.) 50
   C. 15   D. 60

(1 point)
2. $2 \times 5 = \underline{10}$

(1 point)
3. $4 \times 5 = \underline{20}$

(1 point)
4. $5 \times 5 = \underline{25}$

(1 point)
5. $7 \times 5 = \underline{35}$

(1 point)
6. $1 \times 5 = \underline{5}$

(1 point)
7. $3 \times 5 = \underline{15}$

(1 point)
8. $8 \times 5 = \underline{40}$

(1 point)
9. $10 \times 5 = \underline{50}$

(1 point)
10. $6 \times 5 = \underline{30}$

(1 point)
11. $9 \times 5 = \underline{45}$

1 of 1

Unit Review

Lesson Overview

UNIT REVIEW Look Back	20 minutes	**ONLINE**
UNIT REVIEW Checkpoint Practice	20 minutes	**OFFLINE**
⏩ **UNIT REVIEW** Prepare for the Checkpoint		

▶ Unit Objectives

This lesson reviews the following objectives:

- Use concrete objects or sketches of arrays to model multiplication problems.
- Use concrete objects or sketches to model and explain multiplication as repeated addition.
- Use grouping to solve simple multiplication problems.
- Describe linear patterns, such as 3, 6, 9, using the wheels on 1 tricycle, 2 tricycles, 3 tricycles as an example.
- Determine a next term and extend a linear pattern, such as 3, 6, 9, … as the wheels on 1 tricycle, 2 tricycles, 3 tricycles, and extending it to 12 wheels on 4 tricycles as an example.
- Solve problems involving simple number patterns.
- Use models and math symbols to represent multiplication.
- Recognize that the $\times$ sign refers to multiplication.
- Correctly use the symbol $\times$ for multiplication.
- Use counting by multiples of 2 to understand multiplication facts for 2.
- Demonstrate automatic recall of multiplication facts for 2 through 2×10.
- Use counting by multiples of 10 to understand multiplication facts for 10.
- Demonstrate automatic recall of multiplication facts for 10 through 10×10.
- Use counting by multiples of 5 to understand multiplication facts for 5.
- Demonstrate automatic recall of multiplication facts for 5 through 5×10.

Materials to Gather

SUPPLIED
blocks – B
Checkpoint Practice activity page

▶ Advance Preparation

In this lesson, students will have an opportunity to review previous activities in the Multiplication and Number Patterns unit. Look at the suggested activities in Unit Review: Prepare for the Checkpoint online and gather any needed materials.

Keywords	
addition sentence	multiplication facts
array	multiplication symbol ($\times$)
expression	multiply
factor	number sentence
linear pattern	product
multiplication	skip count

UNIT REVIEW Look Back

Objectives

- Review unit objectives.

In this unit, students have learned about multiplication. They have explored arrays as a way to model multiplication. They have related multiplication to repeated addition and equal groups. They have used drawings, models, and symbols to represent multiplication and have used these to solve multiplication computation problems. Students have also learned about number patterns and have learned to recognize rules that describe number patterns involving multiplication and addition. They have learned to use these rules to extend the number patterns. Lastly students have explored the 2s, 5s, and 10s multiplication facts and worked on automatic recall of these basic facts. Students will review these concepts to prepare for the Unit Checkpoint.

UNIT REVIEW Checkpoint Practice

Objectives

- Review unit objectives.

Students will complete a Checkpoint Practice activity page to prepare for the Unit Checkpoint. If necessary, read the directions, problems, and answer choices to students. Have students answer the problems on their own. Carefully review the answers with students.

Give students the circle blocks for Problem 26.

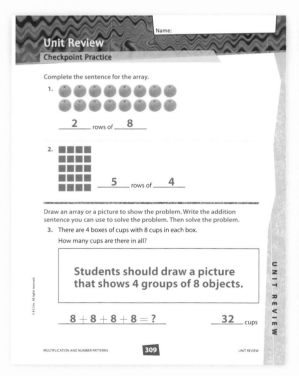

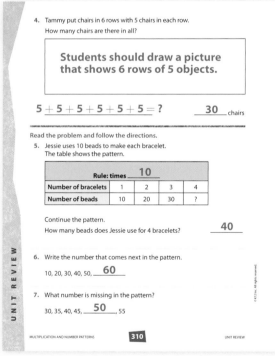

Circle the answer.

8. Corey is arranging his rock collection into groups with 5 rocks in each pile.
   1 group has 5 rocks.
   2 groups have a total of 10 rocks.
   3 groups have a total of 15 rocks.

   Corey has 6 groups of rocks. How many rocks does Corey have?

   A. 26   B. 27
   C. 28   (D.) 30

Corey's Rocks	
Number of groups	Number of rocks
1	5
2	10
3	15
4	20
5	25
6	?

9. Count by 10s to find the answer to 2 × 10.
   A. 18   (B.) 20   C. 30   D. 40

10. Which shows 4 × 2?

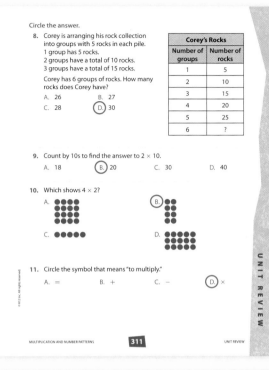

A. (dots)   (B.) (dots)
C. (dots)   D. (dots)

11. Circle the symbol that means "to multiply."
    A. =   B. +   C. −   (D.) ×

12. Steve recycles plastic bottles each week.
    After 1 week, he had recycled 10 plastic bottles.
    After 2 weeks, he had recycled a total of 20 plastic bottles.
    After 3 weeks, he had recycled a total of 30 plastic bottles.

    If this pattern continued, how many plastic bottles would Steve have recycled after 4 weeks?

    A. 25   B. 50   C. 45   (D.) 40

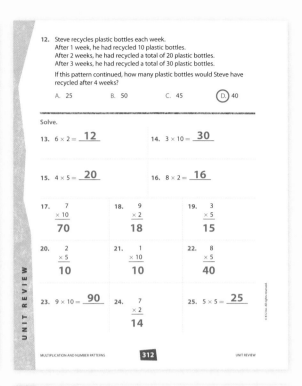

Solve.

13. $6 \times 2 =$ __12__

14. $3 \times 10 =$ __30__

15. $4 \times 5 =$ __20__

16. $8 \times 2 =$ __16__

17.
$$\begin{array}{r} 7 \\ \times\ 10 \\ \hline 70 \end{array}$$

18.
$$\begin{array}{r} 9 \\ \times\ 2 \\ \hline 18 \end{array}$$

19.
$$\begin{array}{r} 3 \\ \times\ 5 \\ \hline 15 \end{array}$$

20.
$$\begin{array}{r} 2 \\ \times\ 5 \\ \hline 10 \end{array}$$

21.
$$\begin{array}{r} 1 \\ \times\ 10 \\ \hline 10 \end{array}$$

22.
$$\begin{array}{r} 8 \\ \times\ 5 \\ \hline 40 \end{array}$$

23. $9 \times 10 =$ __90__

24.
$$\begin{array}{r} 7 \\ \times\ 2 \\ \hline 14 \end{array}$$

25. $5 \times 5 =$ __25__

Read the problem and follow the directions.

26. Use circles to show what 3 × 7 means.

Students should show 3 groups of 7 circle blocks or 3 rows of 7 circle blocks.

27. Look at the groups of stars. Write a multiplication number sentence to represent the groups of stars.

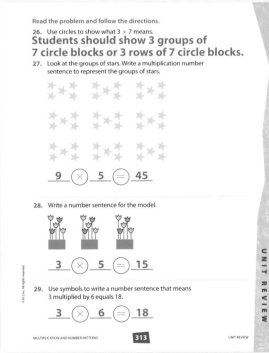

__9__ (×) __5__ (=) __45__

28. Write a number sentence for the model.

__3__ (×) __5__ (=) __15__

29. Use symbols to write a number sentence that means 3 multiplied by 6 equals 18.

__3__ (×) __6__ (=) __18__

30. Count by 10s to find the answer to 10 × 10.

10, 20, 30, 40, 50, 60, 70, 80, 90, 100;
The answer is 100.

31. Count by 5s to find the answer to 10 × 5.

5, 10, 15, 20, 25, 30, 35, 40, 45, 50;
The answer is 50.

32. Sharon does 2 hours of swimming each evening.

Describe the pattern and tell the number of hours of swimming in 7 days.

Rule: times __2__							
Number of days	1	2	3	4	5	6	7
Total number of hours swimming	2	4	6	8	10	12	?

Sharon swam for __14__ hours after 7 days.

→ **UNIT REVIEW** Prepare for the Checkpoint

What you do next depends on how students performed in the previous activity, Unit Review: Checkpoint Practice. If students had difficulty with any of the problems, complete the appropriate review activity listed in the table online.

Unit Checkpoint

Lesson Overview

UNIT CHECKPOINT Offline	20 minutes	OFFLINE
UNIT CHECKPOINT Online	40 minutes	ONLINE

▶ Unit Objectives

This lesson assesses the following objectives:

- Use concrete objects or sketches of arrays to model multiplication problems.
- Use concrete objects or sketches to model and explain multiplication as repeated addition.
- Use grouping to solve simple multiplication problems.
- Describe linear patterns, such as 3, 6, 9, using the wheels on 1 tricycle, 2 tricycles, 3 tricycles as an example.
- Determine a next term and extend a linear pattern, such as 3, 6, 9, … as the wheels on 1 tricycle, 2 tricycles, 3 tricycles, and extending it to 12 wheels on 4 tricycles as an example.
- Solve problems involving simple number patterns.
- Use models and math symbols to represent multiplication.
- Recognize that the $\times$ sign refers to multiplication.
- Correctly use the symbol $\times$ for multiplication.
- Use counting by multiples of 2 to understand multiplication facts for 2.
- Demonstrate automatic recall of multiplication facts for 2 through 2×10.
- Use counting by multiples of 10 to understand multiplication facts for 10.
- Demonstrate automatic recall of multiplication facts for 10 through 10×10.
- Use counting by multiples of 5 to understand multiplication facts for 5.
- Demonstrate automatic recall of multiplication facts for 5 through 5×10.

Materials to Gather

SUPPLIED
blocks – B
paper, drawing – 1 sheet
Unit Checkpoint (printout)

UNIT CHECKPOINT Offline

OFFLINE
20 min

Objectives

- Assess unit objectives.

Students will complete this part of the Unit Checkpoint offline. Students will take a performance-based assessment. Print the Unit Checkpoint. Read the directions, problems, and answer choices to students, if necessary. Use the answer key to score the Checkpoint, and then enter the results online.

Gather the circle blocks and drawing paper. Give students the circle blocks for Problems 2 and 5 and the drawing paper for Problem 3.

Name   Date

Unit Checkpoint Answer Key

Follow the instructions for each item. Choose the response that best
describes how the student performed on the task.

The answer is 45.

1. Say, "Count by 5s to find the answer to 9×5."
   (1 point)
   Did the student count 5, 10, 15, 20, 25, 30, 35, 40, 45?

   A. Yes   B. No

2. Say, "Use the blocks to show that 3×2 means the same as $2 + 2 + 2$."
   (1 point)
   Did the student make 3 groups of 2 blocks, then add the 3 groups
   of 2 to get 6, which is the same result as when you calculate 3×2?
   (The language may vary, but the ideas conveyed should be the same.)

   A. Yes   B. No

3. Say, "Draw an array model for the following multiplication problem: 6×4."
   (1 point)
   Did the student draw correctly? Students should draw objects with
   6 rows of 4 objects.

   A. Yes   B. No

The answer is 12.

4. Say, "Count by 2s to find the answer to 6×2."
   (1 point)
   Did the student count 2, 4, 6, 8, 10, 12?

   A. Yes   B. No

The answer is 10.

5. Say, "Use blocks to model and solve the problem $2 \times 5 = $?."
   (1 point)
   Did the student show 2 groups of 5?

   A. Yes   B. No

The answer is 80.

6. Say, "Count by 10s to find the answer to 8×10."
   (1 point)
   Did the student count 10, 20, 30, 40, 50, 60, 70, 80?

   A. Yes   B. No

Name   Date

The answer is 40.

7. Say, "Count by 5s to find the answer to 8×5."
   (1 point)
   Did the student count 5, 10, 15, 20, 25, 30, 35, 40?

   A. Yes   B. No

8. First build a model of 2 groups of 3 circle blocks, as shown below, and then
   say, "Write a number sentence for this model."

   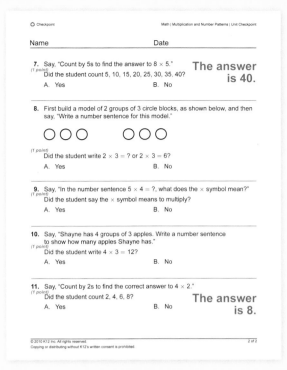

   (1 point)
   Did the student write $2 \times 3 = $? or $2 \times 3 = 6$?

   A. Yes   B. No

9. Say, "In the number sentence $5 \times 4 = $?, what does the $\times$ symbol mean?"
   (1 point)
   Did the student say the $\times$ symbol means to multiply?

   A. Yes   B. No

10. Say, "Shayne has 4 groups of 3 apples. Write a number sentence
    to show how many apples Shayne has."
    (1 point)
    Did the student write $4 \times 3 = 12$?

    A. Yes   B. No

The answer is 8.

11. Say, "Count by 2s to find the correct answer to 4×2."
    (1 point)
    Did the student count 2, 4, 6, 8?

    A. Yes   B. No

ONLINE 40 min

UNIT CHECKPOINT Online

Objectives

Students will complete this part of the Unit Checkpoint online. Read the
directions, problems, and answer choices to students. If necessary, help students
with keyboard or mouse operations

- Assess unit objectives.

Multiplication and Addition Properties

$$2 + 3 = 3 + 2$$

$$2 \times 4 = 4 \times 2$$

- Demonstrate understanding that the order in which numbers are multiplied does not affect the product.
- Demonstrate understanding that any number multiplied by 1 results in the same number ($n \times 1 = n$).
- Demonstrate understanding of the rule for multiplying by zero.
- Demonstrate understanding of the commutative properties of addition and multiplication.
- Use the commutative property in mental calculations.
- Use the commutative property to check results.
- Demonstrate understanding of the associative properties of addition and multiplication.
- Use the associative property in mental calculations.
- Use the associative property to check results.
- Use the commutative and associative properties to simplify expressions.

▶ Big Ideas

The commutative and associative properties can be used to simplify expressions.

▶ Unit Introduction

In this unit, students will learn the commutative and associative properties of addition and multiplication. They also will learn how to multiply with 0 and 1, how to use properties to make problems easier to solve, and how to use the properties to check calculations.

Multiplication Order and Rules

Lesson Overview

Skills Update	5 minutes	ONLINE
LEARN Multiply in Any Order	15 minutes	ONLINE
LEARN Multiply with 0 and 1	15 minutes	ONLINE
LEARN Post the Facts	5 minutes	OFFLINE
TRY IT 0, 1, and Order	10 minutes	OFFLINE
CHECKPOINT	10 minutes	OFFLINE

▶ Lesson Objectives

- Demonstrate understanding that the order in which numbers are multiplied does not affect the product.
- Demonstrate understanding that any number multiplied by 1 results in the same number ($n \times 1 = n$).
- Demonstrate understanding of the rule for multiplying by zero.

▶ Prerequisite Skills

Use models and math symbols to represent multiplication.

▶ Common Errors and Misconceptions

Students might not understand that the two factors in a multiplication expression have different meanings. For example, 3 sets of 6 dots is written as 3×6, not 6×3. However, the product of each expression is 18.

▶ Advance Preparation

Gather the Multiplication Facts Chart from the Multiplication: 5s Facts lesson. If you do not have the chart, refer to the Multiplication: 2s Facts lesson in the Lesson Guide for instructions on how to create it.

▶ Content Background

Students will use arrays and number lines to learn that the order in which numbers are multiplied does not affect the product. They will also use equal groups to learn the rules for multiplying by 0 and 1. Students will post all the new facts they learn on the Multiplication Facts Chart.

An understanding of mathematics properties will help students learn new information about number relationships and transfer that understanding to more difficult concepts later in mathematics. This lesson presents three of those basic properties:

Materials to Gather

SUPPLIED

Multiplication Facts Chart from the Multiplication: 5s Facts lesson

0, 1, and Order activity page

Checkpoint (printout)

ALSO NEEDED

marker, coloring – any color

- The order in which two factors are multiplied does not change the product. For example, the products of 4×3 and 3×4 are both 12. The specific name for this property is the commutative property of multiplication. Informally refer to such facts as "turnaround" facts. This property alone can be an encouraging one for students as they realize how it affects their memorization of multiplication facts. Once they have learned one fact, they actually know two facts.

- Any number when multiplied by 1 results in that same number. For example, $4 \times 1 = 4$, $1 \times 12 = 12$, and $1,234,567 \times 1 = 1,234,567$. The specific name for this property, which students are not required to know, is the identity property of multiplication. By understanding this property, students will understand certain fraction operations more easily as well as a number of concepts of higher math.

- The product of any number and zero is always zero. For example, $4 \times 0 = 0$, $0 \times 12 = 0$, and $1,234,567 \times 0 = 0$. The specific name for this property is the zero property of multiplication. By understanding this property, students can much more easily simplify expressions that may look quite complex but actually result in a simple zero value.

Keywords	**factor** – one of the two or more numbers that are multiplied in a multiplication problem **product** – the answer to a multiplication problem

LEARN Multiply in Any Order

ONLINE **15**min

Students will model multiplication facts with arrays and on number lines to see that the order in which numbers are multiplied does not affect the product. Encourage students to begin using the proper vocabulary: *factors* for the numbers being multiplied and *product* for the answer to a multiplication problem.

Objectives

- Demonstrate understanding that the order in which numbers are multiplied does not affect the product.

LEARN Multiply with 0 and 1

ONLINE **15**min

Students will multiply with 0 and 1. They will see that any number multiplied by 0 is 0 and that any number multiplied by 1 is that same number.

Objectives

- Demonstrate understanding that any number multiplied by 1 results in the same number ($n \times 1 = n$).

- Demonstrate understanding of the rule for multiplying by zero.

LEARN Post the Facts

Students will add the 0s facts, 1s facts, and "turnaround" facts to the Multiplication Facts Chart.

Gather the Multiplication Facts Chart from the Multiplication: 5s Facts lesson and the marker.

1. **Say:** Let's add the 0s facts and 1s facts to the chart. What's 4×0?

   If students are able to quickly recall the product (0), have them write a 0 with a pencil (or marker if they really know it) in the square where the row meets the column. If not, tell them they need to practice 4×0 some more before writing the product on the chart.

2. Repeat Step 1 with all the 0s facts and 1s facts, asking the facts in a random order. Also ask any 2s, 5s, or 10s facts that students may have not yet placed on the chart. Students should only place a fact on the chart when they have it memorized and can say it quickly. Practice facts that students have difficulty with until they can say the facts quickly.

3. When reviewing the 2s, 5s and 10s, if you believe that the students have truly memorized these facts, have students write the products with the marker.

4. Now, include all turnaround facts for 0s, 1s, 2s, 5s, and 10s, such as 0×5, 1×10, or 2×4.

5. If students clearly know other facts within the chart, even without having been formally taught them, encourage them to fill in those facts with a pencil. However, students are only responsible for knowing the facts they have studied and do not need to learn any others at this time.

   Note: The chart demonstrates just how many facts the students have learned. The remaining facts will be left for another time.

   Students have filled out the chart in stages. Keep the chart for use in future lessons and for use as consistent review. At the end of the lesson, the chart should look like the one shown (if students can quickly recall all of these facts) or have some sections written in marker, possibly with stickers, too.

Objectives

- Demonstrate understanding that the order in which numbers are multiplied does not affect the product.
- Demonstrate understanding that any number multiplied by 1 results in the same number ($n \times 1 = n$).
- Demonstrate understanding of the rule for multiplying by zero.

Tips

Filling in this chart is a great motivation for students to memorize and track their facts. Only have students place the product on the chart when they can state the fact quickly—without having to skip count or use a model. You may also want to put a small sticker in the squares of the multiplication facts they know. Consistently return to this chart and practice these facts throughout the year.

Mulitplication Facts Chart

	0	1	2	3	4	5	6	7	8	9	10
10	0	10	20	30	40	50	60	70	80	90	100
9	0	9	18			45					90
8	0	8	16			40					80
7	0	7	14			35					70
6	0	6	12			30					60
5	0	5	10	15	20	25	30	35	40	45	50
4	0	4	8			20					40
3	0	3	6			15					30
2	0	2	4	6	8	10	12	14	16	18	20
1	0	1	2	3	4	5	6	7	8	9	10
0	0	0	0	0	0	0	0	0	0	0	0
×	0	1	2	3	4	5	6	7	8	9	10

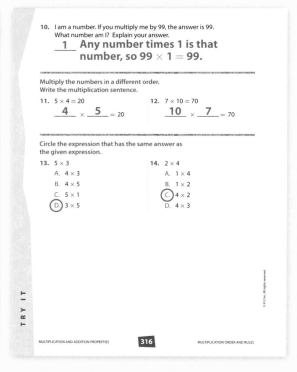

TRY IT 0, 1, and Order

Students will practice solving problems that use 0s facts, 1s facts, and turnaround facts. Give students the 0, 1, and Order activity page from their Activity Book and read the directions with them.

- Demonstrate understanding that the order in which numbers are multiplied does not affect the product.
- Demonstrate understanding that any number multiplied by 1 results in the same number ($n \times 1 = n$).
- Demonstrate understanding of the rule for multiplying by zero.

Multiplication Order and Rules
0, 1, and Order

Name: _____

Solve.

1. $7 \times 1 = \underline{7}$ 2. $0 \times 9 = \underline{0}$

3. $0 \times 12 = \underline{0}$ 4. $50 \times 1 = \underline{50}$

Write the answer. Say your explanation.

5. $6 \times 2 = 12$. What is 2×6? Explain your answer.
$2 \times 6 = \underline{12}$ **The order you multiply the numbers does not change the answer.**

6. $7 \times 5 = 35$. What is 5×7? Explain your answer.
$5 \times 7 = \underline{35}$ **The order you multiply the numbers does not change the answer.**

Write the answer.

7. $2 \times 8 = 16$. What is 8×2?
$8 \times 2 = \underline{16}$

8. $3 \times 0 = 0$. What is 0×3?
$0 \times 3 = \underline{0}$

Write the answer. Say your explanation.

9. I am a number. When you show 10 groups of me, the total is 0. What number am I? Explain your answer.
$\underline{0}$ **Any number times 0 is 0, so if a number is multiplied by 10 and the answer is 0, the number must be 0.**

MULTIPLICATION AND ADDITION PROPERTIES **315** MULTIPLICATION ORDER AND RULES

TRY IT

---

10. I am a number. If you multiply me by 99, the answer is 99. What number am I? Explain your answer.
$\underline{1}$ **Any number times 1 is that number, so $99 \times 1 = 99$.**

Multiply the numbers in a different order. Write the multiplication sentence.

11. $5 \times 4 = 20$
$\underline{4} \times \underline{5} = 20$

12. $7 \times 10 = 70$
$\underline{10} \times \underline{7} = 70$

Circle the expression that has the same answer as the given expression.

13. 5×3
A. 4×3
B. 4×5
C. 5×1
D. 3×5 (circled)

14. 2×4
A. 1×4
B. 1×2
C. 4×2 (circled)
D. 4×3

MULTIPLICATION AND ADDITION PROPERTIES **316** MULTIPLICATION ORDER AND RULES

TRY IT

CHECKPOINT

Print the Checkpoint and have students complete it on their own. Read the directions, problems, and answer choices to students, if necessary. Use the answer key to score the Checkpoint, and then enter the results online.

Objectives

- Demonstrate understanding that the order in which numbers are multiplied does not affect the product.

- Demonstrate understanding that any number multiplied by 1 results in the same number ($n \times 1 = n$).

- Demonstrate understanding of the rule for multiplying by zero.

Checkpoint   Math | Multiplication and Addition Properties | Multiplication Order and Rules

Name _____   Date _____

Checkpoint Answer Key

Solve.

(1 point)
1. $1 \times 6 =$ __6__

(1 point)
2. $490 \times 0 =$ __0__

(1 point)
3. I am a number. When I am multiplied by 80 the answer is 0.
What number am I?

__0__

(2 points)
4. If $9 \times 5 = 45$, what is the answer to 5×9?

Explain your answer.

45; Changing the order you multiply the numbers doesn't change the answer.

Circle the answer.

(1 point)
5. $99 \times 1 = ?$

- **(A.)** 99
- B. 100
- C. 990
- D. 991

1 of 2

Checkpoint   Math | Multiplication and Addition Properties | Multiplication Order and Rules

Name _____   Date _____

(1 point)
6. $48 \times 0 = ?$

- **(A)** 0
- B. 1
- C. 48
- D. 480

(1 point)
7. Choose the problem that has the same answer as 4×2.

- A. 4×9
- B. 3×4
- **(C.)** 2×4
- D. 9×2

(1 point)
8. Choose the problem that has the same answer as 6×5.

- A. 3×4
- **(B.)** 5×6
- C. 7×4
- D. 3×6

2 of 2

The Commutative Property

Skills Update	5 minutes	ONLINE
LEARN Commutative Property	15 minutes	ONLINE
LEARN Use the Commutative Property	20 minutes	ONLINE
TRY IT Use Properties	10 minutes	OFFLINE
CHECKPOINT	10 minutes	OFFLINE

▶ Lesson Objectives

- Demonstrate understanding of the commutative properties of addition and multiplication.
- Use the commutative property in mental calculations.
- Use the commutative property to check results.

▶ Prerequisite Skills

Demonstrate understanding that the order in which numbers are multiplied does not affect the product.

▶ Content Background

Students will learn more about the commutative properties of addition and multiplication. These properties state that they can add or multiply in any order. For example, both $3 + 8$ and $8 + 3$ have the same sum, 11. Also, 2×4 and 4×2 have the same product, 8. Students will use the commutative properties to complete mental calculations and check results.

Materials to Gather

SUPPLIED

Use Properties activity page

Checkpoint (printout)

Keywords

addend — one of the two or more numbers that are added to determine a sum

commutative property of addition — a rule stating that changing the order of two addends does not change their sum

commutative property of multiplication — a rule stating that changing the order of factors does not change their product

LEARN Commutative Property

- Demonstrate understanding of the commutative properties of addition and multiplication.

Students will learn about the commutative properties of addition and multiplication. They will see that they can add numbers in any order and get the same sum. They will also see that they can multiply factors in any order and get the same product. If students ask whether the commutative property is true for subtraction, commend them for asking such a good question and let them know that the commutative property is not true for subtraction. Students will investigate that idea in another lesson.

As students work through the activity, have them ask themselves questions similar to the following:

- What are the numbers in the problem?
- Will changing the order of the numbers make the problem easier to solve?
- What is the sum or product?
- Did the sum or product change when I changed the order of the numbers?

LEARN Use the Commutative Property

- Use the commutative property in mental calculations.
- Use the commutative property to check results.

Students will learn how to use the commutative property to add and multiply mentally and to check answers. They will rearrange the numbers in addition and multiplication expressions to make the numbers easier to add or multiply mentally. They also will check answers by adding or multiplying in a different order.

As students work through the activity, have them ask themselves questions similar to the following:

- Which two numbers can I add to make a friendly tens number?
- Which numbers can I add first so I don't have to regroup?
- Which multiplication facts do I know that will make problems easier to multiply?

TRY IT Use Properties

Students will practice using the commutative properties of addition and multiplication. They will reorder numbers to make them easier to add or multiply. They will also reorder numbers to check answers. Give students the Use Properties activity page from their Activity Book and read the directions with them.

- Demonstrate understanding of the commutative properties of addition and multiplication.

- Use the commutative property in mental calculations.

- Use the commutative property to check results.

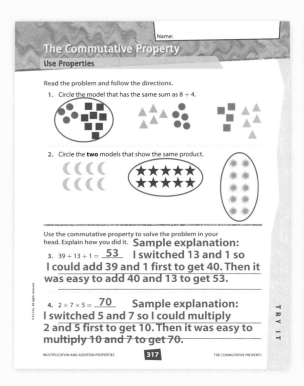

Name: _____

The Commutative Property
Use Properties

Read the problem and follow the directions.

1. Circle the model that has the same sum as $8 + 4$.

2. Circle the **two** models that show the same product.

Use the commutative property to solve the problem in your head. Explain how you did it. **Sample explanation:**

3. $39 + 13 + 1 = $ __53__ **I switched 13 and 1 so I could add 39 and 1 first to get 40. Then it was easy to add 40 and 13 to get 53.**

4. $2 \times 7 \times 5 = $ __70__ **Sample explanation: I switched 5 and 7 so I could multiply 2 and 5 first to get 10. Then it was easy to multiply 10 and 7 to get 70.**

MULTIPLICATION AND ADDITION PROPERTIES **317** THE COMMUTATIVE PROPERTY

T R Y   I T

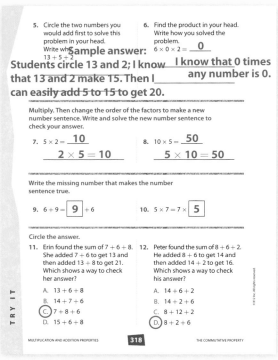

5. Circle the two numbers you would add first to solve this problem in your head. Write why. $13 + 5 + 2$ **Sample answer: Students circle 13 and 2; I know that 13 and 2 make 15. Then I can easily add 5 to 15 to get 20.**

6. Find the product in your head. Write how you solved the problem. $6 \times 0 \times 2 = $ __0__ **I know that 0 times any number is 0.**

Multiply. Then change the order of the factors to make a new number sentence. Write and solve the new number sentence to check your answer.

7. $5 \times 2 = $ __10__ $2 \times 5 = 10$

8. $10 \times 5 = $ __50__ $5 \times 10 = 50$

Write the missing number that makes the number sentence true.

9. $6 + 9 = \boxed{9} + 6$

10. $5 \times 7 = 7 \times \boxed{5}$

Circle the answer.

11. Erin found the sum of $7 + 6 + 8$. She added $7 + 6$ to get 13 and then added $13 + 8$ to get 21. Which shows a way to check her answer?
    A. $13 + 6 + 8$
    B. $14 + 7 + 6$
    C. $7 + 8 + 6$
    D. $15 + 6 + 8$

12. Peter found the sum of $8 + 6 + 2$. He added $8 + 6$ to get 14 and then added $14 + 2$ to get 16. Which shows a way to check his answer?
    A. $14 + 6 + 2$
    B. $14 + 2 + 6$
    C. $8 + 12 + 2$
    D. $8 + 2 + 6$

T R Y   I T

MULTIPLICATION AND ADDITION PROPERTIES **318** THE COMMUTATIVE PROPERTY

CHECKPOINT

Objectives

- Demonstrate understanding of the commutative properties of addition and multiplication.
- Use the commutative property in mental calculations.
- Use the commutative property to check results.

Print the Checkpoint and have students complete it on their own. Read the directions, problems, and answer choices to students, if necessary. Use the answer key to score the Checkpoint, and then enter the results online.

Name _____ Date _____

Checkpoint Answer Key

Circle the answer.

(1 point)
1. What number goes in the box to make this number sentence true?

   $5 \times 3 = 3 \times \square$

   A. 3
   B. 5
   C. 8
   D. 15

(1 point)
2. What number goes in the box to make this number sentence true?

   $6 + 4 = \square + 6$

   A. 4
   B. 5
   C. 6
   D. 10

(1 point)
3. Which numbers can be added together first to make this problem easier to solve?

   $34 + 5 + 6 = \square$

   A. $3 + 4$
   B. $2 + 34$
   C. $34 + 6$
   D. $5 + 4$

Name _____ Date _____

(1 point)
4. Use the commutative property to solve this problem in your head.

   $2 \times 4 \times 5$

   A. 8
   B. 10
   C. 40
   D. 425

(1 point)
5. Yvette found the sum of $10 + 4 + 6$ by adding $10 + 4$ to get 14 and then adding $14 + 6$ to get 20. Which shows a way to check her answer?

   A. $14 + 4 + 6$
   B. $4 + 6 + 10$
   C. $10 + 4 + 10$
   D. $16 + 4 + 10$

(1 point)
6. Susan said that $6 \times 2 = 12$. Which is another way to do this problem to check Susan's answer?

   A. $6 + 2$
   B. 2×6
   C. $6 - 2$
   D. 2×2

The Associative Property

Lesson Overview		
Skills Update	5 minutes	**ONLINE**
LEARN Group to Add and Multiply	20 minutes	**ONLINE**
LEARN Use the Associative Property	15 minutes	**ONLINE**
TRY IT Group Numbers Different Ways	10 minutes	**OFFLINE**
CHECKPOINT	10 minutes	**OFFLINE**

▶ Lesson Objectives

- Demonstrate understanding of the associative properties of addition and multiplication.
- Use the associative property in mental calculations.
- Use the associative property to check results.

▶ Prerequisite Skills

Given a number of objects up through 20, show how those objects can be grouped and regrouped to illustrate the associative property.

▶ Content Background

Students will learn about the associative properties of addition and multiplication. They will use the associative properties to complete mental calculations and check results.

The associative property of multiplication, sometimes known as the grouping property of multiplication, states that changing the way factors are grouped does not change the product. Parentheses can be used to group factors to show which numbers are to be multiplied first. Students will learn about parentheses and will use them to group factors. For example, here are two ways to group the factors to multiply $7 \times 5 \times 2$:

$$(7 \times 5) \times 2 \qquad 7 \times (5 \times 2)$$
$$35 \times 2 \qquad\qquad 7 \times 10$$
$$70 \qquad\qquad\qquad 70$$

Students should group factors in a way that will make the numbers easier to multiply. In the examples, many students will find grouping 5 and 2 a better choice, because multiplying 7 by 10 may be easier for them than multiplying 35 by 2.

The order of operations states that factors in a horizontal row should be multiplied from left to right. If, however, any factors are grouped in parentheses, these factors should be multiplied first.

Materials to Gather

SUPPLIED

blocks – E (red, yellow, blue)

Group Numbers Different Ways activity page

Checkpoint (printout)

associative property of addition – a rule stating that grouping three addends in different ways does not change their sum

associative property of multiplication – a rule stating that grouping factors in different ways does not change their product

ONLINE
20min

LEARN Group to Add and Multiply

Objectives

- Demonstrate understanding of the associative properties of addition and multiplication.
- Use the associative property in mental calculations.
- Use the associative property to check results.

Students will learn about the associative properties of addition and multiplication. They will see that they can group numbers in different ways and get the same sum or product. They will also learn that parentheses show grouping.

As students work through the activity, have them ask themselves questions similar to the following:

- What numbers are in parentheses?
- What is the other number?
- How can I show the groups or arrays?
- What is the sum or product of the numbers in parentheses?
- What is the final sum or product?
- Did the sum or product change when the numbers were grouped in different ways?

ONLINE
15min

LEARN Use the Associative Property

Objectives

- Demonstrate understanding of the associative properties of addition and multiplication.
- Use the associative property in mental calculations.
- Use the associative property to check results.

Students will learn how to use the associative property to add and multiply mentally and to check answers. They will group the numbers in addition and multiplication expressions to make the numbers easier to add or multiply mentally. They also will check answers by grouping the numbers in addition and multiplication expressions in different ways.

As students work through the activity, have them ask themselves questions similar to the following:

- Which two numbers can I add to make a ten?
- Which numbers can I add first so I don't have to regroup?
- Which multiplication facts do I know?
- Which two numbers should I put parentheses around?

TRY IT Group Numbers Different Ways

Students will practice using the associative properties of addition and multiplication. They will group numbers in different ways to make them easier to add or multiply. They will also group numbers in different ways to check answers. Give students the square blocks and the Group Numbers Different Ways activity page from their Activity Book. Read the directions with them.

- Demonstrate understanding of the associative properties of addition and multiplication.
- Use the associative property in mental calculations.
- Use the associative property to check results.

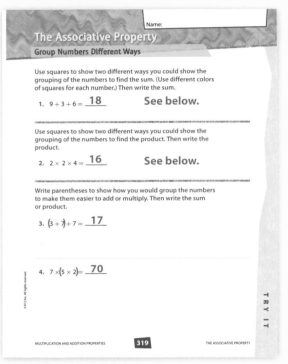

Name:

The Associative Property
Group Numbers Different Ways

Use squares to show two different ways you could show the grouping of the numbers to find the sum. (Use different colors of squares for each number.) Then write the sum.

1. $9 + 3 + 6 = $ __18__   **See below.**

Use squares to show two different ways you could show the grouping of the numbers to find the product. Then write the product.

2. $2 \times 2 \times 4 = $ __16__   **See below.**

Write parentheses to show how you would group the numbers to make them easier to add or multiply. Then write the sum or product.

3. $(3 + 7) + 7 = $ __17__

4. $7 \times (5 \times 2) = $ __70__

TRY IT

MULTIPLICATION AND ADDITION PROPERTIES   **319**   THE ASSOCIATIVE PROPERTY

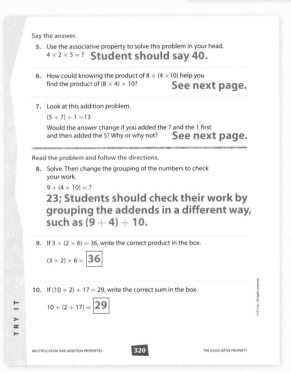

Say the answer.

5. Use the associative property to solve this problem in your head.
   $4 \times 2 \times 5 = ?$ **Student should say 40.**

6. How could knowing the product of $8 \times (4 \times 10)$ help you find the product of $(8 \times 4) \times 10$?   **See next page.**

7. Look at this addition problem.
   $(5 + 7) + 1 = 13$
   Would the answer change if you added the 7 and the 1 first and then added the 5? Why or why not?   **See next page.**

Read the problem and follow the directions.

8. Solve. Then change the grouping of the numbers to check your work.
   $9 + (4 + 10) = ?$
   23; Students should check their work by grouping the addends in a different way, such as $(9 + 4) + 10$.

9. If $3 \times (2 \times 6) = 36$, write the correct product in the box.
   $(3 \times 2) \times 6 = $ __36__

10. If $(10 + 2) + 17 = 29$, write the correct sum in the box.
    $10 + (2 + 17) = $ __29__

TRY IT

MULTIPLICATION AND ADDITION PROPERTIES   **320**   THE ASSOCIATIVE PROPERTY

Additional Answers

1. **Sample answer:**
   Way 1:

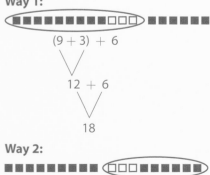

$(9 + 3) + 6$

$12 + 6$

18

   Way 2:

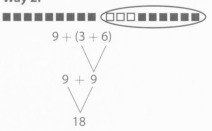

$9 + (3 + 6)$

$9 + 9$

18

2. **Sample answer:**
   Way 1:
   $(2 \times 2) \times 4 = ?$

   $2 \times 2 = 4$ $4 \times 4 = 16$

   Way 2:
   $2 \times (2 \times 4) = ?$

   $2 \times 4 = 8$

   $2 \times 8 = 16$

6. Students should say that the product of $8 \times (4 \times 10)$ is the same as the product of $(8 \times 4) \times 10$. Solve the first problem to know the answer to the second problem. Changing the grouping of factors does not change the product.

7. Students should say no, the answer would not change. Changing the grouping of addends does not change the sum.

CHECKPOINT

Print the Checkpoint. In Part 1, students will take a performance-based assessment. In Part 2, students will complete the problems on their own. Read the directions, problems, and answer choices to students, if necessary. Use the answer key to score the Checkpoint, and then enter the results online.

Objectives

- Demonstrate understanding of the associative properties of addition and multiplication.
- Use the associative property in mental calculations.
- Use the associative property to check results.

Checkpoint   Math | Multiplication and Addition Properties | The Associative Property

Name _____ Date _____

Checkpoint Answer Key

Part 1
Follow the instructions for each item. Choose the response that best describes how the student performed on the task.

1. Say, "How could knowing the product of $4 \times (6 \times 8)$ help you find the product of $(4 \times 6) \times 8$?"
(1 point)
   Did the student say that the product of $4 \times (6 \times 8)$ is the same as the product of $(4 \times 6) \times 8$ because changing the grouping of factors does not change the product?

   A. Yes   B. No

2. Write the addition problem $(9 + 2) + 5 = 16$ on a sheet of paper. Say, "Look at the addition problem.

   Would the answer change if you added the 2 and the 5 first and then added the 9? Why or why not?"
(1 point)
   Did the student say that the sum would not change because

   A. Yes   B. No

Give students Part 2 of the assessment.

1 of 2

Checkpoint   Math | Multiplication and Addition Properties | The Associative Property

Name _____ Date _____

Part 2
Solve.
(1 point)
3. If $2 \times (5 \times 6) = 60$, put the correct product in the box.

   $(2 \times 5) \times 6 = \boxed{60}$

(1 point)
4. If $(8 + 4) + 22 = 34$, put the correct sum in the box.

   $8 + (4 + 22) = \boxed{34}$

Circle the answer.
(1 point)
5. Use the associative property to solve this problem in your head.
   $14 + 7 + 3 = ?$

   A. 10
   B. 21
   Ⓒ 24
   D. 34

(1 point)
6. Larry said that $(7 \times 4) \times 5 = 140$. Which is another way to do this problem to check Larry's answer?

   A. $(7 \times 4) + 5$
   Ⓑ $7 \times (4 \times 5)$
   C. $(7 + 4) \times 5$
   D. $(7 \times 4) - 5$

2 of 2

Use Properties

Skills Update	5 minutes	**ONLINE**
GET READY Mental Calculations	5 minutes	**ONLINE**
LEARN Apply the Commutative Property	15 minutes	**ONLINE**
LEARN Apply the Associative Property	15 minutes	**ONLINE**
TRY IT Use Properties to Simplify	10 minutes	OFFLINE
CHECKPOINT	10 minutes	OFFLINE

▶ Lesson Objectives

Use the commutative and associative properties to simplify expressions.

▶ Prerequisite Skills

- Use the commutative property in mental calculations.
- Use the associative property in mental calculations.

▶ Content Background

Students have learned about the associative and commutative properties of addition and multiplication. They learned that changing the order or grouping of numbers in an addition or multiplication expression does not change the answer. In this lesson, students will continue to learn how to use these properties to make calculations easier.

Materials to Gather

SUPPLIED
Use Properties to Simplify activity page
Checkpoint (printout)

GET READY Mental Calculations

ONLINE
5min

Objectives

- Use the commutative property in mental calculations.
- Use the associative property in mental calculations.

Students will use the commutative and associative properties of addition and multiplication to help them add or multiply expressions more easily.

As students work through the activity, have them ask themselves questions similar to the following:

- Can I change the order or grouping of the addends to make a ten?
- Can I change the order or grouping of the factors to use multiplication facts I know?

LEARN Apply the Commutative Property

ONLINE
15min

Objectives

- Use the commutative and associative properties to simplify expressions.

Students will continue to learn how to apply the commutative property to add and multiply mentally. They will rearrange the numbers in addition and multiplication expressions to make the numbers easier to add or multiply mentally.

As students work through the activity, have them ask themselves questions similar to the following:

- If I add from left to right, can I do the problem in my head?
- If I cannot easily add from left to right, can I change the order of the numbers so that two addends will make a ten?
- If I multiply from left to right, can I do the problem in my head?
- If I cannot easily multiply from left to right, can I change the order of the numbers to use facts that I know?

LEARN Apply the Associative Property

ONLINE
15min

Objectives

- Use the commutative and associative properties to simplify expressions.

Students will continue to learn how to apply the associative property to add and multiply mentally. They will group the numbers in addition and multiplication expressions to make the numbers easier to add or multiply mentally.

As students work through the activity, have them ask themselves questions similar to the following:

- If I add the numbers in the parentheses first, can I do the problem in my head?
- If I cannot easily add the numbers, can I group the numbers differently so that two addends will make a ten?
- If I multiply the numbers in the parentheses first, can I do the problem in my head?
- If I cannot easily multiply the numbers, can I group the numbers differently to use multiplication facts that I know?

OFFLINE 10 min

Objectives

- Use the commutative and associative properties to simplify expressions.

Students will practice using the commutative and associative properties to make addition and multiplication calculations easier. Give students the Use Properties to Simplify activity page from their Activity Book and read the directions with them.

Name:

Use Properties
Use Properties to Simplify

Use the commutative property to rewrite each number sentence to make it easier to solve. Then solve the sentence.

For Problems 1–8, number sentences may vary. Examples are given.

1. $29 + 48 + 11 = ?$

   Number sentence and work:

   $29 + 11 + 48 = 40 + 48 = 88$

   $29 + 48 + 11 = \underline{\ 88\ }$

2. $? = 5 \times 7 \times 2$

   Number sentence and work:

   $5 \times 2 \times 7 = 10 \times 7 = 70$

   $\underline{\ 70\ } = 5 \times 7 \times 2$

3. $? = 9 \times 8 \times 0$

   Number sentence and work:

   $9 \times 8 \times 0 = 0$

   $\underline{\ 0\ } = 9 \times 8 \times 0$

4. $18 + 29 + 52 = ?$

   Number sentence and work:

   $18 + 52 + 29 = 70 + 29 = 99$

   $18 + 29 + 52 = \underline{\ 99\ }$

Use the associative property to rewrite each number sentence to make it easier to solve. Then solve the sentence.

5. $2 \times (3 \times 5) = ?$

   Number sentence and work:

   $(2 \times 3) \times 5 = 6 \times 5 = 30$

   $2 \times (3 \times 5) = \underline{\ 30\ }$

6. $84 + (6 + 7) = ?$

   Number sentence and work:

   $(84 + 6) + 7 = 90 + 7 = 97$

   $84 + (6 + 7) = \underline{\ 97\ }$

7. $? = (36 + 21) + 29$

   Number sentence and work:

   $36 + (21 + 29) = 36 + 50 = 86$

   $\underline{\ 86\ } = (36 + 21) + 29$

8. $? = (6 \times 5) \times 2$

   Number sentence and work:

   $6 \times (5 \times 2) = 6 \times 10 = 60$

   $\underline{\ 60\ } = (6 \times 5) \times 2$

Read the problem and follow the directions.

9. Rewrite this number sentence using the associative property. Then solve the first step of the new number sentence.

   $(76 + 7) + 23 = ?$

   New number sentence:

   $76 + (7 + 23) = ?$

   First step of solving:

   $76 + 30 = ?$

10. Which expression shows one way to use the commutative property make this problem easier to solve? Circle the answer.

    $2 \times 7 \times 5$

    A. $2 \times (7 \times 5)$ B. $2 + 7 \times 5$

    C. $2 \times 5 \times 7$ D. $7 - 2 \times 5$

Read the problem and say the answer.

For Problems 11–13, accept all reasonable answers.

11. Natalie solved this problem: $67 + 25 = 92$.

    How could Natalie's work and the commutative property help you find the sum of $25 + 67$?

    The sum of $25 + 67$ is the same as the sum of $67 + 25$. $67 + 25 = 92$, so $25 + 67 = 92$. The commutative property says that when the order of the numbers changes, the answer stays the same.

12. Explain how to use the associative property to make this problem easier to solve.

    $(38 + 15) + 5$

    Move the parentheses to group the numbers so that they're easier to add mentally: $38 + (15 + 5)$. Add 15 and 5 to make 20. Then add 38 and 20 to get 58.

13. Lori solved this problem: $52 + 11 = 63$.
    Tanner wants to solve to find the sum of $11 + 52$.

    How could Tanner use Lori's work and the commutative property to help him find the sum?

    The sum of $52 + 11$ is the same as the sum of $11 + 52$. So if Tanner knows that $52 + 11 = 63$, he knows that $11 + 52 = 63$. The commutative property states that when the order of the numbers changes, the answer stays the same.

OFFLINE

10min

CHECKPOINT

Objectives

- Use the commutative and associative properties to simplify expressions.

Print the Checkpoint. In Part 1, students will take a performance-based assessment. In Part 2, students will complete the problems on their own. Read the directions, problems, and answer choices to students, if necessary. Use the answer key to score the Checkpoint, and then enter the results online

---

Checkpoint — Math | Multiplication and Addition Properties | Use Properties

Checkpoint Answer Key

Part 1
Follow the instructions for each item. Choose the response that best describes how the student performed on the task.

1. Write the following multipliation problems on a sheet of paper:

$6 \times 10 = ?$

$10 \times 6 = ?$

Say, "Solve the first problem. Explain how knowing the commutative property makes it easier to solve the second problem."
(1 point)
Did the student say that $6 \times 10 = 60$?

A. Yes B. No
(1 point)
Did the student explain that by knowing the answer to the first problem you know the answer to the second problem because changing the order of the factors does not change the product?

A. Yes B. No

2. Write the following addition problems on a sheet of paper:

$47 + 3 + 16 = ?$

$3 + 16 + 47 = ?$

Say, "Solve the first problem. Explain how knowing the commutative property makes it easier to solve the second problem."
(1 point)
Did the student say that $47 + 3 + 16 = 66$?

A. Yes B. No
(1 point)
Did the student say that by solving the first problem they know the answer to the second problem because changing the order of the addends does not change the sum?

A. Yes B. No

Give students Part 2 of the assessment.

© 2010 K12 Inc. All rights reserved.
Copying or distributing without K12's written consent is prohibited.

1 of 2

Checkpoint — Math | Multiplication and Addition Properties | Use Properties

Name _____ Date _____

Part 2
Rewrite the number sentence using the associative property. Then solve the first step of the new number sentence.
(1 point)
3. $43 + (7 + 22) = ?$

New number sentence: $(43 + 7) + 22 = ?$

First step of solving: $50 + 22 = ?$

(1 point)
4. $(8 \times 2) \times 5 = ?$

New number sentence: $8 \times (2 \times 5) = ?$

First step of solving: $8 \times 10 = ?$

Circle the answer.
(1 point)
5. Which expression shows how to use the commutative property to make it easier to solve this problem?

$24 + 38 + 6$

A. $24 - 38 + 6$
B. $24 + 6 + 38$ ⊚
C. $24 - 6 + 38$
D. $24 + 6 - 38$

(1 point)
6. Which expression shows how to use the associative property to make it easier to solve this problem?

$(32 + 2) + 18$

A. $32 + (2 + 18)$ ⊚
B. $(32 - 2) + 18$
C. $(32 + 2) - 18$
D. $32 - (2 + 18)$

© 2010 K12 Inc. All rights reserved.
Copying or distributing without K12's written consent is prohibited.

2 of 2

USE PROPERTIES **467**

Unit Review

UNIT REVIEW Look Back	20 minutes	**ONLINE**
UNIT REVIEW Checkpoint Practice	20 minutes	**OFFLINE**
▶ **UNIT REVIEW** Prepare for the Checkpoint		

▶ Unit Objectives

This lesson reviews the following objectives:

- Demonstrate understanding that the order in which numbers are multiplied does not affect the product.
- Demonstrate understanding that any number multiplied by 1 results in the same number ($n \times 1 = n$).
- Demonstrate understanding of the rule for multiplying by zero.
- Demonstrate understanding of the commutative properties of addition and multiplication.
- Use the commutative property in mental calculations.
- Use the commutative property to check results.
- Demonstrate understanding of the associative properties of addition and multiplication.
- Use the associative property in mental calculations.
- Use the associative property to check results.
- Use the commutative and associative properties to simplify expressions.

▶ Advance Preparation

In this lesson, students will have an opportunity to review previous activities in the Multiplication and Addition Properties unit. Look at the suggested activities in Unit Review: Prepare for the Checkpoint online and gather any needed materials.

Materials to Gather

SUPPLIED

Checkpoint Practice activity page

Keywords

addend
associative property of
    addition
associative property of
    multiplication

commutative property of
    addition
commutative property of
    multiplication
factor
product

UNIT REVIEW Look Back

In this unit, students have learned the commutative and associative properties of addition and multiplication. They also learned how to multiply with 0 and 1. Students used properties to make problems easier to solve. They also learned how to use the properties to check calculations. Students will review these concepts to prepare for the Unit Checkpoint.

- Review unit objectives.

UNIT REVIEW Checkpoint Practice

Objectives

Students will complete a Checkpoint Practice activity page to prepare for the Unit Checkpoint. If necessary, read the directions, problems, and answer choices to students. Have students answer the problems on their own. Carefully review the answers with students.

- Review unit objectives.

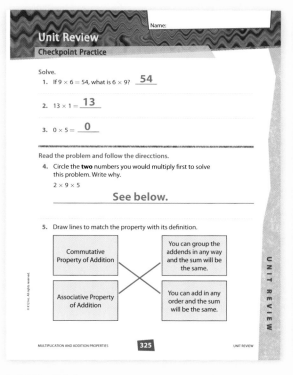

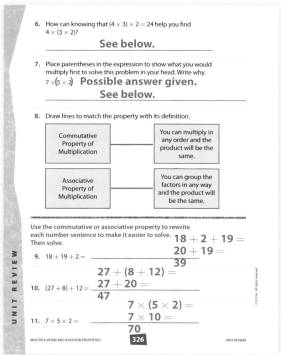

Additional Answers

4. Students should circle 5 and 2 because that will give them 10 and they can multiply 10 and 9. They will have difficulty multiplying the product of any other two numbers by the third factor.

6. Grouping the numbers in different ways gets the same product, so the answer is 24 whether grouping 4×3 or 3×2.

7. Students may put parentheses around 5×2 and explain that it's easier to multiply 7×10 than 35×2.

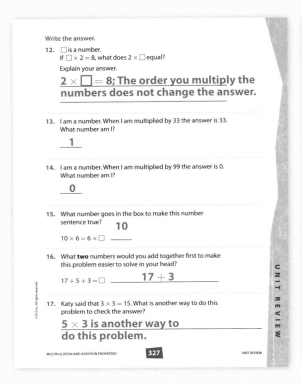

Write the answer.

12. ☐ is a number.
If ☐ × 2 = 8, what does 2 × ☐ equal?
Explain your answer.

2 × ☐ = 8; The order you multiply the numbers does not change the answer.

13. I am a number. When I am multiplied by 33 the answer is 33. What number am I?

1

14. I am a number. When I am multiplied by 99 the answer is 0. What number am I?

0

15. What number goes in the box to make this number sentence true? **10**

10 × 6 = 6 × ☐ _____

16. What **two** numbers would you add together first to make this problem easier to solve in your head?

17 + 5 + 3 = ☐   **17 + 3**

17. Katy said that 3 × 5 = 15. What is another way to do this problem to check the answer?

5 × 3 is another way to do this problem.

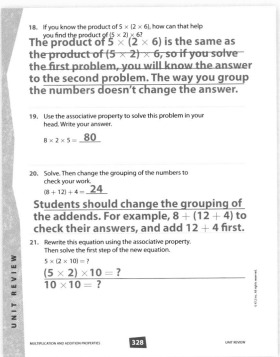

18. If you know the product of 5 × (2 × 6), how can that help you find the product of (5 × 2) × 6?

The product of 5 × (2 × 6) is the same as the product of (5 × 2) × 6, so if you solve the first problem, you will know the answer to the second problem. The way you group the numbers doesn't change the answer.

19. Use the associative property to solve this problem in your head. Write your answer.

8 × 2 × 5 = **80**

20. Solve. Then change the grouping of the numbers to check your work.
(8 + 12) + 4 = **24**

Students should change the grouping of the addends. For example, 8 + (12 + 4) to check their answers, and add 12 + 4 first.

21. Rewrite this equation using the associative property. Then solve the first step of the new equation.

5 × (2 × 10) = ?

(5 × 2) × 10 = ?
10 × 10 = ?

⇥ **UNIT REVIEW** Prepare for the Checkpoint

What you do next depends on how students performed in the previous activity, Unit Review: Checkpoint Practice. If students had difficulty with any of the problems, complete the appropriate review activity listed in the table online.

Unit Checkpoint

| **UNIT CHECKPOINT** Online | 40 minutes | **ONLINE** |
| **UNIT CHECKPOINT** Offline | 20 minutes | **OFFLINE** |

▶ Unit Objectives

This lesson assesses the following objectives:

- Demonstrate understanding that the order in which numbers are multiplied does not affect the product.
- Demonstrate understanding that any number multiplied by 1 results in the same number ($n \times 1 = n$).
- Demonstrate understanding of the rule for multiplying by zero.
- Demonstrate understanding of the commutative properties of addition and multiplication.
- Use the commutative property in mental calculations.
- Use the commutative property to check results.
- Demonstrate understanding of the associative properties of addition and multiplication.
- Use the associative property in mental calculations.
- Use the associative property to check results.
- Use the commutative and associative properties to simplify expressions.

Materials to Gather

SUPPLIED
Unit Checkpoint (printout)

UNIT CHECKPOINT Online

ONLINE 40min

Students will complete this part of the Unit Checkpoint online. Read the directions, problems, and answer choices to students. If necessary, help students with keyboard or mouse operations.

Objectives

- Assess unit objectives.

UNIT CHECKPOINT Offline

OFFLINE 20min

Students will complete this part of the Unit Checkpoint offline. Print the Checkpoint. Students will take a performance-based assessment. Read the directions and problems to students. Use the answer key to score the Checkpoint, and then enter the results online.

Objectives

- Assess unit objectives.

Name   Date

Unit Checkpoint Answer Key

Follow the instructions for each item. Choose the response that best describes how the student performed on the task.

1. Say, "Susie knows the sum of 34 + 53. How can she use that information to find the sum of 53 + 34?"

   (1 point)
   Did the student say that the sum of 34 + 53 is the same as the sum of 53 + 34 because changing the order of addends does not change the sum?

   A. Yes   B. No

2. Say, "Erick found the sum of 4 + 7 + 3 by adding 4 + 7 to get 11 and then adding 11 + 3 to get 14. Explain how to check his answer by changing the order of the numbers."

   (1 point)
   Did the student explain how to check the answer by changing the order of the numbers?

   Sample answer: The sum can be checked by adding 7 + 3 to get 10 and then adding 10 + 4 to get 14.

   A. Yes   B. No

3. Write the addition problem 8 + 4 + 7 on a sheet of paper.

   Say, "Look at the addition problem.

   Would it change the answer if the 4 and the 7 were added first and then the 8 was added? Why or why not?"

   (1 point)
   Did the student explain that the answer would not change because the order the numbers are added does not change the answer?

   A. Yes   B. No

4. Say, "If you know the product of 4 × (9 × 3), how can that help you find the product of (4 × 9) × 3?"

   (1 point)
   Did the student explain that the product of 4 × (9 × 3) is the same as the product of (4 × 9) × 3, so if you solve the first problem, you will know the answer to the second problem (changing the grouping of factors does not change the product)?

   A. Yes   B. No

Name   Date

5. Say, "Asha wanted to solve the problem (4 × 5) × 2. Explain how she could regroup the numbers to make it easier to solve this problem in her head."

   (1 point)
   Did the student explain how Asha could regroup to make it easier to solve the problem?

   Sample answer: Regroup so she solves 4 × (5 × 2), which means she will solve 5 × 2 first, and then multiply 4 × 10.

   A. Yes   B. No

6. Write the number sentence 1 × (3 × 5) = ? on a sheet of paper.

   Say, "Rewrite this number sentence using the associative property. Then solve the first step of the new number sentence."

   (1 point)
   Did the student rewrite the number sentence as (1 × 3) × 5 = ?

   A. Yes   B. No

   (1 point)
   Did the student solve the first step of the new number sentence as 1 × 3 = ?

   A. Yes   B. No

7. Write the number sentence 7 + (9 + 3) = ? on a sheet of paper.

   Say, "Solve. Then change the grouping of the numbers to check your work."

   (1 point)
   Did the student get the answer 19?

   A. Yes   B. No

   (1 point)
   Did the student change the grouping of the addends (for example, (7 + 9) + 3 to check the answer, and add 7 + 9 first)?

   A. Yes   B. No

Name   Date

8. Say, "Billy multiplied 8 × 2 and got 16. What will the answer be if he changes the order of the numbers and multiplies 2 × 8? Explain your answer."

   (1 point)
   Did the student say that 2 × 8 = 16?

   A. Yes   B. No

   (1 point)
   Did the student explain that the order that you multiply the numbers does not change the answer?

   A. Yes   B. No

Introduction to Division

▶ Unit Objectives

- Use repeated subtraction to do division problems.
- Use equal sharing to do division problems.
- Use models and math symbols to represent division.
- Recognize that the ÷ sign refers to division.
- Correctly use the ÷ symbol.
- Use forming equal groups with remainders to solve simple division problems.

▶ Big Ideas

- Division can be understood as repeated subtraction or as division of a quantity into equal groups.
- Models and mathematical symbols can represent multiplication and division.

▶ Unit Introduction

In this unit, students will explore division. They will solve division problems using repeated subtraction and equal sharing. Students will first model repeated subtraction with circle blocks and number lines and learn how to record repeated subtraction. Then they will model equal sharing and solve division story problems. Lastly they will learn about the division symbol, using symbols to record division, and division with remainders.

Division as Repeated Subtraction

Lesson Overview

Skills Update	5 minutes	ONLINE
GET READY Plates of Cookies	5 minutes	ONLINE
LEARN Model Repeated Subtraction	20 minutes	ONLINE
LEARN Division with a Number Line	20 minutes	ONLINE
TRY IT Practice Repeated Subtraction	10 minutes	OFFLINE

▶ Lesson Objectives

Use repeated subtraction to do division problems.

▶ Prerequisite Skills

Use concrete objects or sketches to model and solve addition or subtraction computation problems with sums and minuends up through 30.

▶ Common Errors and Misconceptions

Students might not relate their knowledge of division (its symbols, procedures, and facts) to what they already know in order to make meaningful, everyday connections.

▶ Advance Preparation

Print the Number Line 0–20.

▶ Content Background

Students will learn the meaning of division as repeated subtraction. For example, a problem such as 15 divided by 5 would be solved by finding out how many times 5 could be subtracted from 15 before reaching 0 (3 times). Students will divide by repeatedly subtracting with objects and on a number line.

Materials to Gather

SUPPLIED

blocks – B (any two colors)

Number Line 0–20 (printout)

Practice Repeated Subtraction activity page

ALSO NEEDED

household objects – 6 paper plates

Keywords

divide – to share equally or group an amount into equal parts

division – an operation to share equally or group an amount into equal parts

division symbol (÷) – the symbol that signals division, which is the process of sharing equally or grouping an amount into equal parts

repeated subtraction – a method of dividing by repeatedly subtracting the divisor from the dividend until a value less than the divisor remains

GET READY Plates of Cookies

Students will divide the objects in an array into equal groups. This activity will be a first step in seeing division as repeated subtraction.

Objectives

- Use concrete objects or sketches to model and solve addition or subtraction computation problems with sums and minuends up through 30.

LEARN Model Repeated Subtraction

Objectives

Students will divide to find out how many equal-sized groups of objects a given group of objects contains. For example, suppose students have 8 toys and some baskets. They want to put 2 toys in each basket. How many baskets do they need for all the toys? They would take 2 toys away from the 8 toys over and over, or 4 times, to fill the baskets until they used all the toys. Students would fill 4 baskets.

Objectives

- Use repeated subtraction to do division problems.

Students will be introduced to division as the process of repeated subtraction. Gather the circle blocks and paper plates. Students will use these materials to follow along with the online activity.

Tips

As students complete each problem, ask them following questions:

- How many circle blocks do you subtract each time?
- Can you subtract again or do you have zero left?
- How many times did you subtract?

As students subtract circle blocks, be sure they keep the groups of circles separated on different plates. They can easily count those groups by counting the plates to find how many times they subtracted.

LEARN Division with a Number Line

Objectives

Students will show division as repeated subtraction on a number line. They will make jumps back on a number line, from a starting point to zero, to show how to divide. They will count their jumps to determine the number of times they subtracted from a given number.

Objectives

- Use repeated subtraction to do division problems.

Gather the Number Line 0–20. Have students use their own number lines as they follow along with the online problems.

Discuss the connection between division using repeated subtraction with circle blocks and counting back on a number line.

TRY IT Practice Repeated Subtraction

OFFLINE
10 min

Students will practice dividing by using repeated subtraction. Give students the circle blocks, paper plates, and Practice Repeated Subtraction activity page from their Activity Book. Read the directions with them.

Objectives

- Use repeated subtraction to do division problems.

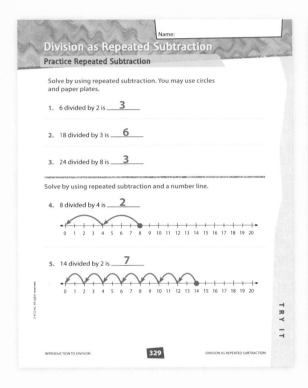

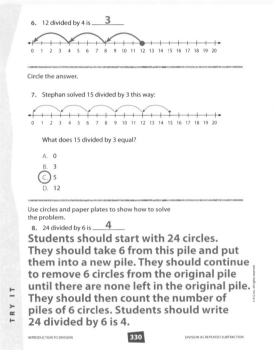

Name:

Division as Repeated Subtraction
Practice Repeated Subtraction

Solve by using repeated subtraction. You may use circles and paper plates.

1. 6 divided by 2 is ___**3**___

2. 18 divided by 3 is ___**6**___

3. 24 divided by 8 is ___**3**___

Solve by using repeated subtraction and a number line.

4. 8 divided by 4 is ___**2**___

5. 14 divided by 2 is ___**7**___

6. 12 divided by 4 is ___**3**___

Circle the answer.

7. Stephan solved 15 divided by 3 this way:

What does 15 divided by 3 equal?

A. 0
B. 3
C. 5
D. 12

Use circles and paper plates to show how to solve the problem.

8. 24 divided by 6 is ___**4**___

Students should start with 24 circles. They should take 6 from this pile and put them into a new pile. They should continue to remove 6 circles from the original pile until there are none left in the original pile. They should then count the number of piles of 6 circles. Students should write 24 divided by 6 is 4.

INTRODUCTION TO DIVISION   **329**   DIVISION AS REPEATED SUBTRACTION

INTRODUCTION TO DIVISION   **330**   DIVISION AS REPEATED SUBTRACTION

TRY IT

TRY IT

Division with Repeated Subtraction

Lesson Overview

Skills Update	5 minutes	ONLINE
GET READY Fast Facts Practice	5 minutes	ONLINE
LEARN Record Repeated Subtraction	15 minutes	ONLINE
LEARN Division Story Problems	15 minutes	ONLINE
TRY IT Practice Division	10 minutes	OFFLINE
CHECKPOINT	10 minutes	OFFLINE

▶ Lesson Objectives

Use repeated subtraction to do division problems.

▶ Prerequisite Skills

Demonstrate automatic recall of subtraction facts with minuends through 20.

▶ Common Errors and Misconceptions

Students might not relate their knowledge of division (its symbols, procedures, and facts) to what they already know in order to make meaningful, everyday connections.

▶ Advance Preparation

Print the Number Line 0–20.

▶ Content Background

Students will continue to solve division problems with repeated subtraction. They will learn how to record repeated subtraction using numbers and symbols. Students will use circle blocks and number lines to explore division. Then they will apply their understanding to solve story problems involving division.

Materials to Gather

SUPPLIED

blocks – B (any two colors)
Number Line 0–20 (printout)
Practice Division activity page
Checkpoint (printout)

ALSO NEEDED

household objects – 5 paper plates

GET READY Fast Facts Practice

ONLINE 5 min

Students will review subtraction facts with minuends, or starting numbers, from 0 to 20. Being able to quickly recall subtraction facts will greatly help students as they prepare to learn divison.

Objectives

- Demonstrate automatic recall of subtraction facts with minuends through 20.

DIRECTIONS FOR USING THE FAST FACTS LEARNING TOOL

1. Have students enter their name and car number as well as choose the color of the car.

2. Choose the following options:
   - Choose the facts you want to practice: Subtraction
   - Work with minuends from 0 to 20
   - Mode: Race Mode

3. As each problem appears on the screen, have students type the answer and then press Enter. After students finish, review the results on the "Fast Facts Results" screen. Note how many problems students answered incorrectly. Also record their time for future reference. You can click under the Lap tables on this screen to see exactly which problems students answered correctly (shown in white) and which ones they missed (shown in red).

4. Repeat the activity. Have students try to beat their time and improve their accuracy.

5. If time remains, customize the "Subtraction" screen and specifically change the range of minuends to give more practice with the facts with which students had difficulty. Then have them run another race.

ONLINE 15 min

LEARN Record Repeated Subtraction

Students will learn how to record repeated subtraction in a way that allows them to count how many times they subtracted. They will learn that the number of times they subtract is the answer. Students will use number lines and circle blocks to solve the division problems in this activity. However, the goal of the lesson is for students to repeatedly subtract to solve a problem.

Gather the circle blocks, paper plates, and Number Line 0–20 printout. Have students use the materials as directed in the activity.

As students progress through the activity, ask them questions such as the following:
- How many do you subtract each time?
- Can you subtract again?
- How many times did you subtract?

ONLINE 15 min

LEARN Division Story Problems

Students will use repeated subtraction to solve division story problems. They will see problems modeled with pictures. They should then try to solve the problems using repeated subtraction. If students have difficulty, have them use their own models or click Hint to see a model for the problems that provide a hint.

As students progress through the activity, ask them questions such as the following:
- How many objects are you dividing?
- How many objects need to be in each group? What number do you need to subtract over and over?
- How many times did you subtract the number? How many groups are there?
- What is your answer?

TRY IT Practice Division

Students will practice dividing by using repeated subtraction. Give students the circle blocks, Number Line 0–20 printout, and Practice Division activity page from their Activity Book. Read the directions with them.

- Use repeated subtraction to do division problems.

Name:

Division with Repeated Subtraction
Practice Division

Solve with repeated subtraction with a number line.

1. 18 divided by 3 equals ___6___   **See below.**

2. 15 divided by 5 equals ___3___   **See below.**

Solve with repeated subtraction. Write the subtraction sentences you use.

3. 10 divided by 5 equals
$$\underline{\quad 2 \quad}$$
$$\begin{array}{r} 10 \\ -5 \\ \hline 5 \end{array} \quad \begin{array}{r} 5 \\ -5 \\ \hline 0 \end{array}$$

4. 6 divided by 2 equals
$$\underline{\quad 3 \quad}$$
$6 - 2 = 4$
$4 - 2 = 2$
$2 - 2 = 0$

Check students' subtraction sentences. They can write horizontal or vertical sentences. Possible answers are shown.

5. 14 divided by 7 equals
$$\underline{\quad 2 \quad}$$
$$\begin{array}{r} 14 \\ -7 \\ \hline 7 \end{array} \quad \begin{array}{r} 7 \\ -7 \\ \hline 0 \end{array}$$

6. 12 divided by 3 equals
$$\underline{\quad 4 \quad}$$
$12 - 3 = 9$
$9 - 3 = 6$
$6 - 3 = 3$
$3 - 3 = 0$

INTRODUCTION TO DIVISION   **331**   DIVISION WITH REPEATED SUBTRACTION

Read the problem and follow the directions.

7. Jenny has 20 oranges. She wants to give each person 2 oranges.   **See below.**

   Use circles to show how many people will get oranges. Then write the answer.   ___10___ people

8. Cheryl has 15 muffins. She wants to put 3 muffins in each bag.   **See below.**

   How many bags of muffins will she have? Solve with repeated subtraction. Then write the answer.   ___5___ bags

Solve.

9. Jeremy has 12 crackers. He eats 2 crackers each day.

   How many days can Jeremy eat crackers before he eats them all?   ___6___ days

10. Mariah has 24 toys. She can fit 8 toys in 1 basket.

    How many baskets does Mariah need to fit all the toys?   ___3___ baskets

11. Jeff has 16 photos. He puts 4 photos on 1 page of a photo album.

    How many pages does Jeff need for all the pictures?   ___4___ pages

Circle the answer.

12. This is how Carla found 10 divided by 2: $10 - 2 = 8$
    $8 - 2 = 6$
    $6 - 2 = 4$
    $4 - 2 = 2$
    $2 - 2 = 0$

    What does 10 divided by 2 equal?
    A. 0   B. 2   (C.) 5   D. 10

INTRODUCTION TO DIVISION   **332**   DIVISION WITH REPEATED SUBTRACTION

Additional Answers

1. Students should start at 18 on number line and jump back by 3s until they reach 0. They should see that there were 6 jumps.

2. Students should start at 15 on number line and jump back by 5s until they reach 0. They should see that there were 3 jumps.

7. Students should move 2 circle blocks into separate piles until they have used all 20 of the circle blocks and then count to find there are 10 piles, so 10 people will get 2 oranges each.

8. Example answer:
   $15 - 3 = 12$
   $12 - 3 = 9$
   $9 - 3 = 6$
   $6 - 3 = 3$
   $3 - 3 = 0$

CHECKPOINT

Objectives

- Use repeated subtraction to do division problems.

Print the Checkpoint. In Part 1, students will take a performance-based assessment. In Part 2, students will complete the problems on their own. Read the directions, problems, and answer choices to students, if necessary. Use the answer key to score the Checkpoint, and then enter the results online.

Gather the circle blocks and Number Line 0–20 printout. Give students the blocks for Problem 1 and the number line for Problem 2.

○ Checkpoint   Math | Introduction to Division | Division with Repeated Subtraction

Name _____ Date _____

Checkpoint Answer Key

Part 1

Follow the instructions for each item. Choose the response that best describes how the student performed on the task.

1. Say, "Use circle blocks to show how to find 21 divided by 3. Then say the answer."
(1 point)

Did the student start by making a pile of 21 circles and then continue to remove piles of 3 circle blocks until there were no more circle blocks in the original pile? Then did the student count the number of piles of 3?

A. Yes   B. No

(1 point)
Did the student say that 21 divided by 3 is 7?

A. Yes   B. No

2. Say, "Rachel has 20 almonds. She wants to eat 5 almonds every day. For how many days can she eat 5 almonds each day? Use a number line to show how to solve this problem. Then say the answer."
(1 point)
Did the student start at 20 and draw backward jumps of 5 until the student got to 0? Then did the student count the jumps?

A. Yes   B. No

(1 point)
Did the student say that 20 divided by 5 is 4?

A. Yes   B. No

Give students Part 2 of the assessment.

   1 of 3

○ Checkpoint   Math | Introduction to Division | Division with Repeated Subtraction

Name _____ Date _____

Part 2
Solve. Show your work.
(1 point)
3. Use a number line to solve.

The ducks laid 12 eggs.

The ducks laid 2 eggs in each nest.

How many nests had eggs in them?

___6___ nests

Students should show their work. Example: Start at 12 on a number line and draw 6 back jumps of 2. Then count the jumps.

Circle the answer.
(1 point)
4. Which answer choice correctly uses repeated subtraction to solve 24 divided by 6?

(A) $\begin{array}{cccc} 24 & 18 & 12 & 6 \\ -6 & -6 & -6 & -6 \\ \hline 18 & 12 & 6 & 0 \end{array}$

Which means that 24 divided by 6 is 4.

B. $\begin{array}{c} 24 \\ -6 \\ \hline 18 \end{array}$

Which means that 24 divided by 6 is 18.

C. $\begin{array}{cc} 24 & 18 \\ -6 & -6 \\ \hline 18 & 12 \end{array}$

Which means that 24 divided by 6 is 12.

D. $\begin{array}{cccc} 24 & 18 & 12 & 6 \\ -6 & -6 & -6 & -6 \\ \hline 18 & 12 & 6 & 0 \end{array}$

Which means that 24 divided by 6 is 0.

   2 of 3

○ Checkpoint   Math | Introduction to Division | Division with Repeated Subtraction

Name _____ Date _____

(1 point)
5. Mark has 6 tires to put on some bicycles. Each bicycle needs 2 tires. How many bicycles can he put tires on?

A. $\begin{array}{ccc} 6 & 4 & 2 \\ -2 & -2 & -2 \\ \hline 4 & 2 & 0 \end{array}$

Mark can put tires on 0 bicycles.

B. $\begin{array}{cc} 6 & 4 \\ -2 & -4 \\ \hline 4 & 0 \end{array}$

Mark can put tires on 2 bicycles.

(C) $\begin{array}{ccc} 6 & 4 & 2 \\ -2 & -2 & -2 \\ \hline 4 & 2 & 0 \end{array}$

Mark can put tires on 3 bicycles.

D. $\begin{array}{cccccc} 6 & 5 & 4 & 3 & 2 & 1 \\ -1 & -1 & -1 & -1 & -1 & -1 \\ \hline 5 & 4 & 3 & 2 & 1 & 0 \end{array}$

Mark can put tires on 6 bicycles.

   3 of 3

Division with Equal Sharing

Lesson Overview

Skills Update	5 minutes	ONLINE
GET READY Model Repeated Subtraction	5 minutes	ONLINE
LEARN Friends Share	20 minutes	ONLINE
LEARN Find Equal Shares	20 minutes	OFFLINE
TRY IT Practice Equal Shares	10 minutes	OFFLINE

▶ Lesson Objectives

Use equal sharing to do division problems.

▶ Prerequisite Skills

Use repeated subtraction to do division problems.

▶ Common Errors and Misconceptions

Students might not relate their knowledge of division (its symbols, procedures, and facts) to what they already know in order to make meaningful, everyday connections.

▶ Content Background

Students have learned that when they know the total and the number in each group, they can divide to find the number of groups.

   The problem 12 divided by 3 could mean 3 groups of 4 or 4 groups of 3. The story in a problem reveals which interpretation is intended for a problem. In one case, students are looking for the number of groups and in the other case, they are looking for how many are in each group. For example, both of these problems would be worked by solving 12 divided by 3:

- There are 12 cookies in the package. How many children could be given 3 cookies?

- There are 12 cookies in the package and 3 children. How many cookies would each child get?

   In this lesson, students will learn that when they know the total and the number of groups, they can divide to find the number in each group.

Materials to Gather

SUPPLIED

blocks – B (all colors)
Practice Equal Shares activity page

ALSO NEEDED

household objects – 12 paper plates

GET READY Model Repeated Subtraction

Students will use repeated subtraction to solve a division problem. They will model the repeated subtraction with circle blocks.

Gather the circle blocks and 6 paper plates. Have students use them as directed in the activity.

As students progress through the activity, ask them these questions:

- How many do you subtract each time?
- Can you subtract again?
- How many times did you subtract?

Objectives

- Use repeated subtraction to do division problems.

LEARN Friends Share

Students will divide to find the number in each group when given the total and the number of groups. They will use equal sharing to find the answer.

Students will also learn that they can equally divide a total into different numbers of groups. For example, 12 objects can be equally shared with 2, 3, 4, or 6 people. Students will also learn that sometimes amounts cannot be shared equally among a certain number of people. For example, 12 objects cannot be divided into 5 equal groups.

Gather the circle blocks and 7 paper plates.

Objectives

- Use equal sharing to do division problems.

Tips

Have students use circles and paper plates to model the problems in the activity.

LEARN Find Equal Shares

Students have learned to divide the total by the number in each group to find the number of groups and also to divide the total by the number of groups to find the number in each group. Help students understand that the same division problem can show either the number of groups or the number in each group. The story described in the problem will help them decide which they are finding.

Gather the circle blocks and 5 paper plates.

1. Remind students that they have used division to solve problems in which they knew the total and how many in each group. They needed to find how many groups.

   Say: Suppose you need to solve the following problem: 6 oranges are placed into bags. There are 3 oranges in each bag. How many bags of oranges are there? You know that "6 divided by 3" in this problem means that the total is 6 and there are 3 in each group. To find how many groups, you can make as many groups of 3 as you can and count how many groups you made.

   Ask: What is 6 divided by 3?
   ANSWER: 2

   Say: There are 2 groups of 3 in 6.

Objectives

- Use equal sharing to do division problems.

Tips

If you wish, draw faces on the plates to help students remember that each plate represents one friend.

2. Explain that students will solve another kind of division problem. They will be given the total and how many groups. They will have to find how many are in each group.

   Say: 3 friends want to share 6 apples equally. How many apples will each friend get? You know that the total is 6 and that you need to make 3 groups. You can find "6 divided by 3" to solve the problem.

3. Display 6 circle blocks.

   Explain that the total is 6 apples and tell students to use 6 circles to show the apples.

4. Display 3 plates.

   Say: You need to make 3 groups of apples for the 3 friends. You will use plates to show the groups.

5. **Say:** You need to give each friend the same number of apples, but you do not know how many apples each will get. You can share the apples equally by giving 1 apple to each friend, then a second apple to each friend, and so on, until you have used all 6 circles that show the total number of apples.

6. Show students how to "share" the circles by placing 1 circle on each plate and then placing a second circle on each plate. When you are finished, point out that you have used all the circles.

7. **Ask:** How many apples did each friend get?
   ANSWER: 2

   Ask: What is 6 divided by 3?
   ANSWER: 2

8. Repeat the activity, having students lay out the plates and share the circles equally, for the following problems:

   - 16 toys and 2 friends (8)
   - 20 marbles and 5 friends (4)
   - 4 sandwiches and 4 friends (1)
   - 7 books and 1 friend (7)

   Note: In the last two problems, dividing a number by itself gives an answer of 1, and dividing a number by 1 gives the number students are dividing—that is, one friend will get all the circles. Point out these ideas to students and discuss them.

TRY IT Practice Equal Shares

Objectives

- Use equal sharing to do division problems.

Students will practice dividing a number into equal shares. Give students the circle blocks, 12 paper plates, and Practice Equal Shares activity page from their Activity Book. Read the directions with them.

Name: _____

Division with Equal Sharing

Practice Equal Shares

Solve. You may use circles and paper plates.

1. There are 6 bananas and 3 friends.
   How many bananas does each friend get?

   6 divided by 3 equals __2__

2. There are 16 bananas and 4 friends.
   How many bananas does each friend get?

   16 divided by 4 equals __4__

3. There are 9 bananas and 3 friends.
   How many bananas does each friend get?

   __3__ bananas

4. There are 12 bananas and 2 friends.
   How many bananas does each friend get?

   __6__ bananas

5. 24 divided by 6 equals __4__

6. 24 divided by 8 equals __3__

TRY IT

---

7. 24 divided by 12 equals __2__

8. 24 divided by 3 equals __8__

Read the problem and follow the directions.

9. Show how to divide 20 circles into 5 equal groups.
   How many circles are in each group? __4__

   Students should divide 20 circles into 5 groups of 4 circles each.

10. Use circles to divide. Then complete the number sentence.
    10 divided by 2 equals __5__

    Students should divide 10 circles into 2 groups of 5 each.

11. Maria wants to know the answer to 24 divided by 4.
    Use circles to make 4 equal groups.
    What is the answer to 24 divided by 4? __6__

    Students should divide 24 circles into 4 groups of 6 each.

12. Dario wants to know the answer to 20 divided by 4.
    Use circles to make 4 equal groups.
    What is the answer to 20 divided by 4? __5__

    Students should divide 20 circles into 4 groups of 5 each.

TRY IT

Equal Share Division

Lesson Overview

Skills Update	5 minutes	ONLINE
LEARN Equal Share Problems	15 minutes	ONLINE
LEARN Draw to Divide	20 minutes	OFFLINE
TRY IT Practice Story Problems	10 minutes	OFFLINE
CHECKPOINT	10 minutes	OFFLINE

▶ Lesson Objectives

Use equal sharing to do division problems.

▶ Prerequisite Skills

Use repeated subtraction to do division problems.

▶ Common Errors and Misconceptions

Students might not relate their knowledge of division (its symbols, procedures, and facts) to what they already know in order to make meaningful, everyday connections.

▶ Content Background

Students will learn more about division. Students have learned that when they know the total and the number in each group, they can divide to find the number of groups.

The problem 12 divided by 3 could mean 3 groups of 4 or 4 groups of 3. The story in a problem reveals which interpretation is intended for a problem. In one case, students are looking for the number of groups and in the other case, they are looking for how many are in each group. For example, both of these problems would be worked by solving 12 divided by 3:

- There are 12 cookies in the package. How many children could be given 3 cookies?

- There are 12 cookies in the package and 3 children. How many cookies would each child get?

In this lesson, students will continue to learn that when they know the total and the number of groups, they can divide to find the number in each group. They will solve division problems that involve finding the number in each group when given the total and the number of groups. Students will apply what they learn to solve division story problems.

Materials to Gather

SUPPLIED

blocks – B (all colors)
Draw to Divide activity page
Practice Story Problems activity page
Checkpoint (printout)

LEARN Equal Share Problems

Students will use division to solve story problems. They will learn how to create a number sentence for a division story problem. Emphasize that if a problem uses equal sharing, students can use division to find the answer. Also emphasize that students should divide the total by the number of groups or by how many are in each group, depending on what the problem asks.

- Use equal sharing to do division problems.

LEARN Draw to Divide

Students will use drawings to solve division story problems.

Give students the Draw to Divide activity page from their Activity Book and read the directions with them.

- Use equal sharing to do division problems.

1. Read aloud Problem 1.

   Say: First you will write a number sentence for this problem. Alexander wants to plant the same number, or an equal number, of onions in each plot. He wants to make equal groups, so you need to divide.

   Ask: What is the total in this problem?
   ANSWER: 18

   Ask: Where should you write the total in the division sentence?
   ANSWER: You should write the total as the first number in the sentence.

   Say: You start a division sentence with the total. Write 18 on the first line.

2. **Ask:** What number do you need to divide the total by?
   ANSWER: 2

   Explain that Alexander is dividing the 18 onions between 2 plots, so students need to divide 18 into 2 equal groups. Ask them to write 2 on the second line.

3. Explain that students can make a drawing to solve the number sentence. Have them draw 2 large rectangles to show the 2 groups.

4. **Say:** You will use circle sketches to show the onions. Draw a circle in the first rectangle. Count aloud "1" as you draw it. You put 1 onion in the first group, so now you need to put an onion in the second group. Draw a circle in the second rectangle, and say "2."

5. Have students continue to draw circles alternately in the 2 rectangles, counting aloud as they draw each one, until they have counted to 18. They should have drawn 9 circles in each rectangle.

6. **Say:** You have drawn 18 circles, and Alexander has 18 onions. You drew 9 circles in each rectangle, so 18 divided by 2 equals 9. Alexander should place 9 onions in each plot. Write the answer, 9.

7. Guide students through the remaining problems using the process described in Steps 1–6.

Equal Share Division
Draw to Divide

Write a number sentence to match the story problem. Then make a drawing to model and solve the number sentence. You can use sketches of circles for the models in the problems. Write the answer.

1. Alexander wants to plant 18 onions. He has 2 garden plots. He wants to plant the same number of onions in each plot.

   How many onions should Alexander plant in each plot?

   __18__ divided by __2__ equals _?_

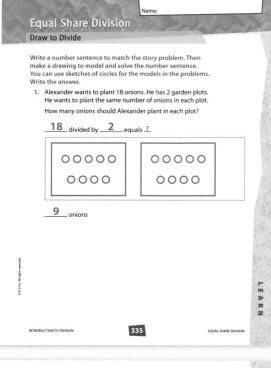

   __9__ onions

2. Alexander picked 21 carrots. He's going to make 3 big salads. He wants to put the same number of carrots in each salad.

   How many carrots should Alexander put in each salad?

   _?_ equals __21__ divided by __3__

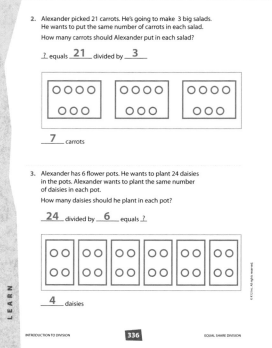

   __7__ carrots

3. Alexander has 6 flower pots. He wants to plant 24 daisies in the pots. Alexander wants to plant the same number of daisies in each pot.

   How many daisies should he plant in each pot?

   __24__ divided by __6__ equals _?_

   __4__ daisies

4. Alexander picked 18 ripe peppers. He wants to give the peppers to his 9 friends. Alexander wants to give the same number of peppers to each friend.

   How many peppers should Alexander give to each friend?

   __18__ divided by __9__ equals _?_

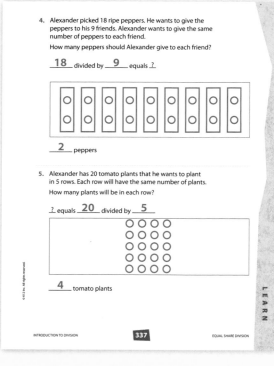

   __2__ peppers

5. Alexander has 20 tomato plants that he wants to plant in 5 rows. Each row will have the same number of plants.

   How many plants will be in each row?

   _?_ equals __20__ divided by __5__

   __4__ tomato plants

6. After a long day on the farm, Alexander decided to put his 24 baseball cards into an album. Each page holds 4 cards.

   How many pages will Alexander need?

   _?_ equals __24__ divided by __4__

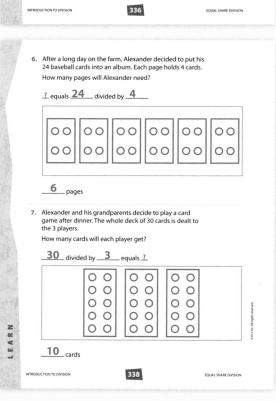

   __6__ pages

7. Alexander and his grandparents decide to play a card game after dinner. The whole deck of 30 cards is dealt to the 3 players.

   How many cards will each player get?

   __30__ divided by __3__ equals _?_

   __10__ cards

LEARN

TRY IT Practice Story Problems

Students will practice using equal sharing to solve division story problems. Give students the circle blocks and Practice Story Problems activity page from their Activity Book. Read the directions with them.

Objectives

- Use equal sharing to do division problems.

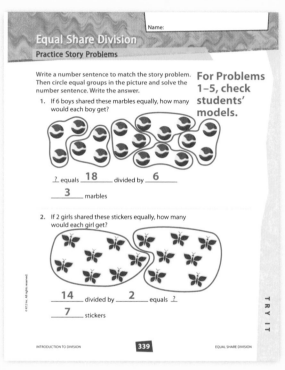

Equal Share Division
Practice Story Problems

Write a number sentence to match the story problem. Then circle equal groups in the picture and solve the number sentence. Write the answer.

For Problems 1–5, check students' models.

1. If 6 boys shared these marbles equally, how many would each boy get?

   ? equals __18__ divided by __6__
   __3__ marbles

2. If 2 girls shared these stickers equally, how many would each girl get?

   __14__ divided by __2__ equals ?
   __7__ stickers

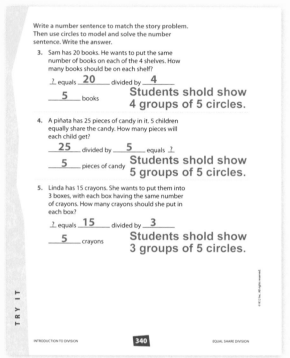

Write a number sentence to match the story problem. Then use circles to model and solve the number sentence. Write the answer.

3. Sam has 20 books. He wants to put the same number of books on each of the 4 shelves. How many books should be on each shelf?

   ? equals __20__ divided by __4__
   __5__ books
   Students shold show 4 groups of 5 circles.

4. A piñata has 25 pieces of candy in it. 5 children equally share the candy. How many pieces will each child get?

   __25__ divided by __5__ equals ?
   __5__ pieces of candy
   Students shold show 5 groups of 5 circles.

5. Linda has 15 crayons. She wants to put them into 3 boxes, with each box having the same number of crayons. How many crayons should she put in each box?

   ? equals __15__ divided by __3__
   __5__ crayons
   Students shold show 3 groups of 5 circles.

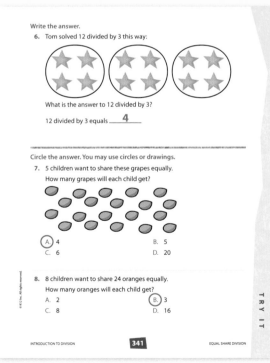

Write the answer.

6. Tom solved 12 divided by 3 this way:

   What is the answer to 12 divided by 3?

   12 divided by 3 equals __4__

Circle the answer. You may use circles or drawings.

7. 5 children want to share these grapes equally. How many grapes will each child get?

   A. 4   B. 5
   C. 6   D. 20

8. 8 children want to share 24 oranges equally. How many oranges will each child get?

   A. 2   B. 3
   C. 8   D. 16

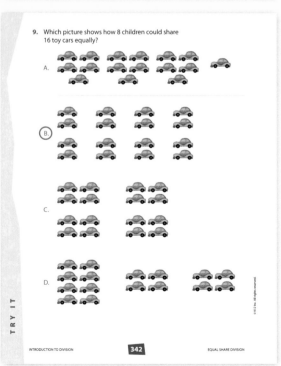

9. Which picture shows how 8 children could share 16 toy cars equally?

   A.

   B.

   C.

   D.

CHECKPOINT

Print the Checkpoint. In Part 1, students will take a performance-based assessment. In Part 2, students will complete the problems on their own. Read the directions, problems, and answer choices to students, if necessary. Use the answer key to score the Checkpoint, and then enter the results online.

Gather the circle blocks and give them to students for Problem 1. Students also may use them for Problems 4–6.

- Use equal sharing to do division problems.

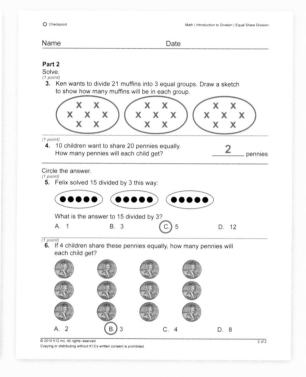

○ Checkpoint   Math | Introduction to Division | Equal Share Division

Name _____   Date _____

Checkpoint Answer Key

Part 1
(1 point)
Follow the instructions for each item. Choose the response that best describes how the student performed on the task.

1. Say, "Jack has 18 apples. Using your circle blocks as apples, show how you can divide the apples into 6 equal groups."
(1 point)
   Did the student explain how to use circles to help solve the problem?

   For example: show a group of 18 circles, and then place 1 circle in each of 6 groups, followed by a second circle in each of 6 groups, followed by a third circle in each of 6 groups.

   A. Yes   B. No

2. Say, "Lucas has 24 pencils. He wants to put them into 6 boxes, with each box having the same number of pencils. Explain how to solve this problem."
(1 point)
   Did the student explain how to solve the problem?

   For example: draw 6 groups, such as boxes or circles, and then draw a mark, such as an X, in each of the 6 groups, followed by a second mark in each of the 6 groups, and so on, until there are 24 marks.

   A. Yes   B. No
(1 point)
   Did the student say that Lucas should put 4 pencils in each box?

   A. Yes   B. No

Give Part 2 of the assessment to students.

○ Checkpoint   Math | Introduction to Division | Equal Share Division

Name _____   Date _____

Part 2
Solve.
(1 point)
3. Ken wants to divide 21 muffins into 3 equal groups. Draw a sketch to show how many muffins will be in each group.

(1 point)
4. 10 children want to share 20 pennies equally. How many pennies will each child get?   **2** pennies

Circle the answer.
(1 point)
5. Felix solved 15 divided by 3 this way:

   What is the answer to 15 divided by 3?

   A. 1   B. 3   Ⓒ 5   D. 12
(1 point)
6. If 4 children share these pennies equally, how many pennies will each child get?

   A. 2   Ⓑ 3   C. 4   D. 8

Represent Division

Lesson Overview

Skills Update	5 minutes	ONLINE
GET READY Model Division	5 minutes	ONLINE
LEARN The Division Symbol	15 minutes	ONLINE
LEARN Write Division Sentences	15 minutes	ONLINE
TRY IT Division Sentences	10 minutes	OFFLINE
CHECKPOINT	10 minutes	OFFLINE

▶ Lesson Objectives

- Use models and math symbols to represent division.
- Recognize that the ÷ sign refers to division.
- Correctly use the ÷ sign.

▶ Prerequisite Skills

- Use repeated subtraction to do division problems.
- Use equal sharing to do division problems.
- Recognize that the × symbol refers to multiplication.

▶ Content Background

Students understand the meaning of division and know how to model division problems. They have used repeated subtraction and equal sharing to solve division problems. In this lesson, students will learn about the division symbol and how to use it to write division number sentences.

Division is an operation used to separate an amount into equal groups. The division symbol (÷) is used to say "divided by." For example, 21 objects divided into 3 equal groups would be shown with the expression 21 ÷ 3. The second number in a division expression may also indicate how many are in each group. For example, 21 ÷ 3 may indicate 21 objects divided into groups with 3 objects in each group.

Materials to Gather

SUPPLIED
base-10 blocks – ones cubes
Division Sentences activity page
Checkpoint (printout)

GET READY Model Division

ONLINE 5min

Students will solve two division problems to review the two meanings of division: repeated subtraction and equal sharing. Point out that in the first problem, the second number in the division sentence (3) represents the number of objects in each group. Point out that in the second problem, the second number in the division sentence (4) represents the number of groups.

Objectives

- Use repeated subtraction to do division problems.
- Use equal sharing to do division problems.

LEARN The Division Symbol

ONLINE 15min

Students will learn about the division symbol (÷), which is read as "divided by." They will write division number sentences using the division symbol and equals symbol. They will also interpret division sentences that use these symbols. Lastly students will be introduced to the terms used for each part of a division sentence: dividend ÷ divisor = quotient. Students are not expected to memorize these terms at this time but will hear them used in lessons.

Objectives

- Use models and math symbols to represent division.
- Recognize that the ÷ sign refers to division.
- Correctly use the ÷ symbol.

LEARN Write Division Sentences

ONLINE 15min

Students will use the division symbol (÷) and equals symbol (=) to write number sentences to match a given picture or story problem. They will begin by filling in the missing symbols. They will choose the correct number sentence from four choices, and then they will write their own sentence. At the end of the activity, students will review all the meanings of the division symbol.

Focus on students' understanding of the division symbol and the equals symbol. Guide students to write number sentences that match the pictures and story problems, reinforcing that the number being divided represents a total and is called the *dividend*, the *divisor* is the number that students are dividing by, and the answer to the division problem is the *quotient*.

Objectives

- Use models and math symbols to represent division.
- Recognize that the ÷ sign refers to division.
- Correctly use the ÷ symbol.

TRY IT Division Sentences

OFFLINE 10min

Students will practice writing and interpreting division number sentences. Give students the Division Sentences activity page from their Activity Book and read the directions with them.

Objectives

- Use models and math symbols to represent division.
- Recognize that the ÷ sign refers to division.
- Correctly use the ÷ symbol.

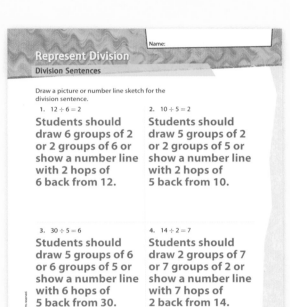

Name: _____

Represent Division
Division Sentences

Draw a picture or number line sketch for the division sentence.

1. $12 \div 6 = 2$

Students should draw 6 groups of 2 or 2 groups of 6 or show a number line with 2 hops of 6 back from 12.

2. $10 \div 5 = 2$

Students should draw 5 groups of 2 or 2 groups of 5 or show a number line with 2 hops of 5 back from 10.

3. $30 \div 5 = 6$

Students should draw 5 groups of 6 or 6 groups of 5 or show a number line with 6 hops of 5 back from 30.

4. $14 \div 2 = 7$

Students should draw 2 groups of 7 or 7 groups of 2 or show a number line with 7 hops of 2 back from 14.

TRY IT

Write a division sentence to match the picture.

5.

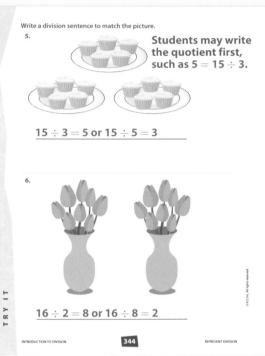

Students may write the quotient first, such as $5 = 15 \div 3$.

$15 \div 3 = 5$ or $15 \div 5 = 3$

6.

$16 \div 2 = 8$ or $16 \div 8 = 2$

TRY IT

Write a division sentence to match the story problem and include the answer in your division sentence.

7. 16 crayons are divided equally in 4 boxes.

$16 \div 4 = 4$

8. 24 children get into 3 equal groups.

$24 \div 3 = 8$

9. 6 strawberries are shared equally among 3 friends.

$6 \div 3 = 2$

10. 40 books are placed equally among 5 shelves.

$40 \div 5 = 8$

TRY IT

Circle the answer.

11. Eddy wrote the problem $12 \div 4$. What operation should he use to solve the problem?

(A.) division
B. multiplication
C. addition
D. subtraction

12. Which symbol should be placed in the circle to show 6 divided by 2?

$6 \bigcirc 2$

A. $+$
B. $\times$
(C.) $\div$
D. $-$

TRY IT

OFFLINE
10min

Objectives

- Use models and math symbols to represent division.
- Recognize that the ÷ sign refers to division.
- Correctly use the ÷ symbol.

Print the Checkpoint. In Part 1, students will take a performance-based assessment. In Part 2, students will complete the problems on their own. Read the directions, problems, and answer choices to students, if necessary. Use the answer key to score the Checkpoint, and then enter the results online.
  Gather the ones cubes and give them to students for Problem 1.

○ Checkpoint   Math | Introduction to Division | Represent Division

Name _____ Date _____

Checkpoint Answer Key

Part 1
Follow the instructions for each item. Choose the response that best describes how the student performed on the task.

1. Say, "Use ones cubes to show how to solve this problem:
   10 ÷ 5 = _____."
   (1 point)
   Did the student show a group of 10 ones cubes, and then place 1 cube in each of 5 groups, followed by a second cube in each group? Or did the student start with 10 cubes and then subtract one group of 5 cubes, followed by a second group of 5 cubes?

   A. Yes   B. No

2. Write the following equation on a sheet of paper and draw an arrow pointing to the division symbol.
   10 ÷ 5 = 2
   Say, "Look at the symbol where the arrow is pointing. What does this symbol mean?"
   (1 point)
   Did the student say the symbol means to divide, share, or separate the 10 into 5 equal groups?

   A. Yes   B. No

Give Part 2 of the assessment to students.

○ Checkpoint   Math | Introduction to Division | Represent Division

Name _____ Date _____

Part 2
Circle the answer.
(1 point)
3. Which division sentence matches the picture?

   A. 2 ÷ 2 = 1
   B. 4 ÷ 2 = 2 (circled)
   C. 4 ÷ 4 = 2
   D. 2 ÷ 4 = 2

(1 point)
4. Which symbol should be used to describe sharing 15 crackers equally among 3 friends?

   15 ◯ 3

   A. +
   B. ×
   C. ÷ (circled)
   D. −

Remainders in Division

▶ ## Lesson Objectives

Use forming equal groups with remainders to solve simple division problems.

▶ ## Prerequisite Skills

Use models and math symbols to represent division.

▶ ## Common Errors and Misconceptions

Students might not relate their knowledge of division (its symbols, procedures, and facts) to what they already know in order to make meaningful, everyday connections.

▶ ## Content Background

Students will learn that when they divide one number by another number, they might have some left over. The leftover amount is called the *remainder*. Students will solve problems involving division with remainders. They will learn that sometimes the solution to the problem includes the remainder and sometimes it does not.

Keywords	**quotient** – the answer to a division problem; the dividend divided by the divisor equals the quotient
	remainder – the amount left over after dividing evenly

Materials to Gather

SUPPLIED

blocks – B (all colors)

Remainders in Story Problems activity page

Practice with Remainders activity page

Checkpoint (printout)

ALSO NEEDED

household objects – 14 paper plates

GET READY Division Sentences

ONLINE 5min

Objectives

- Use models and math symbols to represent division.

Students will determine which division sentence matches a given picture or story problem. As students progress through the activity, have them ask themselves questions such as the following:

- What is the total amount, or what is the dividend?
- How many groups are there, or what is the divisor?
- How many are in each group, or what is the quotient?

LEARN Explore Remainders

ONLINE 15min

Objectives

- Use forming equal groups with remainders to solve simple division problems.

Students will learn what a remainder is, and they will solve division problems with a remainder. They will use both equal sharing and repeated subtraction to find remainders.

LEARN Remainders in Story Problems

OFFLINE 15min

Objectives

- Use forming equal groups with remainders to solve simple division problems.

Students will use models, sketches, and a number line to solve division story problems that have remainders. They will need to decide whether the remainder or the quotient is the answer to the story problem. Give students the circle blocks, 5 paper plates, and Remainders in Story Problems activity page from their Activity Book. Read the directions with them.

1. Read aloud Problem 1. Explain that because each dog will get the same number of bones, students can divide to solve the problem.

2. Ask students to tell you the total. (18) Have them write the total on the first line in the division sentence.

3. Ask students what number they need to divide the total by. (4) Have them write this number on the second line in the number sentence.

4. Display 4 paper plates and 18 circles.

   Say: The 18 bones are being divided among 4 dogs, so you need to divide 18 into 4 equal groups. You'll use 4 plates to show the 4 dogs. You'll use 18 circles to show the 18 bones.

5. Have students model division by first passing out 1 circle to each plate. Ask students if they can give another circle to each plate. (Yes)

6. Repeat Step 5 until students have put 4 circles on each plate. Point out that there are only 2 circles left. Ask students if they can put another circle on each plate and still have equal groups. (No)

7. Ask students what the circles on each plate represent. (the number of bones each dog will get) Ask them what the leftover circles represent. (the number of extra bones, or the remainder)

8. Explain that students can use the model to answer the story problem. Point out that the problem asks how many bones each dog will get.

   Ask: Is the answer the number of circles on each plate or the remainder?
   ANSWER: the number of circles on each plate

   Have students write the answer. (4)

9. Read aloud Problem 2. Help students write the number sentence using the process describe in Steps 1–3.

10. **Say:** In this story problem, you know the total and the number in each group. You can use a sketch to divide.

11. Have students draw 3 target areas, such as 3 plates. They should then draw 3 circles within each plate. Ask students if they can put all 11 circles on their plates and still have equal groups. (No) They should draw the 2 leftover circles to the side of either plate.

12. Ask students what the circles on their plates show. (the number of containers that can be filled) Ask them what the circles not on the plates show. (the number of leftover tennis balls, or the remainder)

13. Explain that students can use their sketch to answer the story problem. Point out that the problem asks how many balls are left over.

   Ask: Is the answer to the question the number of times you subtracted 3 or the remainder?
   ANSWER: the remainder

   Have students write the answer. (2)

14. Guide students through Problem 3 using the process described in Steps 9–13.

15. Guide students through writing the number sentence for Problem 4 using the process described in Steps 1–3. For this problem, students will use the number line and repeated subtraction. Students should start at 15 and count back 2 until they cannot count back 2 before reaching 0. Have them count the number of jumps, or the number of times they subtracted 2, to answer the problem.

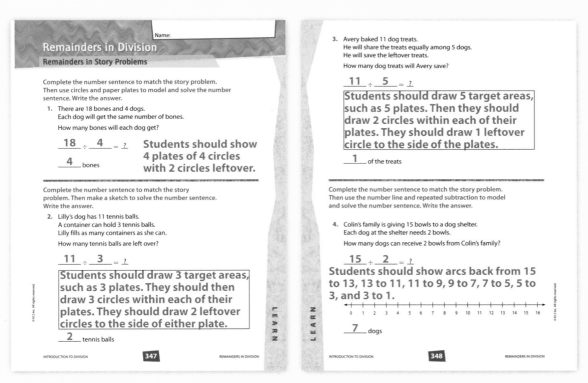

TRY IT Practice with Remainders

Objectives

Students will practice solving division computation and story problems that have remainders. Give students the circle blocks, 9 paper plates, and Practice with Remainders activity page from their Activity Book. Read the directions with them.

- Use forming equal groups with remainders to solve simple division problems.

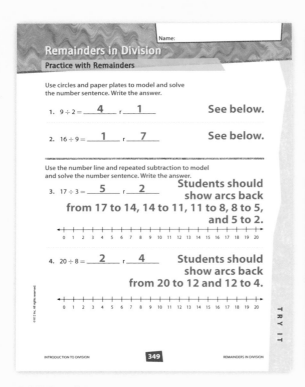

Name:

Remainders in Division
Practice with Remainders

Use circles and paper plates to model and solve the number sentence. Write the answer.

1. $9 \div 2 =$ **4** r **1**   See below.

2. $16 \div 9 =$ **1** r **7**   See below.

Use the number line and repeated subtraction to model and solve the number sentence. Write the answer.

3. $17 \div 3 =$ **5** r **2**   **Students should show arcs back from 17 to 14, 14 to 11, 11 to 8, 8 to 5, and 5 to 2.**

0 1 2 3 4 5 6 7 8 9 10 11 12 13 14 15 16 17 18 19 20

4. $20 \div 8 =$ **2** r **4**   **Students should show arcs back from 20 to 12 and 12 to 4.**

0 1 2 3 4 5 6 7 8 9 10 11 12 13 14 15 16 17 18 19 20

T R Y   I T

INTRODUCTION TO DIVISION   **349**   REMAINDERS IN DIVISION

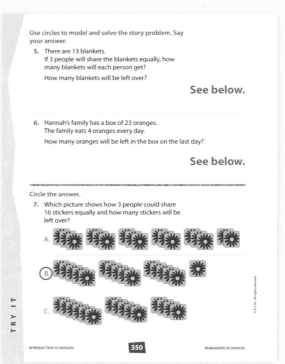

Use circles to model and solve the story problem. Say your answer.

5. There are 13 blankets.
   If 3 people will share the blankets equally, how many blankets will each person get?

   How many blankets will be left over?

   See below.

6. Hannah's family has a box of 23 oranges.
   The family eats 4 oranges every day.

   How many oranges will be left in the box on the last day?

   See below.

Circle the answer.

7. Which picture shows how 3 people could share 16 stickers equally and how many stickers will be left over?

A.

B.

C.

T R Y   I T

INTRODUCTION TO DIVISION   **350**   REMAINDERS IN DIVISION

Additional Answers

1. Students should place 1 circle on 1 plate and 1 on a second plate. Then they should place another circle on the first plate, another on the second plate, and so on until they've placed 4 circles on each plate. They should not place the 1 leftover circle.

2. Students should place 1 circle on each of 9 separate plates. They should not place the 7 leftover circles.

5. Students should place 1 circle in each of 3 separate groups. Then they should place a second circle in each group, then a third circle in each group, and then a fourth circle in each group. They should not place the 1 leftover circle. Students should say that each person will get 4 blankets and there will be 1 blanket left over.

6. Students should place 1 circle in each of 4 separate groups, then place a second circle in each group, then a third circle in each group, then a fourth circle in each group, and then a fifth circle in each group. They should not place the 3 leftover circles. Students should say that there will be 3 oranges left in the box on the last day.

CHECKPOINT

Objectives

- Use forming equal groups with remainders to solve simple division problems.

Print the Checkpoint. In Part 1, students will take a performance-based assessment. In Part 2, students will complete the problems on their own. Read the directions, problems, and answer choices to students, if necessary. Use the answer key to score the Checkpoint, and then enter the results online.

Gather the circle blocks and give them to students for Problem 1.

Checkpoint Math | Introduction to Division | Remainders in Division

Name _____ Date _____

Checkpoint Answer Key

Part 1

Follow the instructions for each item. Choose the response that best describes how the student performed on the task.

1. Say, "Seven people want to share 10 circles equally. Show how to solve this problem using your circles. How many circles will each person get? How many circles will be left over?"
   (1 point) Did the student divide the circle blocks into 7 equal groups, with one circle block in each group and 3 left over?
   A. Yes   B. No
   (1 point) Did the student say that each person will get 1 circle and there will be 3 left over?
   A. Yes   B. No

Give Part 2 of the assessment to students.

1 of 3

Checkpoint Math | Introduction to Division | Remainders in Division

Name _____ Date _____

Part 2

Solve. You may draw a sketch to help you solve the problems.
(1 point)
2. Josie has 17 bracelets to give to her friends.
   She wants to give each friend 3 bracelets.

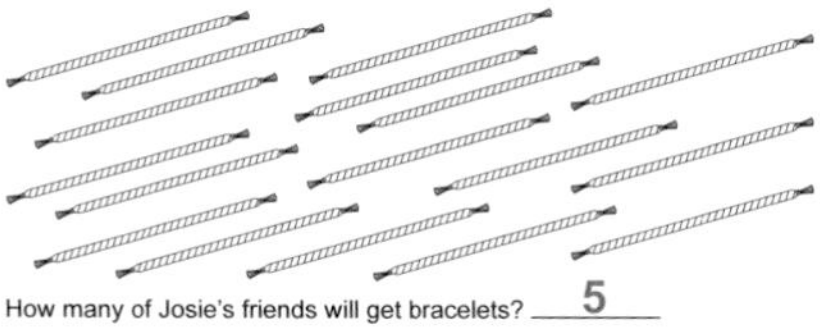

   How many of Josie's friends will get bracelets? __5__

   How many bracelets will she have left over? __2__

(1 point)
3. Ryan has 13 markers.
   He wants to give 2 markers to each friend.

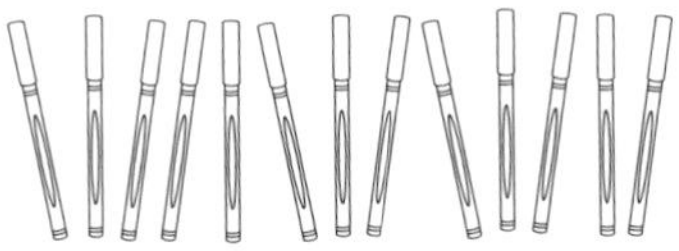

   How many of Ryan's friends will get markers? __6__

   How many markers will be left over? __1__

2 of 3

Checkpoint Math | Introduction to Division | Remainders in Division

Name _____ Date _____

(1 point)
4. 4 children want to share 14 pencils equally.

   How many pencils will each child get? __3__

   How many pencils will be left over? __2__

(1 point)
5. Which picture shows a way that 4 people could share 23 books equally, and how many books will be left over?

   Ⓐ
   B.
   C.

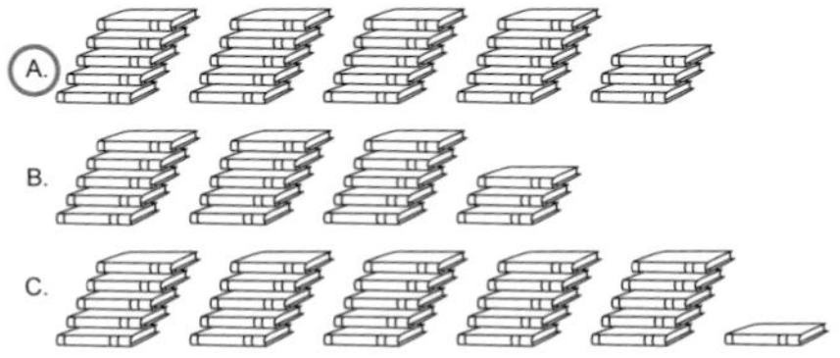

(1 point)
6. Which picture shows how 5 people could share 14 books equally, and how many books will be left over?

   A.
   Ⓑ
   C.

3 of 3

Unit Review

Lesson Overview

UNIT REVIEW Look Back	20 minutes	ONLINE
UNIT REVIEW Checkpoint Practice	20 minutes	OFFLINE
⏩ **UNIT REVIEW** Prepare for the Checkpoint		

▶ Unit Objectives

This lesson reviews the following objectives:

- Use repeated subtraction to do division problems.
- Use equal sharing to do division problems.
- Use models and math symbols to represent division.
- Recognize that the ÷ sign refers to division.
- Correctly use the ÷ symbol.
- Use forming equal groups with remainders to solve simple division problems.

▶ Advance Preparation

In this lesson, students will have an opportunity to review previous activities in the Introduction to Division unit. Look at the suggested activities in Unit Review: Prepare for the Checkpoint online and gather any needed materials.

Materials to Gather

SUPPLIED
Checkpoint Practice activity page

Keywords		
	divide	quotient
	division	remainder
	division symbol (÷)	repeated subtraction

UNIT REVIEW Look Back

ONLINE
20min

Objectives

- Review unit objectives.

In this unit, students have explored division and have solved division problems using repeated subtraction and equal sharing. First students have modeled repeated subtraction with circle blocks and number lines and learned how to record repeated subtraction. Then they have modeled equal sharing and solved division story problems. Lastly they have learned about the division symbol, how to use symbols to record division, and how to do division with remainders. Students will review these concepts to prepare for the Unit Checkpoint.

UNIT REVIEW Checkpoint Practice

Objectives

• Review unit objectives.

Students will complete a Checkpoint Practice activity page to prepare for the Unit Checkpoint. If necessary, read the directions, problems, and answer choices to students. Have students answer the problems on their own. Carefully review the answers with students.

Allow students to use circle blocks for Problems 3–10, if they wish.

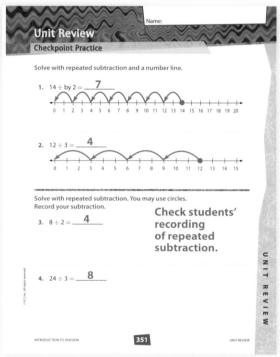

Name: _____

Unit Review

Checkpoint Practice

Solve with repeated subtraction and a number line.

1. $14 \div$ by $2 =$ __7__

   0 1 2 3 4 5 6 7 8 9 10 11 12 13 14 15 16 17 18 19 20

2. $12 \div 3 =$ __4__

   0 1 2 3 4 5 6 7 8 9 10 11 12 13 14 15

Solve with repeated subtraction. You may use circles.
Record your subtraction.

3. $8 \div 2 =$ __4__   **Check students' recording of repeated subtraction.**

4. $24 \div 3 =$ __8__

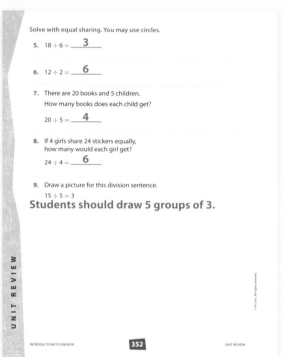

Solve with equal sharing. You may use circles.

5. $18 \div 6 =$ __3__

6. $12 \div 2 =$ __6__

7. There are 20 books and 5 children.
   How many books does each child get?

   $20 \div 5 =$ __4__

8. If 4 girls share 24 stickers equally,
   how many would each girl get?

   $24 \div 4 =$ __6__

9. Draw a picture for this division sentence.
   $15 \div 5 = 3$
   Students should draw 5 groups of 3.

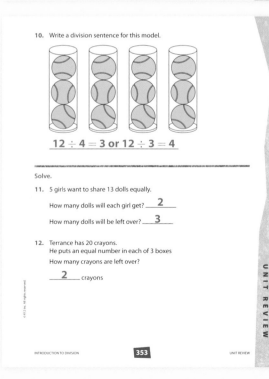

10. Write a division sentence for this model.

    $12 \div 4 = 3$ or $12 \div 3 = 4$

Solve.

11. 5 girls want to share 13 dolls equally.

    How many dolls will each girl get? __2__

    How many dolls will be left over? __3__

12. Terrance has 20 crayons.
    He puts an equal number in each of 3 boxes
    How many crayons are left over?

    __2__ crayons

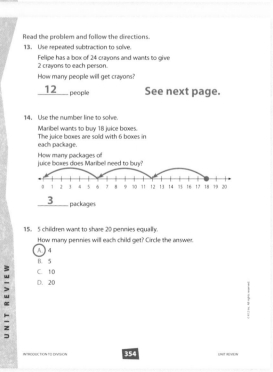

Read the problem and follow the directions.

13. Use repeated subtraction to solve.

    Felipe has a box of 24 crayons and wants to give
    2 crayons to each person.

    How many people will get crayons?

    __12__ people   **See next page.**

14. Use the number line to solve.

    Maribel wants to buy 18 juice boxes.
    The juice boxes are sold with 6 boxes in
    each package.

    How many packages of
    juice boxes does Maribel need to buy?

    0 1 2 3 4 5 6 7 8 9 10 11 12 13 14 15 16 17 18 19 20

    __3__ packages

15. 5 children want to share 20 pennies equally.
    How many pennies will each child get? Circle the answer.

    Ⓐ 4
    B. 5
    C. 10
    D. 20

16. Barbie wants to divide 15 cherries into 5 equal groups. Draw a sketch to show how many cherries will be in each group.

> **Students should draw a sketch of 15 cherries arranged into 5 groups of 3 cherries. Drawings may vary, but the 5 distinct groups of 3 cherries should be clear.**

17. Write a division sentence for the model.

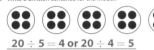

20 ÷ 5 = 4 or 20 ÷ 4 = 5

18. Look at the symbol where the arrow is pointing. What does this symbol mean? Say the answer.

$12 \div 4 = 3$

Students should say the division sign means to divide, to share, or to separate the 12 into 4 equal groups. Accept any one of these answers.

19. Which symbol goes in the circle to make the number sentence true? Circle the answer.

$12 \bigcirc 6 = 2$

A. +
B. −
C. ×
D. ÷

20. 6 children are playing tennis. There are 22 tennis balls.

If the children share the tennis balls equally, how many will each child get and how many will be left over?

__**3**__ tennis balls each

__**4**__ tennis balls left over

Additional Answers

13. **Example:** $24 - 2 = 22, 22 - 2 = 20, 20 - 2 = 18, 18 - 2 = 16,$
$16 - 2 = 14, 14 - 2 = 12, 12 - 2 = 10, 10 - 2 = 8, 8 - 2 = 6,$
$6 - 2 = 4, 4 - 2 = 2,$ and $2 - 2 = 0$
12 people can be given crayons.

→ UNIT REVIEW Prepare for the Checkpoint

What you do next depends on how students performed in the previous activity, Unit Review: Checkpoint Practice. If students had difficulty with any of the problems, complete the appropriate review activity listed in the table online.

Unit Checkpoint

▶ Unit Objectives

This lesson assesses the following objectives:

- Use repeated subtraction to do division problems.
- Use equal sharing to do division problems.
- Use models and math symbols to represent division.
- Recognize that the ÷ sign refers to division.
- Correctly use the ÷ symbol.
- Use forming equal groups with remainders to solve simple division problems.

Materials to Gather

SUPPLIED
blocks – B
Unit Checkpoint (printout)

ONLINE **30**min

UNIT CHECKPOINT Online

Students will complete this part of the Unit Checkpoint online. Read the directions, problems, and answer choices to students. If necessary, help students with keyboard or mouse operations.

Objectives

- Assess unit objectives.

OFFLINE **30**min

UNIT CHECKPOINT Offline

Students will complete this part of the Unit Checkpoint offline. In Part 1, students will take a performance-based assessment. In Part 2, students will complete the problems on their own. Print the Unit Checkpoint. Read the directions, problems, and answer choices to students, if necessary. Use the answer key to score the Checkpoint, and then enter the results online.

Gather the circle blocks and give them to students for Problem 6.

Objectives

- Assess unit objectives.

Name _____ Date _____

Unit Checkpoint Answer Key

Part 1

Follow the instructions for each item. Choose the response that best describes how the student performed on the task.

1. Say, "Three people wanted to share 10 circle blocks equally. Show how to solve this problem using your circle blocks.
   How many circle blocks will each person get?
   How many will be left over?"
   (1 point)
   Did the student divide the circle blocks into 3 groups, with 3 circle blocks in each group and 1 left over?

   A. Yes   B. No

   (1 point)
   Did the student say that each person would get 3 circle blocks and there would be 1 left over?

   A. Yes   B. No

Give students Part 2 of the assessment.

Name _____ Date _____

Part 2
Read the problem and follow the directions.
(2 points)

2. Use repeated subtraction to show your work.

   Frank wants to put his 21 rocks into boxes.
   He wants to put 7 rocks into each box.
   How many boxes will Frank need?

   Sample answer:
   $21 - 7 = 14, 14 - 7 = 7, 7 - 7 = 0$

   ___3___ boxes

   (2 points)
3. Use repeated subtraction to show your work on a number line.

   Barbara had 18 beads.
   She put 9 beads on each necklace.
   How many necklaces did she make?

   0 1 2 3 4 5 6 7 8 9 10 11 12 13 14 15 16 17 18 19 20

   ___2___ necklaces

Name _____ Date _____

(2 points)
4. Draw circles around groups of balloons to solve the problem.

   There are 24 balloons.
   6 children want to share the balloons equally.
   How many balloons will each child get?

   ___4___ balloons

(1 point)
5. Write a division sentence for the model.

   0 1 2 3 4 5 6 7 8 9 10 11 12 13 14 15 16 17 18 19

   Division sentence: $18 \div 6 = 3$ or $18 \div 3 = 6$

(1 point)
6. Look at the symbol where the arrow is pointing. What does this symbol mean?

   ↓
   $12 \div 2 = 6$

   The symbol means **Sample answers: divide, share, separate the 12 into 2 equal groups**

Name _____ Date _____

Circle the answer.
(1 point)
7. Which symbol goes in the circle to make the number sentence true?

   $6 \bigcirc 3 = 2$

   A. +   B. −   C. ×   **D.** ÷

(1 point)
8. 10 children want to share 90 marbles equally.

   How many marbles will each child get?

   A. 9   B. 10   C. 80   D. 100

Data Representations and Analysis

▶ Unit Objectives

- Systematically record numerical data.
- Represent the same data set with more than one representation, such as a tally, picture graph, or bar graph.
- Ask and answer simple questions related to data representations.
- Solve addition or subtraction problems by using data from charts, picture graphs, and number sentences.
- Determine the range for a set of data.
- Identify the mode in a data set.

▶ Big Ideas

Graphs and charts are good ways to represent and compare numerical data.

▶ Unit Introduction

Students will explore different ways to represent and analyze data in this unit. They will make horizontal and vertical bar graphs and learn how to read them. Students will show the same set of data multiple ways, in charts, tables and graphs. They will ask and answer questions and solve addition and subtraction problems using data from tally charts, picture graphs, and bar graphs. Lastly students will find the range and mode of data sets.

Display Data

Skills Update	5 minutes	ONLINE
GET READY Show Data in a Tally Chart	5 minutes	ONLINE
LEARN Make Bar Graphs	10 minutes	ONLINE
LEARN More Bar Graphs	5 minutes	OFFLINE
LEARN Same Data, Different Displays	15 minutes	OFFLINE
TRY IT Make Graphs and Charts	10 minutes	OFFLINE
CHECKPOINT	10 minutes	OFFLINE

▶ Lesson Objectives
- Systematically record numerical data.
- Represent the same data set with more than one representation, such as a tally, picture graph, or bar graph.

▶ Prerequisite Skills
- Write numerals through 500.
- Use pictures and picture graphs to represent data.
- Use tally charts to represent data.

▶ Advance Preparation
Print two copies of the Horizontal Bar Graph and one copy of the Vertical Bar Graph.

▶ Content Background
Students will learn how to make and read a bar graph. They will also learn that the same data can be shown in different charts and graphs. They will recognize when different graphical displays are showing the same data.

The term *data* is the plural of *datum*. Data are pieces of information that can be gathered. For example, the ages of each member of a family are data. There are several ways to record data. Usually, pieces of data are recorded in tables or graphs. Students can use numbers, tallies, pictures, or graphs to represent data.

A picture graph is a graph that uses pictures to represent data. A key is provided to describe how many objects each picture represents.

A *set* is a group of objects. *Set* is a mathematical term for *group*. Use *set* and *group* interchangeably in conversation with students.

Materials to Gather

SUPPLIED

Horizontal Bar Graph (printout) – 2

Vertical Bar Graph (printout)

Same Data, Different Displays activity page

Make Graphs and Charts activity page

Checkpoint (printout)

ALSO NEEDED

crayons

Keywords

bar graph – a graph that uses nonadjacent bars to show quantities for comparison purposes
data – pieces of information; the singular is *datum*
picture graph – a graph that uses pictures to represent data
tally chart – a chart used to record the frequency of data, displaying hand-drawn marks in groups of five, called tally marks

---

GET READY Show Data in a Tally Chart

ONLINE 5min

Students will represent data in a tally chart. They will sort some objects, count them, and record their counts. They will also answer questions about their data.

Objectives

- Use tally charts to represent data.

LEARN Make Bar Graphs

ONLINE 10min

Students will learn how to record information in a bar graph. They'll use both vertical and horizontal bar graphs.

Objectives

- Systematically record numerical data.

LEARN More Bar Graphs

OFFLINE 5min

Students will create their own bar graph.
Gather the crayons and Horizontal Bar Graph.

1. Read this information to students:
- Mr. Green's farm has 5 cows, 9 sheep, 3 pigs, and 4 horses.

2. Help students with the following tasks:
- Label the title at the top of the graph "Animals on Mr. Green's Farm."
- Write "Kinds of animals" on the long line along the left side of the graph.
- Write "Number of animals" on the long line under the graph.
- Write "Cow," "Sheep," "Pig," and "Horse" on the short lines beside the vertical label.
- Write numbers under the chart, starting with 0 beneath the far-left box and ending with 10.

3. Say: Now make the bars to show the data. There are 5 cows. Look for the Cow row. Start at the left of the Cow row and move to the right, coloring 5 boxes. That's one box for each cow.

4. Guide students to start on the left when they color the boxes for each animal. Have them complete the rest of the graph for the other animals.

Objectives

- Systematically record numerical data.

Tips

If you wish, have students show each animal with different-colored snap cubes. Join the like-colored cubes to make trains. Then position the trains next to each other to see the bars.

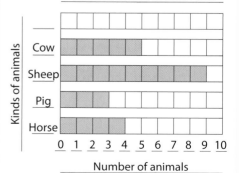

Animals on Mr. Green's Farm

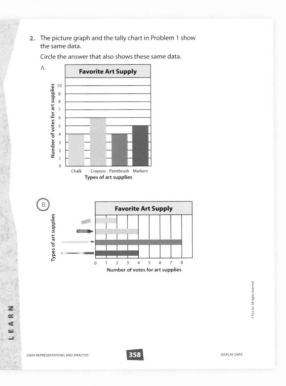

LEARN Same Data, Different Displays

OFFLINE
15min

Objectives

- Systematically record numerical data.
- Represent the same data set with more than one representation, such as a tally, picture graph, or bar graph.

Students will see graphs that show the same data represented in different ways and will explain how they know the graphs display the same data. They will also identify a graph that shows the same data set as another chart or graph. Lastly students will make a bar graph that represents the same data set as a tally chart.

Gather the Vertical Bar Graph, crayons, and Same Data, Different Displays activity page. Give the materials to students and read the directions on the activity page with them.

1. Have students look at the tally chart and the picture graph in Problem 1. Explain that they show the same data in different ways. Point out that they both have the same title. Ask students to point to other parts of the chart and graph that show that the data are the same.

2. Guide students to look for both similarities and differences in the chart and graph as they work on Problems 2 and 3. They should point out examples of data values that are the same and are different.

3. Explain that students will use the data in the tally chart to create their own bar graph in Problem 4.

Guide students to write a title for the graph and label each column on the Vertical Bar Graph the same way as in the tally chart. Students may want to represent each fruit with a different color bar in their graph.

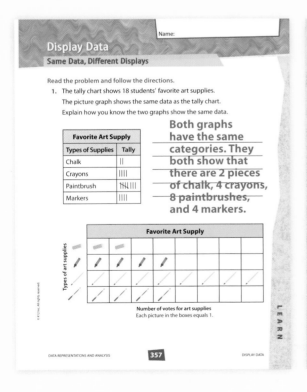

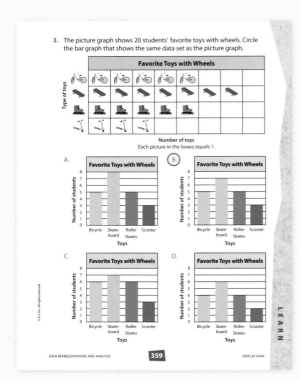

3. The picture graph shows 20 students' favorite toys with wheels. Circle the bar graph that shows the same data set as the picture graph.

L E A R N

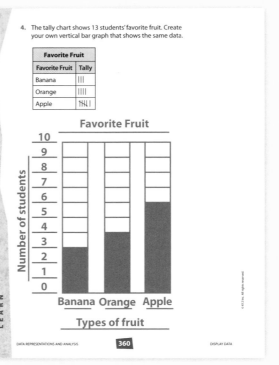

4. The tally chart shows 13 students' favorite fruit. Create your own vertical bar graph that shows the same data.

OFFLINE
10 min

TRY IT Make Graphs and Charts

Students will practice making and identifying a tally chart and different graphs to show data. Give students the Horizontal Bar Graph and Make Graphs and Charts activity page from their Activity Book. Read the directions with them.

Have students tell you what goes on the graph or chart labels, and then write it for them, if necessary. Students should use the Horizontal Bar Graph for Problem 3.

Objectives

- Systematically record numerical data.
- Represent the same data set with more than one representation, such as a tally, picture graph, or bar graph.

Display Data
Make Graphs and Charts

Name: _____

Read the problem and follow the directions.

1. Make a tally chart to show the data set. Remember to label all parts of your chart.

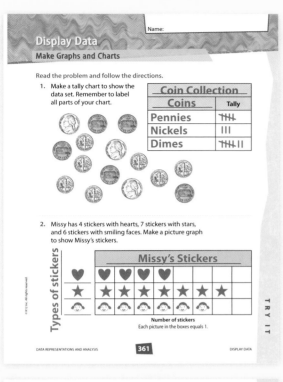

Coin Collection	
Coins	**Tally**
Pennies	卌
Nickels	|||
Dimes	卌||

2. Missy has 4 stickers with hearts, 7 stickers with stars, and 6 stickers with smiling faces. Make a picture graph to show Missy's stickers.

Missy's Stickers

Types of stickers

Number of stickers
Each picture in the boxes equals 1.

TRY IT

---

3. Make a bar graph to show the same data as in the tally chart.

Favorite Berries	
Strawberries 🍓	卌
Raspberries 🫐	||||
Blueberries ●	卌|

See below.

4. Draw a picture graph to show the data in this tally chart.

Favorite Fruit	
Fruit	**Number**
Oranges	卌
Apples	|||
Pears	卌|

Favorite Fruit

Types of fruit

Number of votes for fruit
Each picture in the boxes equals 1.

TRY IT

Circle the answer.

5. Which tally chart shows the correct number of toys shown here?

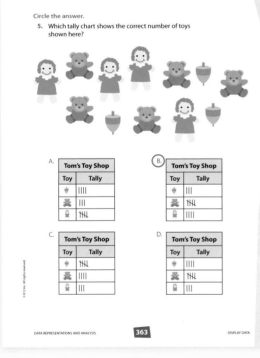

A.
Tom's Toy Shop	
Toy	**Tally**
🪀	||||
🧸	|||
🎎	卌

B.
Tom's Toy Shop	
Toy	**Tally**
🪀	|||
🧸	卌
🎎	||||

C.
Tom's Toy Shop	
Toy	**Tally**
🪀	卌
🧸	||||
🎎	|||

D.
Tom's Toy Shop	
Toy	**Tally**
🪀	|||
🧸	卌
🎎	||

TRY IT

---

6. This bar graph shows how many books were sold each day at a bookstore. Which picture graph shows the same data as the bar graph?

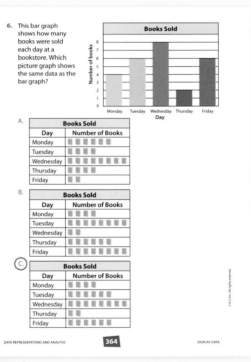

A.
Books Sold	
Day	**Number of Books**
Monday	▪▪▪▪▪▪
Tuesday	▪▪▪
Wednesday	▪▪▪▪▪▪▪▪
Thursday	▪▪▪▪
Friday	▪▪

B.
Books Sold	
Day	**Number of Books**
Monday	▪▪▪▪
Tuesday	▪▪▪▪▪▪▪▪
Wednesday	▪▪
Thursday	
Friday	▪▪▪▪▪▪▪▪

C.
Books Sold	
Day	**Number of Books**
Monday	▪▪▪▪
Tuesday	▪▪▪▪▪▪
Wednesday	▪▪▪▪▪▪▪▪
Thursday	▪▪
Friday	▪▪▪▪▪▪

TRY IT

Additional Answers

3.

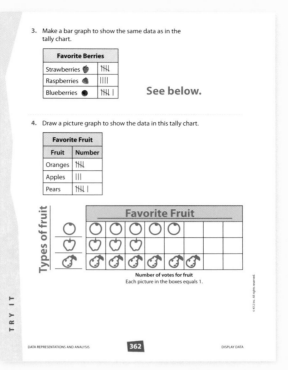

Favorite Berries

Kinds of berries: Strawberries, Raspberries, Blueberries

0 1 2 3 4 5 6 7 8 9 10
Number of votes for berries

CHECKPOINT

Objectives

Print the Checkpoint and have students complete it on their own. Read the directions, problems, and answer choices to students, if necessary. Use the answer key to score the Checkpoint, and then enter the results online.

- Systematically record numerical data.
- Represent the same data set with more than one representation, such as a tally, picture graph, or bar graph.

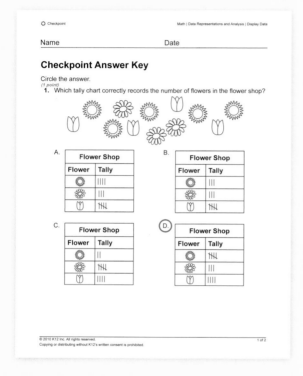

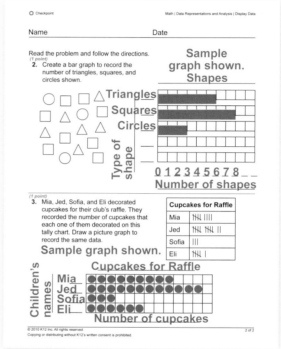

Data Questions

Lesson Overview

Skills Update	5 minutes	**ONLINE**
GET READY Match Data Displays	5 minutes	**ONLINE**
LEARN Questions for Tally Charts and Graphs	15 minutes	**ONLINE**
LEARN Bar Graph Questions	15 minutes	**ONLINE**
TRY IT Chart and Graph Questions	10 minutes	**OFFLINE**
CHECKPOINT	10 minutes	**OFFLINE**

Lesson Objectives

Ask and answer simple questions related to data representations.

Prerequisite Skills

Represent the same data set with more than one representation, such as a tally, picture graph, or bar graph.

Content Background

Students will learn that they can use charts and graphs to answer questions about data. They also will learn how to ask a question that can be answered with information in a particular chart or graph.

Materials to Gather

SUPPLIED

Chart and Graph Questions activity page

Checkpoint (printout)

GET READY Match Data Displays

ONLINE 5min

Students will identify representations that show the same data set.

As students move through the activity, have them ask themselves questions such as the following:

- What are the categories?
- Which chart or graph shows the same numbers for each category as the chart or graph in the question?

Objectives

- Represent the same data set with more than one representation, such as a tally, picture graph, or bar graph.

LEARN Questions for Tally Charts and Graphs

ONLINE 15min

Objectives

- Ask and answer simple questions related to data representations.

Students will answer questions about data in a tally chart, picture graph, and bar graph. They will also create and answer their own questions about the data.

Encourage students to ask a variety of questions; for example, have them ask one that asks about the quantities, one that asks about the most or the fewest, and one that compares two quantities. Guide students to write down at least one question and then answer it. They can express the other questions and answers verbally.

LEARN Bar Graph Questions

ONLINE 15min

Objectives

- Ask and answer simple questions related to data representations.

Students will answer questions about data in vertical and horizontal bar graphs. They will also create and answer their own questions about the data.

Encourage students to ask a variety of questions; for example, have them ask one that asks about the quantities, one that asks about the most or the fewest, and one that compares two quantities. Guide students to write down at least one question and answer it. They can express the other questions and answers verbally.

TRY IT Chart and Graph Questions

OFFLINE 10min

Objectives

- Ask and answer simple questions related to data representations.

Students will practice creating questions that can be answered by data in graphs and tally charts. Give students the Chart and Graph Questions activity page from their Activity Book and read the directions with them.

Data Questions

Chart and Graph Questions

Name:

Use the picture graph for Problems 1–3. The picture graph shows students' responses when they were asked to name their favorite flower.

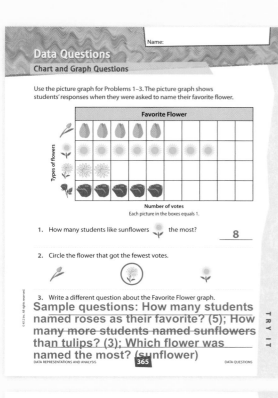

Favorite Flower

Types of flowers

Number of votes
Each picture in the boxes equals 1.

1. How many students like sunflowers 🌻 the most? _____8_____

2. Circle the flower that got the fewest votes.

3. Write a different question about the Favorite Flower graph.
   Sample questions: How many students named roses as their favorite? (5); How many more students named sunflowers than tulips? (3); Which flower was named the most? (sunflower)

Use the bar graph for Problems 4–6. The graph shows students' responses when they were asked what kind of pet they have.

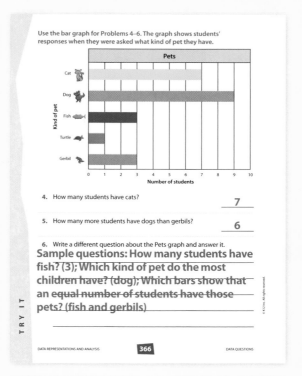

Pets

Kind of pet: Cat, Dog, Fish, Turtle, Gerbil

Number of students

4. How many students have cats? _____7_____

5. How many more students have dogs than gerbils? _____6_____

6. Write a different question about the Pets graph and answer it.
   Sample questions: How many students have fish? (3); Which kind of pet do the most children have? (dog); Which bars show that an equal number of students have those pets? (fish and gerbils)

Read the problem and follow the directions.

7. Write a question that could be answered with information from the graph and then answer it.

Lemonade Sold	
Day	**Tally**
Monday	|||
Tuesday	卌	
Wednesday	卌 ||

Sample questions: How many glasses of lemonade were sold on Tuesday? (6); How many more glasses of lemonade were sold on Wednesday than on Tuesday? (1); How many glasses of lemonade were sold on Monday and Tuesday? (9)

8. Look at the graph. Write a question that could be answered with information from the graph.

Favorite Color

Number

Blue, Red, Green, Orange
Color

Sample questions: What color did most people like? (green); How many more people liked blue than orange? (2); How many people liked green best? (6)

9. Look at the tally chart. Write a question that could be answered with information from the tally chart and then answer it.

Favorite Muffin	
Muffin	**Tally**
Strawberry	卌 ||
Blueberry	卌
Lemon	卌 卌	
Orange	卌 |||

Sample answers: How many people liked strawberry muffins best? (7); How many more people liked orange better than blueberry muffins? (3); What is the total number of people who liked lemon and strawberry muffins? (18)

For Problems 3, 6, and 7–9, students should write a valid question based on the data in the graph or chart. They should correctly answer the question they asked.

TRY IT

OFFLINE
10 min

Print the Checkpoint and have students complete it on their own. Read the directions, problems, and answer choices to students, if necessary. Use the answer key to score the Checkpoint, and then enter the results online.

- Ask and answer simple questions related to data representations.

Name _____ Date _____

Checkpoint Answer Key

Write a question that could be answered with information from the graph or chart. Then answer your question.
(2 points)

1.

Tacos Eaten

Children's names							
Brittney	🌮	🌮	🌮	🌮	🌮	🌮	
Steve	🌮	🌮	🌮				
Emily	🌮	🌮	🌮	🌮	🌮		

Number of tacos
Each picture in the boxes equals 1.

(1 point) Students should write a valid question based on the data in the graph.

(1 point) Students should correctly answer the question they asked.

Sample questions: How many tacos did Brittney eat? 8

How many more tacos did Emily eat than Steve? 3

How many tacos did Steve and Brittney eat altogether? 11

Name _____ Date _____

(2 points)
2.

Favorite Pizza

Pizza Flavor	Tally
Cheese	||||| ||||
Pepperoni	||||| |||||
Black Olive	||||| |||
Ham and Pineapple	|||||

(1 point) Students should write a valid question based on the data in the tally chart.

(1 point) Students should correctly answer the question they asked.

Sample questions: How many liked pepperoni pizza best? 10

How many more people liked cheese than ham and pineapple pizza? 4

What was the total number of people who liked pepperoni and cheese? 19

Name _____ Date _____

(2 points)
3.

Surfboards Sold

(bar graph: Friday 8, Saturday 4, Sunday 6, Monday 1)
Number sold / Days

(1 point) Students should write a valid question based on the data in the bar graph.

(1 point) Students should correctly answer the question they asked.

Sample questions: How many surfboards were sold on Friday? 8

How many more surfboards were sold on Sunday than on Saturday? 2

What was the total number of surfboards sold on Friday and Monday? 9

Use Data to Solve Problems

▶ Lesson Objectives

Solve addition or subtraction problems by using data from charts, picture graphs, and number sentences.

▶ Prerequisite Skills

Ask and answer simple questions related to data representations.

▶ Content Background

Students will use data from charts and graphs to solve addition and subtraction problems. They will write number sentences to show how to find the answer.

Materials to Gather

SUPPLIED

Problems About Data activity page

Checkpoint (printout)

GET READY Ask and Answer

ONLINE
5 min

Objectives

- Ask and answer simple questions related to data representations.

Students will ask and answer their own questions about data in a bar graph. If students have difficulty thinking of questions, prompt them with the following questions:

- What does the chart or graph show?
- What can you ask about the different categories (ladybugs, butterflies, bees, and spiders)?
- What questions can you ask that would compare two amounts?

Sample questions and answers may include the following:

- How many bees are in the garden? (7)
- Which bug is there the least of in the garden? (butterflies)
- How many fewer ladybugs than spiders are there in the garden? (1)
- There are more ladybugs than which other kind of bug? (butterflies)

LEARN Number Sentences for Graphs and Charts **15** min | Objectives

Students will learn how to write and solve addition and subtraction number sentences to answer questions about picture graphs and tally charts. When students are writing number sentences based on a tally chart, make sure they count each group of 5 tally marks as 5, not 1.

- Solve addition or subtraction problems by using data from charts, picture graphs, and number sentences.

LEARN Number Sentences for Bar Graphs **15** min | Objectives

Students will learn how to write and solve addition and subtraction number sentences to answer questions about horizontal and vertical bar graphs. Guide students to read bar graphs by finding the end of the bar for a given category and following the line to the number grid to see the number of objects for that category.

- Solve addition or subtraction problems by using data from charts, picture graphs, and number sentences.

TRY IT Problems About Data **10** min | Objectives

Students will practice writing and solving addition and subtraction number sentences to answer questions about graphs and charts. Give students the Problems About Data activity page from their Activity Book and read the directions with them.

- Solve addition or subtraction problems by using data from charts, picture graphs, and number sentences.

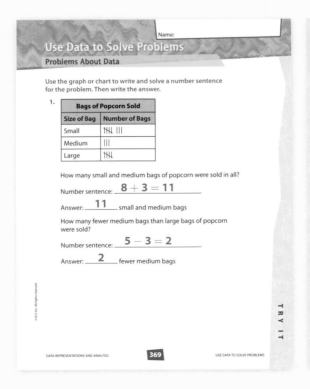

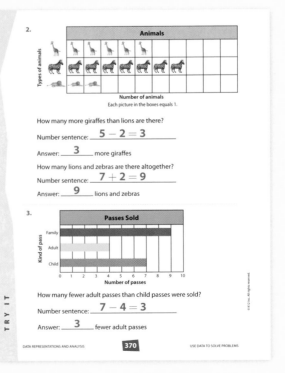

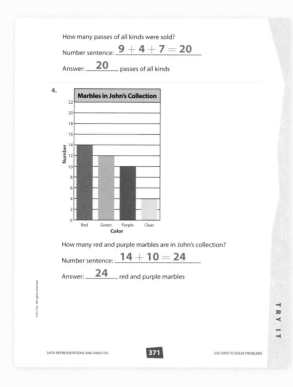

How many passes of all kinds were sold?

Number sentence: $9 + 4 + 7 = 20$

Answer: __20__ passes of all kinds

4.

Marbles in John's Collection

How many red and purple marbles are in John's collection?

Number sentence: $14 + 10 = 24$

Answer: __24__ red and purple marbles

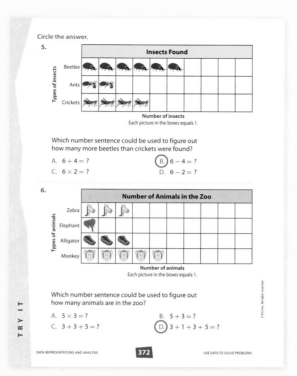

Circle the answer.

5.

Insects Found

Which number sentence could be used to figure out how many more beetles than crickets were found?
A. $6 + 4 = ?$ 　B. $6 - 4 = ?$
C. $6 \times 2 = ?$ 　D. $6 - 2 = ?$

6.

Number of Animals in the Zoo

Which number sentence could be used to figure out how many animals are in the zoo?
A. $5 \times 3 = ?$ 　B. $5 + 3 = ?$
C. $3 + 3 + 5 = ?$ 　D. $3 + 1 + 3 + 5 = ?$

OFFLINE
10 min

CHECKPOINT

Print the Checkpoint and have students complete it on their own. Read the directions, problems, and answer choices to students, if necessary. Use the answer key to score the Checkpoint, and then enter the results online.

Objectives

- Solve addition or subtraction problems by using data from charts, picture graphs, and number sentences.

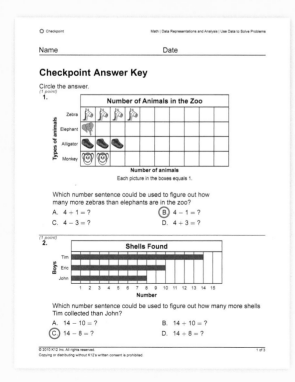

Checkpoint　Math | Data Representations and Analysis | Use Data to Solve Problems

Name　Date

Checkpoint Answer Key

Circle the answer.
(1 point)
1.

Number of Animals in the Zoo

Which number sentence could be used to figure out how many more zebras than elephants are in the zoo?
A. $4 + 1 = ?$ 　B. $4 - 1 = ?$
C. $4 - 3 = ?$ 　D. $4 + 3 = ?$

(1 point)
2.

Shells Found

Which number sentence could be used to figure out how many more shells Tim collected than John?
A. $14 - 10 = ?$ 　B. $14 + 10 = ?$
C. $14 - 8 = ?$ 　D. $14 + 8 = ?$

1 of 3

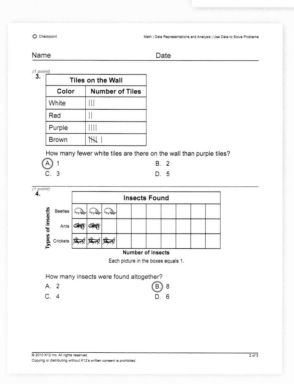

Checkpoint　Math | Data Representations and Analysis | Use Data to Solve Problems

Name　Date

(1 point)
3.

Tiles on the Wall	
Color	Number of Tiles
White	|||
Red	||
Purple	||||
Brown	|||||	

How many fewer white tiles are there on the wall than purple tiles?
A. 1 　B. 2
C. 3 　D. 5

(1 point)
4.

Insects Found

How many insects were found altogether?
A. 2 　B. 8
C. 4 　D. 6

2 of 3

Name _____   Date _____

(1 point)

5.

Number of Animals in the Zoo

Types of animals										
Zebra	🦓	🦓	🦓							
Elephant	🐘									
Alligator	🐊	🐊	🐊							
Monkey	🐵	🐵	🐵	🐵	🐵					

Number of animals

Each picture in the boxes equals 1.

What is the total number of alligators and monkeys
in the zoo?

A. 3

B. 5

C. 8

D. 12

Range and Mode of Data Sets

Skills Update	5 minutes	ONLINE
GET READY Spin and Tally	5 minutes	ONLINE
LEARN Find the Range	15 minutes	ONLINE
LEARN Find the Mode	15 minutes	ONLINE
TRY IT Range and Mode	10 minutes	OFFLINE
CHECKPOINT	10 minutes	OFFLINE

▶ Lesson Objectives

- Determine the range for a set of data.
- Identify the mode in a data set.

▶ Prerequisite Skills

Systematically record numerical data.

▶ Content Background

Students will learn how to compute the range and identify the mode for a set of data. In mathematics, the range of a set of data does **not** indicate two boundaries of the data, such as from 5 to 33, as range might typically imply. The range is, in fact, the *difference* between the piece of data with the greatest value and the piece of data with the least value. The range is a single value. The range of the data set 17, 33, 23, 5, 14, 30 is found by subtracting 5, the least value, from 33, the greatest value, to get a difference of 28.

The mode of a set of data is the value within the data that occurs most often. A data set may have no modes, 1 mode, or several modes. The data set 17, 33, 23, 5, 14, 30 has no modes, whereas the data set 5, 10, 7, 5, 8 has a mode of 5, since 5 appears most often. In this lesson, students will only see data sets that have 1 mode.

Students will be encouraged to arrange the data in numerical order to more easily determine the values of the range and the mode.

Materials to Gather

SUPPLIED
Range and Mode activity page
Checkpoint (printout)

Keywords	**mode** – the pieces of data that occur most often in a set of data; data may have 0, 1, or many modes
	range – the difference between the greatest value in a data set and the least value; for example, the range of the data set {2, 3, 4, 5} is 5 – 2, or 3

GET READY Spin and Tally

Students will generate data with an on-screen spinner and record the data in a tally chart. When students complete the activity, discuss the data in their tally chart with them by asking questions such as the following:

- Which number did you spin the least often?
- How many more times did the spinner land on red than blue?
- What patterns do you see in the recorded spins?
- If you repeat the activity, do you think you would get the same results?

LEARN Find the Range

Students will learn to find the range for a set of data. They will generate the first set of data with an online experiment and find the range. The range is the difference between the greatest and least numbers in a data set. To find the range, students should first identify the greatest and least values in the set. Then they should subtract to find the difference between those numbers.

Other data sets are given in charts and in lists. Hint buttons throughout the activity will help students visualize the numbers in the data set on an on-screen number line. The number line allows them to see the data set ordered from least to greatest and should make it easier for students to identify the least and greatest values.

LEARN Find the Mode

Students will learn how to determine the mode for a set of data. The mode is the number that appears most often in a data set. To find the mode, students should first order the numbers in the set from least to greatest. Then they should be able to find which number is repeated the most times.

TRY IT Range and Mode

Students will practice finding the range and mode of data sets. Give students the Range and Mode activity page from their Activity Book and read the directions with them.

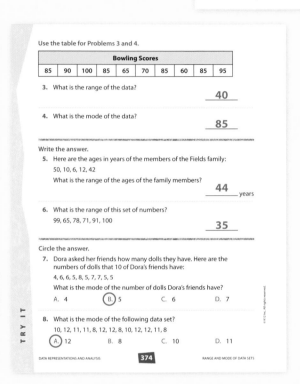

Range and Mode of Data Sets
Range and Mode

Name: _____

Use the table for Problems 1 and 2.

Softball Team Roster

Name	Age
Vicky	⑪
Becky	9
Molly	10
Hannah	9
Tori	8
Emma	⑦
Lauren	7
Kayla	8
Teresa	8

1. Circle the youngest age and the oldest age in the table.
   What is the range of the ages on the softball team?
   4 years

2. Write the numbers in the table in order from least to greatest.
   7, 7, 8, 8, 8, 9, 9, 10, 11
   What is the mode of the ages?
   8 years

Use the table for Problems 3 and 4.

Bowling Scores

| 85 | 90 | 100 | 85 | 65 | 70 | 85 | 60 | 85 | 95 |

3. What is the range of the data?
   40

4. What is the mode of the data?
   85

Write the answer.

5. Here are the ages in years of the members of the Fields family:
   50, 10, 6, 12, 42
   What is the range of the ages of the family members?
   44 years

6. What is the range of this set of numbers?
   99, 65, 78, 71, 91, 100
   35

Circle the answer.

7. Dora asked her friends how many dolls they have. Here are the numbers of dolls that 10 of Dora's friends have:
   4, 6, 6, 5, 8, 5, 7, 7, 5, 5
   What is the mode of the number of dolls Dora's friends have?
   A. 4   B. 5   C. 6   D. 7

8. What is the mode of the following data set?
   10, 12, 11, 11, 8, 12, 12, 8, 10, 12, 12, 11, 8
   A. 12   B. 8   C. 10   D. 11

DATA REPRESENTATIONS AND ANALYSIS   **373**   RANGE AND MODE OF DATA SETS

DATA REPRESENTATIONS AND ANALYSIS   **374**   RANGE AND MODE OF DATA SETS

CHECKPOINT

Objectives

- Determine the range for a set of data.
- Identify the mode in a data set.

Print the Checkpoint and have students complete it on their own. Read the directions, problems, and answer choices to students, if necessary. Use the answer key to score the Checkpoint, and then enter the results online.

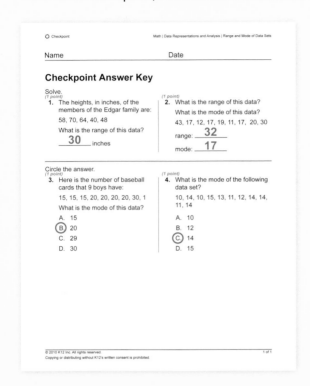

○ Checkpoint   Math | Data Representations and Analysis | Range and Mode of Data Sets

Name _____ Date _____

Checkpoint Answer Key

Solve.
(1 point)
1. The heights, in inches, of the members of the Edgar family are:

   58, 70, 64, 40, 48

   What is the range of this data?

   30 inches

(1 point)
2. What is the range of this data?
   What is the mode of this data?

   43, 17, 12, 17, 19, 11, 17, 20, 30

   range: **32**

   mode: **17**

Circle the answer.
(1 point)
3. Here is the number of baseball cards that 9 boys have:

   15, 15, 15, 20, 20, 20, 30, 1

   What is the mode of this data?

   A. 15
   B. 20 ← *(circled)*
   C. 29
   D. 30

(1 point)
4. What is the mode of the following data set?

   10, 14, 10, 15, 13, 11, 12, 14, 14, 11, 14

   A. 10
   B. 12
   C. 14 ← *(circled)*
   D. 15

1 of 1

Unit Review

Lesson Overview

UNIT REVIEW Look Back	20 minutes	ONLINE
UNIT REVIEW Checkpoint Practice	20 minutes	OFFLINE
⏩ **UNIT REVIEW** Prepare for the Checkpoint		

▶ Unit Objectives

This lesson reviews the following objectives:

- Systematically record numerical data.
- Represent the same data set with more than one representation, such as a tally, picture graph, or bar graph.
- Ask and answer simple questions related to data representations.
- Solve addition or subtraction problems by using data from charts, picture graphs, and number sentences.
- Determine the range for a set of data.
- Identify the mode in a data set.

▶ Advance Preparation

In this lesson, students will have an opportunity to review previous activities in the Data Representations and Analysis unit. Look at the suggested activities in Unit Review: Prepare for the Checkpoint online and gather any needed materials.
Print the Horizontal Bar Graph.

Materials to Gather

SUPPLIED
Horizontal Bar Graph (printout)
Checkpoint Practice activity page

Keywords

bar graph	**picture graph**
data	**range**
mode	**tally chart**

ONLINE
20min

UNIT REVIEW Look Back

Objectives

- Review unit objectives.

In this unit, students have explored different ways to represent and analyze data. They have made horizontal and vertical bar graphs and learned how to read them. Students have showed the same set of data multiple ways in charts, tables, and graphs. They have asked and answered questions and solved addition and subtraction problems using data from tally charts, picture graphs, and bar graphs. Lastly students have found the range and mode of data sets. Students will review these concepts in preparation for the Unit Checkpoint.

UNIT REVIEW Checkpoint Practice

- Review unit objectives.

Students will complete a Checkpoint Practice activity page to prepare for the Unit Checkpoint. If necessary, read the directions, problems, and answer choices to students. Have students answer the problems on their own. Carefully review the answers with students.

Gather the Horizontal Bar Graph and give it to students for Problem 1.

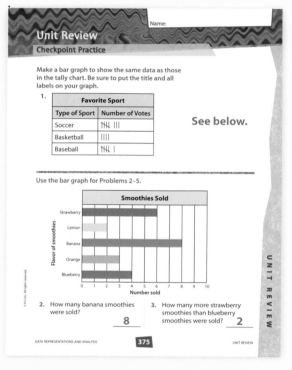

Unit Review
Checkpoint Practice

Make a bar graph to show the same data as those in the tally chart. Be sure to put the title and all labels on your graph.

1.

Favorite Sport	
Type of Sport	Number of Votes
Soccer	ⅢⅡ Ⅲ
Basketball	ⅢⅠ
Baseball	ⅢⅠ Ⅰ

See below.

Use the bar graph for Problems 2–5.

Smoothies Sold

2. How many banana smoothies were sold? **8**

3. How many more strawberry smoothies than blueberry smoothies were sold? **2**

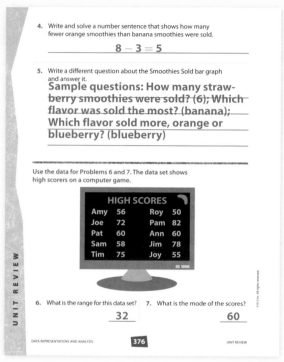

4. Write and solve a number sentence that shows how many fewer orange smoothies than banana smoothies were sold.

$$8 - 3 = 5$$

5. Write a different question about the Smoothies Sold bar graph and answer it.

Sample questions: How many strawberry smoothies were sold? (6); Which flavor was sold the most? (banana); Which flavor sold more, orange or blueberry? (blueberry)

Use the data for Problems 6 and 7. The data set shows high scorers on a computer game.

HIGH SCORES

Amy	56	Roy	50
Joe	72	Pam	82
Pat	60	Ann	60
Sam	58	Jim	78
Tim	75	Joy	55

6. What is the range for this data set? **32**

7. What is the mode of the scores? **60**

Additional Answers

1.

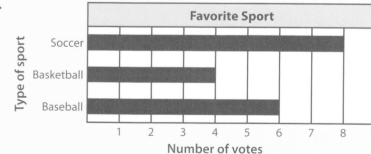

Favorite Sport

Read the problem and follow the directions.

8. Create a tally chart to record the number of each type of ball shown here.

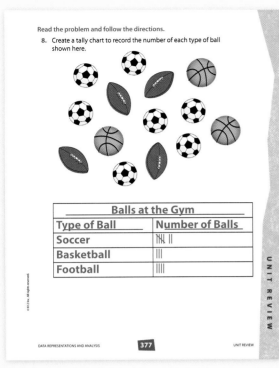

Balls at the Gym	
Type of Ball	Number of Balls
Soccer	||||| ||
Basketball	|||
Football	||||

9. The bar graph records the number of turtles Raymond saw at the zoo.

Draw a picture graph to record the same data.

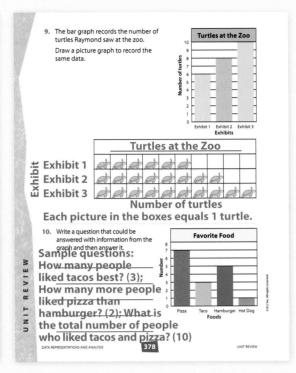

Turtles at the Zoo

Exhibit	Turtles at the Zoo
Exhibit 1	
Exhibit 2	
Exhibit 3	

Number of turtles

Each picture in the boxes equals 1 turtle.

10. Write a question that could be answered with information from the graph and then answer it.

Favorite Food

Sample questions: How many people liked tacos best? (3); How many more people liked pizza than hamburger? (2); What is the total number of people who liked tacos and pizza? (10)

11. Look at the graph. Write a question that could be answered with information from the graph.

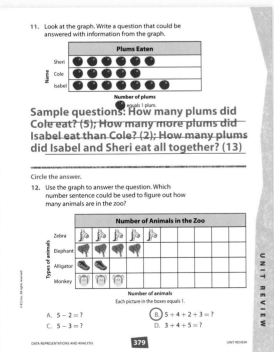

Plums Eaten

equals 1 plum.

Sample questions: How many plums did Cole eat? (5); How many more plums did Isabel eat than Cole? (2); How many plums did Isabel and Sheri eat all together? (13)

Circle the answer.

12. Use the graph to answer the question. Which number sentence could be used to figure out how many animals are in the zoo?

Number of Animals in the Zoo

Each picture in the boxes equals 1.

A. $5 - 2 = ?$
B. $5 + 4 + 2 + 3 = ?$ (circled)
C. $5 - 3 = ?$
D. $3 + 4 + 5 = ?$

13. Use the graph to answer the question. Which number sentence could be used to figure out how many more zebras than elephants are in the zoo?

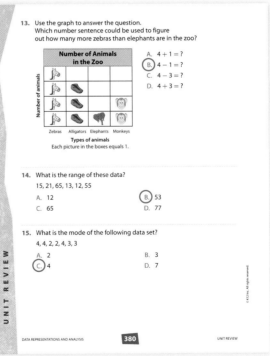

Number of Animals in the Zoo

Each picture in the boxes equals 1.

A. $4 + 1 = ?$
B. $4 - 1 = ?$ (circled)
C. $4 - 3 = ?$
D. $4 + 3 = ?$

14. What is the range of these data?

15, 21, 65, 13, 12, 55

A. 12
B. 53 (circled)
C. 65
D. 77

15. What is the mode of the following data set?

4, 4, 2, 2, 4, 3, 3

A. 2
B. 3
C. 4 (circled)
D. 7

➜ UNIT REVIEW Prepare for the Checkpoint

What you do next depends on how students performed in the previous activity, Unit Review: Checkpoint Practice. If students had difficulty with any of the problems, complete the appropriate review activity listed in the table online.

Unit Checkpoint

▶ Unit Objectives

This lesson assesses the following objectives:

- Systematically record numerical data.
- Represent the same data set with more than one representation, such as a tally, picture graph, or bar graph.
- Ask and answer simple questions related to data representations.
- Solve addition or subtraction problems by using data from charts, picture graphs, and number sentences.
- Determine the range for a set of data.
- Identify the mode in a data set.

▶ Advance Preparation

Print the Picture Graph.

Materials to Gather

SUPPLIED

Picture Graph (printout)

Unit Checkpoint (printout)

UNIT CHECKPOINT Online

ONLINE 30min

Students will complete this part of the Unit Checkpoint online. Read the directions, problems, and answer choices to students. If necessary, help students with keyboard or mouse operations.

Objectives

- Assess unit objectives.

UNIT CHECKPOINT Offline

OFFLINE 30min

Students will complete this part of the Unit Checkpoint offline. Print the Checkpoint and have students complete it on their own. Read the directions, problems, and answer choices to students, if necessary. Use the answer key to score the Checkpoint, and then enter the results online.

Gather the Picture Graph and give it to students for Problem 1.

Objectives

- Assess unit objectives.

Name _____ Date _____

Unit Checkpoint Answer Key

Read the problem and follow the directions.

(1 point)
1. Teresa and George ran a lemonade stand for the last week. The tally chart shows the number of lemons they used each day. Draw a picture graph to record the same data.

See below.

Lemons Used for Lemonade Stand	
Day	**Number of lemons**
Monday	ⅢⅢ Ⅱ
Tuesday	ⅢⅢ ⅢⅢ
Wednesday	Ⅱ
Thursday	ⅢⅢ Ⅰ
Friday	ⅢⅢ

Write a question that could be answered with information from the graph or chart. For Problem 4, also answer the question.

(1 point)
2.
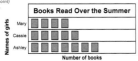

Books Read Over the Summer

Names of girls: Mary, Cassie, Ashley
Number of books
Each rectangle equals 1 book.

Sample questions:
How many books did Ashley read? Who read the most books? How many more books did Cassie read than Mary? What is the total number of books that Cassie and Ashley read?

Name _____ Date _____

(1 point)
3.

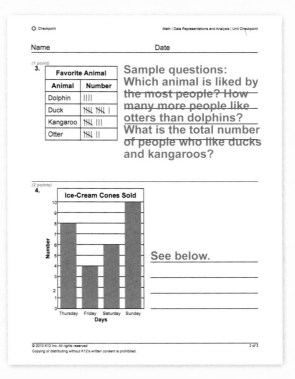

Favorite Animal	
Animal	**Number**
Dolphin	ⅢⅠ
Duck	ⅢⅢ ⅢⅢ Ⅰ
Kangaroo	ⅢⅢ Ⅲ
Otter	ⅢⅢ Ⅱ

Sample questions:
Which animal is liked by the most people? How many more people like otters than dolphins? What is the total number of people who like ducks and kangaroos?

(2 points)
4.

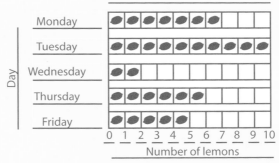

Ice-Cream Cones Sold

Number / Days (Thursday, Friday, Saturday, Sunday)

See below. _____
_____
_____

Name _____ Date _____

Write the answer.

5. What is the range of this data?
   What is the mode of this data?
   15, 12, 11, 12, 9, 10, 12, 11, 19

(1 point) range: **10**

(1 point) mode: **12**

6. John wants to know how many more green marbles than clear marbles he has in his collection. Write a number sentence to figure this out, and then solve the number sentence.

(1 point) Number sentence:
   13 − 4 = ?

(1 point)
   9 more green marbles

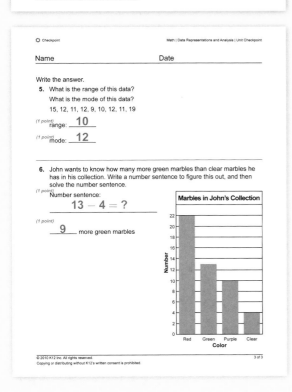

Marbles in John's Collection

Number / Color (Red, Green, Purple, Clear)

Additional Answers

1.

Lemons Used for Lemonade Stand

Day: Monday, Tuesday, Wednesday, Thursday, Friday
Number of lemons: 0 1 2 3 4 5 6 7 8 9 10

4. (1 point) Students should write a valid question based on the data in the graph.

(1 point) Students should correctly answer the question they asked.

Sample questions:
On which day were the most ice-cream cones sold? (Sunday); How many fewer ice-cream cones were sold on Saturday than on Thursday? (2); How many ice-creams cones were sold in all? (28)

Introduction to Fractions

- Demonstrate that a fraction can represent the relationship of equal parts to a whole or parts of a set.
- Explain that when all fractional parts of a whole are included, such as $\frac{4}{4}$, the result is equal to one whole.
- Recognize and name unit fractions from $\frac{1}{12}$ to $\frac{1}{2}$.
- Demonstrate how fractions and whole numbers can be plotted on a number line.

- Generate fraction representations (for example, show $\frac{2}{3}$ of a shape or $\frac{2}{3}$ of a set of objects or $\frac{2}{3}$ of an interval on a number line).
- Use concrete objects or given drawings to compare unit fractions from $\frac{1}{12}$ to $\frac{1}{2}$.
- Identify a few simple equivalent fractions, such as $\frac{1}{2} = \frac{2}{4}$.

▶ Big Ideas

Fractions represent the ratio of a part to a whole, including a part of a set to the whole set.

▶ Unit Introduction

In this unit, students will learn that they can write fractions to describe parts of a whole and parts of a set. They will also learn that fractions are numbers that can be plotted on the number line. They will learn how to create models that represent fractions, including unit fractions and fractions equal to 1, how to compare unit fractions, and how to identify a few simple equivalent fractions.

Fractional Parts of a Whole

Skills Update	5 minutes	**ONLINE**
GET READY Cracker Pieces	5 minutes	**ONLINE**
LEARN What's a Fraction?	20 minutes	**ONLINE**
LEARN Paper Fractions	20 minutes	**OFFLINE**
TRY IT Parts of a Whole	10 minutes	**OFFLINE**

▶ ## Lesson Objectives

- Demonstrate that a fraction can represent the relationship of equal parts to a whole or parts of a set.
- Explain that when all fractional parts of a whole are included, such as $\frac{4}{4}$, the result is equal to one whole.

▶ ## Prerequisite Skills

Demonstrate that a fraction can represent the relationship of equal parts to a whole or parts of a set.

▶ ## Common Errors and Misconceptions

- Students might think that a fraction compares one part to another part rather than recognizing that a fraction compares one part to the whole.
- Students might view the numerator and denominator of a fraction as separate, isolated numbers that can be operated on independently. This may lead to students "memorizing" rather than understanding fraction algorithms, and then using them incorrectly.

▶ ## Advance Preparation

- Make a square and a rectangle out of a sheet of drawing paper by folding the top left corner down to align along the right side of the paper and then trimming the remaining rectangle at the bottom.

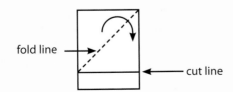

fold line →

← cut line

- Print the Fraction Circles. Cut out one each of the three types of circles (one halves circle, one thirds circle, and one fourths circle).

Materials to Gather

SUPPLIED
Fraction Circles (printout)
Parts of a Whole activity page

ALSO NEEDED
scissors, adult
crayons
paper, drawing – 1 sheet

▶ Content Background

Students will see how a whole can be divided into equal parts. They will learn that fractions are numbers that can compare a part of a whole to the entire whole. They will also learn that when *all* fractional parts are represented, the result is 1 whole. Students will later be introduced to fractions as numbers that describe representations other than parts to a whole.

As students begin their study of fractions, emphasize these key points throughout the activities:

- A fraction is a single number that has two parts, a numerator and denominator. The fraction should be thought of as a single number that shows a comparison between parts of the whole and the entire whole.

- Each part of a whole must be equal in size, or have the same area. Students may believe, for example, that in the diagram on the left, the green triangle represents $\frac{1}{3}$, since the whole is made up of 3 shapes. This is incorrect, because each of the 3 shapes *must* be the same size, as shown in the diagram on the right. In that diagram, each rhombus does represent $\frac{1}{3}$.

- The whole can be any shape, including shapes such as ⚑ or ♡.

Although students will most often see fractions written with a horizontal fraction bar in math, such as $\frac{2}{3}$ or $5\frac{5}{6}$, they will occasionally see a diagonal fraction bar, such as 2/3 or 5 5/6. Students will very likely see the diagonal fraction bar in everyday experiences, but be sure they understand that using the horizontal fraction bar in their work will make problems involving fractions easier to interpret and solve.

Keywords	**equal parts** – portions of a shape that are equal in area or portions of a group that are equal in quantity **fraction** – a number that shows part of a set, a point on a number line, a part of a whole, a quotient, or a ratio **whole** – the entire amount, such as $\frac{5}{5}$ of a whole

ONLINE 5 min

GET READY Cracker Pieces

Students will learn that they can break a cracker into equal pieces to share between two friends or among four friends. This is one way students can begin to relate division to fractions.

As students progress through the activity, have them ask themselves questions similar to the following:

- How does Ron know the number of equal pieces he needs before he breaks the cracker?

- How does Ron know that he has shared the cracker equally?

Objectives

- Demonstrate that a fraction can represent the relationship of equal parts to a whole or parts of a set.

LEARN What's a Fraction?

Students will learn about fractional parts of a whole. They will also learn that when they have all the fractional parts of a particular whole, such as $\frac{6}{6}$, they have 1 whole.

As students work through the activity, reinforce that a fraction is a number that tells the relationship between the parts and the whole. The whole must be defined first. In the block set, a fraction that a part represents depends on the whole that has been defined. For example, if the yellow hexagon is defined as the whole, the green triangle is $\frac{1}{6}$ of the whole because all 6 triangles are the same size and fill the whole hexagon. But, if the red trapezoid is defined as the whole, the same green triangle is $\frac{1}{3}$, because all 3 triangles are the same size and fill the whole trapezoid.

Emphasize that the bottom number in a fraction (or denominator) tells the number of parts that the whole contains. The top number (or numerator) tells the number of parts that the fraction represents. Although the activities discuss the numerator and denominator separately, help students think of the fraction as a single number that describes the relationship of the parts to the whole.

Objectives

- Demonstrate that a fraction can represent the relationship of equal parts to a whole or parts of a set.
- Explain that when all fractional parts of a whole are included, such as $\frac{4}{4}$, the result is equal to one whole.

Tips

Allow students to use the K, L, M, and N blocks to create the models shown online.

LEARN Paper Fractions

Students will use paper folding and fraction circles to learn about fractions. They will fold paper to divide a whole into equal parts. Then they will use the paper and fraction circles to name fractions.

Gather the crayons, rectangular and square sheets of paper, and cut-out fraction circles.

1. Display the rectangular paper. Tell students to imagine the paper is a cracker.

   Ask: How can we share it equally between two people?
   ANSWER: Divide it into two pieces

2. Guide students to fold the paper to form two equal parts.

   Fold ⟶ [rectangle with dashed fold line]

3. Have them use a yellow crayon to lightly shade the top part of the rectangle. Point to that part.

   Say: The entire rectangle is one whole. Your yellow section is a part, or fraction, of the whole. It is one of two equal parts or one-half of the whole. We can use the fraction one-half to represent this part of the whole.

4. Write $\frac{1}{2}$ on a separate sheet of paper. Use a horizontal fraction bar, as shown here. Point to the 1 and remind students that this is called the *numerator*. Point to the 2 and remind students that this is called the *denominator*. Circle the entire fraction and say that this is a number that shows how the yellow part compares to the whole rectangle.

Objectives

- Demonstrate that a fraction can represent the relationship of equal parts to a whole or parts of a set.
- Explain that when all fractional parts of a whole are included, such as $\frac{4}{4}$, the result is equal to one whole.

5. Have students fold the paper in half again to form four equal parts.

Ask: How many equal parts are there now?
ANSWER: 4

6. Have students use a blue crayon to shade the bottom left part of the rectangle. Point to that part.

Say: The section that you shaded blue is one of four equal parts or one-fourth of the whole. We can use the fraction one-fourth to represent this part of the paper.

7. Write $\frac{1}{4}$ on the separate sheet of paper. Use a horizontal fraction bar, as shown here. Point to the 1 and remind students that this is called the *numerator*. Point to the 4 and remind students that this is called the *denominator*. Circle the entire fraction and say that this is a number that shows how the blue part compares to the whole rectangle.

8. Have students shade the remaining part yellow.

9. Point to the three yellow parts.

Say: Each of these yellow parts is one-fourth of the whole rectangle. To find out what fraction of the whole the yellow parts represent, count the fourths with me: one-fourth, two-fourths, three-fourths. The yellow parts show three-fourths of the whole.

10. Write $\frac{3}{4}$ on the separate sheet of paper. Use a horizontal fraction bar, as shown here. Point to the 3 and ask students what this number is called. (numerator)
Point to the 4 and ask students what this number is called. (denominator)
Circle the entire fraction and ask students to explain what this number shows. (how the yellow part compares to the whole rectangle)

11. Explain that there are four-fourths in the whole rectangle. Write $\frac{4}{4}$ on the separate sheet of paper.

Say: Four-fourths is equal to one whole.

12. Display the square paper.

Say: This square is now the whole.

13. Fold the square in half diagonally.

Say: This square has two equal parts.

14. Point to one part.

Ask: What fraction is this part? How do you know?

ANSWER: One-half, because there are two equal parts and this is one of them.

15. Fold the paper to form four equal parts. Review the different fractions that can be used to represent the parts of the square. Have students write $\frac{1}{4}$, $\frac{2}{4}$, $\frac{3}{4}$, and $\frac{4}{4}$ with horizontal fraction bars and shade those parts of the square with a single color as they write the fractions. Have them explain that $\frac{4}{4}$ of the square is all the parts, or the whole square.

16. Display the thirds fraction circle.

Say: This time the whole is a circle.

Ask: How many equal parts are shown?

ANSWER: 3

Say: There are three parts in the whole, so each part is one-third of the whole.

17. Have students write $\frac{1}{3}$ on the separate sheet of paper.

Say: Count the thirds with me: one-third, two-thirds, three-thirds. If you have one of the parts, you have one-third. If you have all of the parts, you have three-thirds or the whole circle.

18. Repeat Steps 16 and 17 with the halves and fourths fraction circles.

OFFLINE

10 min

TRY IT Parts of a Whole

Students will practice identifying, representing, and explaining fractions and fractional models. Give students the Parts of a Whole activity page from their Activity Book and read the directions with them. Use the answer key to check students' answers, and then enter the results online.

Objectives

- Demonstrate that a fraction can represent the relationship of equal parts to a whole or parts of a set.

- Explain that when all fractional parts of a whole are included, such as $\frac{4}{4}$, the result is equal to one whole.

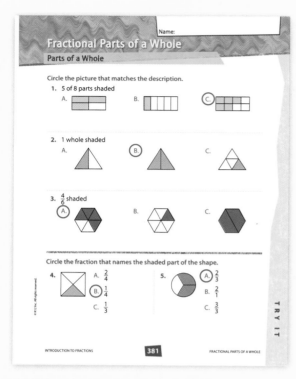

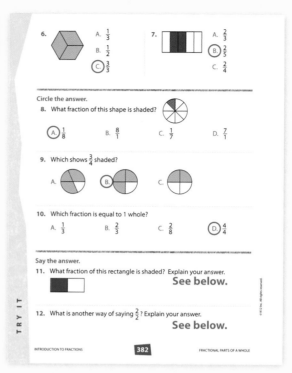

Additional Answers

11. Students should say that $\frac{1}{2}$ of the rectangle is shaded.

They should then explain that the rectangle is divided into 2 equal parts, and 1 part is shaded.

12. Students should say 1 whole, or 1. They should say that $\frac{2}{2}$ means that an object has been divided into 2 equal parts, and both parts are selected. The whole object is selected.

Fractional Parts of a Group

Lesson Overview

Skills Update	5 minutes	ONLINE
GET READY Fractional Parts	5 minutes	ONLINE
LEARN Parts of a Set	15 minutes	ONLINE
LEARN Mixed-Up Sets	10 minutes	ONLINE
LEARN Unit Fractions	15 minutes	ONLINE
TRY IT Identify Fractions	10 minutes	ONLINE

▶ Lesson Objectives

- Demonstrate that a fraction can represent the relationship of equal parts to a whole or parts of a set.
- Recognize and name unit fractions from $\frac{1}{12}$ to $\frac{1}{2}$.

▶ Prerequisite Skills

Demonstrate that a number can be composed of other numbers in various ways.

▶ Common Errors and Misconceptions

- Students might think that a fraction compares one part to another part rather than recognizing that a fraction compares one part to the whole.
- Students might view the numerator and denominator of a fraction as separate, isolated numbers that can be operated on independently. This may lead to students "memorizing" rather than understanding fraction algorithms, and then using them incorrectly.

▶ Content Background

Students will learn that a fraction can show the relationship of equal parts to a set as well as equal parts to a whole. For example, if they have 3 objects and 2 of them are red, they can say that $\frac{2}{3}$ of the objects are red (or that $\frac{2}{3}$ of the set is red). Students will also learn that unit fractions are fractions with a numerator, or top number, of 1.

As students continue their study of fractions, emphasize these key points throughout the activities:

- A fraction is a single number that has two parts, a numerator and denominator. The fraction should be thought of as a single number that shows a comparison between parts of the whole and the entire whole.

Materials to Gather

There are no materials to gather for this lesson.

- Each part of a whole must be equal in size, or have the same area. Students may believe, for example, that in the diagram on the left, the green triangle represents $\frac{1}{3}$, since the whole is made up of 3 shapes. This is incorrect, because each of the 3 shapes *must* be the same size, as shown in the diagram on the right. In that diagram, each rhombus does represent $\frac{1}{3}$.

- The whole can be any shape, including shapes such as or ♡.

- Fractions can represent more than just part of a whole. They can represent a part of a set compared to the entire set. When students first study fractions as part of a set, the objects in the set are generally similar in some way, such as all squares, all letters, or all pieces of fruit. Unlike parts of a whole, parts of a set *do not* have to be the same size. Students will learn that a set can be made up of items or objects of all sorts.

Although students will most often see fractions written with a horizontal fraction bar in math, such as $\frac{2}{3}$ or $5\frac{5}{6}$, they will occasionally see a diagonal fraction bar, such as 2/3 or 5 5/6. Students will very likely see the diagonal fraction bar in everyday experiences, but be sure they understand that using the horizontal fraction bar in their work will make problems involving fractions easier to interpret and solve.

Keywords	**denominator** – the number in a fraction that is below the fraction bar **numerator** – the number in a fraction that is above the fraction bar **unit fraction** – a fraction with a numerator of 1, such as $\frac{1}{3}$ or $\frac{1}{7}$

ONLINE

5 min

GET READY Fractional Parts

Objectives

Students will review a fraction as a number that represents part of whole. They will also learn that sets can model fractions.

As students progress through the activity, have them ask themselves questions such as the following:

- How many parts are in the whole?
- How many parts are blue?
- What fraction shows the blue parts compared to the whole?
- How many objects are in the set?
- How many objects are blue?
- What fraction shows the blue cubes compared to the entire set?

- Demonstrate that a fraction can represent the relationship of equal parts to a whole or parts of a set.

LEARN Parts of a Set

ONLINE 15 min

Objectives

- Demonstrate that a fraction can represent the relationship of equal parts to a whole or parts of a set.

Students have learned about fractions as representing parts of a whole. Now they'll learn that fractions can also represent parts of a set.

Emphasize that when a fraction represents parts of a set, the top number, or numerator, tells the number in the part. The bottom number in the fraction, or denominator, tells the total number in the set. For example, the fraction $\frac{2}{3}$ represents the shaded stars in the set. The fraction $\frac{2}{3}$ is a single value that compares the number shaded in this set to the entire set.

LEARN Mixed-Up Sets

ONLINE 10 min

Objectives

- Demonstrate that a fraction can represent the relationship of equal parts to a whole or parts of a set.

Students will learn that fractions can compare parts of sets with unlike objects. They will learn how to write fractions for sets with varied objects. They will also learn that a set can show different fraction values depending on what is being compared to the entire set. For example, this set shows all the fractions listed and other fractions as well.

- The fraction $\frac{5}{5}$ shows the comparison of fruit to the entire set.

- The fraction $\frac{3}{5}$ shows the comparison of red fruit to the entire set.

- The fraction $\frac{1}{5}$ shows the comparison of bananas to the entire set.

LEARN Unit Fractions

ONLINE 15 min

Objectives

- Recognize and name unit fractions from $\frac{1}{12}$ to $\frac{1}{2}$.

Students will learn that a unit fraction is a fraction with a numerator of 1. The fractions $\frac{1}{2}, \frac{1}{4},$ and $\frac{1}{100}$ are all unit fractions. Students will explore unit fractions with denominators between 1 and 12.

TRY IT Identify Fractions

ONLINE 10 min

Objectives

- Demonstrate that a fraction can represent the relationship of equal parts to a whole or parts of a set.

- Recognize and name unit fractions from $\frac{1}{12}$ to $\frac{1}{2}$.

Students will complete an online Try It. If necessary, read the directions, problems, and answer choices to students and help them with keyboard or mouse operations.

Fractional Relationships

Lesson Overview

Skills Update	5 minutes	**ONLINE**
LEARN Make a Fraction	20 minutes	**ONLINE**
TRY IT Model and Name Fractions	25 minutes	**ONLINE**
CHECKPOINT	10 minutes	**OFFLINE**

▶ Lesson Objectives

- Demonstrate that a fraction can represent the relationship of equal parts to a whole or parts of a set.
- Recognize and name unit fractions from $\frac{1}{12}$ to $\frac{1}{2}$.

▶ Prerequisite Skills

Demonstrate that a fraction can represent the relationship of equal parts to a whole or parts of a set.

▶ Common Errors and Misconceptions

- Students might think that a fraction compares one part to another part rather than recognizing that a fraction compares one part to the whole.
- Students might view the numerator and denominator of a fraction as separate, isolated numbers that can be operated on independently. This may lead to students "memorizing" rather than understanding fraction algorithms, and then using them incorrectly.

▶ Content Background

Students will use objects to represent fractions that compare parts to a whole or parts to a set. They will also identify and name fractions, including unit fractions.

As students continue their study of fractions, emphasize these key points throughout the activities:

- A fraction is a single number that has two parts, a numerator and denominator. The fraction should be thought of as a single number that shows a comparison between parts of the whole and the entire whole.
- Each part of a whole must be equal in size, or have the same area. Students may believe, for example, that in the diagram on the left, the green triangle represents $\frac{1}{3}$, since the whole is made up of 3 shapes. This is incorrect, because each of the 3 shapes *must* be the same size, as shown in the diagram on the right. In that diagram, each rhombus does represent $\frac{1}{3}$.

- The whole can be any shape, including shapes such as .

> ### Materials to Gather
>
> **SUPPLIED**
> blocks – B, E, O (all colors)
> Checkpoint (printout)

- Fractions can represent more than just part of a whole. They can represent a part of a set compared to the entire set. When students first study fractions as part of a set, the objects in the set are generally similar in some way, such as all squares, all letters, or all pieces of fruit. Unlike parts of a whole, parts of a set *do not* have to be the same size. Students will learn that a set can be made up of items or objects of all sorts.

Although students will most often see fractions written with a horizontal fraction bar in math, such as $\frac{2}{3}$ or $5\frac{5}{6}$, they will occasionally see a diagonal fraction bar, such as 2/3 or 5 5/6. Students will very likely see the diagonal fraction bar in everyday experiences, but be sure they understand that using the horizontal fraction bar in their work will make problems involving fractions easier to interpret and solve.

LEARN Make a Fraction

ONLINE
20min

Objectives

- Demonstrate that a fraction can represent the relationship of equal parts to a whole or parts of a set.
- Recognize and name unit fractions from $\frac{1}{12}$ to $\frac{1}{2}$.

Students will create models to show different fractions. They will learn that the same fraction can be modeled as part of a whole or part of a set and that, unlike the parts of a whole, the parts of a set need not be the same size. They will also learn about fractions with a numerator of zero.

Gather the blocks. Have students use the blocks as directed online. The last screen is open ended, and you'll need to check students' models and explanations.

As students progress through the activity, have them ask themselves questions such as the following:

- How many parts are in the whole?
- Are all of the parts of the whole the same size?
- How many objects are in the set?
- What does the numerator, or top number, represent?
- What does the denominator, or bottom number, represent?
- What does the fraction represent?

TRY IT Model and Name Fractions

ONLINE
25min

Objectives

- Demonstrate that a fraction can represent the relationship of equal parts to a whole or parts of a set.
- Recognize and name unit fractions from $\frac{1}{12}$ to $\frac{1}{2}$.

Students will practice naming fractions shown by models and creating models to represent fractions. Models will include parts of a whole and parts of a set.

DIRECTIONS FOR USING THE DIFFERENT WAYS TO SHOW FRACTIONS LEARNING TOOL

1. Click Naming Fractions.
2. A model will be shown on the right side of the screen. Have students click the + and − buttons to adjust the numerator and denominator of the fraction to make it match the model.
3. When students have finished adjusting the fraction, have them click Check. If students answer incorrectly, have them try again. If students answer incorrectly a second time, have them click Show Me to see the correct answer.
4. Have students answer 5 more problems.
5. Click Menu, and then click Restart.

6. Click Visualizing Fractions.

7. A fraction will be shown on the left side of the screen. Have students click the + and − buttons to adjust the model so that it represents the denominator of the fraction. Then have them click parts of the model to shade them in order to represent the numerator.

8. When students have finished adjusting the model, have them click Check. If students answer incorrectly, have them try again. If students answer incorrectly a second time, have them click Show Me to see the correct answer.

9. Have students answer 5 more problems.

10. If time allows, have students answer additional problems in either or both modes. Focus students' practice on the mode in which they had the greater difficulty.

CHECKPOINT

OFFLINE
10 min

Print the Checkpoint and have students complete it on their own. Read the directions, problems, and answer choices to students, if necessary. Use the answer key to score the Checkpoint, and then enter the results online.

Objectives

- Demonstrate that a fraction can represent the relationship of equal parts to a whole or parts of a set.

Tips

If you wish, have students say, rather than write, the answers to Problems 1 and 2.

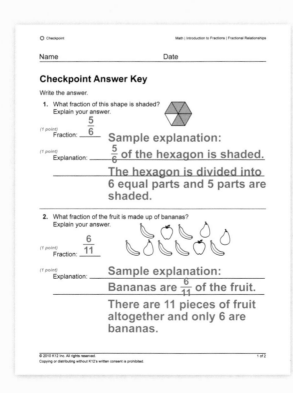

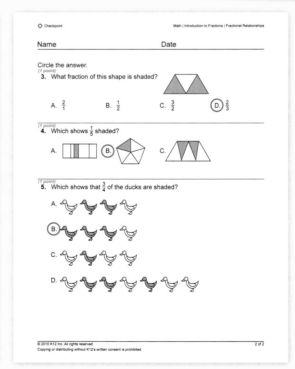

Fractional Parts and 1 Whole

Lesson Overview

Skills Update	5 minutes	ONLINE
GET READY Equal Parts	5 minutes	ONLINE
LEARN Parts Equal to 1 Whole	15 minutes	ONLINE
LEARN Parts on a Number Line	15 minutes	ONLINE
TRY IT Parts and Wholes	10 minutes	OFFLINE
CHECKPOINT	10 minutes	OFFLINE

▶ Lesson Objectives

Explain that when all fractional parts of a whole are included, such as $\frac{4}{4}$, the result is equal to one whole.

▶ Prerequisite Skills

Demonstrate that a fraction can represent the relationship of equal parts to a whole or parts of a set.

▶ Content Background

Students will explain that when all fractional parts of a whole are included, the result is 1 whole. They will explore this concept using blocks and number lines. Students will use objects to represent fractions that compare parts to a whole or parts to a set. They will also identify and name fractions, including unit fractions.

As students continue their study of fractions, emphasize these key points throughout the activities:

- A fraction is a single number that has two parts, a numerator and denominator. The fraction should be thought of as a single number that shows a comparison between parts of the whole and the entire whole.

- Each part of a whole must be equal in size, or have the same area. Students may believe, for example, that in the diagram on the left, the green triangle represents $\frac{1}{3}$, since the whole is made up of 3 shapes. This is incorrect, because each of the 3 shapes *must* be the same size, as shown in the diagram on the right. In that diagram, each rhombus does represent $\frac{1}{3}$.

- The whole can be any shape, including shapes such as ⬠ or ♡.

Although students will most often see fractions written with a horizontal fraction bar in math, such as $\frac{2}{3}$ or $5\frac{5}{6}$, they will occasionally see a diagonal fraction bar, such as 2/3 or 5 5/6. Students will very likely see the diagonal fraction bar in everyday experiences, but be sure they understand that using the horizontal fraction bar in their work will make problems involving fractions easier to interpret and solve.

Materials to Gather

SUPPLIED
Parts and Wholes activity page
Checkpoint (printout)

ALSO NEEDED
crayons

GET READY Equal Parts

Students will identify the fractions that models represent. They will see one model that shows the part of a whole and one model that shows the part of a set. Emphasize the meaning of each fraction.

- Demonstrate that a fraction can represent the relationship of equal parts to a whole or parts of a set.

LEARN Parts Equal to 1 Whole

Objectives

Students will use the Pattern Blocks Learning Tool to make fractions that are part of a whole. They will discover that when the parts completely cover the whole, the fraction representation has the same numerator and denominator.

- Explain that when all fractional parts of a whole are included, such as $\frac{4}{4}$, the result is equal to one whole.

DIRECTIONS FOR USING THE PATTERN BLOCKS LEARNING TOOL

1. Click Free Play. Then read the instructions, and click Start.

2. Drag a yellow hexagon to the canvas.

   Say: This yellow hexagon is 1 whole. Place 2 red trapezoids on the hexagon to cover it.

3. Show students how to rotate and flip the red trapezoids using the arrows. If necessary, help them cover the hexagon.

   Say: Each red trapezoid is one-half of the yellow hexagon, or one-half of the whole, because it is 1 of 2 equal pieces that can cover the whole hexagon.

4. Have students take away 1 of the red trapezoids. Explain that they have taken away one-half of the whole, and one-half of the whole remains.

5. Have students place the red trapezoid back on the hexagon. Explain that they are now showing two-halves, or 1 whole. Write $\frac{2}{2} = 1$ on a sheet of paper.

6. Click the broom to clear the canvas.

7. Repeat Steps 2–6 using the following shapes to cover the hexagon and write the fraction that represents the whole as equal to 1:

   - 3 blue rhombuses (Each rhombus is $\frac{1}{3}$ of the hexagon; when 1 rhombus is removed, $\frac{2}{3}$ of the whole remains.)

   - 6 green triangles (Each triangle is $\frac{1}{6}$ of the hexagon; when 1 triangle is removed, $\frac{5}{6}$ of the whole remains.)

   - 1 yellow hexagon $\left($A hexagon is 1 out of 1 parts of the original hexagon, so the fraction is $\frac{1}{1}.\right)$

8. Emphasize that when all the equal parts are included in a fraction, the fraction equals 1 whole.

   Say: We showed that two-halves, three-thirds, and six-sixths are all equal to 1 whole.

   Ask: What other fractions do you think equal 1 whole? $\left($Any fraction for which the numerator and denominator are equal, such as $\frac{4}{4}$ and $\frac{5}{5}.\right)$

   Say: You could even have $\frac{100}{100}$ show 1 whole.

Tips

Allow students to use the K, L, M, and N blocks to create the models shown online.

LEARN Parts on a Number Line

Students will use a number line to represent and interpret fractions, including fractions that equal 1.

In the second part of the activity, students will use the Different Ways to Show Fractions Learning Tool to compare fractions shown as part of a whole to that same fraction on a number line, with a concentration on fractions that equal 1.

- Explain that when all fractional parts of a whole are included, such as $\frac{4}{4}$, the result is equal to one whole.

DIRECTIONS FOR USING THE DIFFERENT WAYS TO SHOW FRACTIONS LEARNING TOOL

1. Click Parts of a Whole.

2. Click the $+$ symbol in the lower right of the screen four times to divide the square into four equal parts.

   Say: The square is one whole. It's divided into four equal parts. So each part equals one-fourth.

3. Have students click one part of the square to color it.

   Ask: What fraction did you show?
   ANSWER: one-fourth

   Ask: How do you know that this fraction shows one-fourth?
   ANSWER: The whole is divided into four parts. One of the parts is colored.

4. Point to the fraction $\frac{1}{4}$ on the screen, and explain how the 1 represents the colored parts and the 4 represents the total parts in the whole.

5. Have students click another part of the square so that two parts are colored.

   Say: Now two out of four parts are colored. So the fraction changed to two-fourths. The bottom number, 4, stayed the same because the whole is still divided into four parts.

6. Have students click a third part and note how the fraction changed. Then have them click the fourth part.

   Say: Now four out of four parts are colored. The fraction changed to four-fourths. Four-fourths is equals to one whole.

7. Click Show Number Line. Point out that all of the number line from 0 to 1 is shaded. Leave the number line showing.

8. Have students click each colored part of the square again to clear the fraction. They should watch how the fraction changes from $\frac{4}{4}$ to $\frac{3}{4}$ to $\frac{2}{4}$ to $\frac{1}{4}$ to $\frac{0}{4}$ and how the shading on the number line changes.

9. Repeat the activity with thirds and sixths. Students may choose another shape other than the square, if they'd like. As students color each part, have them explain why the top number of the fraction is changing and the bottom number is not. Also, have them explain why the number line is at 1 when all of the parts of the shape are shaded.

TRY IT Parts and Wholes

OFFLINE
10 min

Students will practice identifying fractions that are equal to 1 whole and explaining why these fractions are equal to 1 whole. Give students the crayons and Parts and Wholes activity page from their Activity Book. Read the directions with them.

Objectives

- Explain that when all fractional parts of a whole are included, such as $\frac{4}{4}$, the result is equal to one whole.

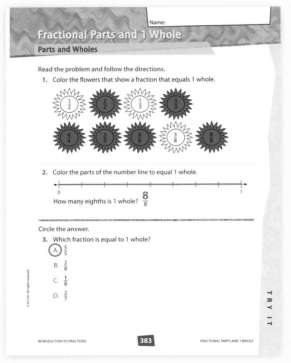

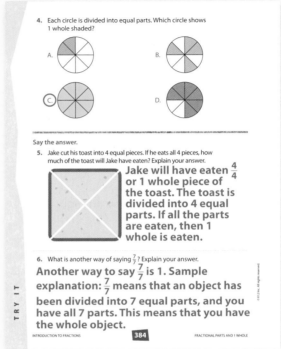

CHECKPOINT

Print the Checkpoint and have students complete it on their own. Read the directions, problems, and answer choices to students, if necessary. Use the answer key to score the Checkpoint, and then enter the results online.

Objectives

- Explain that when all fractional parts of a whole are included, such as $\frac{4}{4}$, the result is equal to one whole.

- Recognize and name unit fractions from $\frac{1}{12}$ to $\frac{1}{2}$.

Tips

If you wish have students say, rather than write, the answer to Problem 2.

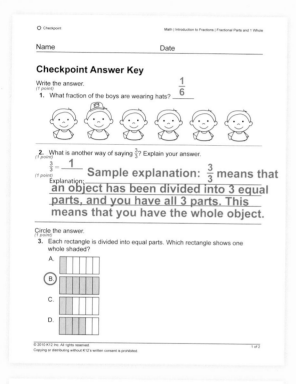

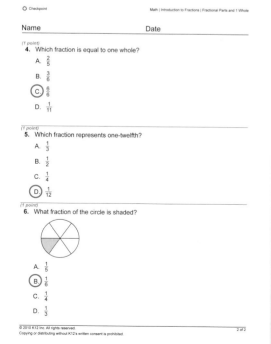

Fractions and Whole Numbers

Lesson Overview		
Skills Update	5 minutes	ONLINE
GET READY One-Half on a Number Line	5 minutes	ONLINE
LEARN Fractions on a Number Line	15 minutes	ONLINE
LEARN Fractions Between 0 and 1	20 minutes	OFFLINE
LEARN Fractions Between 0 and 2	5 minutes	OFFLINE
TRY IT Plot Fractions	10 minutes	OFFLINE

▶ Lesson Objectives

Demonstrate how fractions and whole numbers can be plotted on a number line.

▶ Prerequisite Skills

Demonstrate that a fraction can represent the relationship of equal parts to a whole or parts of a set.

▶ Advance Preparation

Print the Blank Number Lines 0–2 and the Blank Whole to Twelfths Number Lines.

▶ Content Background

Students will identify and plot fractions on a number line. They will learn that fractions remain in the same relative location no matter how many whole numbers are shown on a number line. For example, on a number line from 0 to 1, the fraction $\frac{1}{2}$ is at the center of the number line, exactly between 0 and 1. On a number line from 0 to 3, the fraction $\frac{1}{2}$ is no longer at the center of the number line, but it is still exactly between 0 and 1.

Students will also locate fractions on number lines by folding paper and inspecting number lines with unlabeled sections. The greater concentration will be on fractions between 0 and 1, but students will also count by fractions from 0 to 2.

As students continue their study of fractions, emphasize these key points throughout the activities:

- A fraction is a single number that has two parts, a numerator and denominator. The fraction should be thought of as a single number that shows a comparison between parts of the whole and the entire whole.

Materials to Gather

SUPPLIED

Blank Number Lines 0–2 (printout)

Blank Whole to Twelfths Number Lines (printout)

Plot Fractions activity page

- Each part of a whole must be equal in size, or have the same area. Students may believe, for example, that in the diagram on the left, the green triangle represents $\frac{1}{3}$, since the whole is made up of 3 shapes. This is incorrect, because each of the 3 shapes *must* be the same size, as shown in the diagram on the right. In that diagram, each rhombus does represent $\frac{1}{3}$.

- The whole can be any shape, including shapes such as .

- Fractions can represent more than just part of a whole. They can represent a part of a set compared to the entire set. When students first study fractions as part of a set, the objects in the set are generally similar in some way, such as all squares, all letters, or all pieces of fruit. Unlike parts of a whole, parts of a set *do not* have to be the same size. Students will learn that a set can be made up of items or objects of all sorts.

- Another way to represent fractions is as a location on a number line, as students will explore in this lesson. Each fraction has a unique location on a number line. For example, $\frac{5}{6}$ is always a distance of 5 units out of 6 from 0, and no other fraction holds that same position unless that fraction has the same value as $\frac{5}{6}$. Although equivalent fractions can be represented different ways, each one is located at the same place on a number line. For example, $\frac{5}{2}$ and $2\frac{3}{6}$ are equivalent to $2\frac{1}{2}$, so each of these fractions would fall on the same location on the number line $2\frac{1}{2}$ units from 0.

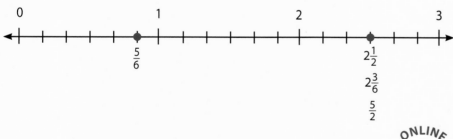

ONLINE
5 min

GET READY One-Half on a Number Line

Students will learn where the fraction $\frac{1}{2}$ is located on several number lines. They will learn that no matter how many numbers are shown on a number line, $\frac{1}{2}$ is always halfway between 0 and 1.

Objectives

- Demonstrate that a fraction can represent the relationship of equal parts to a whole or parts of a set.

ONLINE
15 min

LEARN Fractions on a Number Line

In this activity, students locate the fractions $\frac{1}{2}$, $\frac{1}{4}$, $\frac{2}{4}$, and $\frac{3}{4}$ on a number line and label them. They will learn how to write a fraction. They will learn that the top number is the numerator and the bottom number is the denominator. Students will then see that equivalent fractions will be at the same location on the number line.

Objectives

- Demonstrate how fractions and whole numbers can be plotted on a number line.

LEARN Fractions Between 0 and 1

Students will learn how to label the fractions with denominators up through 12 on number lines.

Give students the Blank Whole to Twelfths Number Lines.

1. Point to the number line at the bottom of the page. Have students place their finger at 0 and move their finger over to 1. Explain that they have moved from $\frac{0}{1}$ to $\frac{1}{1}$, and have them write those values under 0 and 1.

2. Point to the next number line up. Have students count the number of equal parts between 0 and 1. (2)

   Say: The the part of the number line between 0 and 1 represents 1; 1 is divided into 2 equal parts, so you can write 0 as $\frac{0}{2}$.

3. Have students write $\frac{0}{2}$ under 0 and then place their finger at 0 and move it along the number line to the first unlabeled tick mark.

   Say: This part is one-half of the whole, so label the tick mark $\frac{1}{2}$.

4. Have students move their finger from $\frac{1}{2}$ along the number line to 1.

   Say: You have now moved your finger two halves from 0 and have reached 1. Write $\frac{2}{2}$ under 1.

5. Have students count aloud as they point to each half: zero halves, one half, two halves.

6. Point to the next number line up.

7. Have students count the number of equal parts between 0 and 1. (3)

   Say: The part of the number line between 0 and 1 represents 1; 1 is divided into 3 equal parts, so you can write 0 as $\frac{0}{3}$.

8. Have students write $\frac{0}{3}$ under 0 and then place their finger at 0 and move it along the number line to the first unlabeled tick mark.

   Say: This part is one-third of the whole, so label the tick mark $\frac{1}{3}$.

9. Have students move their finger from $\frac{1}{3}$ along the number line to $\frac{2}{3}$.

   Say: You have now moved your finger two thirds from 0. Write $\frac{2}{3}$ under the second tick mark.

10. Have students move their finger from $\frac{2}{3}$ along the number line to 1.

    Say: You have now moved your finger three thirds from 0 and have reached 1. Write $\frac{3}{3}$ under 1.

11. Lastly on the thirds number line, have students count aloud as they point to each third: zero thirds, one third, two thirds, three thirds. This is a key step.

12. Repeat Steps 6–9 for all the other number lines on the page, but skip around as you choose the number lines for students to complete.

Objectives

- Demonstrate how fractions and whole numbers can be plotted on a number line.

Tips

Have students count fractions along the number line to help them understand fractions beyond 1 more easily.

LEARN Fractions Between 0 and 2

- Demonstrate how fractions and whole numbers can be plotted on a number line.

Students will learn to count by fractions from 0 to 2 on number lines. Give students the Blank Number Lines 0–2.

1. Point to the first number line. Remind students that the part of the number line between 0 and 1 represents 1.

   Say: We figure out the denominator of the fractions we will use by counting the number of equal sections between 0 and 1, no matter how far out the number line shows numbers.

2. Have students count the number of equal parts between 0 and 1. (2)

   Say: Since the section of the number line between 0 and 1 is divided into 2 equal parts, we can write 0 as $\frac{0}{2}$.

3. Have students write $\frac{0}{2}$ under 0, $\frac{1}{2}$ under the first tick mark, and $\frac{2}{2}$ under the 1.

4. **Say:** Let's think about what happens beyond 1. First let's count the halves from 0 to 1 together: zero halves, one half, two halves.

5. **Ask:** What do you think would come next?

   Give students a chance to answer. Help them realize that the next half would be three halves and the one after that would be four halves at 2 on the number line.

6. Have students write $\frac{3}{2}$ and $\frac{4}{2}$ on the number line.

7. Help students realize that they could keep counting by halves forever along the number line.

8. Choose at least two more number lines on the page, including the last one (tenths). First find the number of equal sections between 0 and 1 to determine the denominator, and have students count by that denominator from 0 to 2. You may choose whether to have the students write the fractions or just count aloud.

TRY IT Plot Fractions

Students will practice identifying fractions on number lines. Give students the Plot Fractions activity page from their Activity Book and read the directions with them. Use the answer key to check students' answers, and then enter the results online.

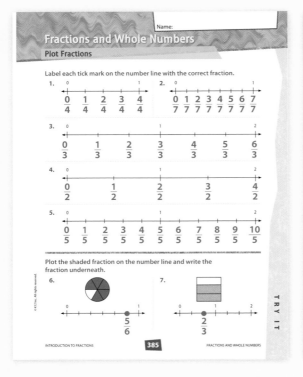

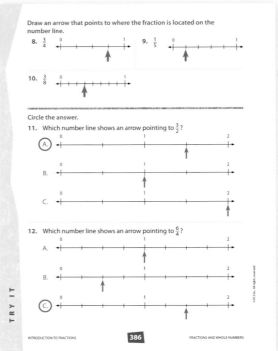

Fractions and Mixed Numbers

Lesson Overview		
Skills Update	5 minutes	ONLINE
GET READY Fractions Greater Than One	5 minutes	ONLINE
LEARN Fraction or Whole Number	10 minutes	ONLINE
LEARN Mixed Numbers	20 minutes	ONLINE
TRY IT Number-Line Models	10 minutes	ONLINE
CHECKPOINT	10 minutes	OFFLINE

▶ Lesson Objectives

Demonstrate how fractions and whole numbers can be plotted on a number line.

▶ Prerequisite Skills

Demonstrate that a fraction can represent the relationship of equal parts to a whole or parts of a set.

▶ Content Background

Students will learn that a mixed number is a number with a whole-number part and a fractional part. The numbers $1\frac{1}{2}$, $3\frac{5}{8}$, and $5\frac{2}{9}$ are all mixed numbers. Students will learn how to locate mixed numbers on the number line.

As students continue their study of fractions, emphasize these key points throughout the activities:

- A fraction is a single number that has two parts, a numerator and denominator. The fraction should be thought of as a single number that shows a comparison between parts of the whole and the entire whole.

- Each part of a whole must be equal in size, or have the same area. Students may believe, for example, that in the diagram on the left, the green triangle represents $\frac{1}{3}$, since the whole is made up of 3 shapes. This is incorrect, because each of the 3 shapes *must* be the same size, as shown in the diagram on the right. In that diagram, each rhombus does represent $\frac{1}{3}$.

- The whole can be any shape, including shapes such as ⌐▷ or ♡.

- Fractions can represent more than just part of a whole. They can represent a part of a set compared to the entire set. When students first study fractions as part of a set, the objects in the set are generally similar in some way, such as all squares, all letters, or all pieces of fruit. Unlike parts of a whole, parts of a set *do not* have to be the same size. Students will learn that a set can be made up of items or objects of all sorts.

Materials to Gather

SUPPLIED

Checkpoint (printout)

- Another way to represent fractions is as a location on a number line; students will continue to explore this representation of fractions in this lesson. Each fraction has a unique location on a number line. For example, $\frac{5}{6}$ is always a distance of 5 units out of 6 from 0, and no other fraction holds that same position unless that fraction has the same value as $\frac{5}{6}$. Although equivalent fractions can be represented different ways, each one is located at the same place on a number line. For example, $\frac{5}{2}$, $2\frac{2}{4}$, and $2\frac{3}{6}$ are all equivalent to $2\frac{1}{2}$, so each of these fractions would fall on the same location on the number line $2\frac{1}{2}$ units from 0.

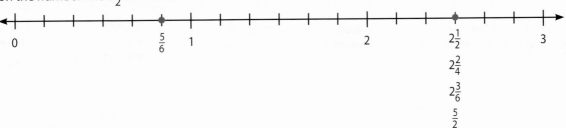

ONLINE
5 min

GET READY Fractions Greater Than One

Objectives

Students will learn that there are numbers between each pair of whole numbers on the number line. For example, the numbers $\frac{1}{2}$ and $\frac{3}{4}$ are between 0 and 1, the numbers $1\frac{1}{4}$ and $1\frac{1}{2}$ are between 1 and 2, and the numbers $2\frac{2}{4}$ and $2\frac{3}{4}$ are between 2 and 3.

- Demonstrate that a fraction can represent the relationship of equal parts to a whole or parts of a set.

ONLINE
10 min

LEARN Fraction or Whole Number

Objectives

Students will differentiate between the locations of fractions and whole numbers on a number line. For example, students may confuse the location of $\frac{1}{2}$, 1, and 2. They will learn that to locate $\frac{1}{2}$, they jump one half space. To locate 1, they jump one whole-number space. To locate 2, they jump two whole-number spaces.

- Demonstrate how fractions and whole numbers can be plotted on a number line.

LEARN Mixed Numbers

ONLINE
20min

Students will learn to locate mixed numbers on a number line. They will learn to first find the whole-number part of the mixed number. Then they will count on by the fractional part to locate the mixed number on the number line.

Objectives

- Demonstrate how fractions and whole numbers can be plotted on a number line.

TRY IT Number-Line Models

ONLINE
10min

Students will complete an online Try It. If necessary, read the directions, problems, and answer choices to students and help them with keyboard or mouse operations.

Objectives

- Demonstrate how fractions and whole numbers can be plotted on a number line.

CHECKPOINT

OFFLINE
10min

Print the Checkpoint and have students complete it on their own. Read the directions, problems, and answer choices to students, if necessary. Use the answer key to score the Checkpoint, and then enter the results online.

Objectives

- Demonstrate how fractions and whole numbers can be plotted on a number line.

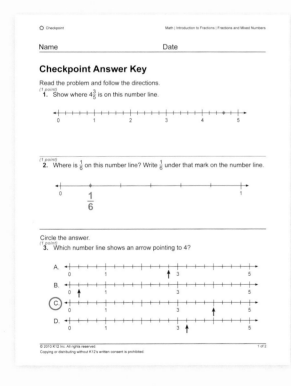

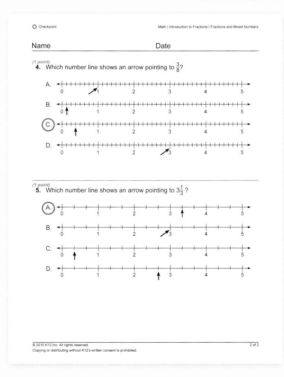

Model and Compare Fractions

▶ Lesson Objectives

Generate fraction representations (for example, show $\frac{2}{3}$ of a shape or $\frac{2}{3}$ of a set of objects or $\frac{2}{3}$ of an interval on a number line).

▶ Prerequisite Skills

Explain that when all fractional parts of a whole are included, such as $\frac{4}{4}$, the result is equal to one whole.

▶ Common Errors and Misconceptions

Students might have difficulty understanding how different models represent fractions because they often see fractions represented as parts of circles—for example, pie and pizza illustrations. They might not recognize, for example, that the following models all represent the fraction $\frac{3}{5}$.

$\frac{3}{5}$ is a point on the number line. $\frac{3}{5}$ of the shapes are triangles. $\frac{3}{5}$ of the rectangle is shaded.

▶ Content Background

In this lesson, students will shade a figure or set to show a given fraction or they will plot the fraction on a number line. They will also use drawings and objects to compare the values of unit fractions.

As students continue their study of fractions, emphasize these key points throughout the activities:

- A fraction is a single number that has two parts, a numerator and denominator. The fraction should be thought of as a single number that shows a comparison between parts of the whole and the entire whole.

- Each part of a whole must be equal in size, or have the same area. Students may believe, for example, that in the diagram on the left, the green triangle represents $\frac{1}{3}$, since the whole is made up of 3 shapes. This is incorrect, because each of the 3 shapes *must* be the same size, as shown in the diagram on the right. In that diagram, each rhombus does represent $\frac{1}{3}$.

Materials to Gather

SUPPLIED

Fraction Practice activity page

Checkpoint (printout)

- The whole can be any shape, including shapes such as ⬠ or ♡.

- Fractions can represent more than just part of a whole. They can represent a part of a set compared to the entire set. When students first study fractions as part of a set, the objects in the set are generally similar in some way, such as all squares, all letters, or all pieces of fruit. Unlike parts of a whole, parts of a set *do not* have to be the same size. Students will learn that a set can be made up of items or objects of all sorts.

- Another way to represent fractions is as a location on a number line; students will continue to explore this representation of fractions in this lesson. Each fraction has a unique location on a number line. For example, $\frac{5}{6}$ is always a distance of 5 units out of 6 from 0, and no other fraction holds that same position unless that fraction has the same value as $\frac{5}{6}$. Although equivalent fractions can be represented different ways, each one is located at the same place on a number line. For example, $\frac{5}{2}$, $2\frac{2}{4}$, and $2\frac{3}{6}$ are all equivalent to $2\frac{1}{2}$, so each of these fractions would fall on the same location on the number line $2\frac{1}{2}$ units from 0.

LEARN Create Fraction Models

ONLINE **20**min

Students will model fractions as parts of wholes, parts of sets, and points on number lines.

DIRECTIONS FOR USING THE DIFFERENT WAYS TO SHOW FRACTIONS LEARNING TOOL

Parts of a Whole

1. Click Parts of a Whole.

2. Click the + symbol in the lower right of the screen three times to divide the square into three equal parts.

   Say: The square is one whole. It's divided into three equal parts, so each part equals one-third.

3. Have students click two parts of the square to color them.

   Ask: What fraction did you show?
   ANSWER: two-thirds

   Ask: How do you know that this model shows two-thirds?
   ANSWER: The whole is divided into three parts. Two of the parts are colored.

4. Point to the fraction $\frac{2}{3}$ on the screen and explain how the numerator 2 represents the colored parts and the denominator 3 represents the total parts in the whole.

Objectives

- Generate fraction representations (for example, show $\frac{2}{3}$ of a shape or $\frac{2}{3}$ of a set of objects or $\frac{2}{3}$ of an interval on a number line).

Tips

Make and display a poster that shows a written fraction, such as $\frac{3}{5}$. Include three models for the fraction:

- Shape divided into 5 equal parts, with 3 of the parts shaded
- Set of 5 objects, with 3 of the objects shaded
- Number line from 0 to 1, with the point $\frac{3}{5}$ labeled

5. Click Show Number Line and help students realize that the colored bar ends at the point that is $\frac{2}{3}$ of the distance between 0 and 1 on the number line. Leave the number line on.

6. Ask students to adjust the model so that it shows $\frac{5}{8}$. Students should click the + and − buttons to adjust the model in order to represent the denominator. They should click parts of the model to color them or remove color from them to represent the numerator. When students have created the correct model, the fraction on the screen will be $\frac{5}{8}$.

7. **Ask:** How do you know this model shows five-eighths?
   ANSWER: The whole is divided into eight parts. Five of the parts are colored. Also, the number line shows the bar ending $\frac{5}{8}$ of the distance between 0 and 1.

8. Repeat Steps 5 and 6 with $\frac{2}{6}$.

Parts of a Set

9. Click Menu and then click Restart.

10. Click Parts of a Set.

11. Click the + symbol in the lower right of the screen seven times to show a set of seven frogs.

12. Have students click four frogs to color them.

   Ask: What fraction did you show?
   ANSWER: four-sevenths

   Ask: How do you know that this model shows four-sevenths?
   ANSWER: There are seven objects in the set. Four of the objects are colored.

13. Point to the fraction $\frac{4}{7}$ on the screen and explain how the numerator 4 represents the colored objects and the denominator 7 represents the total objects in the set.

14. Ask students to adjust the model so that it shows $\frac{2}{9}$. Students should click the + and − buttons to adjust the model in order to represent the denominator. They should click objects to color them or remove color from them to represent the numerator. When students have created the correct model, the fraction on the screen will be $\frac{2}{9}$.

15. **Ask:** How do you know this model shows two-ninths?
   ANSWER: There are nine objects in the set. Two of the objects are colored.

16. Repeat Steps 13 and 14 with $\frac{11}{12}$.

   Have students go to the next screen to continue with the Learn activity.

ONLINE

15min

LEARN Compare Fractions

Objectives

Students will compare unit fractions, which are fractions with numerators of 1 $\left(\frac{1}{2}, \frac{1}{3}, \frac{1}{4},\right.$ and so on$\left.\right)$. They will begin by using models or drawings to compare. Then they will learn that to compare unit fractions, they can compare the denominators. As the denominator of a fraction becomes greater, the model that represents the fraction is divided into more parts. Each part becomes smaller. Unit fractions with greater denominators are less than unit fractions with lesser denominators.

- Use concrete objects or given drawings to compare unit fractions from $\frac{1}{12}$ to $\frac{1}{2}$.

The fraction $\frac{1}{4}$ has a lesser denominator than the fraction $\frac{1}{8}$, so $\frac{1}{4}$ is greater than $\frac{1}{8}$.

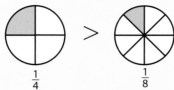

OFFLINE
10 min

TRY IT Fraction Practice

Students will practice modeling and comparing fractions. Give students the Fraction Practice activity page from their Activity Book and read the directions with them.

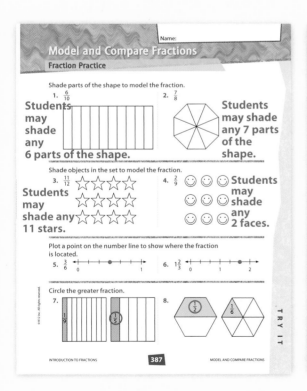

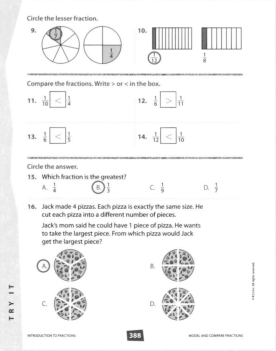

CHECKPOINT

Objectives

Print the Checkpoint and have students complete it on their own. Read the directions, problems, and answer choices to students, if necessary. Use the answer key to score the Checkpoint, and then enter the results online.

- Generate fraction representations (for example, show $\frac{2}{3}$ of a shape or $\frac{2}{3}$ of a set of objects or $\frac{2}{3}$ of an interval on a number line).
- Use concrete objects or given drawings to compare unit fractions from $\frac{1}{12}$ to $\frac{1}{2}$.

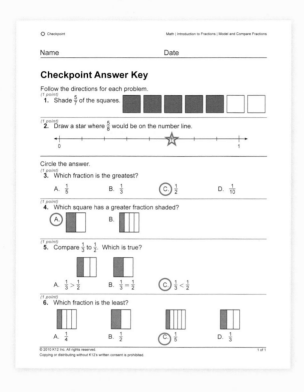

Equivalent Fractions

Lesson Overview

Skills Update	5 minutes	**ONLINE**
LEARN Equivalent Fractions: Shapes	10 minutes	**ONLINE**
LEARN Equivalent Fractions: Number Lines	15 minutes	**ONLINE**
LEARN Find Equivalent Fractions	10 minutes	**OFFLINE**
TRY IT Practice Equivalent Fractions	10 minutes	**OFFLINE**
CHECKPOINT	10 minutes	**OFFLINE**

▶ Lesson Objectives

Identify a few simple equivalent fractions, such as $\frac{1}{2} = \frac{2}{4}$.

▶ Prerequisite Skills

Use concrete objects or given drawings to compare unit fractions from $\frac{1}{12}$ to $\frac{1}{2}$.

▶ Advance Preparation

Print the Whole to Twelfths Number Lines.

▶ Content Background

Fractions that have the same value are called *equivalent fractions*. Students will use shapes, blocks, and number lines to model equivalent fractions. They will work toward memorization of some common equivalent fractions.

Students have been taught that the denominator can guide them in comparing unit fractions, or fractions with a numerator of 1. Unit fractions that have greater denominators are less than unit fractions with lesser denominators. For example, because $\frac{1}{5}$ has a greater denominator than $\frac{1}{2}$, students can tell that $\frac{1}{5}$ is *less than* $\frac{1}{2}$. However, if they were comparing fractions with numerators greater than 1, looking only at the denominator would not necessarily tell them which fraction is greater. For example, if they were comparing $\frac{4}{5}$ to $\frac{1}{2}$, they would find that $\frac{4}{5}$ is the greater fraction, even though the denominator for $\frac{4}{5}$ is greater than the denominator for $\frac{1}{2}$. Be sure to remind students throughout the lesson that because they are comparing unit fractions, comparing the denominators tells them which fraction is greater. This is important to grasp as they begin to understand equivalent fractions as well.

As students continue their study of fractions, emphasize these key points throughout the activities:

- A fraction is a single number that has two parts, a numerator and denominator. The fraction should be thought of as a single number that shows a comparison between parts of the whole and the entire whole.

Materials to Gather

SUPPLIED

blocks – K, L, M, N

Whole to Twelfths Number Lines (printout)

Practice Equivalent Fractions activity page

Checkpoint (printout)

ALSO NEEDED

crayons

- Each part of a whole must be equal in size, or have the same area. Students may believe, for example, that in the diagram on the left, the green triangle represents $\frac{1}{3}$, since the whole is made up of 3 shapes. This is incorrect, because each of the 3 shapes *must* be the same size, as shown in the diagram on the right. In that diagram, each rhombus does represent $\frac{1}{3}$.

- The whole can be any shape, including shapes such as 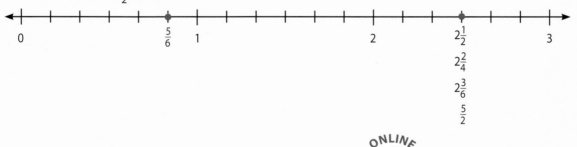 or ♡.

- When students compare fractions from two different wholes, the assumption is that the wholes are exactly the same size and shape.

- Another way to represent fractions is as a location on a number line; students will continue to explore this representation of fractions in this lesson. Each fraction has a unique location on a number line. For example, $\frac{5}{6}$ is always a distance of 5 units out of 6 from 0, and no other fraction holds that same position unless that fraction has the same value as $\frac{5}{6}$. Although equivalent fractions can be represented different ways, each one is located at the same place on a number line. For example, $\frac{5}{2}$, $2\frac{2}{4}$, and $2\frac{3}{6}$ are all equivalent to $2\frac{1}{2}$, so each of these fractions would fall on the same location on the number line $2\frac{1}{2}$ units from 0.

A number line from 0 to 3. Points marked at 0, $\frac{5}{6}$, 1, 2, $2\frac{1}{2}$, 3. Below $2\frac{1}{2}$ are listed $2\frac{2}{4}$, $2\frac{3}{6}$, $\frac{5}{2}$.

LEARN Equivalent Fractions: Shapes

ONLINE

10 min

Objectives

- Identify a few simple equivalent fractions, such as $\frac{1}{2} = \frac{2}{4}$.

Students will learn that fractions that have the same value are called *equivalent fractions*. They will use models to identify equivalent fractions. If two fractions are equivalent, the same amount of each model will be shaded. For example, $\frac{1}{2}$ and $\frac{2}{4}$ are equivalent fractions, so the same amount of each rectangle is shaded.

A rectangle divided in half with the top $\frac{1}{2}$ shaded and the bottom $\frac{1}{2}$ unshaded. Another rectangle divided into fourths, with the top two $\frac{1}{4}$ sections shaded and the bottom two $\frac{1}{4}$ sections unshaded.

LEARN Equivalent Fractions: Number Lines

Students will build on their knowledge that fractions that have the same value are equivalent fractions. They will use number lines to identify and find equivalent fractions. If two fractions are equivalent, the fractions will be the same distance from 0 on the number line. For example, $\frac{1}{2}$ and $\frac{2}{4}$ are equivalent fractions. When the 0s and 1s of the number lines are aligned, then $\frac{1}{2}$ and $\frac{2}{4}$ align because $\frac{1}{2}$ and $\frac{2}{4}$ are the same distance from 0.

Objectives

- Identify a few simple equivalent fractions, such as $\frac{1}{2} = \frac{2}{4}$.

LEARN Find Equivalent Fractions

Students will identify equivalent fractions with number lines.
　Gather the Whole to Twelfths Number Lines printout. Have students use the number lines to find as many fractions as they can that are equivalent to the following fractions:

- $\frac{1}{2}$ $\left(\frac{2}{4}, \frac{3}{6}, \frac{4}{8}, \frac{5}{10}, \frac{6}{12}\right)$
- $\frac{1}{3}$ $\left(\frac{2}{6}, \frac{3}{9}, \frac{4}{12}\right)$
- $\frac{1}{4}$ $\left(\frac{2}{8}, \frac{3}{12}\right)$
- $\frac{3}{4}$ $\left(\frac{6}{8}, \frac{9}{12}\right)$
- $\frac{4}{5}$ $\left(\frac{8}{10}\right)$
- $\frac{10}{12}$ $\left(\frac{5}{6}\right)$
- $\frac{6}{9}$ $\left(\frac{2}{3}, \frac{4}{6}, \frac{8}{12}\right)$
- $\frac{0}{11}$ $\left(0, \frac{0}{2}, \frac{0}{3}, \frac{0}{4}, \frac{0}{5}, \frac{0}{6}, \frac{0}{7}, \frac{0}{8}, \frac{0}{9}, \frac{0}{10}, \frac{0}{11}, \frac{0}{12}\right)$

Objectives

- Identify a few simple equivalent fractions, such as $\frac{1}{2} = \frac{2}{4}$.

Tips

To help students see which fractions are actually aligned, and therefore equivalent, help them place a ruler vertically on the page first at $\frac{1}{2}$ and then at $\frac{1}{3}$, and so on through the fractions given in this activity.

TRY IT Practice Equivalent Fractions

Students will practice modeling and identifying equivalent fractions. Give students the blocks, crayons, and Practice Equivalent Fractions activity page from their Activity Book. Read the directions with them.

Objectives

- Identify a few simple equivalent fractions, such as $\frac{1}{2} = \frac{2}{4}$.

Tips

If you wish, assist students with Problems 1 and 2, so that they understand how they are expected to model the problems with the blocks.

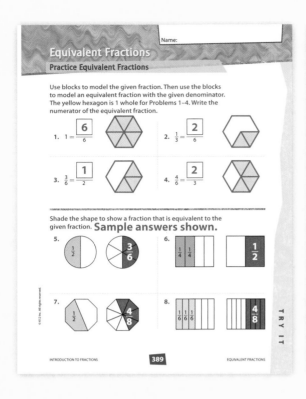

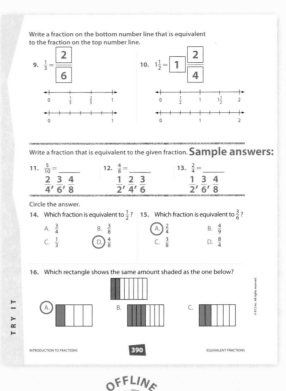

CHECKPOINT

Print the Checkpoint and have students complete it on their own. Read the directions, problems, and answer choices to students, if necessary. Use the answer key to score the Checkpoint, and then enter the results online.

Gather the crayons and give them to students for Problem 2.

Objectives

- Identify a few simple equivalent fractions, such as $\frac{1}{2} = \frac{2}{4}$.

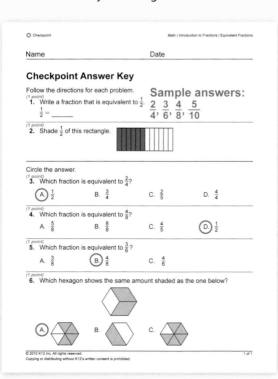

Unit Review

Lesson Overview

UNIT REVIEW Look Back	20 minutes	**ONLINE**
UNIT REVIEW Checkpoint Practice	20 minutes	**OFFLINE**
⇥ **UNIT REVIEW** Prepare for the Checkpoint		

▶ Unit Objectives

This lesson reviews the following objectives:

- Demonstrate that a fraction can represent the relationship of equal parts to a whole or parts of a set.
- Explain that when all fractional parts of a whole are included, such as $\frac{4}{4}$, the result is equal to one whole.
- Recognize and name unit fractions from $\frac{1}{12}$ to $\frac{1}{2}$.
- Demonstrate how fractions and whole numbers can be plotted on a number line.
- Generate fraction representations (for example, show $\frac{2}{3}$ of a shape or $\frac{2}{3}$ of a set of objects or $\frac{2}{3}$ of an interval on a number line).
- Use concrete objects or given drawings to compare unit fractions from $\frac{1}{12}$ to $\frac{1}{2}$.
- Identify a few simple equivalent fractions, such as $\frac{1}{2} = \frac{2}{4}$.

▶ Advance Preparation

In this lesson, students will have an opportunity to review previous activities in the Introduction to Fractions unit. Look at the suggested activities in Unit Review: Prepare for the Checkpoint online and gather any needed materials.

Materials to Gather

SUPPLIED

blocks – K, L, M, N

Checkpoint Practice activity page

Keywords

denominator
equal parts
fraction
mixed number

numerator
unit fraction
whole

UNIT REVIEW Look Back

In this unit, students have learned that they can write fractions to describe parts of a whole and parts of a set and numbers that can be plotted on the number line. They have created models that represent fractions, including unit fractions and fractions equal to 1. Students also have learned how to compare unit fractions and to identify a few simple equivalent fractions. Students will review these concepts to prepare for the Unit Checkpoint.

UNIT REVIEW Checkpoint Practice

Students will complete a Checkpoint Practice activity page to prepare for the Unit Checkpoint. If necessary, read the directions, problems, and answer choices to students. Have students answer the problems on their own. Carefully review the answers with students.

   Gather the blocks and give them to students for Problems 22 and 23.

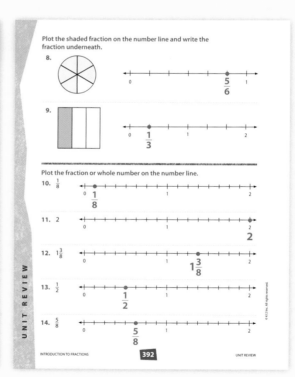

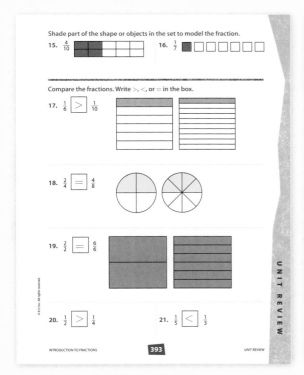

Shade part of the shape or objects in the set to model the fraction.

15. $\frac{4}{10}$ 16. $\frac{1}{7}$

Compare the fractions. Write >, <, or = in the box.

17. $\frac{1}{6}$ > $\frac{1}{10}$

18. $\frac{2}{4}$ = $\frac{4}{8}$

19. $\frac{2}{2}$ = $\frac{6}{6}$

20. $\frac{1}{2}$ > $\frac{1}{4}$ 21. $\frac{1}{5}$ < $\frac{1}{3}$

INTRODUCTION TO FRACTIONS   393   UNIT REVIEW

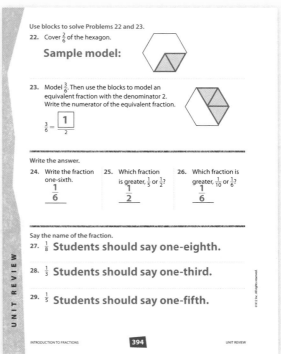

Use blocks to solve Problems 22 and 23.

22. Cover $\frac{2}{6}$ of the hexagon.

Sample model:

23. Model $\frac{3}{6}$. Then use the blocks to model an equivalent fraction with the denominator 2. Write the numerator of the equivalent fraction.

$\frac{3}{6} = \frac{1}{2}$

Write the answer.

24. Write the fraction one-sixth.

$\frac{1}{6}$

25. Which fraction is greater, $\frac{1}{5}$ or $\frac{1}{2}$?

$\frac{1}{2}$

26. Which fraction is greater, $\frac{1}{10}$ or $\frac{1}{6}$?

$\frac{1}{6}$

Say the name of the fraction.

27. $\frac{1}{8}$ **Students should say one-eighth.**

28. $\frac{1}{3}$ **Students should say one-third.**

29. $\frac{1}{5}$ **Students should say one-fifth.**

INTRODUCTION TO FRACTIONS   394   UNIT REVIEW

⮕ UNIT REVIEW Prepare for the Checkpoint

What you do next depends on how students performed in the previous activity, Unit Review: Checkpoint Practice. If students had difficulty with any of the problems, complete the appropriate review activity listed in the table online.

Unit Checkpoint

UNIT CHECKPOINT Online	60 minutes	**ONLINE**

▶ Unit Objectives

This lesson assesses the following objectives:

- Demonstrate that a fraction can represent the relationship of equal parts to a whole or parts of a set.
- Explain that when all fractional parts of a whole are included, such as $\frac{4}{4}$, the result is equal to one whole.
- Recognize and name unit fractions from $\frac{1}{12}$ to $\frac{1}{2}$.
- Demonstrate how fractions and whole numbers can be plotted on a number line.
- Generate fraction representations (for example, show $\frac{2}{3}$ of a shape or $\frac{2}{3}$ of a set of objects or $\frac{2}{3}$ of an interval on a number line).
- Use concrete objects or given drawings to compare unit fractions from $\frac{1}{12}$ to $\frac{1}{2}$.
- Identify a few simple equivalent fractions, such as $\frac{1}{2} = \frac{2}{4}$.

Materials to Gather

There are no materials to gather for this lesson.

UNIT CHECKPOINT Online

ONLINE 60min

Students will complete the Unit Checkpoint online. Read the directions, problems, and answer choices to students. If necessary, help students with keyboard or mouse operations.

Objectives

- Assess unit objectives.

Semester Review

Lesson Overview

SEMESTER REVIEW Look Back	20 minutes	**ONLINE**
SEMESTER REVIEW Checkpoint Practice	20 minutes	**OFFLINE**
⏵ **SEMESTER REVIEW** Prepare for the Checkpoint		

▶ Semester Objectives

This lesson reviews the following objectives:

- Identify the place value for each digit in whole numbers through 1,000.
- Use expanded forms to represent numbers through 1,000, such as 754 = 7 hundreds + 5 tens + 4 ones.
- Order three or more whole numbers through 1,000 by using the symbols $<, =, >$.
- Identify and describe plane figures according to the number of sides and vertices, such as triangle, square, rectangle, circle, oval.
- Classify plane figures according to similarities and differences, such as triangle, square, rectangle, circle, oval.
- Classify solid figures according to the number and shape of faces, such as sphere, pyramid, cube, rectangular prism.
- Find the sum or difference of two whole numbers with sums and minuends up through 1,000.
- Recognize and solve word problems involving sums or minuends up through 1,000 in which one quantity changes by addition or subtraction.
- Write and solve addition or subtraction number sentences to represent problem-solving situations with sums and minuends up through 1,000.
- Justify the procedures selected for addition or subtraction problem-solving situations with sums or minuends up through 1,000.
- Use concrete objects or sketches of arrays to model multiplication problems.
- Use grouping to solve simple multiplication problems.
- Use models and math symbols to represent multiplication.
- Demonstrate understanding of the commutative properties of addition and multiplication.
- Use repeated subtraction to do division problems.
- Use equal sharing to do division problems.
- Use forming equal groups with remainders to solve simple division problems.
- Solve addition or subtraction problems by using data from charts, picture graphs, and number sentences.
- Demonstrate that a fraction can represent the relationship of equal parts to a whole or parts of a set.
- Explain that when all fractional parts of a whole are included, such as $\frac{4}{4}$, the result is equal to one whole.
- Recognize and name unit fractions from $\frac{1}{12}$ to $\frac{1}{2}$.
- Demonstrate how fractions and whole numbers can be plotted on a number line.

Materials to Gather

SUPPLIED

blocks – B
blocks – L (2), N (1)
blocks – P, Q, R, S, V
Checkpoint Practice activity page

Advance Preparation

In this lesson, students will have an opportunity to review previous activities from the semester. Look at the suggested activities in Semester Review: Prepare for the Checkpoint online and be prepared to gather any needed materials.

SEMESTER REVIEW Look Back	**ONLINE** **20**min	Objectives

- Review semester objectives.

In this semester, students have identified, classified, and described plane and solid figures. They have learned about the place value of numbers through 1,000 and have used that knowledge to compare and order numbers. Students have solved story problems with numbers through 1,000. For these story problems, they have justified their solutions and explained their answers.

Students also have explored two new operations this semester: multiplication and division. They have modeled these operations, and they have memorized key facts. Finally students have learned about fractions, including unit fractions, mixed numbers, and fractions equal to 1. They have modeled, compared, and interpreted fractions. Students will review key concepts from the semester to prepare for the Semester Checkpoint.

You may notice that some of the objectives in the Semester Review are not necessarily included in the Semester Checkpoint. Some of these concepts are particularly important to review in order to be successful with the upcoming topics students will encounter, and others contribute to a greater understanding of the concepts that are being assessed. Therefore, a complete review of the objectives in this lesson is recommended.

To review, students will play a Super Genius game. If students answer a problem incorrectly, the correct answer will display. Be sure to help students understand why the answer is correct before students move on to the next problem. If they miss several problems, have students play the game again.

Objectives

- Review semester objectives.

Students will complete a Checkpoint Practice activity page to prepare for the Semester Checkpoint. If necessary, read the directions, problems, and answer choices to students. Have students answer the problems on their own. Carefully review the answers with students.

Gather the blocks and give students the circle blocks for Problems 1–4, hexagon and rhombuses for Problem 5, and geometric solid blocks for Problem 6.

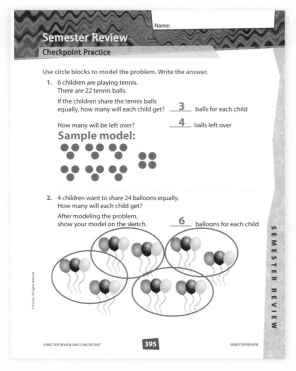

Name: _____

Semester Review

Checkpoint Practice

Use circle blocks to model the problem. Write the answer.

1. 6 children are playing tennis.
   There are 22 tennis balls.

   If the children share the tennis balls equally, how many will each child get? __3__ balls for each child

   How many will be left over? __4__ balls left over

   Sample model:

2. 4 children want to share 24 balloons equally.
   How many will each child get?

   After modeling the problem, show your model on the sketch. __6__ balloons for each child

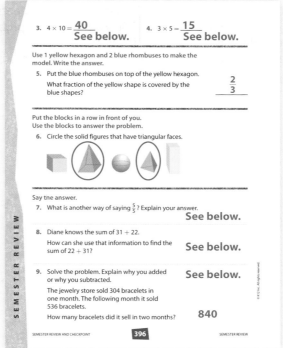

3. $4 \times 10 =$ __40__   See below.

4. $3 \times 5 =$ __15__   See below.

Use 1 yellow hexagon and 2 blue rhombuses to make the model. Write the answer.

5. Put the blue rhombuses on top of the yellow hexagon.

   What fraction of the yellow shape is covered by the blue shapes? __$\frac{2}{3}$__

Put the blocks in a row in front of you.
Use the blocks to answer the problem.

6. Circle the solid figures that have triangular faces.

Say the answer.

7. What is another way of saying $\frac{5}{5}$? Explain your answer.   See below.

8. Diane knows the sum of $31 + 22$.

   How can she use that information to find the sum of $22 + 31$?   See below.

9. Solve the problem. Explain why you added or why you subtracted.   See below.

   The jewelry store sold 304 bracelets in one month. The following month it sold 536 bracelets.

   How many bracelets did it sell in two months?   840

Additional Answers

3. Sample model:

4. Sample model:

7. 1 whole, or 1. Sample explanation: $\frac{5}{5}$ means that an object has been divided into 5 equal parts, and all 5 parts are included.

8. The sum of $31 + 22$ is the same as the sum of $22 + 31$. Changing the order of addends does not change the sum.

9. Students should say that they added to get the answer 840 bracelets. Sample explanation: The total number of bracelets is a greater number than the number of bracelets made each month, so I added.

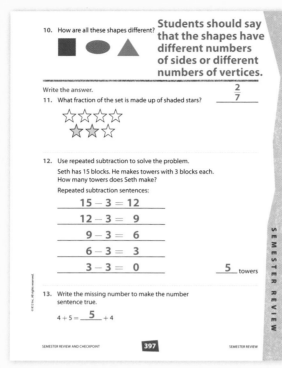

10. How are all these shapes different? **Students should say that the shapes have different numbers of sides or different numbers of vertices.**

Write the answer.

11. What fraction of the set is made up of shaded stars? $\frac{2}{7}$

12. Use repeated subtraction to solve the problem.

Seth has 15 blocks. He makes towers with 3 blocks each. How many towers does Seth make?

Repeated subtraction sentences:

$15 - 3 = 12$

$12 - 3 = 9$

$9 - 3 = 6$

$6 - 3 = 3$

$3 - 3 = 0$

__5__ towers

13. Write the missing number to make the number sentence true.

$4 + 5 = \underline{5} + 4$

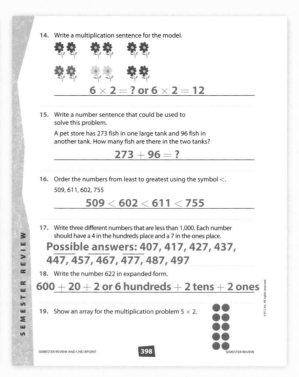

14. Write a multiplication sentence for the model.

$6 \times 2 = ?$ or $6 \times 2 = 12$

15. Write a number sentence that could be used to solve this problem.

A pet store has 273 fish in one large tank and 96 fish in another tank. How many fish are there in the two tanks?

$273 + 96 = ?$

16. Order the numbers from least to greatest using the symbol <.

509, 611, 602, 755

$509 < 602 < 611 < 755$

17. Write three different numbers that are less than 1,000. Each number should have a 4 in the hundreds place and a 7 in the ones place.

Possible answers: 407, 417, 427, 437, 447, 457, 467, 477, 487, 497

18. Write the number 622 in expanded form.

$600 + 20 + 2$ or 6 hundreds + 2 tens + 2 ones

19. Show an array for the multiplication problem 5×2.

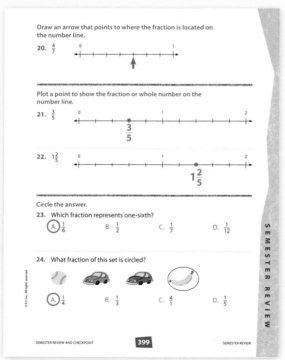

Draw an arrow that points to where the fraction is located on the number line.

20. $\frac{4}{7}$

Plot a point to show the fraction or whole number on the number line.

21. $\frac{3}{5}$

$\frac{3}{5}$

22. $1\frac{2}{5}$

$1\frac{2}{5}$

Circle the answer.

23. Which fraction represents one-sixth?

A. $\frac{1}{6}$ B. $\frac{1}{2}$ C. $\frac{1}{7}$ D. $\frac{1}{12}$

24. What fraction of this set is circled?

A. $\frac{1}{4}$ B. $\frac{1}{3}$ C. $\frac{4}{1}$ D. $\frac{1}{5}$

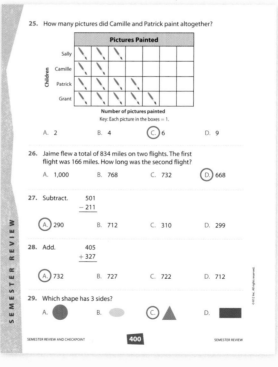

25. How many pictures did Camille and Patrick paint altogether?

Pictures Painted

Children	Number of pictures painted
Sally	
Camille	
Patrick	
Grant	

Key: Each picture in the boxes = 1.

A. 2   B. 4   C. 6   D. 9

26. Jaime flew a total of 834 miles on two flights. The first flight was 166 miles. How long was the second flight?

A. 1,000   B. 768   C. 732   D. 668

27. Subtract.   501 − 211

A. 290   B. 712   C. 310   D. 299

28. Add.   405 + 327

A. 732   B. 727   C. 722   D. 712

29. Which shape has 3 sides?

A.   B.   C.   D.

➔ SEMESTER REVIEW Prepare for the Checkpoint

What you do next depends on how students performed in the previous activity, Semester Review: Checkpoint Practice. If students had difficulty with any of the problems, complete the appropriate review activity listed in the Unit Review tables online.

Because there are many concepts to review, consider using the Your Choice day to continue preparing for the Semester Checkpoint.

Semester Checkpoint

Lesson Overview

SEMESTER CHECKPOINT Offline	60 minutes	OFFLINE

▶ Semester Objectives

This lesson assesses the following objectives:

- Order three or more whole numbers through 1,000 by using the symbols $<, =, >$.
- Classify plane figures according to similarities and differences, such as triangle, square, rectangle, circle, oval.
- Find the sum or difference of two whole numbers with sums and minuends up through 1,000.
- Recognize and solve word problems involving sums or minuends up through 1,000 in which one quantity changes by addition or subtraction.
- Write and solve addition or subtraction number sentences to represent problem-solving situations with sums and minuends up through 1,000.
- Justify the procedures selected for addition or subtraction problem-solving situations with sums or minuends up through 1,000.
- Use grouping to solve simple multiplication problems.
- Use models and math symbols to represent multiplication.
- Demonstrate understanding of the commutative properties of addition and multiplication.
- Use forming equal groups with remainders to solve simple division problems.
- Solve addition or subtraction problems by using data from charts, picture graphs, and number sentences.
- Demonstrate that a fraction can represent the relationship of equal parts to a whole or parts of a set.

Materials to Gather

SUPPLIED

blocks – K (2), N (1)

blocks – A, C, D, E, F, G, H (1 of each)

blocks – B

Semester Checkpoint (printout)

ALSO NEEDED

index cards – 4

crayons – 3

pencils – 2

SEMESTER CHECKPOINT Offline

OFFLINE 60min

Objectives

- Assess semester objectives.

Print the Checkpoint. In Part 1, students will take a performance-based assessment. In Part 2, students will complete the problems on their own. Read the directions, problems, and answer choices to students, if necessary. Use the answer key to score the Checkpoint, and then enter the results online.

Give students the blocks, index cards, crayons, and pencils.

Name _____ Date _____

Semester Checkpoint Answer Key

Part 1
Follow the instructions for each problem. Choose the response that best describes how the student performs on the task.

1. Give students the green triangles and yellow hexagon.
   Say, "Put the 2 green triangles on top of the yellow hexagon.
   What fraction of the yellow hexagon is covered by the green triangles?"
   (1 point) Did the student say $\frac{2}{6}$ or $\frac{1}{3}$?
   A. Yes   B. No

2. Give students the circle blocks.
   Say, "5 children share 11 toys equally. How many toys will each child get and how many toys will be left over? Use circle blocks to model and solve the problem."
   (1 point) Did the student use the circles to find that each child will get 2 toys and that there will be 1 toy left over?
   A. Yes   B. No

3. Give students the circle blocks.
   Say, "Use circle blocks to model and solve 2×2."
   (1 point) Did the student show 2 groups of 2 circles or 2 rows of 2 circles and find that the answer is 4?
   A. Yes   B. No

Name _____ Date _____

4. Display the index cards, crayons, and pencils in a random arrangement.
   Say, "What fraction of this set is made up of index cards? Explain your answer."
   (1 point) Did the student say that $\frac{4}{9}$ of the set is made up of index cards?
   A. Yes   B. No
   (1 point) Did the student explain that there are 9 objects in the set and 4 of the objects are index cards?
   A. Yes   B. No

5. Say, "Tim knows the sum of $15 + 19$. How can he use that information to find the sum of $19 + 15$?"
   (1 point) Did the student say that the sum of $15 + 19$ is the same as the sum of $19 + 15$ because changing the order of addends does not change the sum?
   A. Yes   B. No

6. Say, "Solve this problem, and explain why you solved it the way you did.
   Isaac had 501 rocks in his rock collection. He went digging and found some more rocks. He now has 550 rocks in his collection. How many rocks did he find?"
   (1 point) Did the student say Isaac found 49 rocks?
   A. Yes   B. No
   (1 point) Did the student explain how to solve the problem?
   Sample answer: The number of rocks he found must be less than the total number of rocks so you subtract.
   A. Yes   B. No

Name _____ Date _____

7. Give students 2 circles, 2 squares, 2 rectangles, and 2 triangles.
   Say, "Put all of the shapes with only 3 sides in one group."
   (1 point) Did the student put the 2 triangles in a group?
   A. Yes   B. No

8. Say, "Write a number sentence that could be used to correctly solve this problem, and then solve it.
   A farmer picked 334 red apples and 528 green apples. How many apples did the farmer pick altogether?"
   (1 point) Did the student write $334 + 528 = ?$
   A. Yes   B. No
   (1 point) Did the student say the farmer picked 862 apples altogether?
   A. Yes   B. No

9. Say, "Write a number sentence that could be used to correctly solve this problem, and then solve it.
   Talia's flowers had 145 petals. 75 of them fell off. How many petals are left?"
   (1 point) Did the student write the number sentence $145 - 75 = ?$
   A. Yes   B. No
   (1 point) Did the student solve the problem to find out that there are 70 petals left?
   A. Yes   B. No

Give students Part 2 of the assessment.

Name _____ Date _____

Part 2
Solve.
(1 point)
10. Draw a sketch to help solve the problem 4×2.

    Students should draw a sketch to show 4 groups of 2 objects or a 4 by 2 array.

Write the answer.
(1 point)
11. Tony had $123. He got some more money and now has $798. How much more money did Tony get? $ __675__

(1 point)
12. Think of a strategy to solve this problem in your head first. Then solve on paper.

    799
    + 108
    907

(1 point)
13. Think of a strategy to solve this problem in your head first. Then solve on paper.

    541
    − 303
    238

(1 point)
14. Order the numbers 567, 564, and 569 from least to greatest using the $<$ symbol.

    $564 < 567 < 569$

Name _____ Date _____

(1 point)
15. What number goes in the box to make this number sentence true?

$10 \times 6 = 6 \times$ [10]

(1 point)
16. Write a multiplication sentence for the model.

$3 \times 10 =$? or $3 \times 10 = 30$

Circle the answer.

(1 point)
17. A soccer team collected 658 magazines for recycling in one month. The next month the team collected 239 magazines. How many magazines did the team collect altogether?

   A. 419   B. 421   C. 887   (D.) 897

(1 point)
18. A prize machine had 1,000 prizes. Some children got prizes from the machine. Now the machine has 899 prizes left. How could someone find out how many prizes the children got from the machine?

   A. Add 1,000 and 899 because the machine now has more prizes than it started with.

   B. Subtract 899 from 1,000 because the machine now has more prizes than it started with.

   (C.) Subtract 899 from 1,000 because the machine now has fewer prizes than it started with.

(1 point)
19. Tim is doing an art project. He can only use shapes with 4 sides.

Which **two** of the following shapes can Tim use?

A. △   (B.) ◇   (C.) ▭   D. ⬭